Foundations of Computing

INTERNATIONAL COMPUTER SCIENCE SERIES

Consulting Editor **A D McGettrick** University of Strathclyde

SELECTED TITLES IN THE SERIES

Distributed Systems: Concepts and Design *G Coulouris and J. Dollimore*

Software Prototyping, Formal Methods and VDM *S Hekmatpour and D Ince*

High-Level Languages and Their Compilers *D Watson*

Interactive Computer Graphics: Functional, Procedural and Device-Level Methods *P Burger and D Gillies*

Real Time Systems and Their Programming Languages *A Burns and A Wellings*

Fortran 77 Programming (2nd Edn) *T M R Ellis*

Prolog Programming for Artificial Intelligence (2nd Edn) *I Bratko*

Introduction to Expert Systems (2nd Edn) *P Jackson*

Logic for Computer Science *S Reeves and M Clarke*

Computer Architecture *M De Blasi*

The Programming Process: an Introduction using VDM and Pascal *J T Latham, V J Bush and D Cottam*

Analysis of Algorithms and Data Structures *L Banachowski, A Kreczmar and W Rytter*

Handbook of Algorithms and Data Structures in Pascal and C (2nd Edn) *G Gonnet and R Baeza-Yates*

Algorithms and Data Structures *J H Kingston*

Principles of Expert Systems *P Lucas and L van der Gaag*

Discrete Mathematics for Computer Scientists *J K Truss*

Programming in Ada plus Language Reference Manual (3rd Edn) *J G P Barnes*

Software Engineering (4th Edn) *I Sommerville*

Distributed Database Systems *D Bell and J Grimson*

Software Development with Z *J B Wordsworth*

Program Verification *N Francez*

Comparative Programming Languages (2nd Edn) *L B Wilson and R G Clark*

Concurrent Systems: an Integrated Approach to Operating Systems, Database, and Distributed Systems *J. Bacon*

Concurrent Programming *A Burns and G Davies*

Functional Programming and Parallel Graph Rewriting *R Plasmeijer and M van Eekelen*

Foundations of Computing

System Development with Set Theory and Logic

Thierry Scheurer

University of Manchester
Institute of Science and Technology

ADDISON-WESLEY
PUBLISHING
COMPANY

Wokingham, England · Reading, Massachusetts · Menlo Park, California · New York
Don Mills, Ontario · Amsterdam · Bonn · Sydney · Singapore
Tokyo · Madrid · San Juan · Milan · Paris · Mexico City · Seoul · Taipei

Cover designed by Chris Eley incorporating an original illustration by Pascale Scheurer and printed by Oxted Press Ltd., Oxted, Surrey
Line drawings by Margaret Macknelly Design, Tadley
Typeset by Techset Composition Ltd., Salisbury
Printed in Great Britain by the University Press, Cambridge.

First printed 1994.

British Library Cataloguing in Publication Data
A catalogue record for this book is available from the British Library.

Library of Congress Cataloging in Publication Data
Scheurer, Thierry.
The foundations of computing : system development with set theory and logic / Thierry Scheurer.
p. cm.
Includes bibliographical references and index.
ISBN 0-201-54429-6
1. System design. 2. Set theory. 3. Logic, Symbolic and mathematical. I. Title.
QA76.9.S88S29 1994
004.2′1 dc20 94-16315
CIP

Preface

Aims

Two theses form the basis of this book. The first is that computers are general-purpose machines. Consequently, the control and use of computers, the task of software development, is tantamount to general problem solving. The first aim of this book is to present *a methodology of general problem solving*. This may be applied on its own, independently of computers, or as a methodology of software engineering.

The second thesis is that set theory and logic are ideally suited for this task. Set theory, based on logic, is a universal language in which all problems may be formulated and solved. It is remarkably simple. It is also very natural in the sense that it closely reflects any natural language. In fact, it may be regarded as a highly simplified and regular notation enjoying the same expressive power as natural languages, without suffering from their shortcomings: complexity, verbosity, ambiguity and lack of accuracy. The second aim of this book is *to introduce set theory as a fundamental and practical tool of modelling, or general problem solving*. Set theory is not 'new' – it is well established and has been taught in schools for decades. The novelty of this book is the perspective in which this theory is presented. It seems that the practical relevance of set theory as a language of universal applicability has largely gone unnoticed despite its presence in curricula. This misconception is as harmful as it is widespread. Our goal will be fully achieved the day set theory is used as a tool of the trade by computing scientists on the same scale as Pascal or C, for instance, are today.

This book is not about computers, nor is it an introduction to computer programming. It is about modelling in general, with or without the help of these machines. Electronic digital computers are having an enormous impact on our modelling and problem-solving capabilities. However, it is not the machines in themselves, but the fundamental way they affect our methods and thinking that is the concern of this book. If anything, the reader is encouraged to forget about computers for a while and to start afresh on new foundations. The computer will find its proper place as a means of action in due course.

Readership

This book is written from first principles; it assumes no prior knowledge of either computing or mathematics on the part of readers. However, it is expected that the majority of them will have some acquaintance with computers. Consequently, a few references to aspects of these machines are made without detailed explanations, especially in Chapter 1. However, these are not essential, and the book may be read by anyone interested in general problem solving, even without any knowledge of computers.

The book is aimed at two main groups of people: first, all those engaged in one way or another in software development. It should enable them to improve the quality of their work, by providing them with the means to express their thoughts precisely and rigorously at all stages of the software development process, from requirements analysis up to programming in machine-executable language.

The second group includes all those interested in general problem solving and anxious to develop their analytical skills: scientists, engineers or managers, in fact anybody interested in the way set theory may be used to describe any kind of object, situation, problem and solution in a precise manner. The book should also appeal to those who believe in the importance of the quality of expression and communication in natural language, and what can be learnt in this respect from set theory and logic as a complementary universal notation.

For teaching purposes, the book is suitable for undergraduate or post-graduate introductory courses mainly in computing, but also in all fields of science and engineering with a strong element of general modelling or system design.

Orientation and structure

Set theory and logic underpin many different branches of computing. First and foremost is the area of formal methods, including specification languages such as VDM and Z. Closely related to these are the axiomatic method of (procedural) language specification and program development, algebraic specification methods and denotational semantics. Note that these terms are used in different ways in the literature.

Somewhat further afield are such areas as functional programming, with its numerous languages ranging from LISP to Miranda and ML, logic programming exemplified by PROLOG, and object-oriented programming (Smalltalk, Eiffel, and so on). In addition, a form of set theory is used in important application areas, such as data modelling and database theory. A typical example is the popular relational model of data modelling and the associated language SQL. This is a major and direct application of the theory of relations, itself central to set theory. Further examples could be added: the above list emphasizes key areas of computing, but it is by no means exhaustive.

There is no intention in this book to provide even the beginning of an introduction to these various branches of computing. In most of them, there are numerous specialized textbooks, some excellent, which will provide the necessary introduction to the interested reader. In this respect, the first aim of the book is simply to introduce a number of fundamental ideas of set theory and logic, those which appear to play a major role in all these branches, and to do so in a notation which is as standardized and as widely accepted as possible. The second aim of the book is to put these ideas into practice through numerous concrete applications, ranging from simple examples to large and realistic case studies. The hope is that, having absorbed the contents of this book, the reader should have mastered the foundations, which will make the study of the specialized fields just mentioned that much easier.

Accordingly, the reader will find no new 'language' in this book, just the well-established notation of set theory and logic. The only innovative features of the book are as follows: first, there is the *perspective* in which selected key ideas are presented, emphasizing their universality, interrelationships and theoretical and practical significance. Second, emphasis is put on *exposition* and *explication* of ideas and their concrete illustration. Third, the traditional notation of set theory is extended by a few simple rules, found necessary for the development of large-scale models. These rules are called 'Feature Notation'; they are little more than a discipline for constructing names of objects and their features systematically.

The book is in five parts. The purpose of Part 1, which contains only one chapter, is to 'set the scene', that is, to motivate subsequent theories and methods and establish their link to computing in general. The last section of this chapter gives an overview of the key aims and ideas to be found in the remaining chapters. Part 2 is devoted to a semiformal introduction to set theory. Part 3 introduces propositional and first-order predicate logic. Parts 4 and 5 are essentially devoted to applications of graded complexity, the *practice* of modelling.

Sources

This book owes much to a variety of excellent predecessors. The material on set theory is based on various sources, including primarily H. Enderton's *Elements of Set Theory*. Other important sources are P. Halmos' *Naive Set Theory* and Birkhoff and Mac Lane's *Survey of Modern Algebra* and *Algebra*. The introduction to logic is based mainly on H. Enderton's *A Mathematical Introduction to Logic* and, to a lesser extent, P. Andrews' *An Introduction to Mathematical Logic and Type Theory*. Logic is above all a *formal language*. In the author's view, the best introduction to the key principles of formal languages is through a study of logic, as presented in these two excellent books or any equivalent.

Of all the languages mentioned above, the approach of this book is closest to the specification language Z. In particular, there is much in common between the Feature Notation referred to above and Z schemas. However, there are also important differences. These are briefly explained in the relevant section. Hayes' *Specification Case Studies* and Spivey's *The Z Notation: A Reference Manual* have provided the initial impetus to the development of several application case studies. C. Jones' *Systematic Software Development Using VDM* has also been a source of inspiration.

The indirect influence of other sources must also be acknowledged. Bird and Wadler's *Introduction to Functional Programming* is an excellent exposition of an important complementary approach to software development. Gries' *Science of Programming* is an excellent introduction to the axiomatic approach to procedural program development and is also complementary. Dijkstra and Scholten's *Predicate Calculus and Program Semantics* provides an important formal proof methodology, though primarily for procedural programming. This has had some influence on the approach to model development in this book. The formulation of set-theoretic models has also been influenced by aspects of Per Martin-Löf's type theory, as expounded in *Programming in Martin-Löf's Type Theory* by Nordström *et al.* Finally, the emphasis on certain ideas and constructions – for instance, the systematic search for pairs of *inverse* operations as a modelling strategy – has been inspired by Mac Lane's *Categories for the Working Mathematician*. These are the main sources of influence on this book; many others could be mentioned.

Acknowledgements

I owe a debt of gratitude to the various people who helped me bring this book to completion. I would like to thank, in particular, the reviewers and Professor A.D. McGettrick, who suggested several invaluable improvements; the personnel of Addison-Wesley, especially the Editor-in-Chief, Simon Plumtree, and Susan Keany, who supervised the production of the book with great dedication; and finally my daughter Pascale, who produced the first draft of the figures as well as the cover illustration.

Thierry Scheurer
July 1994

Contents

Sections labelled AT *cover 'advanced topics' and may be skipped on first reading.*

List of symbols

Symbol	*Description*	*Page*

1. General equality

$=$	Equality (numbers, sets, etc.)	40
$\neq$	Inequality	47

2. Natural numbers; numeric relations and operations

Nat	Set of natural numbers: $\{0, 1, 2, \ldots\}$	50
(Nat, 0, S)	Natural numbers as a Peano system	185
Pos	Set of positive natural numbers	141
$<$	Less than	39
$\leqslant$	Less than or equal	38
$>$	Greater than	53
$\geqslant$	Greater than or equal	100
$+$	Addition	50
$-$	Subtraction	50
$\times$	Multiplication	42
DIV	Division	53
MOD	Remainder of division	53

3. Set theory: basic relations and operations

$\{x, y, \ldots\}$	Set construction by enumeration	37
$\{x \mid -x-\}$	Set construction by abstraction	38
$\in$	Membership	44
$x : S$	By definition $x \in S$	84

$\notin$	Negation of membership	45
$\subseteq$	Inclusion	47
$\subset$	Strict inclusion	47
$\varnothing$	Empty set	48
Num, Card, $\lvert\ \rvert$	Cardinality of a set (number of members)	50
$\{x, y\}$	Pair (unordered) of x and y	56
$\cup$	Union (of two sets)	57
$\bigcup$	Union (of a set of sets)	58
$\cap$	Intersection (of two sets)	59
$\bigcap$	Intersection (of a set of sets)	60
$\setminus$	Relative complement	63
$+$	Sum (union of two disjoint sets)	64
Σ	Sum (union of a set of disjoint sets)	64
$-$	Set difference	65
Pow(S)	Powerset (set of subsets of S)	65
Powf(S)	Set of finite subsets of S	66
$\langle a, b\rangle$	Couple (ordered pair) of a and b	91
$(a_1, a_2, \ldots, a_n)$	n-tuple	141, 142
$\times$	Cartesian product	93, 142
Π	Cartesian product (n-ary)	143
$\amalg$	Disjoint union	96, 144
$\coprod$	Disjoint union (of a set of sets)	145
A^n	n-ary cartesian product of n identical sets A	144
$n \times A$	n-ary disjoint union of n identical sets A	145
ω	Set of natural numbers (as concretely defined in set theory)	188
$(\omega, \varnothing, S)$	Peano system associated with ω	188
x^+	$x \cup \{x\}$	188

4. Relations and functions; special functions

$R: A \leftrightarrow B$	Introducing relation R with domain A and codomain B	102
$F: A \nrightarrow B$	Introducing (possibly partial) function F from domain A to codomain B	113, 150
$F: A \rightarrow B$	Introducing total function F from A to B	113, 152
$x \mapsto y$	Member to member association in a relation or a function	104, 113, 151
χ (χ_s)	Characteristic function (of S)	126, 128
$\mathrm{Im}_R(S)$	Image of S under relation R	130
$F(x)$, Fx, F_x	Application of function F to x	110
$F(a_1, a_2, \ldots, a_n)$	Application of F to $(a_1, a_2, \ldots, a_n)$	151
$(F_i \mid i{:}I)$	Family	132

5. Higher-order set operations

$R2 \circ R1$	Composition of relations	164
$G \circ F$	Composition of functions	164
$S \langle R$	Domain restriction of relation R	165
$T \langle\cdot R$	Codomain restriction of relation R	166
$S \diamond R$	Restriction of relation R	166
$(F \mid x \mapsto y)$	Function overriding	167, 307
Id_S	Identity function on set S	167
$\mathrm{Inc}_{S'}$	Inclusion function of a subset S'	168
Opp	Opposite of a relation	169
Inv	Inverse of a relation	171
F^{-1}	Inverse of function F	172
$\cong$	Isomorphism (of any given class of objects)	457

6. String and list operations

Al^*	Set of strings on alphabet Al	220, 251
ε	Empty string	220, 294
$+\!\!+$	Standard concatenation	335, 450

7. Logic

$\neg$ not	Negation	79, 250
$\wedge$ and	Conjunction	79, 250
$\vee$ or	Disjunction	80, 250
$\Rightarrow$ if ... then	Conditional	80, 250
$\Leftrightarrow$ iff	Equivalence or biconditional	80, 250
$\downarrow$ nor	Not or	280
$*$	Any binary logical connective	295
$\forall$ for all	Universal quantifier	81, 287
$\exists$ there exists	Existential quantifier	81, 287
$\exists 1$ there exists one	Existential-unique quantifier	82
ξ	Any quantifier	296
Eq	Equality (first-order logic)	287
m	Truth assignment (propositional logic)	256
	Interpretation extension (first-order logic)	304
M	Interpretation	303
(M, m)	Extended interpretation	304
$\boldsymbol{M}$	Semantic function (propositional logic)	256
$\boldsymbol{M}, \boldsymbol{M}_{(M, m)}$	Semantic function (first-order logic)	305, 308
$\models$	Tautological implication (propositional logic)	266, 268
	Logical implication (first-order logic)	314, 316
$\vdash$	Inference (formal deduction)	324, 335

8. Decoration

9. Punctuation

Part 1

Overview

Prologue

Generality

It is said that many centuries ago, an Indian princess asked the Buddha to summarize his philosophy for her. The wise man obliged, but when he brought his answer to the lady, she asked for a more concise summary. This exchange was repeated a few times. Whenever the Buddha complied with her latest request, the princess kept on demanding an even shorter version. Eventually she asked: 'Can you express your philosophy in just *one* word?' Once more the Buddha obliged. The definition he offered was: '*Today*'.

Can we do in computing what Buddha did in philosophy – express the essence of that subject in a single word? Would such a description enlighten us in any way? This book takes as its starting point the proposition that these questions may be answered in the affirmative and that computing may indeed be summed up in one word: *Generality*. For it is a fact of experience that the study of computing constantly leads to the same conclusion. Ultimately, computing has one fundamental object: to study and to achieve generality. Conversely, without generality, there would be no computing.

The first aim of this book is to justify this proposition: to show that computing has one goal in the last analysis, namely to achieve generality, and that this theme pervades all aspects of this subject. Therefore, it seems fitting to start our enquiry with a brief examination of generality.

The nature of generality

Perhaps the most remarkable of our faculties is our ability to identify and work with *classes* or *sets* of objects. The essential feature of a class is that in general it involves a multiplicity of distinct objects called members or instances of the class. Members are distinguished from non-members by some feature or property common to all members of the class and no other objects. It is this property which gives the class its identity.

Our ability to identify classes means that we may operate, or act, on all the members of the class simultaneously, without referring to each member explicitly and individually. By *operation* on an object we mean performing some task or action on it: for example, producing a new object depending on it, establishing that it has a certain property, or making a statement about it.

How can we 'operate on each member of a class simultaneously'? We do so by choosing a *symbol*, for example a word, to represent *any one* instance of the class, and then performing the operation on the symbol.

For example, consider the statement

S: *Every person has a brain to think with.*

This is a general statement – a statement about every member of the class of all persons. Its purpose is to express a certain fact about every human being, considered individually. Here the word 'person' is a symbol that stands for any human being that has ever existed, now exists or will ever exist in future. The role of 'person' is clarified by the adjective 'every'.

The force of S is that it conveys the same information as the set of all sentences that may be obtained by substituting the name of a specific individual for 'every person' in it. Thus we may replace 'every person' by Albert, Beth or Cathy in S, giving respectively the statement instances

S1: *Albert has a brain to think with.*

S2: *Beth has a brain to think with.*

S3: *Cathy has a brain to think with.*

Many other such propositions may be obtained in the same way: in fact an infinite number. Clearly, the totality of these specific statements is equivalent to S. Therefore, the latter is a very powerful means of expression indeed.

Generality is what we achieve when we create or identify classes, and when we perform general operations – that is, operations on all members of a class simultaneously.

Generality pervades and plays a dominant role in all walks of life – domestic, scientific, artistic, ethical, and so on. Most of our ideas are of a general nature: they are concerned not with individuals but with classes of objects. Most of our statements, descriptions or rules are general ones. Most of our actions are general: they aim at producing classes of results, rather than individual ones.

Generality and computing

To describe the essence of computing in one word is a bold step. The reader is not expected to accept this idea as final, but to consider it as a guiding principle, a working hypothesis to be used with flexibility. However, at this point we may at least test the *plausibility* of this thesis. Here is some initial evidence.

1 The aim of computing is to formulate the principles and methods underpinning the construction and control of computer systems. Computers are general-purpose machines – in fact the most general-purpose that may be conceived. They are potentially capable of solving or assisting with the solution of *any* problem, and are meant to do so. It follows that the primary concern of computing is *general problem solving* – that is, the development of principles and methods applicable to the solution of any problem, present or future. Computers should be regarded as just a means to this end.

2 This first argument is normative rather than based on empirical evidence. Let us turn to the latter and consider how computers are actually used. This too gives strong support to the claim that achieving generality is the fundamental aim of computing.

Given a computer, the primary concrete problem of computing is to construct a program or a suite of programs to control the behaviour of the machine. The visible behaviour of the machine is its 'output': displayed messages, printed reports and so on. Now a program is almost never written to perform just one task, but rather a *set* of tasks. In most cases this generality is achieved by separating the program into two parts: the program proper and further information usually called 'input' or 'data'. The computer's behaviour is determined by the combination of these two elements. While the program proper is constant, the input may vary. Thus what we call 'input' is in fact a *class* of objects, the set of all possible combinations of data which may be used in conjunction with the program proper. Each such combination is an *input instance* and produces a different behaviour of the machine – a different *output instance*.

Consequently, when we write a computer program, we must define the class of possible input instances, the class of possible output instances and the correspondence between these two classes. This correspondence is nothing else than a general operation in the sense introduced above. The proper description of such classes is a major task, and the description of the requisite correspondence between the two is even more difficult.

3 A key feature of programming is the ability to make the computer perform a certain action *repeatedly*. A computer program is interesting and useful only if it contains one or more repetitions; otherwise, it would be just as easy to carry it out by hand.

Now a repetition is a concrete way of achieving generality: it is the production of a whole set of objects, the sequence of machine states brought about by the successive instances of the repeated action. It is well known that designing correct combinations of repetitions is a fundamental problem of computing, and one of the most difficult.

Conclusion

The above examples are just initial evidence for our assertion that achieving generality is the ultimate aim of computing. All the developments presented in this book will provide further support for it. They will also show that this principle has a much wider significance than the given examples suggest.

In conclusion, 'generality' is our cue. To the student of computing, we are not saying: 'Your task is to study computers and how to program them'. This is the wrong goal because it is based on the mistaken belief that to know how computers work and are controlled is to understand their real significance as tools of action. Why is this a fallacy? Because although the way computers work may be described exactly, such a description does not even begin to tell us anything about their full potential and how they should be used in practice.

What we are saying instead to the student of computing is: 'Study generality. Seek to understand its significance. Learn to recognize it in all circumstances. Constantly look for ways of achieving it, for the most general methods. Take this advice and you will stand a better chance of understanding what computing is all about.'

1 A View of System Development

1.1 On systems and computers

1.1A Computing: a new perspective

As a discipline, computing owes its existence to the modern digital electronic computer. It may be defined concretely as the branch of science concerned with the construction and use of computers. These machines are controlled by *programs*, or *software* as these are called collectively. The term 'computing' is also used in a stricter sense, as concerned solely with the creation of software.

In this book, 'computing' is understood in this narrower sense. *Its main aim is to present theories and methods conducive to the development of sound computer software.* However, the difficulty of the task cannot be overstated. Anyone who sets out to create software faces a triple challenge:

(1) How to produce *correct* software, that is, programs which meet their requirements exactly and completely.

(2) How to produce *adaptable* software, that is, programs which are easy to adapt to new requirements and likely changes in their environment.

(3) More generally, how can the *potential* of today's and tomorrow's computers be fully exploited?

Since the advent of the modern electronic computer in the mid-forties, these aims have proved very hard to achieve (see, for example, Brookes, 1975 and Sommerville, 1989). The reasons for these difficulties are not clear. What is now emerging is that we may have been misled by the apparent *transparency* of computer technology. As we shall see, computers may be described exactly and very simply. However this does *not* mean that we truly understand their real, concrete significance. What matters is not so much the machine in itself but *how it can be used* – that is, *integrated into our activities – and how these must be transformed as a result.* In this respect, we seem to have generally failed to recognize one fundamental fact: as Dijkstra put it, *the computer is a radical novelty*, and as such it requires radically new ways of thinking (Dijkstra, 1989).

The following analogy will illustrate the problem. Our 'understanding in principle' of computers is like knowing the rules of chess, but to understand the concrete significance of these machines is similar to knowing how to play chess well. Any educated person knows there is a world of difference between the two. Yet when it comes to computing, this very difference seems to elude us. We have still to discover the methods that will distinguish grandmasters from laymen.

One main example of the limiting effect of 'traditional thinking' is the dominance of procedural programming, still largely prevalent today in computing. It is based on the principle that the fundamental task of computing is to write instructions which exactly determine the sequence of actions to be executed by the computer, where each action is described as a machine state transformation. This idea is common sense, it may be argued: it simply reflects the way computers work! But it is precisely this kind of plausible reasoning which has restricted our thinking. It means that our approach to computing has been driven primarily by the characteristics of the computer, the so-called Von Neumann or sequential machine to be precise, and this has precluded alternative and more fruitful approaches.

The limitations of the traditional procedural view of computing have been pointed out by scientists – for instance, quite forcefully by Backus (1978). Indeed, there are alternative approaches – for example, the *declarative* and the *functional* ones. These are only loosely coupled to the characteristics of computers, and as a result they are often more natural, more flexible and simpler than the procedural view.

For these various reasons, the present book is based on a very different perspective of computing. The starting point is not the question of how to program computers effectively but the following reasoning. Computers are general-purpose machines. They can be used to solve or at least assist with the solution of any type of problem. Therefore, there is a need *to devise general methods of problem solving*, that is, *methods suitable for the solution of the most general classes of problems.* This is taken as the ultimate aim of computing. Computers must, of course, be taken into account, but as means to general ends. As far as they are concerned, the problem is to determine how they are likely to affect our methods. This question must be addressed, but in due course.

Consequently, the aim of this section is to outline a general theory of problem solving, which forms the basis of this book. This theory is first developed in Section 1.1B without reference to computers. The relevant features of the latter are analysed in Section 1.1C. Finally, these two theories are integrated in Section 1.1D.

This approach to computing implies that further references to computers in subsequent chapters are marginal. However, the reader should not conclude that the models developed in this book are remote from their implementation in machine-executable language. On the contrary, they are quite close to implementation, although this aspect will not be discussed.

1.1B General problem solving

Systems

What is a problem, and how do we solve problems in general? This question is tantamount to asking: how do human beings relate to the world and, more specifically, their environment?

Immediate experience tells us that we are immersed in a universe which appears to us as a multiplicity of *objects* or entities *related* in many ways. Some objects are transient and others more permanent; some are features of others; some are physical – that is, perceived by the senses: for example, boats, mountains, people or historical events – whereas others are conceptual – for example, the notions of sets, relations, numbers and other general ideas. An object is anything that may be named and distinguished from other objects.

Many objects consist of *sets* of other objects, often related in various ways. Relations between objects are themselves 'higher-order' objects. These observations lead us to the concept of a *system*. In the most general sense, a system is *any collection of objects related in various ways*. It turns out that practically any phenomenon may be described as a system. Thus, we postulate that any object of our universe consists of a system of some kind.

Here are some examples. Any physical product of daily use is a system. For instance, a car is made up of a set of components: body, chassis, engine, wheels, and so on. These are related in multiple ways. They are rigidly fastened together; their relative spatial position is important; the engine must be connected to the wheels to transmit motion, and to the petrol tank as the source of energy, and so on. In turn, each component is a subsystem described similarly.

A person is a system. He or she is a combination of limbs and organs linked in numerous ways, functionally and otherwise. A town is a system of persons, houses and other resources connected by streets, sewers, electric power lines, telecommunication lines, transport facilities and so forth. Its inhabitants are in perpetual motion and interaction, which are just further forms of relations. A country may be described similarly as a system involving towns connected in multiple ways.

Systems may also be of a conceptual or mixed nature. A language is an example. It involves a hierarchy of symbols: letters, words, phrases, sentences and so on, related by rules of grammar and usage. Human relations involve numerous other examples of rule systems, ranging from simple games to legal and political structures governing millions of individuals. The list of examples may be extended *ad infinitum*.

It must be emphasized that in practice there are many different ways of identifying systems. A system is always a certain *part* of the world, whose selection is for the observer to decide. Consequently, a system may also be regarded as a certain *view* of certain objects, varying with the features selected by the observer. For instance, a car may be described as above. Alternatively, it may be depicted as an object moving in space under the control of its driver. In this second, dynamic description, the position in space and the velocity of the vehicle are part of the system described.

Problems

A second fact of experience is that there are two fundamental relations between any observer and any system. First, the observer has or may obtain a certain *knowledge* of the system, a representation or an understanding of it. Second, the observer may have a *degree of control* over the system – that is, he or she may influence or modify it in some way. Both of these relations may vary in quality and degree. Furthermore, the control of an object is always relative, because any object is determined by its own laws, which necessarily impose limits on the extent and form of its control. For instance, a driver may have complete control of a car, but the form of this control is closely determined by the operating characteristics of the vehicle: these are imposed on the driver.

These two relations between observer and observed are quite distinct but closely linked. Often the control of a system depends on the information available about it. Conversely, the control of a system may be a means of gaining more information on it. Thus in general, information and control closely interact and should be considered simultaneously. Therefore we shall call the ability to influence a system *effective* or *strict control*, and extend the term 'control' to subsume both information and effective control. A general theory of control has been developed along these lines by the mathematician Norbert Wiener under the name 'cybernetics' (from the Greek word for 'pilot'); see Wiener (1954).

We may classify systems by the extent and nature of our control over them. In particular, the control of any system is either *direct*, or more or less *indirect* – that is, through other systems. A system is *distant* if our control of it is limited and indirect, and *close* otherwise. Distance is, of course, a matter of degree. At one extreme, there are systems that are known but over which we have no effective control. Typical examples are the solar system, galaxies, and so on. At the other extreme, there are systems over which our effective control is total and immediate. These are our thoughts, direct actions, the sentences we utter or write, and so on. Other systems fall somewhere in between.

Distant systems are controlled *indirectly*, through other, closer systems. For instance, we control a car by acting on the steering wheel and pedals; a computer by pressing keys and interpreting the messages it returns; an organization by issuing orders to middle managers and analysing their reports; and so on. Often control involves several intermediate systems. For instance, the ultimate aim in controlling a business organization may be to induce a certain market to buy a certain product. The market is the final system to be controlled.

It is our ability to control distant systems via closer ones that creates *problems*. A problem arises when, following our understanding of the world, we seek to transform it in some way, to obtain certain results. These constitute *objectives* to achieve, and the problem is to find and activate the means of achieving them. In each case, the means are closer, intermediate systems connecting the decision-maker to the final system to control. This description holds even in the case where the desired result is purely informational, as a piece of information is an object in its own right, which must be obtained and preserved, and may be used to further ends.

Models

An important class of close systems, used mainly as intermediaries in the control of more distant ones, is the class of models. A model is a *simplified representation of another system*. For instance, an architect's drawing is a model of a house to build; a road map is a model of the road system of a country. A model is a system in its own right. Its distinctive features are as follows:

1 A model is created or selected in order to understand and/or effectively control another, more distant system. Thus, the drawings of a house-to-be are intended to show the main features of the house and to guide the builders at the construction stage. Consequently, the notion of a model implies the existence of two distinct systems: (a) the *represented* system, which the model describes; and (b) the model itself.

2 There must be a certain relationship between the represented system and the model: somehow, the latter must constitute some description of the former. This means that *there must be a suitable correspondence between the features of the represented system and those of the model.* For instance, in a drawing representing the front of a house, the distance between any two points should be proportional to the distance between the represented points. In general, the correspondence between the model and the represented system should be such that an investigation of the model (or other kind of operation on it) will yield information on the main system and possibly the means of effectively controlling it.

3 The correspondence between the model and the represented system is generally achieved by 'incorporating' *some* features of the represented system in the model. Therefore, the features of the represented system fall into two groups: those captured by the model, often very few indeed; and all the others.

This separation is a form of abstraction; the discarded features of the represented object are said to be *abstracted away* in the model. For instance a perspective drawing of the front of a house captures only some of the visible features of the house. All other features, materials, internal layout, plumbing and so on, are ignored.

4 The choice of features captured in the model should be the result of a reasoned decision. In general this depends on the *purpose* for which the model is intended, that is, the type of control it is intended to serve. For example perspective drawings are designed to convey the general appearance of a house in its surroundings to an external observer. The emphasis is not on accuracy but on the total impression which the house is meant to create. Detailed drawings, on the other hand, are more sober, more precise and supplemented with distances and so on. Their purpose is to give precise guidance to all those involved in the construction of the house.

5 Both the represented system and the model are subject to their own (internal) laws. The main reason for resorting to the model is that its laws are different from those of the main system, and consequently it is easier to manipulate – more tightly controlled – than the original. For instance, a drawing is obtained by running a pencil on a sheet of paper, with the help of a straight edge, compasses and other instruments. The necessary techniques of drawing are laws imposed on the draughtsman. The actual building process is subject to entirely different laws: physical laws of mechanics and chemistry, which in turn determine laws of cement mixing, bricklaying, carpentry, etc.; laws of organization and communication to direct and coordinate workers, and so on.

The internal laws to which a model is subject are the rules imposed on its *construction* and its *use*. (Constructing and using a model are two levels of control.) The internal laws governing *symbolic models* (described below) form the *notation* in which the model is expressed. By analogy, we shall say that for *any* type of model, the internal laws to which it is subject form its 'notation'. These rules must be well understood by the model builder.

The term 'model' is often used in a narrow sense. This is to ignore the universality of models and their fundamental role not only in science but in every walk of life: they arise everywhere. Here are some examples. In each case the reader may verify that all the features of models listed above are present.

1 *Static physical models.* Any plan, drawing, blueprint, mock-up or map is a model. The case of architectural drawings has already been discussed. The other examples may be analysed in a similar way. Paintings, photographs, sculptures and so on are models of a similar nature, whether created for artistic or purely functional reasons.

2 *Dynamic physical models.* A model is dynamic if it is 'active', that is, evolves in time. Examples are wind tunnels, reduced-size replicas of engines or other devices and prototypes. Computers themselves may be regarded as general-purpose dynamic models.

3 *Plays and games.* Theatre plays and motion pictures may be viewed as dynamic models involving people: they simulate human relations and situations. Games of all types are models of a similar nature. Chess, for instance, may be interpreted as a model of warlike situations; business games are used to represent interactions between economic agents; and so on.

4 *Symbolic models.* Any form of symbolic expression is a model. This includes the words, sentences and speeches we utter and the texts we write. For instance, a name is a representation of an object or a person. A sentence is a representation of a theory, a fact, a situation or a chain of events. The languages in which we express ourselves are either *natural* – for example, English or Spanish – or extensions of natural languages – for instance, mathematical notation. Natural languages are the most widely and frequently used modelling instruments. They are *universal*, as they may be used to represent *any* idea, fact or situation.

5 *Theoretical models.* Symbolic models must be distinguished from *theoretical* or *conceptual models*, although these two types are closely related. A theoretical model is a concept or a system of concepts representing any other type of reality, itself physical or conceptual. It is a purely *mental* or *ideal* object. For instance, the notion of a person is a theoretical model. It is a representation of any human being, either existing, or past, or to be born, or purely hypothetical. Most of the models developed in subsequent chapters of this book fall into this category.

To sum up, any type of problem-solving or purposeful activity may be described as follows. An agent seeks to control some distant system, either to obtain information about it or to influence it in some desired way. This is the agent's goal. It is achieved through the control of one or more intermediate systems, the agent's means of information and action. The intermediate systems are closer to the agent and therefore easier to control. They are essentially *models* of the distant system. Controlling them means, as for any system, either studying them and their relationships to the distant system and/or manipulating them in some way. In general, the whole process involves a chain of intermediate systems between the agent and the distant system. Henceforth, we shall regard any relatively close system as a model. This very theory is a conceptual model of the general process of problem solving.

1.1C Radical novelties

We now return to computers. We must establish their essential properties and how these are likely to affect problem solving in general. Computers are models. They are close systems, which we know and effectively control. They also mediate between us and distant systems, mainly by providing information on the latter but also, though less commonly, by effectively controlling the latter. Their essential features may be described by a very simple model. This is as follows, ignoring input and output devices (keyboard, screen and so on).

A digital electronic computer is an assembly of interconnected physical devices, which we shall simply call *registers*. At any time, each register is in a certain state, and the collection of the registers' states defines the overall state of the computer. These registers fall into different categories: registers proper, main and backup store locations and so on, but these distinctions are not essential for our purpose.

The possible states of a register are *discrete*. This means that they are well separated from one another. It also means that a register has a finite number of possible states, and that these may be replicated exactly. It is useful to think of a register state as the representation of a natural number in a fixed range, 0 to 255 for instance. Practically, registers are used to represent any information that may be *coded* as a list of numbers.

The *behaviour* of the computer is the sequence of states $(S_0, S_1, S_2, \ldots)$ that it takes on over time, given a certain initial state S_0. Each state S_i in the sequence is entirely and exactly determined by its immediate predecessor, S_{i-1}. Consequently, the whole sequence is exactly determined by its starting state S_0, and to control the computer is a matter of fixing S_0. This is done by a *program*. In fact, we may define a program as the first state S_0 of the sequence it determines. As the program is fixed by the user (programmer), the computer's behaviour is entirely determined by the user. This completes our model of the computer. Although very simple, this theoretical model is entirely rigorous.

As such, our model does not yet fully explain the nature and extent of our control (knowledge and effective control) of computers. Four further related characteristics must be added to complete the picture; we describe these in turn, in the light of our elementary model.

1 *Very high storage capacity.* The number of registers in a computer is very high. For instance, the storage capacity of a good personal computer today may be five million bytes of main store and 100 million bytes of backup store, typically hard disk. (A byte is a number in the range 0 to 255.) For mainframes and supercomputers, these figures are much higher.

2 *Very high processing speed.* The processing speed of a computer may be defined as the average speed at which it moves from one state to the next. This is very high by comparison with the speed of common human actions. Nowadays, the speed of computers is measured in multiples of millions of operations per second, where an operation is an elementary state change.

3 *Total determinism.* Consider the property that at any time the state of the computer is exactly determined by its immediate predecessor in time. This may also be expressed by saying that any machine state is an exactly determined *function* of its immediate predecessor. It is emphasized that this function is a constant, physical characteristic of the computer (the 'hardware'). It is called the *state transition function.* This property, together with the discrete nature of the registers' possible states, has the following implications.

First, each possible machine state is completely distinct from all the others. Moreover, it may be *exactly replicated*, either on the same machine at different times, or on a different but equivalent machine (one with the same state transition function).

Second, if at any time t the computer is in a given state S_0, then the whole sequence of states $(S_0, S_1, S_2, \ldots)$ from time t onward is exactly determined by S_0. Consequently any state *sequence* $(S_0, S_1, S_2, \ldots)$ may be exactly replicated, either on the same machine at different times, or on another, equivalent machine, simply by fixing the starting state as S_0. For the same reason, given the state transition function, for any given state S_0, we may potentially predict its successors $S_1, S_2, \ldots$ with complete accuracy.

4 *Potentially very high sensitivity.* The three previous properties have a final consequence. Consider two state sequences $S = (S_0, S_1, S_2, \ldots)$ and $S' = (S'_0, S'_1, S'_2, \ldots)$. Just as they are entirely identical if their initial states S_0 and S'_0 are equal, *the slightest difference between S_0 and S'_0 may produce two very different sequences,* except for a few initial states perhaps. The implication of this fact is crucial: in a *computer program or a set of data, every feature, however minute – literally every 'bit' – may be just as important as the program as a whole.*

To put it another way, the behaviour of the computer may be extremely sensitive to the slightest change in programs or data, however small. This is not to say that *any* small change must necessarily produce major differences in the computer's behaviour, but that in general *some* small variations will completely alter the subsequent behaviour of the machine.

In conclusion, computers are modelling tools of enormous power. They enable us to create a quasi-infinite variety of models of practically unbounded complexity – namely, their various state sequences $(S_0, S_1, S_2, \ldots)$ and the outputs they determine. These are capable of simulating any kind of reality, often in relatively little time. However, in the last analysis these computer-generated objects are entirely determined by our own actions, through the programs we write. Therefore we are faced with a formidable *choice problem,* compounded by the need for complete accuracy implied by the potentially very high sensitivity of the computer to the smallest program variations.

Another major implication of the characteristics of computers is this. As the behaviour of a computer is entirely and exactly determined by its initial state and its state transition function, in principle any aspect of this behaviour may be predicted solely by *deductive reasoning.* Consequently, this type of reasoning must play a dominant role in computer system development. It is indeed central to the modelling methodology developed in this book. The whole of Part **3** may be regarded as a formalization of this kind of reasoning, and the various developments of Parts **4** and **5** are entirely based on it.

1.1D Computers and general problem solving

Finally, we return to the main question: what is the influence of computers on our ability to solve problems in general? How are they integrated into our general problem-solving methods? How *should* they be?

We repeat that our ultimate concern is *not* the control of computers in itself, but general problem solving: how to control – that is, know and/or effectively control – more or less distant systems such as organizations, resource systems, complex projects or national economies. This we do by building and manipulating models of various types: symbolic, conceptual, physical and so on. It is through these intermediaries that we control distant systems.

In general, a single application requires not one but a multiplicity of models of different types. These are related in many different ways: they form a *system* of models. For instance, the building of a house requires multiple narratives, drawings, mock-ups, bills of materials, execution plans that list tasks to perform with their resource and other requirements, schedules of tasks, etc. All these elements form a complex hierarchy of models and submodels, a close system in its own right. The central problem in each application is to find the appropriate overall model, that is, the right combination of models, each of the right type and expressed in the right notation.

Computers and computer programs are just models of a certain type. In any application, computer programs are only *part* of the appropriate total model. They must be supplemented with many other models. These fall roughly into two main groups. Some are *preliminary descriptions* which pave the way to the programs. The others, such as user manuals, serve other, related purposes.

Why do programs require preliminary descriptions? The answer is that because of the very general nature of computers and their enormous modelling potential, the construction of adequate programs is a complex task. It involves myriads of choices, which must not be arbitrary but based on reasoned analysis. The main steps needed before programming are:

(1) analysis of the problem domain and determination of the functional and other requirements which the programs must satisfy;

(2) program specification – that is, precise and complete description of the effects of the programs as they will be seen by the user (as opposed to the programmer);

(3) program design – that is, decomposition of the programs into components and subcomponents and specification of their interrelationships.

For all but the most trivial applications, each of these steps is a complex task, which requires great care and effort. Its outcome must be an *appropriate description* of the relevant factors. Such a description is nothing else than a model, to be constructed in the most effective notation: the proper combination of natural language, special symbolic notation, diagrams and so on. Although the first stage tends to be more informal than the others, *every* stage requires the right mix of formal and informal methods.

These models mediate between us, our computer programs and, beyond these, the distant system(s) we seek to control. Therefore they must not be considered in isolation. An understanding of the relation between each model and the next in the chain is as important as each model on its own. This relation has been described above essentially as a control link (of information and effective control) from one model to the next.

One of the main challenges of computing today is to devise appropriate notations, methods and tools in support of each stage. These must allow in particular for the need to relate successive models as indicated, that is, to integrate them in a coherent whole. The theories and conceptual models presented in this book are a contribution to this endeavour.

1.2 Universal features of systems

A distant system is closely linked to the multiple intermediate systems, the models, through which we control it. Indeed, we perceive and/or effectively control the former *entirely* through the latter. Thus although these various objects are distinct, their interrelationships are essential. Consequently *a distant system together with all its models* is a system in its own right, which we shall call a *total system*. It is generally appropriate to take total systems as primary objects of consideration, as they include 'everything we may be interested in'. Henceforth 'system' will generally mean a total system unless otherwise indicated by the context.

This section describes a number of fundamental features of total systems. These characteristics are universal: they can be found in all systems. The purpose of this section is threefold: first, to motivate the theory presented in subsequent chapters; second, to clarify the link between this theory and modelling as such; and third, to pave the way for the construction of the various illustrative models we develop later, especially in Parts **4** and **5**. These applications will amply demonstrate the relevance of the analysis below.

Six universal features of systems appear to be relevant to our purposes. As will be seen, these features closely reflect the principle of generality adopted as our starting proposition. They are as follows:

(1) structure
(2) taxonomy
(3) modules: components and interfaces
(4) notation
(5) transformation
(6) establishment: specification and analysis

We now consider these in turn.

1.2A Structure

A system has been defined above as a collection of objects related in various ways (Section **1**.1B). This is a very general and abstract description. For our purposes we need a more comprehensive or 'concrete' concept. Consequently we shall regard this initial definition as capturing only one feature of a system, albeit a fundamental one. This aspect is called the *structure* of the system.

More precisely, a structure consists of a set of objects and a set of relations between these objects. The objects may be any entities, including components, aspects or features of other objects. They may themselves be sets of other objects or even substructures in their own right. A relation may be defined informally as a collection of 'links', each of which 'connects' two or more given objects. Like any object, a link may be physical (for example, a road between two cities) or conceptual (for example, the property that 0 precedes 1 in the set of natural numbers).

As a structure is defined in almost the same way as a system, how do these two notions differ? A structure is a 'pure' concept: we regard it as entirely described by the above definition. However, as mentioned above, we want a more comprehensive definition of a system. In particular, we wish to include the various other features mentioned above in our concept of system. These features are not necessarily present in a structure, which is why a distinction is made between these two notions. Note, however, that the structure of a system is its most general aspect: other features too have structure, in particular the other universal features mentioned above.

The concept of structure is central to all subsequent developments. The theory of sets introduced in Part **2**, including relations and functions, may be viewed as a mathematical theory of structures. Logic, treated in Part **3**, is mainly concerned with the formalization of this theory.

1.2B Taxonomy

An important task in constructing systems is to identify *general categories* or *classes* of objects and how these relate to one another. The categories may be more or less *general* and *abstract*. Altogether they form the *taxonomy* or *classification* of the system. The construction of a taxonomy is itself called classification.

The universality of this feature may be demonstrated as follows. When we refer to an object, we very rarely mean a certain, individual thing. In most cases, we actually mean a certain *class* of objects (considered 'one at a time'). This is the principle of generality introduced in the prologue. We sometimes emphasize this fact by using the phrase 'object type' instead of merely 'object'. Accordingly, we assume that whenever we consider a system we actually regard it as a member of some class of systems, more precisely as a variable ranging over the class. The same applies to any component or any other feature of the system.

For the same reasons, we are generally led to consider not just one but a multiplicity of classes of objects. Indeed, a class is an object in its own right, which we may want to vary like any object. So we may vary classes within classes within classes, and so on, to any number of levels of variation.

In conclusion, the description of a system always involves implicitly or explicitly defining multiple classes of instances of the system or any of its features. These classes form the taxonomy of the system described. What matters is to determine which classes are worth defining explicitly – that is, to construct a *suitable* taxonomy.

The process of classification is important in all fields of scientific or technological activity, a fact which has been known at least since Greek antiquity. It is particularly relevant to the construction of software systems, because of the enormous potential of computers. Any system may involve many different features: functions mainly, but also modes of action or 'contexts', relations with other systems such as compatibility, and so on. These features generally fall into many different classes or varieties. These should be made explicit in order to clarify the nature of the system and to master its complexity.

The need for taxonomy is reinforced by the fact that many systems are 'open': their features may be expected to evolve substantially during their lifetime. This is a further factor calling for the identification of classes and subclasses of features and systems, possibly of a high degree of generality. The main point is: always think of an object or a feature not as fixed but as liable to vary over any number of classes or 'dimensions' of variation.

1.2C Modules: components and interfaces

The central problem in constructing a system is to establish the various components of the system and their interrelationships, to the extent that they are controlled. It must be emphasized that this is very much a matter of *choice* by the constructor, and usually there are numerous alternatives to choose from.

In order to control (know or influence) the components of a system, we must be able to *separate* them from one another in some suitable sense, physically, conceptually or otherwise. We must also be able to *combine* them – that is, to (re)establish their interrelationships, as the latter are essential features of the system. Thus as a rule, when building a system, we should always seek to maximize the separability and combinability of its components; the ideal construction is one in which each component is controlled in total isolation from, and yet is easy to integrate with, the rest of the system. Note that these two properties are closely linked: they are the two sides of the same coin.

The concept of a *module* addresses this fundamental aim. In a very general sense, a module is any component of a system which is 'well separated' from the other parts, and whose relationships to the rest of the system are 'simple' and established as completely and precisely as possible. This implies that in any (ideal) module, we may identify *two parts*: its *body* and its *interface*.

The *body* of a module is its set of 'internal' features. It comprises all the elements which must be present when the module is completely isolated from the rest of the system. The *interface* of a module consists of all the connections, conceptual or physical, between the module and the rest of the system. It is the linchpin holding these two together.

The role of a module's interface is crucial in two ways. On the one hand, it must contain all the elements needed to control the body completely. For instance, it should provide all the information needed to determine how the body should be constructed, what its essential properties should be, what it should 'do'; no references to other parts of the system should be necessary for this purpose. On the other hand, the interface should contain all the essential relations between the module and the rest of the system. In particular, it should provide all the information needed to determine what the module 'requires' from its environment, or how it is or can be 'used' by the rest of the system; no references to the body should be necessary for this purpose.

In conclusion, it is only by breaking down a system into components and *fully specifying their interfaces* that we may completely separate the control (knowledge and/or construction) of each component from its integration within the rest of the system, and thus master the latter's complexity. Therefore, in constructing any system we should always seek as far as possible to establish its components and subcomponents as modules in the sense just defined. Note that what we have given above is a very general definition of a module, which it is better to leave somewhat vague. It is an *ideal*, which it may not always be possible to achieve completely.

The concept of a module is natural and indeed universal. Its application can be observed in human organizations, complex physical products, computer systems, the organization of mathematics, and so on. For instance, this last discipline proceeds by building systems of theorems and proofs. A theorem and its proof may be regarded as a module: the interface is the theorem itself, the body is the proof, and these are built and used as described above. Software systems may be described in the same way.

A fundamental idea of software development theory is the so-called principle of *separation of concerns*. It is that different aspects of a system should be handled separately, ideally as separate modules – see for instance Liskov and Guttag (1986). This is essentially another way of advocating the modular approach to system development. The theoretical models built in Parts **4** and **5** will provide comprehensive illustrations of these principles.

1.2D Notation

As we have seen, any (total) system has a *notation*, the collection of (internal) laws governing the various models of which it is made up: the grammatical rules of the author; the drawing methods of the draughtsman; the carving techniques of the sculptor; the programming languages of the computer programmer, and so on. If the system comprises models of different types, its 'notation' is the sum of the notations of its various constituent models.

For any model, notational rules are of two types. Some are imposed by nature – they are laws of physics or mathematics. The others are conventional – established not by observation but by 'decree', as it were, and therefore more or less arbitrary. These two types of rule interact closely: a notation must be *established* in the sense defined below (Section **1**.2F).

There is no absolute divide between establishing a notation and building models in a given notation. These are two aspects of modelling or system construction, and they are best regarded as two interacting components of a common process. The notation designer is concerned with establishing a certain set of models, all those which may be built in the specified notation, but this set is a system in its own right. Conversely the model builder is often actually concerned with not one but a whole family of models, and so, often, a key part of modelling is to extend or refine a basic notation.

The rules of a notation fall into three main categories: *syntax*, *semantics* and *calculi*. These are universal. They are particularly apparent in symbolic models, which are our primary concern, but they can also be found in other types of model. They are extensively illustrated in logic, developed in Part **3**. We introduce these categories in turn.

1 *Syntax.* Any notation starts with two groups of *syntactic rules*. The first specifies a set of primitive or basic objects, and the second how these may be combined to produce a model. These laws form the syntax of the notation. In the case of symbolic models, the basic objects are called *symbols*. They are distinct from one another and (normally) finite in number. Their set is called the *alphabet* of the notation. In diagrammatic models, typical primitive objects are 'boxes' of various shapes, such as circles and rectangles, and lines or arrows to connect them.

The second group of syntactic rules determines how the primitive objects may be legally assembled to form more complex objects or '*valid units*'. In most symbolic notations, valid units are linear: they are lists of basic symbols to be 'read' in the order of the list. In formal notations, they are called (well-defined) *expressions*, more specifically *terms* or *formulas*. In natural languages, the valid units are words, sentences, paragraphs and so on. Clearly not all sequences of characters constitute legal words or sentences: the syntax is there to separate the valid from the invalid ones. In diagrammatic notations, these syntactic rules typically determine how boxes may be linked by connecting lines, their allowed relative positions, and so on.

In general, the set of valid units has a hierarchical structure: valid combinations of basic objects may in turn be used as building blocks of more complex units, and this may be repeated indefinitely. The various units may be further separated into multiple classes. Such classified hierarchical structure is quite apparent in natural languages.

2 *Semantics.* The second set of rules of any notation defines the 'meaning' of each valid unit. These rules form the semantics of the notation. They determine the correspondence between the various features of any model built in the notation, and the aspects of the object which the model represents. The syntax and semantics of a notation are closely related. Whereas the description of syntax is independent of semantics, the latter closely depends on and follows the former.

3 *Calculi.* Any notation may contain a third category of rules. In general these may fall into different subgroups called '*calculi*'. A calculus for a given notation is a set of rules on the objects (models or model components) defined by the syntax. The main purpose of these rules is to represent the semantics of the notation, but in an entirely 'formal' way – that is, solely by the objects which the syntax defines and by operations on these objects. Therefore, although a calculus 'expresses semantics', *its rules are of the same nature as syntactic rules*, a fact of crucial importance.

1.2E Transformation

Many aspects of systems may be described as transformations of some kind. A transformation is a rule or a process which, given the features of a first object in some class, determines the features of a second object. Thus, a transformation does not generally apply to a single object, but to a whole class of objects: with each of them it associates a second object and determines all its features. A transformation is essentially the same as a function, one of the most important concepts of mathematics. Indeed, the terms 'transformation', 'function' and 'operation' are often used interchangeably. The following examples clearly demonstrate the universality of this feature.

1 By definition, any effectively controllable system may be viewed as a transformation. It converts the actions on it to certain responses, that is, to a certain behaviour. For instance, a computer program may be described in this way. It transforms a sequence of 'inputs' (for example, commands) into a sequence of 'outputs' (messages and so on), different inputs generally producing different outputs. This 'black box' view of a program is very appropriate.

2 The various models making up a total system are generally related in many ways, as we have seen. Often the most important relation between two constituent models is a transformation of one of them into the other. For instance, consider the successive models leading to a computer program briefly described in Section **1**.1D. Each description must be the result of a transformation of its predecessor(s). Thus, the initial semiformal description of user requirements and the precise program specification which follows are not independent: the latter must be a faithful translation of the former. Likewise, the design of the program is determined by – that is, must be a function of – its specification. Finally, the actual program in machine-executable language must be a function of its design.

3 We have just outlined two dimensions of transformation of a system. A third dimension is the *evolution* of the system in time. It is generally important to view a system as *open* and *in permanent evolution*. Clearly its successive versions are not independent: each is normally the result of a transformation ('update') of its predecessor.

Many other examples could be given. Serious efforts should be made by system builders to identify the various transformations arising in systems and system development, and to establish their rules as precisely as possible. This, however, is one of the most difficult (and seemingly neglected) tasks of system construction.

1.2F Establishment: specification and analysis

The last universal feature of systems we consider is *establishment*. This term is used here in a new and specific sense, which is now to be defined and justified. It reflects the observation made earlier that the two aspects of control, information and effective control, usually interact closely.

The features of any total system fall into two main categories. Some characteristics are *specified* in the strict sense of the term: they are selected by arbitrary choice from some set of alternatives. The others are *derived* or *implied*: they are determined by the specified characteristics and by the laws (of logic, physics, convention, and so on) imposed on the controlling agent (system builder or user). Consequently, the control (construction or use) of any system may be broken down into two corresponding groups of activities:

(1) *specification*, the selection of the specified features of the system
(2) *analysis*, the identification of the derived features of the system

Two important facts must now be pointed out. First, specified and derived features are in general closely intertwined. Whenever an additional feature is specified, a number of consequences immediately follow, often including a reduction in the range of choices remaining to the system builder. In principle these consequences should be immediately determined – if only because the range of available alternatives with respect to any feature should always be well defined. Consequently, the two corresponding types of activity, specification and analysis, are tightly interdependent and should be regarded as part of a single process. The term 'establishment' is applied to this joint process as it has the double meaning of either laying down a rule or determining a fact. This term is also used to refer to the system's features themselves as they have been established – that is, either specified or derived by analysis.

Second, in general the establishment status of any system feature is *relative*: for the same system, a feature may be specified in one description and derived in another. Naturally the status of the various features is interdependent: if a feature is specified in description *D1* and derived in description *D2* of a given system, there must be another feature that is derived in *D1* and specified in *D2*. The establishment status of system features typically reflects the chronological or priority order in which features are established. It may be appropriate to leave this status open to revision in the course of system development. These are further reasons for emphasizing the interactive nature of specification and analysis.

It is emphasized that establishment pertains to each main stage of software development in particular. For instance, 'specification of requirements' is a misnomer. Like any other features, the user's requirements are never laid down entirely freely. Very often they are themselves implied at least partly by deeper motives, and by constraints imposed on the user. Moreover they must be *consistent* – they must conform to the general laws of logic, physics, and so on imposed on the system builder. In a nutshell, it must be possible to build a system which satisfies them all. This is why the 'specification of requirements' generally includes substantial elements of analysis, just like any other stage of the development process, and 'establishment of requirements' is the appropriate term.

The concept of establishment is a fundamental principle of the modelling method described in Parts **4** and **5**. It is elaborated on in these two parts and thoroughly illustrated by the various conceptual models developed there.

1.3 System development with set theory and logic

In the previous two sections, we have introduced a certain view of computing, systems and system development. This view is at the basis of the theories and methods which form the main subject matter of this book and are developed in Parts **2** to **5**. This introductory chapter concludes with an overview of these theories and methods, focusing on the key ideas which motivate them.

The main purpose of this book is to present a general methodology of system development, or problem solving. This methodology is based on set theory and logic. The intention is not to provide a comprehensive coverage of mathematical methods in computing. The general aims of the book are more limited, and as follows.

The first aim is to introduce the reader to a small number of fundamental ideas, carefully selected for their relevance and universality, both in theory and in practice. These ideas should not simply be 'studied'; they should be truly *mastered.*

The second aim is to illustrate these ideas by numerous applications, ranging from simple examples to large case studies. These have been selected for their concrete and practical value, as well as relevance to the specific points they are to illustrate. These applications are more than mere illustrations. They are intended to provide the reader with ample opportunities to put into practice the theories and methods taught here within a rich and realistic 'problem situation'. It is only through intensive practice that the reader will fully master the methodology and turn it into an effective – and enjoyable – tool of the trade.

We now turn to the more specific objectives of the book.

1.3A Introduction to set theory

The first objective is to introduce the basic concepts of set theory in a semiformal manner and to show their relevance to system development in the sense understood here: the total description of any type of object, any (distant) system we may be interested in. The key goal is to present set theory as a *modelling instrument of universal applicability*, and as a primary tool of the trade for computing professionals: programmers, analysts, theoreticians and general users of computer tools or packages. This goal will be fully achieved when practitioners are seen to use set theory as naturally and extensively as they use programming languages such as Pascal or C today.

The branch of mathematics known as set theory is well established. Its fundamental concepts and notation are standard and widely accepted in all scientific and engineering disciplines, give or take some variations of presentation. What is not generally understood is the full significance of set theory. The 'importance' of this subject is universally acknowledged in principle. However, it seems to be generally regarded as little more than an interesting theory, occasionally useful in the solution of practical problems. In computing in particular, set theory plays a major role in advanced research, but its practical relevance does not seem to be understood by more than a small group of specialists.

However, there is far more to set theory. This subject precisely meets the fundamental requirements of computing, defined as general problem solving. First, set theory is a *universal* language. It is accepted that the whole body of mathematics may be expressed in the language of set theory, and this surely must include any problem solvable by computer. Second, as a language, set theory is extremely *simple* and *natural*. In particular, it is very close to natural language. This fact cannot be overstated, as it is far from being understood even among computing professionals.

The simplicity and naturalness of set theory are so remarkable that they are worth demonstrating at once by an example. Consider any simple concept, for example the notion of a 'parent', which children understand from a very early age. It turns out that *all the symbols of set theory are illustrated by the definition of this concept*. How do we define a parent? A reasonable answer is that it is *a person who is the mother or the father of another person*. This may be reformulated more precisely as follows:

> *Any person P is a parent if and only if there exists another person C such that P is the mother of C or P is the father of C.*

Clearly these two definitions are equivalent, and they express one of the simplest ideas that may be conceived. Thus it may come as a surprise to learn that: (a) the translation of the second version into set theory is immediate – that is, it is just a matter of substituting a few special symbols for their English counterparts; (b) as mentioned, this translation illustrates *all* the symbols of set theory, hence all the symbols necessary to define any concept, formulate any problem, express any solution. Here is this translation:

$$\forall\, P \in \text{Persons} \cdot$$
$$P \in \text{Parents iff}$$
$$\exists\, C \in \text{Persons} \cdot P = \text{Mother}(C) \text{ or } P = \text{Father}(C)$$

This formula may be understood with a minimum of explanations. '$\forall\, P$' means 'for any P'; '$P \in$ Persons' means 'P is in the set of all persons'; 'iff' stands for 'if and only if'; '$\exists$' means 'there exists'; and 'Mother(C)' means 'the mother of C'. The dot '$\cdot$' is a punctuation mark, and the whole expression has been split and indented to enhance readability.

This little example illustrates perfectly well what set theory is all about. It is a very simple notation, very close to natural language, as powerful as the latter but with major advantages over the latter: it is much simpler and more concise, and totally regular, unambiguous and accurate. It is hard to understand how we have for so long failed to grasp its universal modelling potential!

The basic ideas of set theory are covered in Chapters **2** and **3**. These ideas are illustrated by simple but practical examples at this stage; the more advanced and comprehensive applications are treated in Parts **4** (theory of lists, trees and related objects) and **5** (application case studies).

1.3B Induction and recursion

Induction and recursion are twin notions of fundamental importance in computing. A second objective of this book is to put these two concepts on a firm foundation and to show their *practical* relevance. The distinction between induction and recursion must be clarified. Induction is the more primitive of the two concepts. In the strict sense, it refers to a certain method of constructing a *set*, which is then said to be *inductively generated*. A recursion is a *function*, based on an inductively generated set. One cause of confusion is that the term 'inductive definition' is often used to mean a recursive function. We refer to induction and recursion jointly as *inductive constructions*.

Inductive constructions are powerful, and generally quite elegant and natural. They are very frequent in computing, although often in an implicit form. A first main application area is the definition of programming and other formal languages. The syntax of a formal language is almost inevitably defined inductively, and its semantics recursively. These definitions are entirely natural. Consider, for instance, the following statement: "To find the value of the expression '$a + (b - c)$', first find the values of the two subexpressions 'a' and '$(b - c)$'; then add these two values." This is a recursive definition; it is perfectly simple and natural.

Given the universality of inductive constructions, it seems important for computer scientists to be at least able to identify these constructions as they arise. This is not so easy, as the inductive nature of a definition is not always clear. One aim therefore is to clarify the nature of induction and recursion, and to develop the reader's skill at recognizing them.

Although it is relatively easy to understand *given* inductive constructions, it is more difficult to define them correctly. In general an inductive construction is correct only if certain conditions are satisfied. Given the importance of these constructions, computing students should be well aware of these conditions. The inductive generation of a set is relatively straightforward. The main difficulties start with recursion. In general, a function may be defined recursively on the basis of an inductively generated set only if the latter satisfies a fundamental condition: it must be *freely* generated, which roughly means that each of its elements must be produced in exactly one way by the generating rules. This is the import of the *recursion theorem*, which is fundamental. It provides the standard justification of the main recursive functions constructed in practice, such as the semantics of formal languages. Any student of computing should at least be aware of it and able to justify it intuitively. This theorem is treated in mathematical textbooks but rarely mentioned in computing ones, even when it is greatly relied upon, for example, in language theory or functional programming. Consequently, another aim is to introduce this theorem and explain its concrete significance. Induction and recursion are the topics of Chapter **4**.

1.3C Formal notation and symbolic logic

The next key topics of this book are the notions of *formal notation* or language, and *symbolic logic*. These are closely related. In particular, we regard logic primarily as a formal notation, ideally suited by its simplicity to illustrate the main principles of formal language specification. These topics are treated in Part **3**.

In Section **1**.2D, we pointed out that notation is a universal feature of any total system (that is, a distant system together with all its models). As *all* our work consists of creating models or descriptions of various kinds, the quality of our products greatly depends on the quality and suitability of the various notations we use, including natural languages. A notation may be more or less precisely and consciously defined. An imprecise notation leads to inaccurate or ambiguous models. A verbose and irregular notation increases the risks of errors. Therefore, we have a strong incentive to design and use notations which are simple, clear and regular, and totally accurate and unambiguous. A notation is called *formal* if it meets these requirements.

Programming languages are necessarily formal. For the reasons stated, the notations required at the previous stages of the software development process also tend to be highly formal. Therefore, the design and use of formal notations is central to computing, and any practitioner should have a thorough understanding of their nature. Moreover, all formal languages are subject to the same general principles, outlined in Section **1**.2D. Specifically, any notation must have a syntax, a semantics, and possibly various calculi. These features are universal and consequently of central interest to any student of computing.

Accordingly, the first objective of Part **3** is to describe how formal notations are specified, using symbolic logic as the main example. The recourse to logic for this purpose has a double advantage. First, as a language logic is very simple, in fact far more so than most high-level programming languages, for instance. Second, all three features of logic, its syntax, semantics and calculus, are entirely formally described. Thus the establishment of logic provides a *complete* example of formal language specification. Again, the aim of this part is to introduce a number of key principles, *not* to provide a comprehensive coverage of language specification methods or formal language theory. The latter is a mature subject, based on set theory but beyond the scope of this book. Two references are Hopcroft and Ullman (1979) and Wood (1987).

The second objective of Part **3** is to present symbolic logic as such. As pointed out at the end of Section **1**.1C, *deductive reasoning* plays a central role in computing. Logic has been defined as 'a model of deductive thought' (Enderton, 1972). Thus the aim of logic is to explain this type of reasoning and establish its rules. More precisely, it is to explain how certain facts may be deduced from other facts and to define what constitutes a valid deduction.

The distinctive feature of logic is that it is concerned primarily with the *form* in which facts and deductions are expressed. It focuses on the way in which objects and their properties are represented as symbolic expressions, and describes deductions as lists of such expressions entirely determined by symbol manipulation rules. The difference between logic in general and symbolic logic is that the latter imposes a strict discipline on the form of expressions. As this appears to be essential to the success of logic, we shall consider only symbolic logic and use the term 'logic' in this specific sense.

There are many varieties of logic. Only two of them are described in Part **3**, namely (classical) *propositional logic* and *first-order logic*, as these are the most fundamental and meet all the needs of this book. After a short introduction to logic in general in Chapter **5**, propositional logic is treated in Chapter **6** and first-order logic in Chapters **7** (syntax and semantics) and **8** (formal deduction).

Another way of describing logic is to say that its chief purpose is to *formalize* theories. This again emphasizes the nature of logic as a formal language primarily. This role is vividly illustrated in Chapter **9** by the formalization of set theory itself. Thus, while this theory is treated only semiformally in Part **2**, we show in this chapter how it can be completely formalized in first-order logic or, as we shall say, *axiomatized.* This is not to say that all subsequent developments are entirely formal. We continue relying on intuition in the applications of Parts **4** and **5**. Our aim is just to show how semiformal theories may be turned into completely formal ones, and to give the reader the means to do so.

On proof

The concept of deduction is closely related to that of *proof*, which is essentially equivalent. The notion of a proof is frequently misinterpreted, and this often leads to serious misconceptions about the nature of formal specification methods of the type described in this book. There are two different types of proof. In the first sense, a proof is an argument, expressed in any form, for example natural or mixed language, and sufficiently rigorous *to convince a suitably competent person of the truth of some proposition.* In the second sense, a proof is a completely formal deduction, determined by purely symbolic rules as described above. We shall call these two types of proof *semiformal* and (completely) *formal*, respectively.

The main misconception is that proofs must necessarily be entirely formal, and that there is no place for semiformal ones. This belief is wrong, as it is contradicted by all the achievements of mathematics and related sciences. *Most proofs in these disciplines are semiformal.* They do not give an absolute guarantee of correctness, a fact which mathematicians are the first to acknowledge. What they give is a very high degree of confidence in the validity of their conclusions, and this is the best that can be hoped for from *any* kind of reasoning, including completely formal ones.

In conclusion, the proper exercise of deductive reasoning is first to establish semiformal proofs, and then to seek to formalize these progressively and selectively. The two types of proof are complementary. Semiformal ones help us (a) to determine what has to be proved formally and (b) to understand formal proofs, once these have been produced. Formal proofs, once worked out, confirm their semiformal counterparts. Moreover the *concept* of a formal proof supports semiformal ones by telling us what they should be: the ideal semiformal proof is such that we can clearly see how to formalize it completely. These points are elaborated on in Chapter **8** and are illustrated in this and subsequent chapters.

1.3D The practice of model establishment

Parts **2** and **3** form the theoretical foundations of this book. Parts **4** and **5** are devoted to applications of the theory. The common theme of these last two parts is modelling in the round, the establishment of theoretical models of progressively increasing complexity and realism, using the concepts of Parts **2** and **3** as basic building blocks. Thus it is in Parts **4** and **5** that the related ideas of *taxonomy* and *modularity* will take on their full significance.

Feature Notation, lists and trees

Part **4** has three chapters. In Chapter **10** we introduce the concept of a 'complex model' and the various models described in the next two chapters, namely lists, trees and related objects. These have important common features. Then we introduce a simple notation called *Feature Notation.* The need for this notation stems from the *scale* of realistic models. Systems are described quite naturally as objects with multiple features. An advanced model may easily involve tens, even hundreds, of different objects and features of objects, and the problem is to name these in a systematic fashion. This is the aim of our notation.

Feature Notation is not a new 'language'. It is mainly a discipline for constructing feature names more systematically and meaningfully than is usually done in mathematics. It has two distinctive features: *word orientation* and *tree structure*. Word orientation means that feature names are constructed mainly as concatenations of word prefixes, which means that they closely reflect their natural language counterparts. The tree structure of the notation mirrors this construction. The feature names constructed as concatenations of prefixes are regarded as the paths of a tree. Each path is viewed as leading from a complex object to progressively simpler ones, each being a feature of its predecessor on the path. This simple principle lends great coherence to the family of feature names built in this way, and gives a natural hierarchic organization to large-scale models.

In Chapter **11**, we introduce various types of *list* and related concepts. The description of these objects is somewhat different from the view prevalent in computing, and closer to the mathematicians' definition. Whereas a list is often defined recursively in computing – especially in functional programming – it is described as a function from the set $\{1, 2, \ldots, n\}$ to some set of 'values' (for example, characters) by mathematicians.

This alternative view has been adopted, with qualifications, for several reasons. First, it is more in line with the set-theoretic prespective of the book: a function from $\{1, 2, \ldots, n\}$ is a simpler concept, once the notion of function has been understood, than the recursive construction. Second, this approach is part of a unified description of a wider category of objects, including forests and trees. In this general theory, any object under consideration consists of a 'base set' that is structured in some way, together with a function from the base to a set of values. In the case of a list, the base is any set ordered like the natural numbers. This general definition is quite natural and has various advantages. For instance, it simplifies the description of a subobject of a given object – for example, a sublist of a tree. Third, our model of a list is essentially equivalent to the concept of a *linked list* in computer programming theory. It is therefore very close to the data structures which programmers are familiar with. This underscores the point made earlier that our models are in fact quite close to their implementation as computer programs.

Chapter **12** is devoted to *trees* of various types, and related notions. Trees are of prime importance in several branches of computing and, more generally, science and technology. As abstract models, they arise in many different forms. For instance, any type of text has a tree structure. Further examples of applications are: menus in computer programs; directories in operating systems; organization charts; and taxonomies of any type. This list could be extended *ad infinitum*. In computing, trees of various types are also implementation data structures of major importance.

Trees are described in the same way as lists, that is, as functions from a structured 'base' to a set of values. The essential difference between a list and a tree is the structure of the base. In a list, a point or element has only one immediate successor, whereas in a tree a point may have several immediate 'successors' (or 'children'). Consequently, lists are special cases of trees, and all the features of trees are already present in lists.

To sum up, Part **4** is concerned primarily with two important families of 'complex models': lists and trees. These are halfway between the theory of Parts **2** and **3**, and the concrete applications of Part **5**. They serve as a basis for one of the more advanced cases treated in this last part.

Application case studies

Part **5** presents four application case studies of graded complexity. Each consists of a *theoretical model* of a concrete and practical type of object or situation (what we have called a 'distant system'). The emphasis at this stage is put on *modelling*, that is, the connection between the theoretical model and the type of object it is meant to describe. Each model is highly generic, describing many varieties of instances.

After a general introduction in Chapter **13**, the first model describes a set as *an evolving object*, undergoing successive transformations over time. Many concrete examples may be given: a human or animal population; a stock of parts; the stock of books of a lending library; the set of spare seats in an aeroplane; and so on. In each case, the set is first created, and then progressively modified by the insertion of new members or the removal of current ones. Each such transformation is represented as an *operation* on the set.

The second model represents a *dictionary*, also viewed as an evolving object. The term 'dictionary' is again taken generically. It covers many concrete instances of routine practical importance: language dictionaries, telephone directories, birthday books, address books, data dictionaries in computer programs, catalogues and so on. This model is an extension of the previous one. A dictionary is described as an evolving set of *couples*, each of which consists of a 'word' and the associated 'definition'. Its evolution is determined by operations very similar to those of simple evolving sets. These two models are developed in Chapters **14** and **15**. They are particularly simple and may be read before Chapters **11** and **12**.

The third model is more comprehensive and builds on Chapters **11** and **12**. It represents a so-called *tree editor*, which is a generalization of familiar text editors. A tree in this context is understood as a purely logical concept, independent of any physical representation, and evolving in time like the objects of the first two applications. The values associated with the base points are (typically) characters or lines of characters. The tree is supplemented with a 'cursor', which represents the selection of a small set of base points. The evolution of the tree is determined by two main groups of operations. *Navigation operations* 'move' the cursor to an adjacent point, such as the current point's parent or first child. *Tree transformation operations* modify the tree itself, by inserting a new-valued point at the location indicated by the cursor, removing the subtrees determined by the cursor, or reinserting previously removed subtrees. This application is presented in Chapter **16**.

The fourth model describes a *resource allocation system.* Such a system is made up of evolving sets of tasks to perform, resources of various types and possibly agents (employees, users and so on), together with multiple relations between these sets. At any time a task is either active – that is, being executed – or inactive. If active, it must be allocated individual resources in adequate quantities. The transformation laws of the system are operations to add and remove tasks, resource units and agents from their respective sets, and to activate and deactivate tasks. These operations must be established so as to preserve all the relations of the system.

This model is very general. Instances include: a lending library, where the resources are books and the tasks are uses of books; a conference centre, where the resources are conference rooms and ancillary facilities, and tasks are events such as lectures, seminars and so on; a vehicle depot of a transport company, described similarly; and the execution of a complex project, that is, a large predefined set of tasks subject to multiple precedence and resource constraints. The model is presented in Chapter **17**.

'Core' versus 'advanced topics'

In subsequent chapters, topics are split into two categories: 'core' and 'advanced'. The former consist of basic material which the reader should absorb first. This material is self-contained as far as possible. Advanced topics are generally more difficult and sometimes incidental. On first reading, the reader may choose to survey this material but skip the details. Sections containing advanced topics are labelled 'AT'.

Part 2

Set Theory and Induction

2 Sets and Basic Set Operations

In the prologue, it was pointed out that the ultimate aim of computing is to achieve generality, and that to think in terms of classes is perhaps the most important of our intellectual faculties. Therefore, it is not surprising that the concept of *set* or *class* should be at the centre of our preoccupations throughout this book.

This chapter has two main purposes. The first is to describe the basic features of sets, operations on sets and properties of these operations. The second is to introduce the notion of *formal notation* and familiarize the reader with the notation used throughout the book. One important skill which the reader should seek to acquire is fluency in this notation, and the ability to translate ideas back and forth between it and English.

Section 2.1 first introduces and illustrates the notion of a set, describes how sets are specified, and discusses some basic features of this concept. It then introduces some fundamental relations between sets, and certain important special cases of sets. Finally, it establishes and justifies some initial rules or *axioms* of set theory.

Section 2.2 describes the basic *operations* of set theory, that is, rules to construct new sets from existing ones. The notion of an operation or *function* is fundamental in mathematics, and this section provides many initial illustrations of this concept. The general concept itself is treated in Chapter 3.

Section 2.3 is devoted to some properties of set operations. These features are analogous to the properties of arithmetic operations, although there are important differences. The properties described here are generally intuitively obvious, but this material is somewhat dry and daunting for beginners. Therefore, this section is flagged as 'advanced' and may be skipped on first reading.

One rather surprising fact is that the formal notation we use is actually much *simpler* than a natural language. Indeed by the end of Section 2.2 we will have already encountered all the types of symbol needed in this book and, arguably, in the whole of computing and mathematics! Consequently in Section 2.4 we systematically review these various types of symbol and discuss the nature of each type.

There is a standard set theory which is well established in mathematics and which we shall call pure set theory. It is often appropriate to extend this standard in various ways for theoretical or pragmatic reasons. The relevant variants are discussed in Section 2.5.

2.1 Basic definitions

2.1A The concept of a set

We begin our study of set theory with a definition of the concept of a set. *A set is a collection of objects.* These may be physical, for example, books, houses, towns or people; or they may be conceptual, for example, numbers, concepts or statements. The nature of the objects that may make up a set does not matter. All that is required is that they are clearly identifiable and distinct from one another. Note that the concept of a set is a primitive notion. It is assumed to be understood immediately and intuitively. To sum up:

Definition 2.1A.1

A set is a collection of objects which are clearly identifiable and distinct from one another. ■

The following are examples of sets of physical objects:

- The set of citizens of the USA
- The set of houses in London

- The set of books stocked by a library
- The set of entries in the Oxford English Dictionary (OED), where each entry is regarded as a piece of printed text

The following are examples of sets of conceptual objects:

- The Roman alphabet
- The set of polygons
- The set made up of the four numbers 5, 6, 7 and 8
- The set of all natural numbers: 0, 1, 2, 3, ...
- The set of definitions in the OED, where each definition is now viewed as a conceptual object

These examples illustrate the following features of sets. In each case, the set considered can be seen as an entity with various components. The components of a set are called its *members* or *elements*. A set is an entity in its own right, distinct from each of its members. For instance, the Roman alphabet is an object in its own right, distinct from each letter. It has its own properties, and these are different from those of the letters taken individually. One of these is the number of its members – 26; the letters themselves have no similar property.

2.1B Defining and denoting sets

In order to refer to a particular set, we must provide a *definition* or *specification* of it, and this must be done in a certain notation. There are essentially two ways of specifying a set. The first is to *enumerate* its members – give a list of them. An example is the set consisting of the numbers 5, 6, 7 and 8. We represent such a set by listing its elements separated by commas and enclosed in braces, as follows:

{5, 6, 7, 8}

Clearly this method is feasible only if the set has a small number of members. Here are other examples:

- A set of capitals from five different continents:

  {Washington, London, Cairo, Peking, Canberra}

- The vowels:

  {a, e, i, o, u}

- A group of people:

  {Albert, Beth, Charles}

The second method of defining a set is to specify a property which is common to all its members, and to its members only. This property is called a *defining property*. An example is the 'set of natural numbers from 5 to 8 inclusive'. Any object is a member of this set if and only if it is a natural number no less than 5 and no greater than 8. Another example is 'the set of all letter-groups (*strings*) of at least one and no more than four letters'. A few random examples are 'a', 'bc', 'pl', 'r', 'plm' and 'rrrr'.

Our notation for this second method is as follows. A *name* or *identifier* is introduced, which stands for any member of the set being specified. This is then followed by a statement of the defining property of the set. These two elements are separated by a vertical bar and enclosed in braces. For instance, the first example above is represented as

$$\{num \mid num \text{ is a natural number and } 5 \leqslant num \text{ and } num \leqslant 8\}$$

In this definition, '*num*' is a name that stands for any member of the set. The defining property is

$$num \text{ is a natural number and } 5 \leqslant num \text{ and } num \leqslant 8$$

The expression '$5 \leqslant num$' means '5 is less than or equal to *num*'. Note that we may simplify the expression of the defining property if this does not alter its meaning. For instance, in this example the form

$$\{num \mid 5 \leqslant num \text{ and } num \leqslant 8\}$$

would be equally acceptable in a context in which only natural numbers are being considered. A further simplification often used in this and similar cases is

$$\{num \mid 5 \leqslant num \leqslant 8\}$$

This clearly has the same meaning as the previous expressions.

The second example given above is specified as follows in this notation:

$$\{Word \mid Word \text{ is a string of } n \text{ letters, where } 1 \leqslant n \leqslant 4\}$$

In this example, '*Word*' is again an arbitrary name standing for any member in the set being defined. Any other name could have been used, for example, '*w*' or '*W*'. This means that the set just described is exactly the same as the set defined by

$$\{W \mid W \text{ is a string of } n \text{ letters, where } 1 \leqslant n \leqslant 4\}$$

In particular, the names or identifiers we use to denote set members, or any object for that matter, may consist of only one letter. In any specification, the choice of identifier is left to the discretion of the author of the specification.

This second method of specifying a set is called *abstraction*. This term also means the expression used to describe the set. Note that the term 'abstraction' is used here in a technical sense, quite distinct from its usual meaning.

In an abstraction, the name standing for any member of the set specified is also called a *variable*. This is because it is not meant to represent one particular member, but any member – that is, all members of the set, but taken 'one at a time'.

In expressing a defining property, we often use a combination of formal and informal expressions. An expression like '$1 \leqslant n$ and $n \leqslant 4$' is entirely formal, whereas 'W is a string of n letters' is informal, even though it is entirely clear if we know what a string is.

Once more, it is emphasized that the notation we have introduced is first of all a convenient and standardized *shorthand*. It removes the *verbosity* and *ambiguity* of its natural language counterpart. For instance, one way of reading the last abstraction in English is

'The set of strings of n letters, where n is between 1 and 4.'

This is the meaning conveyed by the notation. However, it is more verbose, and above all ambiguous. Is 'between' to be interpreted strictly or not? We may, of course, clarify questions of this type by adding phrases like 'exclusive' or 'inclusive', but even such devices have their limitations. Thus, it is not easy to see how we can express the following set in English, using 'between':

$$\{n \mid 5 \leqslant n < 8\}$$

These remarks should convince the reader of the advantage of using the notation described. However, the reader is urged to check constantly that the intended meaning of the notation is well understood. The best way to do that is to practise translating from English into the notation and vice versa. Moreover, we must not be dogmatic about the medium of expression to use. We should always have recourse to the most convenient form, be it natural language, formal notation or even a mixture of both, as several of the above examples illustrate. Professional mathematicians often express their ideas in both forms, natural language to outline key features, and formal notation for precision.

In many cases, the defining property of an abstraction is expressed in terms of other set(s), implicitly or explicitly. For instance, the definition $\{n \mid 5 \leqslant n < 8\}$ implicitly refers to the set of natural numbers, as n must clearly be such a number. Obviously, reference to other sets in a definition makes sense only if these other sets themselves have been defined beforehand or are at least well understood. Here in particular we rely (provisionally) on the reader's intuitive understanding of the set of natural numbers, $\{0, 1, 2, \ldots\}$.

2.1C Identifiers

In an abstraction, a name is used to represent any member of the set specified. This illustrates an important idea, which we apply generally and frequently. The idea is to give names to the various specific objects we are dealing with, in order subsequently to refer to them precisely. A name is also called an identifier, as its purpose is to identify uniquely the entity it represents: in a given context, each name should refer to a *single* object.

The *meaning* of a name is the object it represents. Note that the meaning of a name always depends on the *context* in which the name occurs. For instance, the name n is used above in two different abstractions:

$$\{W \mid W \text{ is a string of } n \text{ letters, where } 1 \leqslant n \leqslant 4\}$$

and

$$\{n \mid 5 \leqslant n < 8\}$$

Each of these abstractions forms a different context for n. In the first, n is an auxiliary variable used in the definition of any member W of the set specified. In the second context, n represents the members themselves of the defined set, again taken 'one at a time', individually.

The practice of naming objects as we do is one major departure from the standard usage of natural languages. It adds substantial accuracy to the language. Note that the use of names is not restricted to formal notations. They may very well be used in natural language.

Names may be used to refer to entities of any type. In particular, we use them to identify sets. Their convenience may be illustrated at once. The various abstractions introduced above have not been named. Consequently, the only way to refer to any one of them is to rewrite it completely, or to use rather cumbersome descriptions like 'the first abstraction given above'. We give a name to a set, or any other entity, by equating the name with the definition of the entity. For instance, to introduce the set of words of one or two letters and give it the name 'A', we write

$$A = \{W \mid W \text{ is a string of } n \text{ letters, where } 1 \leqslant n \leqslant 2\}$$

This means that from now on and until the end of the present context, 'A' has the meaning given by this definition. We also say that it is *bound* to the defined set. We usually write names in italics to emphasize their special role and the fact that their meaning may vary from context to context.

In a given context, the meaning of a name is either *constant* or *variable*. In the current context 'A' denotes a constant set but within the definition of A, both 'W' and 'n' denote *variable* objects. This may seem to contradict the principle that a name should refer to a single object, but this contradiction is only apparent.

For instance, consider the use of 'W' within the definition of A. In this context, W is always meant to represent *exactly one* object. However, this object is *any* member of A, so, as already mentioned, W is meant to represent all members of A, but taken 'one at a time'. We say that *W varies over A*. This idea is subtle, but it is crucial. We shall come back to it in Section **2**.4D.

A final remark about names: some authors use the term 'name' to mean any symbolic construction which identifies an object uniquely. In this sense, an abstraction is a 'name' for a set, and expressions like '$2+2$' or '$n-6$' are names of certain numbers (the number 4 in the first case). We prefer to call such forms 'expressions' and use the term 'name' in the usual sense.

2.1D Equivalent definitions

From our informal definition of a set, such an object is entirely determined by its members. Thus, *we regard two sets as identical if they have the same members*. This is the so-called *principle of extensionality*, which is discussed further in Section **2**.1I. For the moment, we only illustrate a consequence of this principle. This is that, in general, a set may be defined in many different ways. In other words, two different definitions may be *equivalent*, in the sense that they define the same set. Here are two examples.

First, consider the set S defined by the following abstraction:

$$S = \{n \mid 5 \leqslant n < 8\}$$

In English, this says that S is the set of natural numbers greater than or equal to 5, and less than 8. Clearly, we may also enumerate this set: its members are 5, 6 and 7. Therefore S is also given by the definition

$$S = \{5, 6, 7\}$$

Thus, S is defined in two different ways, and in fact by the two different methods we have described.

Second, consider the following set defined as an abstraction by

$$P = \{n \mid n \text{ is a natural number divisible by exactly two natural numbers}\}$$

It turns out that P is the set of prime numbers. A *prime number* is officially defined as any natural number n greater than 1 and divisible only by 1 and by itself. Let P' be the set of prime numbers defined in this way. Thus, P' is described by the following abstraction:

$$P' = \{n \mid 2 \leqslant n \text{ and } n \text{ is divisible only by 1 and by } n\}$$

It is easy to see that P and P' have the same members. Any number n greater than 1 is in P' if and only if it is divisible by exactly two numbers, 1 and itself.

The number 1, which is *not* a prime number – that is, not a member of P' – is not a member of P either, as it is divisible only by itself. As for 0, this is divisible by any number: $n \times 0 = 0$ for all n. Therefore, 0 belongs neither to P' nor to P. In this second example, the same set is determined by two different abstractions.

2.1E On the caution required in defining sets

Care must be taken in defining sets. For instance, consider the sentence

'Every human is mortal, but not every mortal is human.'

What is the set of words in this sentence? There are at least *three* possible answers to this question:

Answer 1 Words occupying different positions in the sentence are regarded as distinct. So the set is

{(1, 'Every'), (2, 'human'), (3, 'is'), (4, 'mortal'), (5, 'but'), (6, 'not'), (7, 'every'), (8, 'mortal'), (9, 'is'), (10, 'human')}

In this enumeration, each word has been written with its position number to make the intended distinctions explicit.

Answer 2 Any two words are regarded as distinct if and only if they differ by at least one (positioned) character. For example, 'all' is distinct from 'are' because the second characters differ (and also because the third characters differ). In this case the set of words in the above sentence is

{'every', 'human', 'is', 'mortal', 'but', 'not'}

In this answer, it is assumed that 'Every' spelt with an upper-case first letter, is *not* distinct from 'every' with a lower-case first letter. But the opposite convention may be adopted, giving the third answer.

Answer 3 Words are distinct if they differ in the sense of answer (2) *or* if they differ in the case (lower or upper) of one or more of their component letters. In this case the set is

{'Every', 'every', 'human', 'is', 'mortal', 'but', 'not'}

All three answers are equally reasonable, so it is important to state which of the three is intended. This depends on the *purpose* for which the definition is made. This purpose must be carefully established before the set is defined.

Many other examples could be given, but this particular one is typical and arises frequently. A common way of distinguishing between definitions (1) and (2) is to call the members of the first set 'word *occurrences*' (in the sentence), and the members of the second set simply 'words'.

Note that the question considered here does not pertain to set theory as such. It is a matter of *modelling* – it concerns the way we apply our concepts to the real world. Nevertheless, questions of this kind are just as important in practice as purely theoretical considerations.

2.1F Three fundamental features of sets

As already stated, a set is entirely determined by its members. If we are given a full description of its members, we have all the information that may be given about a set. This fundamental characteristic of sets has several important consequences.

1 *A set must be distinguished from its description.* As we have seen, in general a set may be defined in many different ways. Consequently, it is important to make a distinction between a set on the one hand, and the definition of the set, the *symbolic expression* describing it, on the other.

For instance, as strings of characters, the following expressions are clearly different:

'$\{2, 3, 4\}$' '$\{3, 2, 4\}$' '$\{2, 2, ,3, 4, 4, 4\}$'

'$\{n | 2 \leqslant n \leqslant 4\}$' '$\{m | 2 \leqslant m \leqslant 4\}$' '$\{n | 1 < n < 5\}$'

However, all these descriptions are equivalent: they denote the same set, namely the set whose members are 2, 3 and 4.

Note that the distinction between an object X and a description or representation of X is not confined to sets. It is an important principle, which applies to any type of entity whatsoever.

2 *All the elements of a set are distinct.* In other words no element may 'occur' more than once in a set. This is because an object x cannot be a member of a set S in more than one way. Either x is a member of S, or it is not; there is no notion of 'multiple membership' of a set.

This is one respect in which sets differ from their descriptions. As the third example above shows, an object (for example, 4) may occur several times in a *description* of S. This does not imply that such a member has several occurrences in the set S itself.

A definition of a set in which a member occurs several times is called *redundant*. Such descriptions are valid and sometimes inevitable. However they may cause confusion and should be avoided whenever possible.

Note that it is possible to define an alternative concept, which is like a set except for the fact that its members may have multiple occurrences in it. Such a concept is called a *bag*; it is a *different* concept, and is described later.

3 *The elements of a set are not ordered in any way.* This again is a consequence of the fact that the members of a set determine it completely. To know that x and y are members of a set cannot tell us in which order they occur. Therefore, the members of a set are essentially unordered.

In this respect, too, sets differ from their descriptions. In an enumeration of the members of a set, the members are necessarily ordered. However, *this order is irrelevant.* This is why the two expressions '$\{2, 3, 4\}$' and '$\{3, 2, 4\}$', for instance, represent the same set.

Given any set, we may also extend it by imposing some order on its members. However, the resulting object is no longer a set: it is a different kind of object. An example of a set whose elements are totally ordered is a *list*. This concept, too, is described later.

2.1G Membership and inclusion

Two concepts are closely associated with the notion of a set: *membership* and *inclusion.* We describe these in turn.

Membership

For any set S, and any object x, either x is a member of S, or it is not. In order to indicate that x is a member of S, we write

$$x \in S$$

In this notation, '$\in$' is a stylized Greek letter, an epsilon, called *membership symbol.* The expression '$x \in S$' is shorthand for the sentence:

x is a member of S

These two expressions are entirely equivalent. We may also read '$x \in S$' as the sentence '*x belongs to S*'.

For any given set S and any object x, the statement '$x \in S$' is either true or false. It is true if indeed x is a member of S, and false otherwise. Thus, '$x \in S$' describes a certain *property* that S and x may or may not have.

Consider the various possible pairs made up of an object x and a set S. We repeat: any such pair either has, or has not, the property that $x \in S$. A property which is true for certain pairs of objects is called a *relation.* The property expressed by the statement '$x \in S$', and which is true for some pairs of objects x and S, and false for the others, is called the *membership relation.*

The notion of a relation is fundamental. It is described systematically in Chapter 3. For the moment we may note that we have already come across several relations in addition to set membership. For instance, the symbol '$<$' denotes the relation 'less than' on the set of natural numbers: for any pair of natural numbers m and n, '$m < n$' is a property which m and n may or may not have – that is, '$m < n$' is either true or false.

Example 2.1G.1

Here are a few more examples of statements asserting that some object is a member of some set:

(1) $3 \in \{3, 4, 5\}$

(2) $7 \in \{x | x$ is divisible by exactly two numbers$\}$

(3) Rome $\in \{C | C$ is a capital city$\}$ ■

We often want to assert that a certain object x is *not* a member of a set S. The shorthand for that is $x \notin S$.

Example 2.1G.2

The following are true statements:

(1) $2 \notin \{3, 4, 5\}$

(2) Berlin $\notin \{T | T$ is a town of no more than 20,000 inhabitants$\}$

■

Sets as members of sets *Any object* may be a member of a set. Consequently, a set may have other sets as members. Likewise, a set may have a mixture of sets and non-sets as members.

Example 2.1G.3

(1) $S1 = \{\{a\}, \{b, q\}, \{t, u\}\}$	A set of sets of letters
(2) $S2 = \{2, \{3, 4\}, 3, \{3, 5\}, 6\}$	A set of numbers and sets of numbers
(3) $S3 = \{1, \{1, q\}, 2, \{6, \{3, b\}\}, m\}$	A set of numbers, letters, sets of numbers and letters, etc.
(4) $S4 = \{S1, S2, S3\}$	The set of the previous sets

■

Note In this and subsequent examples, we often use individual letters as set members. These are used to represent *distinct* elements, and must not be regarded as identifiers, as in general two different identifiers *may* denote the same object. To simplify, they are written unquoted, unless this might cause confusion – for example, within English text. On the other hand, strings of characters are enclosed in quotes. ■

All these instances of sets given in Example 2.1G.3 are enumerations. We may also construct sets of sets by abstraction.

Example 2.1G.4

Let $S1$, $S2$, etc. be defined as in Example **2**.1G.3

(1) $A1 = \{S \mid S \in S4 \text{ and } S \text{ has 5 members}\}$
$A1$ is equal to $\{S2, S3\}$, as the reader should verify.

(2) $A2 = \{S \mid S \in \{S1, S2\} \text{ or } S = S3\}$
It is easy to see that $A2$ is equal to $S4$. ■

Nontransitivity of membership

In natural language, the preposition 'in' expresses a relation similar to set membership. However, there is a crucial difference, which must be stressed. In many cases, we take for granted that, given any three objects A, B and C, if A is in B and B in C, then A is in C. For instance, if we are told that Baltimore is in the state of Maryland and that Maryland is in the USA, we naturally conclude that Baltimore is in the USA. What we assume implicitly in this reasoning is that the relation denoted by 'in' is *transitive*. That is, we assume that *for all* objects A, B and C, if A is in B and B in C then necessarily A is in C.

Now because of the resemblance between set membership and the relation defined by 'in', it is tempting to assume that membership is also transitive. *This is not the case.* It *is* true that a set may be a member of another set, as the previous examples illustrate. However, if for any three sets $S1$, $S2$ and $S3$ we have $S1 \in S2$ and $S2 \in S3$, *this does not imply that* $S1 \in S3$! Nor is the contrary property implied, by the way: $S1 \in S3$ may be true, or it may be false.

Example 2.1G.5

Consider the following sets:

$$S1 = \{a, 3\}$$
$$S2 = \{4, 7, q\}$$
$$S3 = \{1, S1, 4, S2\} = \{1, \{a, 3\}, 4, \{4, 7, q\}\}$$

In this example, 'a' $\in S1$ and $S1 \in S3$. However, 'a' is *not* a member of $S3$. On the other hand, $4 \in S2$, $S2 \in S3$ and $4 \in S3$, but this last property is *not* due to the previous two facts. We know that $4 \in S3$ only because 4 is explicitly listed as a member of $S3$. ■

To sum up:

Principle 2.1G.1

If A is a member of B and B is a member of C, this does *not* imply that A is a member of C. ■

Inclusion

Next, we introduce the notion of set inclusion. Consider first a simple example. Let A and B be any two sets defined by $A = \{3, 4\}$ and $B = \{3, 4, 5\}$. Every member of A is also a member of B. We say that A is *included* in B or, equivalently, that A is a *subset* of B.

Definition 2.1G.1

A set S is *included in* another set T if and only if every member of S is a member of T. In this case, we also say that S is a *subset* of T. ■

To express formally the fact that a set S is included in a set T, we write

$$S \subseteq T$$

The symbol '$\subseteq$' must not be confused with '$\in$'. The former denotes *inclusion*, the latter *membership*.

Inclusion is another example of a relation. It is a relation between sets. For any two sets S and T, the property '$S \subseteq T$' is either true or false. Note that inclusion is entirely determined by the membership relation. Here is the formal counterpart of the definition of inclusion, based on the definition of the membership relation $\in$. The reader should work it out first before reading on.

Definition 2.1G.2 (formal counterpart)

For any two sets S and T, $S \subseteq T$ if and only if for all x, if $x \in S$ then $x \in T$. ■

Remarks on inclusion

1 From Definition **2**.1G.1 (or **2**.1G.2), any set S is a subset of itself. This is because every member x of S is a member of S. Formally:

Property 2.1G.1

For any set S, $S \subseteq S$. ■

2 For any two sets S and T, we say that S is a *strict* subset of T if $S \subseteq T$ but T has a member which does not belong to S. In this case we write

$$S \subset T$$

We express this formally as follows:

Definition 2.1G.3

For any sets S and T, $S \subset T$ if and only if $S \subseteq T$ and there exists x such that $x \in T$ and $x \notin S$ (which implies that $S \neq T$). If $S \subset T$ then S is a *strict* or *proper* subset of T. ■

2.1H Special sets and set cardinality

We now describe some special types of set: the empty set, singletons and finite sets. The definition of the last category depends on the notion of set cardinality, which is introduced informally at the same time.

Empty set

A set is *empty* if it has no members. The idea of an empty set is perfectly proper but may be somewhat hard to conceive. An example showing how such a set is obtained may be of help here.

Consider the set $S2 = \{\text{You, Me}\}$. Remove Me from $S2$, giving the new set $S1$. Thus, $S1 = \{\text{You}\}$. Now what we have done with $S2$, we should be able to repeat with $S1$! Therefore, next, remove You from $S1$ giving $S0$. $S0$ is *not* nothing. Just as $S1$ is a set constructed from $S2$, $S0$ is also a set, constructed from $S1$ by the same operation. $S0$ is the empty set, $\{\ \}$. To sum up the process we have carried out:

$S2 = \{\text{You, Me}\}$

Remove Me giving

$S1 = \{\text{You}\}$

Remove You giving

$S0 = \{\ \}$

The alert reader will have noticed a slight change of phraseology. Whilst initially we referred to *a* set being empty, we concluded with the sentence that $S0$ is *the* empty set. This is simply a consequence of the principle of extensionality, which is that if two sets S and T are empty then they must be equal. Consequently, there can be only *one* empty set.

Definition 2.1H.1

The *empty set* is the set with no members and is unique, by the principle of extensionality. It is denoted by $\varnothing$. Thus, formally, $\varnothing$ is defined by the condition that for any object x, $x \notin \varnothing$. ■

The existence of the empty set is a principle which we take for granted but cannot logically prove. Principles of this kind are called axioms. In general, an *axiom* is a statement taken as a starting point in a theory and which cannot be proved by the rules of logic. It is accepted either because it is intuitively obvious or because it reflects a certain *view* of things which is not contradicted by our intuition (even though alternatives would also be acceptable).

An immediate property of the empty set is that it is included in every set, including itself:

Property 2.1H.1

For any set S, $\varnothing \subseteq S$. ■

This property directly follows from the definition of $\subseteq$. Given any set S, as $\varnothing$ has *no* members then it must be true that every member x of $\varnothing$ is a member of S. We say that this property of 'all members' of $\varnothing$ is *vacuously true*, precisely because there are no such members.

This mode of reasoning may prove strange to beginners, yet it is important and quite frequent in practice. One useful way of justifying the reasoning is as follows. For any two sets Q and S, on what condition can we say that Q is *not* included in S? The answer is that *there must exist an object x such that $x \in Q$ and $x \notin S$.* But if Q has no members, this condition is not satisfied for any set S. Therefore if $Q = \varnothing$, it is included in every set.

Example 2.1H.1

Here are two further cases of sets involving the empty set.

(1) $\varnothing \neq \{\varnothing\}$. The first set is the empty set: it contains no members. The second set is *not* empty: it has one member, and this member itself is the empty set.

(2) Consider the set S of all *sets* of natural numbers less than or equal to 2. We define this set formally, first by enumerating its members and second using the abstraction method. The reader should try to do this before reading on.

The definition of S by enumeration is

$$S = \{\varnothing, \{0\}, \{1\}, \{0, 1\}, \{2\}, \{0, 2\}, \{1, 2\}, \{0, 1, 2\}\}$$

Note that each member of S is a set. Moreover, $\varnothing$ is a member of S, by Property **2**.1H.1. The definition of S by abstraction is

$$S = \{T \mid T \subseteq \{n \mid 0 \leqslant n \leqslant 2\}\}$$

■

Singletons

A set S containing exactly one element is called a *singleton*.

Example 2.1H.2

The following sets are singletons:

(1) $S1 = \{1\}$	The single member is 1
(2) $S2 = \{\text{'pqr'}\}$	The single member is the string 'pqr'
(3) $S3 = \{\{2, \text{'ttb'}, \{a, 3, 9\}\}\}$	The single member is a set
(4) $S4 = \{S3, \{\{2, \text{'ttb'}, \{a, 3, 9\}\}\}\}$	The single member is a set

$S3$ has a single member, although this member is itself a set of several elements. To see that $S4$ is a singleton requires closer scrutiny. $S4$ is defined as the set with members *S3* and $\{\{2, \text{'ttb'}, \{a, 3, 9\}\}\}$. But these two objects are equal! Therefore the above definition of *S4* is redundant, and $S4 = \{S3\}$ – it is a singleton. ■

Note that in all the examples of sets S given so far, we can see that $S \neq \{S\}$. $\{S\}$ is necessarily a singleton, but S need not be.

Cardinality

The number of members of a set S is called the *cardinality* of S. This is only an informal definition. The cardinality of a set S is denoted by $|S|$. In this book the notation Num(S) is generally used, standing for 'number of members of S'. Other authors use Card(S) for 'cardinality of S'. Thus if $S = \{a, b, c\}$, Num(S) = 3. The empty set is the only set with cardinality zero: Num($\varnothing$) = 0.

It is important to distinguish a set from its cardinality. The confusion between these two notions is not uncommon and may cause errors.

Finite and infinite sets

A set S is *finite* if its cardinality Num(S) is a natural number: 0, 1, 2, ... Not every set is finite. If a set S is not finite, it is called *infinite*.

An example of an infinite set is the set of all natural numbers, which we denote by Nat. Thus, we may write

$$\text{Nat} = \{0, 1, 2, 3, \ldots\}$$

Intuitively it is obvious that Nat is infinite. For any number n, Nat must contain all numbers less than n – that is $0, 1, \ldots, n-1$, plus n itself, $n+1$, $n+2$, and so on. Therefore, Nat must have *more* than n members.

As each set S is called finite if its cardinality is a number $n \in \text{Nat}$, we also say that the number n itself is finite.

The cardinality of infinite sets may also be defined, but as a new type of number which does *not* belong to the set Nat of natural numbers. This topic is beyond the scope of this book. The interested reader is referred to Enderton (1977). The two important facts to remember at this stage are stated in the following:

Principle 2.1H.1

(1) The set Nat of natural numbers is infinite.

(2) However, each number $n \in \text{Nat}$ is finite: there is *no* infinite natural number. In particular there is no natural number equal to the cardinality of Nat. ■

2.1I Principle of extensionality

The principle of extensionality was introduced informally in Section **2.**1D. We now examine this principle in greater detail.

Recall that, informally, this principle asserts that *if two sets S and T have the same members, then $S = T$.* Here is the formal definition:

Principle of extensionality

Let A and B be any two sets.

(1) If $A \subseteq B$ and $B \subseteq A$ then $A = B$. ■

In other words, if every member of A is a member of B and every member of B is a member of A, then $A = B$. We may also express this principle directly in terms of the more basic membership relation as follows:

For any two sets A and B, $A = B$ if for all x, $x \in A$ if and only if $x \in B$.

The reader should verify that these two definitions are indeed equivalent. Note that the assertion of the principle in terms of $\subseteq$ is markedly clearer than the second alternative.

Remark

The principle of extensionality is a one-way conditional: it does not contain the converse

(2) If $A = B$ then $A \subseteq B$ and $B \subseteq A$.

This does *not* mean that (2) is false. (2) is not stated as an explicit principle simply because it directly follows from the definition of equality: if two sets are equal then they must have exactly the same properties. Hence, they must have the same members. More formally: by Property **2.**1G.1, $A \subseteq A$. If $A = B$, we may substitute B for A first on the right and then on the left of '$A \subseteq A$', giving '$B \subseteq A$' and '$A \subseteq B$' respectively. Consequently these two inclusions follow from $A = B$. ■

In contrast, the principle of extensionality cannot be deduced formally from other facts. It is an *axiom*, which reflects a certain choice on our part, a certain view of sets. We could conceivably adopt a different definition of sets in which this principle did not hold.

2.1J On the method of abstraction

As we have seen, the abstraction method consists of defining a set S by specifying a *property* or *condition* satisfied by every member of S and no other objects.

For instance, the set S given by enumeration as $S = \{3, 4, 5\}$, is defined by abstraction as

$$S = \{x \mid x \in \text{Nat and } 3 \leqslant x \leqslant 5\}$$

the defining property of S being '$x \in \text{Nat}$ and $3 \leqslant x \leqslant 5$'.

From this example, we can see that the general form of an abstraction is

(1) $S = \{x \mid P(x)\}$

In this abstraction, x is the local name standing for any member of S. $P(x)$ is a formula containing 'x' and which expresses the defining property of S. Thus for any x, $P(x)$ is either true or false, and an object x is a member of the set S defined if and only if $P(x)$ is true. In the above example $P(x) =$ '$x \in \text{Nat}$ and $3 \leqslant x \leqslant 5$' and therefore $S = \{3, 4, 5\}$.

The method of abstraction cannot be used without restrictions of two types. First, some rules must be imposed on the *form* of the property $P(x)$ in order to ensure that $P(x)$ is *well defined* and truly specifies a set. Failing to do so may produce paradoxes invalidating the reasoning. An example is given in Enderton (1977). The necessary rules are quite natural, and we shall apply them without spelling them out in Part **2**. Their rigorous definition will be given in Part **3**.

Second, even well-formed formulas may lead to paradoxes and so may fail to define sets properly. The most famous example was discovered by Bertrand Russell (1872–1970) in 1902. The contradiction which it leads to is called *Russell's paradox* and is discussed in Section **2**.5A. In order to resolve this second difficulty, the standard method is to require that the defining property $P(x)$ be of the form

(2) $P(x) = x \in A$ and $P'(x)$

where $P'(x)$ may itself be any well-formed formula, and A is a *predefined* set (a set that has already been defined by means other than unrestricted abstraction). In other words, the method of abstraction is restricted to the definition of a *subset* of a given set only, for clearly if $P(x)$ is of the form '$x \in A$ *and* $P'(x)$' then the defined set S must be included in A.

The rule that if A is a set and $P'(x)$ any well-formed formula then

(3) $S = \{x \mid x \in A \text{ and } P'(x)\}$

is also a well-defined set is called a *subset axiom*. Note that there is a whole family of subset axioms: there is one such axiom per set A and formula P. Subset axioms are also called *comprehension axioms*. As the part '$x \in A$' is standard in the allowed form $P(x)$, a set defined by restricted abstraction as in

(3) is often written in the abbreviated form

(4) $S = \{x \in A \mid P'(x)\}$

In the sequel we generally but not always use this restricted form of defining property. We do not specify the subset A when A is clear from the context; or $P'(x)$ is such that it is guaranteed to define a set on its own; or the object we intend to define need not be a strict set – for example, it may be a '*proper class*', in the sense defined in Section **2**.5.

EXERCISES

2.1.1 Using the notation illustrated in this section (a combination of English and special symbols), define the sets listed below (a) by semiformal abstraction and (b) by (nonredundant) enumeration. All numbers used here are natural. The symbol 'iff' is an abbreviation for 'if and only if'. A number is *even* if it is divisible by 2, *odd* otherwise. A *prime number* is a number p *greater than* 1 and divisible only by 1 and by p. The first four prime numbers are 2, 3, 5 and 7. Use divisibility without defining it here; it is formally defined in Exercise **2**.1.3 below.

(a) The set of even numbers less than 5
(b) The set of multiples of 3 in the range 5–13
(c) The set of prime numbers in the range 5–19
(d) The set of numbers which are either odd or divisible by 5, and in the range 5–13

2.1.2 Consider the sets of letters given below.

(a) Indicate which representations are redundant.
(b) The same set may be represented several times. For each given set, indicate its various representations.

$A = \{a, b, c\}$ $B = \{b, a\}$ $C = \{c, a, b, d\}$
$D = \{b, c, a\}$ $E = \{b, b, a, a\}$ $F = \{a, c, d, a\}$
$G = \{b, a, d, c\}$ $H = \{c, a, b\}$

2.1.3 The division of natural numbers, say n by d, produces a *quotient* q and a *remainder* r. These are the natural numbers which satisfy the two conditions

(a) $(q \times d) + r = n$
(b) $0 \leqslant r < d$

They are defined, and *unique*, for any n and any $d > 0$. We denote the main result, the quotient q, by n DIV d and the remainder r by n MOD d (read 'n modulo d').

n is *divisible by d*, or is a *multiple of d*, iff $r = 0$. Calculate n DIV d and n MOD d for the following values of n and d, and indicate when n is divisible by d.

n	d
5	2
13	3
18	6
23	5
49	7

2.1.4 Give a completely formal definition of the set of prime numbers using MOD.

2.1.5 Express the sets of Exercise 2.1.1 completely formally using MOD.

2.1.6 What can you say about n DIV d and n Mod d in the following cases? (a) $n = 0$ and $d > 0$; (b) $d = 0$ (and n is any number).

2.1.7 Represent each of the following sets in enumeration form and indicate which sets are equal.

$A = \{n | 3 < n \leqslant 5\}$
$B = \{m | 2 \times m \leqslant 7\}$
$C = \{p | 1 < p < 4\}$
$D = \{x | (5 \leqslant x < 10) \text{ or } (12 \leqslant 3 \times x \leqslant 20\}$
$E = \{x | (5 \leqslant x < 10) \text{ and } (12 \leqslant 3 \times x \leqslant 20\}$
$F = \{n | (1 < n < 6) \text{ and 6 is divisible by } n\}$

2.1.8 Express the set $\{0, 3, 6, 9\}$ as an abstraction, using $\leqslant$ and MOD.

2.1.9 Consider $A = \{x \in \text{Nat} | x + x = x \times x\}$. Represent A by enumeration.

2.1.10 Translate the following symbolic statements into English:

(a) $x \in S$ (b) $x \notin S$ (c) $X \subseteq Y$
(d) $A \subset B$ (e) $A \in B$ (f) $B \notin C$

2.1.11 Define the inclusion relation $\subseteq$ formally in terms of the membership relation $\in$.

2.1.12 Give the formal definition of '$A \subset B$'

(a) in terms of $\subseteq$

(b) in terms of $\in$

2.1.13 Write all the subsets S of $A = \{m, n, p\}$. Underline the *proper* subsets of A.

2.1.14 How many members does each of the following sets contain? Enumerate the members of the sets defined by abstraction.

$A = \{a,b\}$ $\quad$ $B = \{\{a,b,c\}, \{b,d\}, \{a,c,d\}\}$

$C = \{\{b,c\}, a, \{a,c\}, \{b\}, c\}$ $\quad$ $D = \{S \mid S \subset \varnothing\}$

$E = \{S \mid S \subseteq \varnothing\}$ $\quad$ $F = \{S \mid S \subseteq \{k\}\}$

$G = \{S \mid S \subseteq \{k, m\}\}$ $\quad$ $H = \{S \mid S \subseteq \{k,m,n\}\}$

2.1.15 Let $B = \{x \in \text{Nat} \mid x \times x \text{ is prime}\}$. What can you say about B?

2.1.16 Enumerate the members of the following sets. Which is the singleton? (Caution: redundancy may arise!)

(a) $S1 = \{a, \{a\}, b, \{a, b, c\}, \{a, c, c, b\}\}$

(b) $S2 = \{b, \{a, b, c\}, S1\}$

(c) $S3 = \{x \mid x \text{ is a vowel in the range b, c, } \ldots, \text{p}\}$

(d) $S4 = \{S \mid S \in S1 \text{ and } b \in S\}$

(e) $S5 = \{S4, S3, \{\{a, b, c\}\}\}$

2.2 Basic set operations

An *operation* is a rule which defines how objects, here sets, may be constructed from other objects, the *operands*. Our purpose now is to establish a catalogue of set operations. These are called *basic*, as their definition is simple and expressed entirely in terms of the membership relation $\in$, and as they are used later as 'building blocks' in defining more complex operations. Another feature of the catalogue worth mentioning is that it is *complete*. Any set we may be interested in, however complex, may be obtained by a combination of these basic operations. This 'construction principle' is universal; it arises in all areas of computing and mathematics.

Basic set operations are very much like the elementary operations of arithmetic: addition, multiplication and so on. The difference is that here, instead of operating on numbers, we operate on sets. Moreover, set operations share many important properties with arithmetic operations, but there are also important differences between these two types of operation. Some fundamental properties of set operations are presented in Section 2.3.

In general, we use capitals – A, B, C, S, T, and so on – to denote sets and x, y, etc. to denote objects (potential set members). Recall, however, that a member x of a set may itself be a set, with its own members. Furthermore, 'iff' will henceforth be used as shorthand for the phrase 'if and only if'.

2.2A Pair

Consider any two objects x and y. They may but need not be sets. Our first operation is to construct the set whose members are just x and y. It is defined thus:

Definition 2.2A.1

Any two objects x and y form a set called *pair* and denoted by $\{x, y\}$. This set is formally defined by the condition

for all z, $z \in \{x, y\}$ iff $z = x$ or $z = y$ ■

As can be seen, any pair $P = \{x, y\}$ is represented by enumerating its members, x and y. In Section **2**.1B, we have already assumed that we can define a set by enumerating its members. What we are doing now is slightly different. First, we are postulating that one *operation*, or rule for producing a certain set P, is to take two objects x and y, and declare that P is the set whose members are x and y. Here we emphasize the idea of operation, of 'acting' on two objects x and y to form a new object. Second, this operation is defined formally using the membership relation. Third, we are now more specific. In this operation, we restrict the number of members in the result to at most two.

Note the use of the conjunction 'or' in Definition **2**.2A.1. The statement '$z = x$ or $z = y$' precisely means that z is equal to x, or to y, or to both x and y. We emphasize this by saying that or is *non-exclusive*. The symbol 'or' is called a *logical connective*. The exact meaning of logical connectives is given in Section **2**.4C.

An important point must be made now. In Definition **2**.2A.1, 'x' and 'y' are two *names* or identifiers. They are symbols which stand for certain (variable) objects. The question is: are the two objects represented by x and y necessarily different? The answer is *no*! *Nothing tells us that they are different*. Therefore, it is important to bear in mind that the objects denoted by x and y may be identical, unless this is explicitly ruled out.

The conclusion is that the set $\{x, y\}$ given by Definition **2**.2A.1 has exactly *one* member if $x = y$, or *two* members if $x \neq y$. This point is simple, but must be made. It is a good illustration of the care required in devising concepts and systems. Note that there is an analogy between this situation and the problem of defining the set of words of a sentence (Section **2**.1E); the reader is invited to compare these two questions.

This observation sheds some light on the nature of a name, and reminds us of the distinction we must always make between an object and its representation, as was mentioned in Section **2**.1F. It also tells us something about the meaning of *equality*. What does '$x = y$' mean exactly? Simply, that 'x' *denotes the same object as* 'y'. As symbols, 'x' and 'y' are different, but to assert '$x = y$' is to state that the objects they *represent* are the same.

Recall the above claim that our catalogue of basic set operations is complete. Here is a first opportunity to put this claim to the test. Our operations should enable us to construct singletons, among other sets. Well, the pair operation meets this requirement, as we have just observed. Given any object x, we may form the pair $S = \{x, x\}$ and this is just the singleton $\{x\}$. The point is that *we do not need to introduce a separate singleton constructor*. The pair operation already does the job.

2.2B Union

The second operation is the *union* of given sets. This comes in two variants. The first version operates on two sets, say A and B. The result of the operation is a new set called the union of A and B and is denoted by

$$A \cup B$$

This new set is defined as follows. For any object x, x is a member of $A \cup B$ iff x is a member of A, or B, or both.

In order to express this definition formally, we may proceed in one of two ways. Both of them are used in the following.

Definition 2.2B.1

The union of two sets A and B is the set denoted by $A \cup B$ and defined by the condition:

for all x, $x \in A \cup B$ iff $x \in A$ or $x \in B$

Equivalently, $A \cup B$ is given by

$$A \cup B = \{x \mid x \in A \text{ or } x \in B\}$$

■

The two alternatives used in Definition **2**.2B.1 are clearly equivalent. Here, '$x \in A$ or $x \in B$', precisely means that x is a member of A, or x is a member of B, or x is a member of both A and B.

Example 2.2B.1

(1) Let $A = \{1, 3, 5, 6\}$ and $B = \{2, 3, 6, 7\}$. Then

$$A \cup B = \{1, 2, 3, 5, 6, 7\}$$

(2) Let $A = \{x \in \text{Nat} \mid x \leqslant 3\}$ and $B = \{x \in \text{Nat} \mid 2 \leqslant x \leqslant 6\}$. Then

$$A \cup B = \{x \in \text{Nat} \mid x \leqslant 6\} = \{0, 1, 2, 3, 4, 5, 6\}$$

(3) Let $A = \{x \mid x \text{ is a girl}\}$ and $B = \{x \mid x \text{ is a boy}\}$. Then

$$A \cup B = \{x \mid x \text{ is a child}\}$$

■

The second variant of the union is a generalization of the first. Instead of starting with just two sets, we assume that a set A of sets is given. Then the result, denoted by $\cup A$, is the set of objects each of which belongs to at least one member of A.

This construction is best explained by a simple example. Suppose $A = \{S, T, U\}$, where S, T and U themselves are sets. Then the union of A, which is the same as saying the union of S, T and U, is the set of which any member belongs to S, T or U. More concretely, suppose $S = \{1, 2\}$, $T = \{\text{b}, \text{t}\}$ and $U = \{1, 3, \text{t}\}$. Then

$$\cup A = \cup\{S, T, U\} = \{1, 2, \text{b}, \text{t}, 3\}$$

Definition 2.2B.2

Let A be any set of which each member is a set. The union of A is the set denoted by $\cup A$ and defined by the following condition: any object x is a member of $\cup A$ iff x is a member of at least one of the members of A. Formally:

for all x, $x \in \cup A$ iff there exists a set S such that $x \in S$ and $S \in A$

Equivalently, $\cup A$ is given by

$$\cup A = \{x \mid \text{there exists a set } S \text{ such that } x \in S \text{ and } S \in A\}$$ ■

Example 2.2B.2

(1) Let $A = \{\, \{\text{a}\}, \{\text{b}, \text{q}\}, \{\text{a}, \text{r}, \text{q}\} \,\}$. Then

$$\cup A = \{\text{a}, \text{b}, \text{q}, \text{r}\}$$

(2) Let $S1 = \{3, \text{'me'}\}$, $S2 = \{\text{m}, 5, \text{'rrr'}\}$, $S3 = \{\text{'me'}, 5, 8\}$ and $A = \{S1, S2, S3\}$. Then

$$\cup A = \{3, \text{'me'}, \text{m}, 5, \text{'rrr'}, 8\}$$

$3 \in \cup A$ because $3 \in S1$ and $S1 \in A$. 'me' $\in \cup A$ because 'me' $\in S1$ and $S1 \in A$, and also because 'me' $\in S3$ and $S3 \in A$.

(3) Let $S = \{\text{x}, \text{y}, \text{z}\}$ and $A = \{S\}$. Then

$$\cup A = \{\text{x}, \text{y}, \text{z}\} = S$$ ■

A simple and safe method of computing the union of a number of enumerated sets is to copy all the members of each set into a new set. This in general gives a redundant description of the result. Then, cross out unnecessary duplicate members. Using the second part of Example **2**.2B.2, for instance,

$$\begin{aligned} &\cup\{S1,\ S2,\ S3\} \\ &= \{3, \text{'me'}, \text{m}, 5, \text{'rrr'}, \text{'me'}, 5, 8\} \\ &= \{3, \text{'me'}, \text{m}, 5, \text{'rrr'}, 8\} \end{aligned}$$

Clearly, for any sets A and B, we have

$$A \cup B = \cup\{A, B\}$$

For instance, if $A = \{2, 4, 6\}$ and $B = \{1, 4, 7\}$ then

$$A \cup B = \{1, 2, 4, 6, 7\} = \cup\{A, B\}$$

It is for this reason that the second variant of the union is said to be a generalization of the first.

Consider three (or more) sets – for example, S, T, U. Officially, we denote their union by $\cup\{S, T, U\}$. However, there is an alternative way of representing it, which is to write $S \cup T \cup U$. We use this alternative occasionally, as it is somewhat more natural.

Technically, the notation '$S \cup T \cup U$' is an *iterated application* of the union $\cup$ of *two* sets, and we should ask whether this is well defined. The question is: does '$S \cup T \cup U$' mean $S \cup (T \cup U)$ or $(S \cup T) \cup U$? Fortunately the answer is that '$S \cup T \cup U$' means both, as $S \cup (T \cup U) = (S \cup T) \cup U$. (This property is treated in Section **2**.3.) Therefore we may use '$S \cup T \cup U$' without ambiguity.

Representation of union by a Venn diagram

A convenient way of representing the union of two (or more) sets is a Venn diagram (Figure **2**.2B.1). In this diagram each set S is depicted by a circle, and the members of S are represented by the points lying within the circle. If two

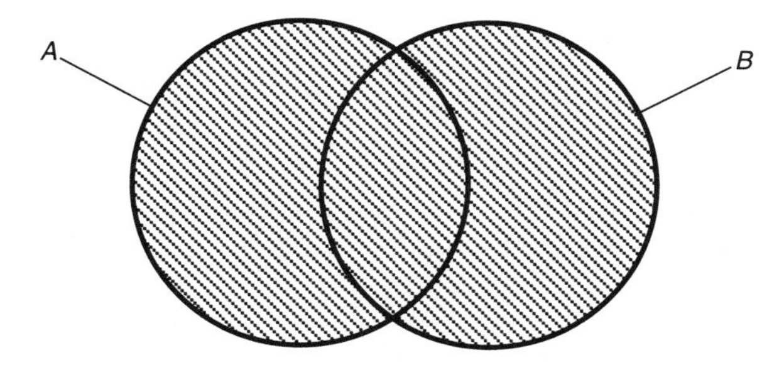

Figure 2.2B.1 Venn diagram of the union of two sets. $A \cup B$ is the shaded area.

sets *S1* and *S2* have common members, these are naturally represented by the points lying in the area where the corresponding circles overlap. Given such a picture of several sets, their union is represented by all the elements occurring in the total enclosed area.

2.2C Intersection

The next operation, called *intersection*, also comes in two variants. The first version operates on two sets, the second on a set of sets.

Consider first the intersection of two sets A and B. This is denoted by

$$A \cap B$$

and is defined as follows: for any object x, x is a member of $A \cap B$ iff x is a member of both A and B. More formally:

Definition 2.2C.1

The intersection of two sets A and B is the set denoted by $A \cap B$ and defined by the condition:

$$\text{for all } x,\ x \in A \cap B \text{ iff } x \in A \text{ and } x \in B$$

Equivalently, $A \cap B$ is given by

$$A \cap B = \{x \mid x \in A \text{ and } x \in B\}$$ ■

The two alternatives used in this definition are clearly equivalent.

Example 2.2C.1

(1) Let $A = \{1, 3, 5, 6\}$ and $B = \{2, 3, 6, 7\}$. Then

$$A \cap B = \{3, 6\}$$

(2) Let $A = \{x \in \text{Nat} \mid x \leqslant 3\}$ and $B = \{x \in \text{Nat} \mid 2 \leqslant x \leqslant 6\}$. Then

$$A \cap B = \{x \in \text{Nat} \mid 2 \leqslant x \leqslant 3\} = \{2, 3\}$$

(3) Let $A = \{x \mid x \text{ is a girl}\}$ and $B = \{x \mid x \text{ is a boy}\}$. Then

$$A \cap B = \varnothing$$ ■

The second variant of intersection generalizes the first. Given a set A of sets, the intersection of A, denoted by $\cap A$, is the set of objects each of which belongs to *every* member of A.

Here is a simple example. Suppose $A = \{S, T, U\}$, where S, T and U themselves are sets. Then the intersection of A, that is, the intersection of S, T

and U, is the set of which any member belongs simultaneously to S, T and U. Thus, if $S = \{1, 2, 3, \text{t}\}$, $T = \{\text{b}, 1, \text{t}\}$ and $U = \{1, \text{b}, 3, \text{t}\}$ then

$$\cap A = \cap \{S, T, U\} = \{1, \text{t}\}$$

Note that $\cap A$ is defined only if $A \neq \emptyset$.

Definition 2.2C.2

Let A be any *nonempty* set of which each member is a set. The intersection of A is the set denoted by $\cap A$ and defined by the following condition: any object x is a member of $\cap A$ iff x is a member of every member of A. Formally:

$$\text{for all } x,\ x \in \cap A \text{ iff for all sets } S \text{ such that } S \in A,\ x \in S$$

Equivalently, $\cap A$ is given by

$$\cap A = \{x \mid \text{for all sets } S \text{ such that } S \in A,\ x \in S\}$$ ∎

Example 2.2C.2

(1) Let $A = \{ \{\text{a, q, s}\}, \{\text{a, b, q}\}, \{\text{a, q, r}\} \}$. Then

$$\cap A = \{\text{a, q}\}$$

(2) Let $S1 = \{3, \text{m}, \text{'rr'}\}$, $S2 = \{\text{m}, 5, \text{'rr'}\}$, $S3 = \{\text{m}, \text{'me'}, 5, 8, \text{'rr'}\}$ and $A = \{S1, S2, S3\}$. Then

$$\cap A = \{\text{m}, \text{'rr'}\}$$

(3) Let $S = \{\text{x, y, z}\}$ and $A = \{S\}$. Then

$$\cap A = \{\text{x, y, z}\} = S$$ ∎

A simple method of computing the intersection of a finite set A of enumerated sets is as follows. First, make a copy of the first member of A. Then examine each member x of this copy in turn and check that x occurs in every other member of A. If x fails this test then delete it from the new set. Using the second part of Example **2**.2C.2, for instance:

- Start with a copy of $S1$:

  $\{3, \text{m}, \text{'rr'}\}$

- Consider 3. This occurs neither in $S2$ nor in $S3$, so drop 3:

  $\{\text{m}, \text{'rr'}\}$

- Consider m. m is also a member of $S2$ and $S3$, so keep m:

  {m, 'rr'}

- Consider 'rr'. 'rr' $\in S2$ and 'rr' $\in S3$, so keep 'rr'. Conclude that

  $\cap A = \{$m, 'rr'$\}$ ■

As with union, the intersection $A \cap B$ of two sets A and B is equal to $\cap \{A, B\}$, as the reader may verify on some examples. For instance, if $A = \{2, 4, 6, 7\}$ and $B = \{1, 4, 7\}$ then

$$A \cap B = \{4, 7\} = \cap \{A, B\}$$

In Definition **2**.2C.2, the intersection $\cap A$ of a set A of sets is defined only if A is not the empty set. The reason for this is as follows. Suppose $\cap \varnothing$ *were* a set. Then every possible object would have to be a member of this 'set', because there is no constraint whatsoever restricting its membership. However, we cannot allow a set containing all objects, in particular all sets (including itself), as this would lead to a contradiction. This point is discussed in Section **2**.5A, in connection with Russell's paradox.

As with union, we also use the notation $S \cap T \cap U \cap \ldots$ to represent the intersection of three sets or more. This too is unambiguous as $S \cap (T \cap U) = (S \cap T) \cap U$. We treat this property in Section **2**.3.

Representation of intersection by a Venn diagram

The Venn diagram introduced in Section **2**.2B is also useful to represent the intersection of two or more sets. Given n circles depicting n different sets, the intersection of these sets is represented by the points lying within the area where the circles overlap. Two examples are given in Figure **2**.2C.1.

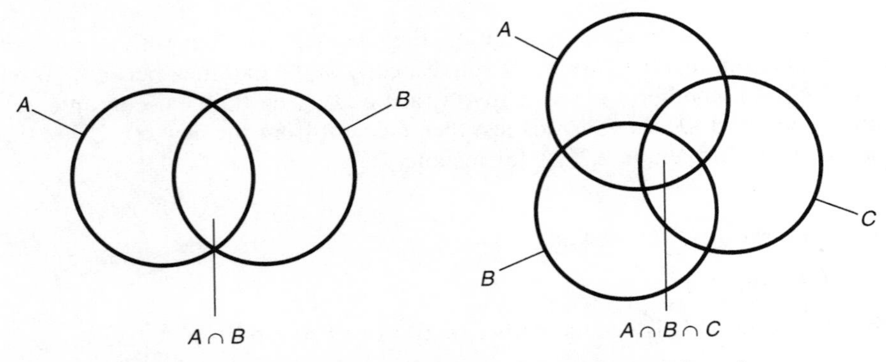

Figure 2.2C.1 Venn diagrams representing the intersection of sets.

2.2D Relative complement

For any two sets A and B, their *relative complement* is the set whose members belong to A and not to B. It is denoted by $A \backslash B$.

For instance, let $A = \{1, 4, 6\}$ and $B = \{2, 6, 7\}$. Then $A \backslash B = \{1, 4\}$. To obtain the result, take a copy of A and delete the members of B from this copy. Note that $A \backslash B$ is defined even if B is *not* included in A.

Definition 2.2D.1

The relative complement of two sets A and B is the set denoted by $A \backslash B$ and defined by the following condition:

for all x, $x \in A \backslash B$ iff $x \in A$ and $x \notin B$

Equivalently,

$$A \backslash B = \{x \mid x \in A \text{ and } x \notin B\}$$ ■

Example 2.2D.1

(1) Let $A = \{1, 3, 5, 6\}$ and $B = \{2, 3, 6, 7\}$. Then

$$A \backslash B = \{1, 5\}$$

(2) Let $A = \{x \in \text{Nat} \mid x \leqslant 3\}$ and $B = \{x \in \text{Nat} \mid 2 \leqslant x \leqslant 6\}$. Then

$$A \backslash B = \{x \in \text{Nat} \mid x < 2\} = \{0, 1\}$$

(3) Let $A = \{x \mid x \text{ is a girl}\}$ and $B = \{x \mid x \text{ is a boy}\}$. Then

$$A \backslash B = A = \{x \mid x \text{ is a girl}\}$$

Consider (2) above. The result is justified as follows (details in square brackets):

$A \backslash B$

$= \{x \mid x \in A \text{ and } x \notin B\}$ [by Definition **2**.2D.1]

$= \{x \in \text{Nat} \mid x \leqslant 3 \text{ and not } (2 \leqslant x \leqslant 6)\}$ [by definition of A and B]

$= \{x \in \text{Nat} \mid x < 2\}$ [simplifying the defining property]

$= \{0, 1\}$ ■

Some authors use the symbol '$-$' to denote the relative complement. We also use this symbol, but only in the special case where $B \subseteq A$. This is introduced in Section **2**.2E.

2.2E Disjointness and related operations

Consider any two sets A and B. We say that these two sets are *disjoint* if they have no common members, that is, if $A \cap B = \varnothing$. Likewise, for any set of sets, we say that these are *pairwise disjoint* if there is no object x which belongs to more than one of them. The precise definition is as follows.

Definition 2.2E.1

(1) Two sets A and B are disjoint iff $A \cap B = \varnothing$.

(2) Let A be any set of sets. A is pairwise disjoint iff for any two different members S and T of A,

$$S \cap T = \varnothing$$ ■

Union of disjoint sets

Disjointness is an important property of sets. In applications, we frequently operate on sets which are pairwise disjoint, and this feature is crucial. For this reason, we now introduce a special notation for the union of disjoint sets.

Definition 2.2E.2

(1) For any two sets A and B, if A and B are disjoint then their union $A \cup B$ is called *set sum* and denoted by

$$A + B$$

(2) Let A be a set of sets. If A is pairwise disjoint, then the union $\cup A$ is called *set sum* of A and denoted by

$$\Sigma A$$ ■

The two symbols '$+$' and 'Σ' are borrowed from arithmetic, where they have an *analogous* meaning. For instance, if two finite sets A and B are disjoint then the cardinality of the union of A and B equals the sum of the cardinalities of A and B:

(1) $\text{Num}(A+B) = \text{Num}(A) + \text{Num}(B)$

However, this property is not satisfied if A and B are *not* disjoint. Note that in (1) the first '$+$' denotes the union of disjoint sets while the second denotes addition of two numbers. We see this clearly from the respective types of the operands, so there is no confusion about the meaning of each occurrence of '$+$' (we say that '$+$' is *overloaded*).

The advantage of this notation is to remind the reader of the fact that the operands are, or must be, pairwise disjoint. This property is often crucial, and to emphasize it in this way enhances the readability of the notation significantly. However, this notation is not standard. Note that it must not be confused with the so-called *disjoint union* of sets. The latter is introduced in Chapter **3**.

Relative complement of a subset

Similar reasoning leads us to represent the relative complement $A \backslash B$ by '$A - B$' *when* B *is included in* A. This is again because of the analogy between this case and the subtraction of two numbers. By writing '$A - B$', we emphasize that $B \subseteq A$, a property that may play the same crucial role as disjointness in the union of sets.

Definition 2.2E.3

For any two sets A and B, if $B \subseteq A$ then their relative complement $A \backslash B$ is called their *set difference* and denoted by

$$A - B$$ ■

Clearly, for any two finite sets A and B, if $B \subseteq A$ then they satisfy the property

(2) $\quad \text{Num}(A - B) = \text{Num}(A) - \text{Num}(B)$

However this property is *not* satisfied if B is *not* a subset of A.

There is also an important relation between the union '$+$' of disjoint sets and the relative complement '$-$'. If the set $C = A + B$, then $B \subseteq C$ and therefore $C - B$ is defined. Moreover, it is clear that $C - B = A$. These are other properties shared with arithmetic addition and subtraction. Note, however, that if A and B are *not* disjoint and $C = A \cup B$ then $C - B$ is still defined but $C - B \neq A$.

2.2F Powerset

The last basic operation we introduce is the *powerset* of a given set S. This is defined as the set of subsets of S and is written $\text{Pow}(S)$.

Definition 2.2F.1

For any set S, the *powerset* of S is the set $\text{Pow}(S)$ defined by

$$\text{for all } x,\ x \in \text{Pow}(S) \text{ iff } x \subseteq S$$

Equivalently,

$$\text{Pow}(S) = \{x \mid x \subseteq S\}$$ ■

From this definition it follows that in order to express the fact that a set x is included in a set S, we may write either '$x \subseteq S$' or '$x \in \text{Pow}(S)$'; the two notations are equivalent. However, we use the form '$x \subseteq S$' whenever possible, as it is found to be more natural than the alternative.

Example 2.2F.1

(1) Let $S1 = \{a, b\}$. Then the subsets of $S1$ are $\emptyset$, $\{a\}$, $\{b\}$ and $\{a, b\}$. Consequently

$$\text{Pow}(S1) = \{\emptyset, \{a\}, \{b\}, \{a, b\}\}$$

(2) Let $S2 = \{2, 5, 8\}$. Then

$$\text{Pow}(S2) = \{\emptyset, \{2\}, \{5\}, \{2, 5\}, \{8\}, \{2, 8\}, \{5, 8\}, \{2, 5, 8\}\}$$

(3) Let $S3 = \{2\}$. Then

$$\text{Pow}(S3) = \{\emptyset, \{2\}\}$$

(4) Let $S4 = \emptyset$. Then

$$\text{Pow}(S4) = \{\emptyset\}$$

■

We also introduce a related notion, namely the set of *finite* subsets of a set S. This is denoted by Powf(S).

Definition 2.2F.2

For any set S, Powf(S) is the set defined by

$$\text{Powf}(S) = \{x \mid x \subseteq S \text{ and } x \text{ is finite}\}$$

■

Obviously if S itself is finite then Powf(S) = Pow(S). However, this is no longer the case when S is infinite. For instance, Nat is infinite and consequently Pow(Nat) $\neq$ Powf(Nat). Indeed, there are many different *infinite subsets* of Nat. Some examples are Nat itself, the set of all even numbers, the set of all odd numbers and the set of numbers divisible by 3. These are members of Pow(Nat) but not of Powf(Nat).

This concludes our catalogue of basic set operations.

2.2G Application

John and Kate are pen-friends. Each of them keeps a 'list' of correspondents. John's is

$$LJ = \{\text{Albert, Beth, Kate, Linda, Mike, Olaf}\}$$

and Kate's is

$$LK = \{\text{Beth, John, Mike, Peter}\}$$

From our point of view, these are sets in the strict sense of the term, but we continue to call them lists here to reflect common usage.

The two friends decide to compare their lists.

1 Kate, anxious to extend her circle of pen-friends, suggests pooling the two lists. The result is

$$\begin{aligned} LTotal &= LJ \cup LK \\ &= \{\text{Albert, Beth, John, Kate, Linda, Mike, Olaf, Peter}\} \end{aligned}$$

2 There is a qualitative difference between the original lists on the one hand, and the new one on the other. Can you tell what it is?

Answer John is not a member of LJ, as John is not in the habit of writing letters to himself. Similarly, Kate $\notin LK$. But as they are pen-friends, they belong to each other's lists. As a result, both of them belong to the new list:

$$\text{John, Kate} \in LTotal$$

Therefore, $LTotal$ is not entirely suitable as a new list for either John or Kate. In some applications, to adopt $LTotal$ as a new list might even prove to be a serious error. This fact may be unexpected. It illustrates the kind of pitfalls to which we are always exposed and which analysis is designed to uncover.

3 Kate decides to rectify this anomaly. Her final list is therefore

$$LK' = LTotal - \{\text{Kate}\}$$

John follows suit, and his final list is

$$LJ' = LTotal - \{\text{John}\}$$

In both definitions, the operator '$-$' is correct as $\{\text{Kate}\} \subseteq LTotal$ and $\{\text{John}\} \subseteq LTotal$.

4 'What friends do we have in common?' asks John. The answer is:

$$LJ \cap LK = \{\text{Beth, Mike}\}$$

Note that this result does not include {John, Kate}. Therefore it describes the set of their friends other than themselves, which is probably what most people would regard as the correct answer.

5 Kate wishes to know who her new pen-friends will be. She computes:

$$NFK = LK' - LK = \{\text{Albert, Linda, Olaf}\}$$

John's set of new pen-friends is found in the same way:

$$NFJ = LJ' - LJ = \{\text{Peter}\}$$

6 John thinks that nobody can simultaneously be a new friend of both himself and Kate. He verifies:

$$NFJ \cap NFK = \{\text{Peter}\} \cap \{\text{Albert, Linda, Olaf}\} = \varnothing$$

7 Kate concludes that the final list *LTotal* may be *partitioned* into four pairwise disjoint subsets:

(a) themselves:	$T =$	{John, Kate}
(b) their common friends:	$C = LJ \cap LK =$	{Beth, Mike}
(c) John's new friends:	$NFJ =$	{Peter}
(d) Kate's new friends:	$NFK =$	{Albert, Linda, Olaf}

She checks that indeed these four sets are pairwise disjoint and their total (union of disjoint sets) is *LTotal*:

$$\begin{aligned}
&\Sigma\{T, C, NFJ, NFK\} \\
&= \Sigma\{\{\text{John, Kate}\}, \{\text{Beth, Mike}\}, \{\text{Peter}\}, \{\text{Albert, Linda, Olaf}\}\} \\
&= \{\text{Albert, Beth, John, Kate, Linda, Mike, Olaf, Peter}\} \\
&= LTotal
\end{aligned}$$

EXERCISES

Note Difficult exercises are marked with an asterisk.

2.2.1 Calculate $X \cup Y$, $X \cap Y$, $X \backslash Y$ and $Y \backslash X$ for the following pairs of sets X and Y:

X	Y
{a,b,c}	{b,c,d}
{b,c,e}	{a,d,e,f}
{a,d,e}	{b,c,f}
{c,e,f}	{c,d}

2.2.2 For any set A, determine $A \cup A$, $A \cap A$ and $A \backslash A$.

2.2.3 Let $A = \{n \in \text{Nat} \mid 3 \leqslant n \leqslant 7\}$ and $B = \{n \in \text{Nat} \mid 5 \leqslant n \leqslant 9\}$.

(a) Calculate $A \cup B$, $A \cap B$, $A \backslash B$ and $B \backslash A$.
(b) What relationships between these four sets can you identify?

2.2.4 Let $S1 = \{n \in \text{Nat} \mid 3 < n < 9\}$, $S2 = \{n \in \text{Nat} \mid n \text{ is a prime}\}$ and $S3 = \{n \in \text{Nat} \mid n \text{ is even}\}$. Let $S4 = S1 \cap S2$ and $S5 = S1 \cap S3$.

(a) Enumerate $S1$, $S4$ and $S5$.
(b) What interesting relationships between these three sets can you identify?

2.2.5 For any English word w, let $L(w)$ denote the set of letters occurring in w. Different occurrences of a letter are *not* regarded as distinct; for instance, if $w =$ 'abracadabra' then $L(w) = \{\text{a, b, r, c, d}\}$. Let W be any set of words.

(a) Give a formula to express the set of letters occurring in W.
(b) Let $w1 =$ 'alas', $w2 =$ 'balcony', $w3 =$ 'saddle' and $W = \{w1, w2, w3\}$. Use your formula to work out the set of letters occurring in W.

2.2.6 Let A and B be two *disjoint* sets and $C = A + B$.

(a) Calculate $A \backslash B$ and $B \backslash A$.
(b) Calculate $C - A$ and $C - B$.
(c) Show how the various relationships between these sets are reflected in the relationships between their cardinalities.
(d) Show by a counterexample that your answers to (c) would not be valid if A and B were not disjoint.

2.2.7 Let A be any set.

(a) Let S be any subset of A. What is the relationship between $\text{Pow}(S)$ and $\text{Pow}(A)$?
(b) Show that $\cup \text{Pow}(A) = A$ and $\cap \text{Pow}(A) = \varnothing$.
(c) Assume every member of A is a set. Show that $A \subseteq \text{Pow}(\cup A)$.
(d) Give an example to show that A, as defined in (c), is not in general equal to $\text{Pow}(\cup A)$.

2.2.8 Let A be any set and $P = \text{Pow}(A)$.

(a) Show that for any two members X and Y of P, $X \cup Y$, $X \cap Y$ and $X \backslash Y$ are members of P.
(b) Give examples to show that in general $X \in P$ does *not* imply $\text{Pow}(X) \in P$, although $\text{Pow}(X)$ *may* belong to P.

2.2.9 Enumerate the powersets $\mathrm{Pow}(A_i)$ of the following sets A_i:

(a) $A_0 = \varnothing$
(b) $A_1 = \{\mathrm{m}\}$
(c) $A_2 = \{\mathrm{m, n}\}$
(d) $A_3 = \{\mathrm{m, n, p}\}$

2.2.10* In Exercise 2.2.9 each set A_i is obtained by inserting a *new* member into the previous set A_{i-1}. For instance:

$$A_1 = A_0 + \{m\}$$
$$A_2 = A_1 + \{n\}$$

and so on. How can we construct $\mathrm{Pow}(A_i)$ from $\mathrm{Pow}(A_{i-1})$ for each $i > 0$? Hence, give a systematic method of enumerating the powerset $\mathrm{Pow}(A)$ of any finite set A.

2.2.11* Using your solution to Exercise 2.2.10, show that if $\mathrm{Num}(A) = n$ then

$$\mathrm{Num}(\mathrm{Pow}(A)) = 2^n.$$

2.3 Properties of basic set operations

This section briefly describes some fundamental laws or properties of the set operations presented in Section 2.2. Some of these laws are studied under the heading *algebra of sets*. They are the properties of the operations of union ($\cup$), intersection ($\cap$), relative complement ($\backslash$) and inclusion ($\subseteq$). As already mentioned, the laws of set algebra are similar to those of arithmetic, but there are also important differences.

2.3A Commutativity and associativity

Commutative laws of $\cup$ *and* $\cap$

The two operations of union and intersection applied to two sets are *commutative*. This means that the result is independent of the order of the operands. Formally: for any sets A and B,

(1) $A \cup B = B \cup A$

(2) $A \cap B = B \cap A$ ■

For instance, if $A = \{1, 2, 3, 4\}$ and $B = \{3, 4, 5, 6\}$ then both $A \cup B$ and $B \cup A$ equal $\{1, 2, 3, 4, 5, 6\}$. This result is independent of the order of A and B in the operation. Likewise, both $A \cap B$ and $B \cap A$ equal $\{3, 4\}$: the order of the operands makes no difference. In contrast, the relative complement is *not* commutative. For instance, using the same sets A and B, $A\backslash B = \{1, 2\}$ but $B\backslash A = \{5, 6\}$.

That the relation $A \cup B = B \cup A$ holds is intuitively clear, from a Venn diagram for instance, but how can we *prove* that this relation is true for any sets A and B? Here is the answer in outline. We must show that

for any x, $x \in A \cup B$ iff $x \in B \cup A$

If this is proved then we may conclude that $A \cup B = B \cup A$ by the principle of extensionality. Now to prove this we consider each of the four possible cases which may hold for any x:

(a) $x \in A$ and $x \in B$ (b) $x \in A$ and $x \notin B$

(c) $x \notin A$ and $x \in B$ (d) $x \notin A$ and $x \notin B$

For each case, we check that x is a member of both $A \cup$ B and $B \cup A$, or neither of these two sets. For instance, any x which satisfies case (b) belongs to both $A \cup$ B and $B \cup A$ because $x \in A$. Any x that satisfies case (d) belongs neither to $A \cup B$ nor to $B \cup A$.

The remaining laws may be proved using the same method. Note that here we had to consider four distinct cases because the relation to be proved involves two basic sets, A and B. When three basic sets are involved there are $2^3 = 8$ different cases to consider, and in general when n basic sets are involved there are 2^n cases to consider.

We shall not give further proofs here; they are left as exercises. In Chapter **9** we show how these proofs may be formalized completely within axiomatic set theory, which is based on first-order logic.

Associative laws of ∪ *and* ∩

Both the union and the intersection of three (or more) sets are *associative*. To see what this means, consider any sets A, B and C. We may obtain the union of these three sets in two ways. One way is to apply ∪ first to A and B, and then to $(A \cup B)$ and C. The second way is to apply ∪ first to B and C, and then to A and $(B \cup C)$. The results of these two methods are the same.

Example 2.3A.1

Let $A = \{1, 3\}$, $B = \{2, 3, 4\}$ and $C = \{5\}$. Then on the one hand

$$A \cup B = \{1, 2, 3, 4\}$$

and

$$(A \cup B) \cup C = \{1, 2, 3, 4\} \cup \{5\} = \{1, 2, 3, 4, 5\}$$

On the other hand,

$$(B \cup C) = \{2, 3, 4, 5\}$$

and

$$A \cup (B \cup C) = \{1, 3\} \cup \{2, 3, 4, 5\} = \{1, 2, 3, 4, 5\}$$ ■

This example shows that the final results are equal, although they are reached through two different routes.

The same property holds for intersection. Apply $\cap$ first to A and B, and then to $(A \cap B)$ and C. The final result is the same as the one obtained by applying $\cap$ first to B and C, and then to A and $(B \cap C)$.

Example 2.3A.2

Let $A = \{1, 2, 3, 4\}$, $B = \{2, 3, 4, 5, 6\}$ and $C = \{1, 3, 4, 6\}$. Then on the one hand

$$A \cap B = \{2, 3, 4\}$$

and

$$(A \cap B) \cap C = \{2, 3, 4\} \cap \{1, 3, 4, 6\} = \{3, 4\}$$

On the other hand,

$$(B \cap C) = \{3, 4, 6\}$$

and

$$A \cap (B \cap C) = \{1, 2, 3, 4\} \cap \{3, 4, 6\} = \{3, 4\}$$ ■

We now express the associativity of union and intersection formally. For any sets A, B and C,

(1) $(A \cup B) \cup C = A \cup (B \cup C)$

(2) $(A \cap B) \cap C = A \cap (B \cap C)$

As mentioned in Sections **2**.2B and **2**.2C, these two properties mean that we may write '$A \cup B \cup C$' and '$A \cap B \cap C$' without ambiguity. Moreover, it may be shown that associativity extends to any finite number of sets (generalized associative laws). For any number n, in

$$A_1 \cup A_2 \cup \ldots \cup A_n$$

we may apply $\cup$ in any order. This also holds for

$$A_1 \cap A_2 \cap \ldots \cap A_n$$

2.3B Distributivity and De Morgan's laws

The remaining laws are stated without supporting examples. These laws are given here as they apply to the minimum number of sets. Several of them may be generalized in various ways to sets of sets. These generalizations are not given here, as they are more complex to describe, without bringing much additional insight. We begin with the distributive laws and De Morgan's laws.

Distributivity of $\cup$ *and* $\cap$

Consider any sets A, B and C.

(1) Union is distributive over intersection

$$A \cup (B \cap C) = (A \cup B) \cap (A \cup C)$$

(2) Intersection is distributive over union

$$A \cap (B \cup C) = (A \cap B) \cup (A \cap C)$$

■

De Morgan's laws

For any sets A, B and C,

(1) $C \backslash (A \cup B) = (C \backslash A) \cap (C \backslash B)$

(2) $C \backslash (A \cap B) = (C \backslash A) \cup (C \backslash B)$ ■

Note that the distributive laws and De Morgan's laws come in pairs. In each case, one of the laws is obtained from the other by interchanging $\cup$ and $\cap$. The two components of the pair are said to be *dual*.

2.3C Laws of the empty set, idempotence and absorption

The next laws are fairly obvious. We begin with three properties involving the empty set.

Laws of the empty set

For any sets A and B,

(1) $A \cup \varnothing = A$

(2) $A \cap \varnothing = \varnothing$

(3) $A \cap (B \backslash A) = \varnothing$ ■

There are two properties called *idempotence*. These laws are dual.

Idempotence of $\cup$ *and* $\cap$

For any set A,

(1) $A \cup A = A$

(2) $A \cap A = A$ ■

The next two properties are called *laws of absorption*. They are also dual.

Absorption of $\cup$ *and* $\cap$

For any sets A and B,

(1) $A \cap (A \cup B) = A$

(2) $A \cup (A \cap B) = A$ ■

2.3D Laws of inclusion

The relation of inclusion also satisfies important properties. These are fairly obvious and are as follows.

Property 2.3D.1

For any sets S, A, T and B with $S \subseteq A$ and $T \subseteq B$,

(1) $S \cup A = A$

(2) $S \cap A = S$

(3) $A \subseteq A \cup B$

(4) $A \cap B \subseteq A$

(5) *If* $A \cap B = \varnothing$ then $S \cap T = \varnothing$ ■

Monotonicity of inclusion

For any sets S, A and B with $S \subseteq A$,

(1) $S \cup B \subseteq A \cup B$

(2) $S \cap B \subseteq A \cap B$

(3) If in addition A is a set of sets then

$$\cup S \subseteq \cup A$$ ■

Antimonotonic laws of inclusion

For any sets S, A and B such that $S \subseteq A$,

(1) $B \backslash A \subseteq B \backslash S$

(2) If in addition A is a set of sets and $S \neq \varnothing$ then

$$\cap A \subseteq \cap S$$

■

Note that in these last two laws, the order of S and A is *reversed.*

2.3E Properties of operations on disjoint sets

Recall that for any two sets A and B, we write $A+B$ to denote the union of A and B and at the same time state that A and B are *disjoint*. Likewise, we write $A - B$ to denote the relative complement $A \backslash B$ and simultaneously express the fact that B is a *subset* of A. These two special operations have the following properties.

Property 2.3E.1

For any sets A, B, X and Y,

(1) *Cancellation law*

If $A+X = A+Y$ then $X = Y$

(2) $(A+B) - B = A$

(3) $A+X = B$ iff $X = B - A$

■

EXERCISE

2.3.1 Prove the various laws of this section using the method illustrated for commutativity.

2.4 Review of notation

One of the most remarkable aspects of set theory is the *simplicity* of its notation, set against its *expressive power.* One cannot exaggerate the importance of this fact. The key point is this: *every type of symbol we may ever need, not only in this book but arguably in the whole of computing and mathematics, has now been introduced.*

Consequently, it seems appropriate at this stage to review the notation introduced so far. We may draw up a list of its various types of symbol, in the knowledge that there will be nothing to add to it later. This is our aim now. The reader is urged to study the categories below carefully, and to identify the types of the symbols encountered in all subsequent developments. Note that these categories arise in both natural language descriptions and their formal counterparts.

The various symbols of our notation fall into six main categories. These are as follows:

- variables
- function symbols (including constant symbols)
- predicate symbols
- logical connective symbols
- quantifiers
- punctuation marks

These categories are first illustrated with a simple example. Then they are described in turn.

2.4A Example

Recall the formal definition of a parent given in Section **1**.3A:

$$\forall\, P \in \text{Persons} \cdot P \in \text{Parents iff}$$
$$\exists\, C \in \text{Persons} \cdot P = \text{Mother}(C) \text{ or } P = \text{Father}(C)$$

All six categories of symbols are already represented in this simple example. It is reproduced in Figure **2**.4A.1 with an indication of the type of each symbol. Recall that '$\forall$' means 'for all' and '$\exists$' means 'there exists'.

In the next sections, we describe the six categories of symbols of our notation in turn. This taxonomy is borrowed from first-order logic. We give it in broad, informal outline. In the context of logic, these categories are much more precisely defined. We begin with variables, function symbols and predicate symbols.

$\forall$ Quantifier	P Variable	$\in$ Predicate symbol	**Persons** Constant	• Punctuation
P	$\in$	**Parents** Constant	**iff** Connective	
$\exists$ Quantifier	C Variable	$\in$	**Persons**	•
P	$=$ Predicate	**Mother** Function	(C Punctuation	) Punctuation
or Connective	P	$=$	**Father** Function	(C)

Figure 2.4A.1 Analysis of a definition.

2.4B Variables, functions and predicates

Variables

A variable is a symbol or name used to refer to an object in some given set or class. The symbol itself is fixed: the word 'variable' means that the object referred to may vary over the given set. Note that a variable is always meant to represent exactly *one* object. For instance when 'x' is used to represent *any* member of a set S, 'x' stands for all the members of S but taken *individually*, 'in turn' as it were. This is a fundamental and subtle idea. It may be explained precisely in connection with the quantifier '$\forall$' ('for all').

In any theory, a variable may denote any kind of object. In particular one may introduce function and predicate variables. It is up to the author of the theory to decide exactly which objects may be represented by a given variable in any context. In an informal theory such decisions are often implicit, but in a formalized theory they must be made explicitly.

Function symbols

The various operations on sets introduced in Section **2**.2 are examples of *functions*. Further examples are the various operations of arithmetic: addition, subtraction, and so on. Thus we have already come across many instances of this concept. In each case, we have a rule which produces a certain object, the result, *depending* on some other object(s), the argument(s) or operand(s). The theory of functions is treated in Chapter 3.

A *function symbol* is a name for a function. It is also often called an *operator*. Examples of such symbols in set theory are '$\cup$', and '$\cap$'. These have the constant meaning defined in previous sections. Likewise in arithmetic, the symbols '$+$', '$-$' and so on are function symbols. Their meaning too is constant. Note that we may also define *sets* of functions, and variables ranging over such sets. Therefore in general, depending on the context, we may also have variable function symbols, as stated above.

A *constant symbol* denotes a constant. There are two different ways of defining the notion of a constant. In one sense, it is a fixed object of any kind, possibly a function or a predicate. In this sense a constant symbol may be regarded as a special case of a variable, namely one ranging over a set consisting of just one object.

In the second sense, a constant is an object which does not depend on other objects. In this sense it is equivalent to a function with no arguments, a *nullary* function. It is mainly in this sense that the term is used in this book.

Predicate symbols

Recall the concept of a relation, which we have briefly introduced in Section 2.1G. It is a property that certain pairs of objects may or may not have and is also called a *predicate*. Predicates are close to functions, as a predicate may be described as a special function which returns the value 'true' if its arguments have the relevant property, 'false' otherwise. In general a predicate may have any number of arguments, not just two. The theory of relations is the topic of Chapter 3.

A predicate symbol is a name for a relation. Several examples of predicate symbols were used in Section 2.1: '$<$' and '$\leqslant$' express relations between numbers; the membership symbol '$\in$' denotes a relation between objects and sets; '$\subseteq$' and '$\subset$' represent relations between sets; '$=$' denotes a relation between objects of the same type, for example numbers or sets. In all these cases the meaning of the symbol is constant. However, as with functions, we may define sets of relations and variables ranging over such sets. Consequently in a given context the relation denoted by a predicate symbol is either fixed or variable.

2.4C Logical connective symbols

The various words used to link components of sentences, such as 'not', 'or' and 'and' are called *logical connective symbols*. We have already used most of them several times. The full list is as follows. Each connective is given in two forms: a special symbol and the English word equivalent.

$\neg$	not
$\wedge$	and
$\vee$	or
$\Rightarrow$	if ... then
$\Leftrightarrow$	iff

Logical connectives are studied systematically in Chapter **6**, as part of propositional logic. In Part **2**, they are regarded mainly as a shorthand for the corresponding English phrases. However, they have a precise meaning, which we now define.

Connectives are applied to propositions. A proposition is a statement of a property that is true or false of a certain object or group of objects, such as '$n < p$' or '$x \in S$'. Connectives enable us to construct new propositions by linking more elementary ones as described below. In these definitions, we use the letters 'P' and 'Q' to represent any propositions.

Not Given a proposition P, 'not P', alias '$\neg P$', is the negation of P. Therefore if P is true then 'not P' is false, and if P is false then 'not P' is true. This rule is summarized in the following *truth table*:

P	$\neg P$
true	false
false	true

Note that the negation of a predicate symbol may also be represented by crossing the symbol. For instance, '$x \notin S$' means 'not ($x \in S$)'.

And For any two propositions P and Q, 'P and Q', alias '$P \wedge Q$', states that both P and Q are true. Thus 'P and Q' is true when both P and Q are true and false in all other cases. This is summarized in the following truth table, which gives the truth value of 'P and Q' for each combination of truth values of P and Q.

P	Q	$P \wedge Q$
true	true	true
true	false	false
false	true	false
false	false	false

Or For any two propositions P and Q, 'P or Q', alias '$P \vee Q$', states that at least one of the two propositions P, Q is true. Therefore '$P \vee Q$' is true in all cases except when both P and Q are false. The truth table is:

P	Q	$P \vee Q$
true	true	true
true	false	true
false	true	true
false	false	false

Note that 'or' is *inclusive*: '$P \vee Q$' is true when *both* P and Q are true.

If . . . then For any two propositions P, Q, 'if P then Q', alias '$P \Rightarrow Q$', states that if P is true then so is Q. If P is false, Q may have any truth value. Therefore '$P \Rightarrow Q$' is false *in only one case*, namely when P is true and Q is false. Here is the truth table:

P	Q	$P \Rightarrow Q$
true	true	true
true	false	false
false	true	true
false	false	true

Iff For any two propositions P, Q, 'P iff Q', alias $P \Leftrightarrow Q$', states that P and Q are either both true, or both false. Therefore, '$P \Leftrightarrow Q$' is true exactly when P and Q have the same truth value. The truth table is:

P	Q	$P \Leftrightarrow Q$
true	true	true
true	false	false
false	true	false
false	false	true

We also say that '$P \Leftrightarrow Q$' states that P and Q are *equivalent*.

2.4D Quantifiers

There are two quantifiers, the *universal* and the *existential*. They are now described in turn. '$\cdot$' is a punctuation mark: its use is explained below.

The *universal quantifier* is expressed in English by the phrase 'for all' or by other similar forms like 'for any' or 'for each'. It is denoted by the special symbol '$\forall$'. For instance, the proposition

$$\forall x \cdot x \notin \varnothing$$

is read 'for all x, x is not a member of the empty set', or 'for any x, ...'. In general, if x is a variable and P a proposition which may contain x, for example '$x \notin \varnothing$' above,

$$\forall x \cdot P$$

means that the proposition P is true for any object represented by x. In other words, '$\forall x \cdot P$' states: 'Whatever x may stand for, P is true'. '$\forall x \cdot P$' is called a *generalization* of P. In '$\forall x \cdot P$', x is said to be (universally) quantified. We also call '$\forall x$' a (universal) quantifier. Often the quantified variable is constrained to range over a given set A. We may express this by writing

$$\forall x \in A \cdot P$$

which is read: 'for any member x of A, P is true'. This form is equivalent to '$\forall x \cdot$ if $x \in A$ then P', or '$\forall x \cdot x \in A \Rightarrow P$'.

The *existential quantifier* is represented in English by the phrase 'there exists ... such that' or any equivalent form. It is denoted by the special symbol '$\exists$'. For example the proposition

$$\exists x \cdot \varnothing \neq x$$

is read 'there exists (an object) x, such that the empty set is not equal to x', or 'for some x, $\varnothing$ is not equal to x'. In general, if x is a variable and P a proposition which may contain x,

$$\exists x \cdot P$$

means that there exists an object such that P is true when 'x' stands for this object.

In '$\exists x \cdot P$', x is said to be (existentially) quantified. '$\exists x$' is also called an (existential) quantifier. If x is constrained to range over a given set A, this may be written

$$\exists x \in A \cdot P$$

which is read: 'there exists a member x of A such that P is true'. This form is equivalent to '$\exists x \cdot x \in A$ and P', or '$\exists x \cdot x \in A \wedge P$'.

The quantifiers '$\forall$' and '$\exists$' are closely related. Clearly, '$\exists x \cdot P$' is equivalent to '$\neg(\forall x \neg P)$'. Therefore we could do all our work with one quantifier only, say '$\forall$'.

We also sometimes use the variant '$\exists 1$' of the existential quantifier: for any variable x and any proposition P, '$\exists 1 x \cdot P$' means 'there exists *exactly one* x such that P is true'. For instance,

$$\exists 1 x \, \forall y \cdot y \notin x$$

reads: 'there exists exactly one x such that for all y, y is not a member of x'. (This is a true proposition: the x in question is $\varnothing$, and this set is unique by the principle of extensionality.)

On the nature of variables and generalization

Consider a proposition about natural numbers, for example,

$$P = \text{'If } n \text{ is odd then } n+1 \text{ is even'}$$

and its generalization '$\forall n \cdot P$'. (The fact that $n \in \text{Nat}$ is implicit.) How can the variable 'n' simultaneously stand for *all* natural numbers and for exactly *one* of them in '$\forall n \cdot P$'? A precise explanation is as follows.

The problem is to determine the exact meaning of '$\forall n \cdot P$'. Each natural number, 0, 1, 2 and so on, is an *instance* of n and may be substituted for 'n' in P, giving an instance of P. Thus the instances of P are:

$$P_0 = \text{'If 0 is odd then } 0+1 \text{ is even'}$$
$$P_1 = \text{'If 1 is odd then } 1+1 \text{ is even'}$$
$$P_2 = \text{'If 2 is odd then } 2+1 \text{ is even'}$$

and so on. Now we can clearly see the intended meaning of '$\forall n \cdot P$': it is that *all these instances of P are true*. It is the same as asserting

$$P_0 \text{ and } P_1 \text{ and } P_2 \text{ and } \ldots$$

This example gives a precise explanation of generalization. It also explains how a variable may stand simultaneously for exactly one member of a set and for all of its members. In any one instance of P, n is replaced by one specific number, but considering all the instances of P we can see that in this proposition n also stands for all natural numbers.

2.4E Punctuation

A punctuation mark is 'any of the marks (for example, full stop or comma) used in writing to separate sentences, phrases and so on and to clarify meaning'

(Oxford English Dictionary). Punctuation marks play the same role in formulas. The main ones we use are the parentheses '(' and ')'. Their purpose is to group items – that is, to indicate that the symbols they enclose must be read as a *unit* in its own right. We occasionally use square brackets '[' and ']' to facilitate the matching of corresponding left and right parentheses.

Another alternative to parentheses is the dot '·', used as follows. Consider any expression containing parentheses. If we replace a *left* parenthesis by '·' and eliminate the *matching right* parenthesis, we obtain a new expression which we regard as equivalent. For instance

$$\exists x \ (\varnothing \neq x)$$

is equivalent to

$$\exists x \cdot \varnothing \neq x$$

A judicious combination of dots and parentheses may enhance readability substantially. With a little practice, it is easy to reconstruct the fully parenthesized expression from the equivalent 'dotted' one. The rule is: replace the dots *from left to right* by left parentheses. Whenever a dot is replaced, *insert a matching right parenthesis as far right as possible*, that is, at the end of the expression or before the first ')' whose matching '(' *precedes* the dot being replaced. For instance, the formula

$$\exists 1 \ x \cdot \forall y \cdot y \notin x$$

is reconstructed as

$$\exists 1 \ x \ (\forall y \cdot y \notin x)$$

and finally

$$\exists 1 \ x \ (\forall y (y \notin x))$$

For the moment, we use parentheses and '·' freely, but in Part **3** their use will be subject to precise rules.

In set theory, the braces '{' and '}' have a special role, namely to enclose the description of a set. The comma has a more limited role than in natural language. It is used solely as a separator of successive elements in an enumeration.

2.4F Introducing names

Before a name may be used, it must be introduced or defined – that is, its meaning must be specified. It is useful to indicate in the text when a name is either introduced for the first time or given a new meaning. We shall do so by decorating the relevant relation symbol with the subscript 'd', meaning 'by definition'. For instance,

$$A =_{\mathrm{d}} \{1, 2, 3\}$$

introduces A as the set $\{1, 2, 3\}$. It is to be read: 'A is *by definition* equal to $\{1, 2, 3\}$'. Likewise to introduce an object S as a subset of a given set T, we may write

$$S \subseteq_{\mathrm{d}} T$$

meaning 'S is by definition a subset of T'.

To introduce an object x as a *member* of a given set or class S, we write

$$x : S$$

This means: 'By definition, $x \in S$'. This use of ':' is common, which is why ':' is here preferred to '$\in_{\mathrm{d}}$'.

This completes our notation review. The taxonomy of symbols we have introduced is further developed in Part **3**.

2.5 Variants of set theory

There are several variants of set theory. In the purest form, the only objects to be considered are sets as obtained by certain precise rules, the so-called Zermelo–Fraenkel (ZF) axioms, some of which have already been given. This is the theory which mathematicians regard as standard today. We refer to it as ZF or *pure set theory*.

The other variants are essentially extensions of pure set theory. These extensions are used for various reasons. Thus it may be convenient on theoretical grounds to make a distinction between strict sets and certain 'larger' collections called *classes* (understood in a technical sense). The origin of this distinction lies in the resolution of contradictions such as Russell's paradox in pure set theory. Section **2**.5A is devoted to this paradox and to classes.

Other extensions are motivated by pragmatic reasons. Recall that the purpose of this book is not just to describe set theory in itself. It is to show how this theory can be used as a modelling language, to represent any aspect of the world one may be interested in, concrete or abstract. This calls for some practical adaptations of the theory, which are outlined in Section **2**.5B.

Finally, a distinction must be made regarding the *form* of set theory. This theory may be expressed either *semiformally*, or *axiomatically* – that is, *completely formally*. These two alternatives are discussed in Section **2**.5C.

2.5A Russell's paradox and classes

As stated in Section **2**.1J, the unrestricted definition of sets by the method of abstraction leads to certain paradoxes, the most famous of which is due to Bertrand Russell and is as follows. Suppose any formula may be used to define a set by abstraction. Then the following equality introduces A as the set of all sets:

$$A =_{\mathrm{d}} \{x \mid x = x\}$$

In this definition, the defining property is a formula which is true for every x; any other formula with this property, such as 'true' or '$\varnothing \subseteq \varnothing$', would be equally suitable. Now as $A = A$, it follows that $A \in A$; that is, the set of all sets belongs to itself. This leads us to define the set R of all sets which do *not* belong to themselves:

$$R =_{\mathrm{d}} \{x \mid x \notin x\}$$

The question is: does R belong to itself or not? Suppose it does: $R \in R$. Then, substituting R for x in the definition of R, we must conclude that $R \notin R$. However, if the latter is true then R is an object satisfying the defining condition of R and we must conclude that $R \in R$. So the definition of R leads to a *contradiction*: a situation in which a statement and its negation are simultaneously true. We cannot possibly allow this, for otherwise any statement whatsoever would have to be regarded as true according to the rules of logic, as will be seen in Part **3**.

There is only one way out of this dilemma. It is to accept that definitions such as those of A and R above cannot be used to define *sets*. This is why only the restricted form of abstraction defined in Section **2**.1J has been allowed in general. Under this restriction, it can then be *proved* that there is no set which contains every set. The proof is fairly simple: for any set A, there is a set B which does not belong to A, namely $B =_{\mathrm{d}} \{x \in A \mid x \notin x\}$. $B \notin A$, for otherwise the definition of B would create the same contradiction as R above.

The consequence of this restriction is that in pure set theory, in which all objects under consideration are sets, we are not allowed to refer to the set of all sets. This is a drawback. In describing the theory, it is often convenient to refer to the collection of all sets or other similar totalities. Moreover, the inability to name such totalities makes the formulation of the theory more difficult.

An alternative approach is to allow reference to such totalities but as collections *distinct from sets*. The collections to be considered are called *classes*. They are separated into two categories: *strict sets* on the one hand, and *proper classes* on the other. A set in the standard sense is a class, but *not* a proper one. Intuitively, a proper class is a collection which is 'too large' to qualify as a set.

This distinction may now be used to refer to the collection of all sets, which we shall name Set. This is defined as a *proper class*. Its various subclasses are either strict sets or proper classes. Only sets may be members of Set or any of its subclasses; proper classes may not. For instance, consider the class of all sets which are not members of themselves. This is a subclass of Set. The resolution of Russell's paradox means that it is a proper class.

This variant of set theory is referred to as von Neumann–Bernays (VNB) or Gödel–Bernays (GB) set theory (Enderton, 1977). Allowing proper classes in addition to sets facilitates the exposition of the theory substantially. It makes it possible to introduce and name various collections of objects which are essentially proper classes. Most of the classes of objects we shall establish in Parts **4** and **5** are of this type. Henceforth we shall systematically distinguish between sets and classes. These two terms will always be used in the sense defined, unless otherwise stated. In particular, whenever we introduce a specific entity as a 'class', the reader should be alerted to the fact that it may be a proper class.

2.5B Set theory as a modelling language

As mentioned above, it is appropriate to adapt set theory in various ways if it is to be applied as a practical modelling tool. We now outline two main extensions motivated by this requirement.

The first extension is as follows. In addition to sets we may wish to refer to objects which are not naturally described as sets, but may be regarded as members of sets. We have already adopted this viewpoint in the previous sections. Indeed, most of the examples given so far were sets of such objects: physical entities such as houses, rivers or persons, or conceptual ones such as numbers or geometric figures. Such objects are referred to collectively as *atoms*, to indicate that they cannot be decomposed as a set can be decomposed into its members.

In pure set theory atoms and sets of atoms are not allowed. The reason for this limitation is that it simplifies the theory without causing any essential loss: the universe of discourse is homogeneous, as every object is a set, and operations such as union, intersection and so on are naturally defined for all objects under consideration. The penalty is the inability to refer to objects which are not sets.

Taking pure set theory as a starting point, there are two ways of introducing atoms. One is to *represent* them by pure sets, in the same way, for instance, that letters are represented in a computer by numbers according to some coding convention. An example of this method is given in Section **4**.1D. It is the representation of the natural numbers by pure sets. Thus in this approach the correspondence between sets and the objects they represent is established outside the theory.

The alternative is to postulate the existence of the various sets of atoms we are interested in, as well as any relevant properties they satisfy, in addition to the axioms of pure set theory. This is a natural approach; we have already used it implicitly earlier, and we shall continue to follow it in future applications.

The second extension is this. A common way of representing any kind of object is to describe its 'features'. This approach is both natural and universal, and we shall follow it in the applications. Specifically, we shall introduce various classes of objects, and each class will be established by describing each member as an atom, a set or an object with certain *features* or *attributes*. Any feature of an object is regarded as an object in its own right – that is, it belongs to a certain class and it is described like any other type of object. One consequence is that a feature may have its own features, and so on.

This style of description is used systematically in Parts **4** and **5**. Note that it constitutes no fundamental departure from set theory. It would be straightforward to convert this description to a purely set-theoretical one in which each object is either an atom or a strict set, though this will not be done explicitly.

2.5C Naive versus axiomatic set theory

A final distinction must be made regarding the form of set theory. There are two main ways of expressing the theory. The first is *semiformal*, or *naive*, and the second *axiomatic* or *completely formal*. The semiformal style is the one we have used so far and shall continue to use in the remainder of Part **2**. In this alternative, ideas are expressed as a combination of natural language and expressions in special symbols. The latter are nothing more than a regular shorthand for natural language expressions, defined more or less precisely. Moreover, reasoning on the objects described is largely intuitive.

In axiomatic set theory, objects and their relationships are entirely represented by so-called *well-formed expressions* (*wfes*), more specifically *terms* and *well-formed formulas* (*wffs*) respectively. These are defined as sequences of certain symbols constructed according to exact rules, which form the *syntax* of the wfes defined. The correspondence between wfes and the objects or relationships they represent is also defined exactly, by so-called *semantic* rules.

Above all, in axiomatic set theory *reasoning* on the objects described is itself entirely represented by *expression transformation rules*. These rules form so-called *deductive calculi*. They are similar to syntax rules in that *they refer solely to wfes as such*, that is as pure, finite strings of symbols, and not to the objects they represent.

The rules governing axiomatic theories in general are the subject of symbolic logic, which is presented in Part **3**. Axiomatic set theory itself is but one application of these rules. It will be illustrated in Chapter **9**.

Relations and Functions

The concepts of relation and function are perhaps the most important in mathematics and science in general. The reason is that, in a sense, 'everything' may be described entirely by relations, or by functions. (The full justification of this assertion depends on an understanding of first-order predicate logic, which is treated in Part **3**.) This chapter is devoted to these two notions.

In Section **3**.1, a few basic preliminary concepts are introduced: *couples* or *ordered pairs, cartesian products* and *disjoint unions*. Cartesian products are defined in terms of couples and disjoint unions are constructed as special cases of cartesian products.

Section **3**.2 is devoted to relations, and Section **3**.3 to functions. Because of their fundamental importance, these two notions are studied in detail and abundantly illustrated. *Relations* may be defined in three different ways, but the most widely used definition is as a subset of a cartesian product. *Functions* are defined as special cases of relations. One main aim of the examples given is to show how universal these two concepts are, not only in theory but also as conceptual models of 'concrete' objects or situations of practical significance: relations and functions arise in all walks of life. Recall that functions are also called *transformations* or *operations*; this last term is also used more specifically, as we shall see.

In Section **3**.4, we treat various fundamental applications of functions. By this is meant objects which are special cases of functions, yet may be regarded as basic notions in their own right. In particular, we show that relations and functions are in fact *equivalent* notions: functions are special cases of relations, but relations may themselves be described as special cases of functions – a typical mathematical twist! Section **3**.5 is devoted to an important generalization of relations and functions, so-called *n-ary relations and functions*. This extension is not as fundamental as the two basic notions it generalizes, but it is very useful in practice, as numerous further examples show.

The elements which may be connected by relations and functions may be any objects. In particular, they may be sets or even (more elementary) relations and functions. We are therefore led to construct so-called *higher-order sets, relations and functions*, whose elements are themselves more elementary sets, relations or functions. These are introduced in Section **3**.6. At first, objects of this kind may seem rather daunting. Yet they are perfectly natural and in fact no more complex than many notions most people use almost routinely. Coming to grips with these is mainly a matter of practice.

By the end of this chapter, we shall have constructed an impressive collection of conceptual objects. These are all instances of theoretical models, as defined in Section **1**.1B. They form a *hierarchy*, in the sense that they may be broadly classified into successive groups or 'levels', each defined in terms of objects of previous levels. These are (roughly): (a) sets; (b) couples; (c) relations and functions; (d) higher-order relations and functions. Yet the remarkable fact about these concepts is that in the last analysis, they all reduce to one notion: in a certain sense, *they are all sets (or classes)*. Thus, the end of this chapter will be the right place at which to reflect once more upon the nature of set theory as a universal modelling notation.

3.1 Couples, cartesian product and disjoint union

3.1A Couples

The two fundamental concepts of relation and function hinge upon the notion of *couple* or *ordered pair*. Intuitively, this concept is simple. However, this simplicity is deceptive, for a couple is not so easy to define precisely in set-theoretical terms. We first describe this notion intuitively. Then we state the fundamental property which this description suggests, and which any specification should satisfy. Finally, we give its standard set-theoretical definition.

Intuitive notion and notation

Intuitively, a *couple* or *ordered pair* consists of two objects a and b *taken in a certain order*. It is denoted by

$$\langle a, b\rangle$$

The two components a and b are called the *first* and *second coordinates* of $\langle a, b\rangle$ respectively. They may be of any type; in particular, they may be any sets. Moreover, they may be different or identical. However, whether identical or not, they are always regarded as *distinct, at least by their position* within the couple.

It is important to make the distinction between a *couple* $\langle a, b\rangle$ and a *pair* $\{a, b\}$. First, $\langle a, b\rangle$ has always exactly two distinct components, a first and a second, as just stated. Thus if $a = b$ then $\langle a, b\rangle = \langle a, a\rangle$, where a occurs in two different positions. However, *we cannot write* $\langle a, a\rangle = \langle a\rangle$, because '$\langle a\rangle$' does not denote a couple – in fact the expression '$\langle a\rangle$' has not been defined. In contrast, if $a = b$, the pair $\{a, b\} = \{a, a\} = \{a\}$, a set with one member.

Second, by definition $\langle a, b\rangle$ is essentially ordered. Consequently, if $a \neq b$, then $\langle a, b\rangle \neq \langle b, a\rangle$. In contrast, $\{a, b\} = \{b, a\}$, as a set is unordered. Of course, *if* $a = b$ *then* $\langle a, b\rangle = \langle b, a\rangle$, simply because both couples are equal to $\langle a, a\rangle$.

Fundamental property of couples

In general, there are two main ways of defining a concept or class of objects. One is to describe the 'anatomy' of any member, its constituent parts and how they are related to one another. This is the *concrete* approach. The other way is to describe some essential relation(s) which any member of the class must bear to other members. This is the *abstract* – one could also say 'behavioural' – approach. The two methods serve different but complementary purposes. This duality of approaches is a key idea in mathematics.

The introduction of couples gives us an opportunity to illustrate these two approaches by a simple, though important, example. We begin with the abstract approach, because it is more important for our purposes than the concrete one.

From the 'abstract' point of view, the question is this: what is the property of couples which is essential in their applications – for example, the definition of relations or functions? The answer is as follows:

Property 3.1A.1
For any two couples $\langle a, b\rangle$ and $\langle u, v\rangle$,

$$\langle a, b\rangle = \langle u, v\rangle \text{ iff } a = u \text{ and } b = v$$ ■

This property is in agreement with our intuitive notion of a couple, but it does not tell us what a couple is 'concretely'. All it does is spell out a certain key relation between couples – it is only an *abstract view* of such objects. For the moment, this relation is a goal to achieve. It is a condition that any suitable concrete definition of a couple must satisfy.

Kuratowski's definition AT

We may now turn to specifying the concept of couple concretely and rigorously. Just to say that the two elements making up a couple are *ordered* is not sufficient, because we have no definition of the meaning of 'order', just an intuitive understanding.

Our aim now must be spelt out clearly. What we want is to construct, for any objects a and b, a new object C able to *represent* the couple $\langle a, b\rangle$. This means that for any such C, *we must have a method of extracting from C the two components a and b, and the information that a is 'first' and b 'second'.*

Moreover, C must be defined rigorously. This means that it must be defined using the set-theoretical operations we have already established. In particular, C must be some kind of set, but of course it can *not* be $\{a, b\}$, as we have already seen. If we succeed in our aim, then our definition of a couple must satisfy Property **3**.1A.1, and this too has to be verified.

There are several possible solutions. Here we consider the alternative which is now standard in set theory. This definition was proposed by Kuratowski in 1921.

Definition 3.1A.1
For any two objects a and b, the couple $\langle a, b\rangle$ is the set given by

$$\langle a, b\rangle =_{\text{d}} \{\{a\}, \{a, b\}\}$$ ■

In this definition, a couple is defined as a set of sets, using the pair operation *three* times. Let $C =_{\text{d}} \{\{a\}, \{a, b\}\}$ for any two objects a and b. To see that Definition **3**.1A.1 works, we must establish a method of extracting a and b in this order from C. The key idea is as follows.

Two cases must be considered.

Case 1 $a = b$. In this case, $\{a, b\} = \{a\}$. Consequently, C itself must be the *singleton* $\{\{a\}\}$, and the single member of C must also be a singleton.

Case 2 $a \neq b$. In this case, $\{a, b\} \neq \{a\}$. Consequently, C must have *exactly two* different members. One member must be the singleton $\{a\}$. The other member must be the set $\{a, b\}$, and this too must have *exactly two* different members.

Our method of extracting a and b from C in this order follows immediately. If we find that C is a singleton (case 1), then we conclude that C represents the couple $\langle a, a\rangle$, where a is the member of the member of C. Otherwise (case 2), we determine which member of C is a singleton. This singleton must be $\{a\}$, and so from it we extract a, which we label 'first'. Then we consider the other member of C, which must be $\{a, b\}$. From this set we may extract b: it is the member which differs from a. So we have b, which may be labelled 'second'.

It remains to verify that Kuratowski's definition of a couple satisfies Property **3**.1A.1. We only outline the demonstration. Consider two sets $C1$ and $C2$ built like C above, that is, for some objects a, b, c and d,

$$C1 =_{\mathrm{d}} \{\{a\}, \{a, b\}\} \text{ and } C2 =_{\mathrm{d}} \{\{c\}, \{c, d\}\}$$

First, suppose that $a = c$ and $b = d$. Then it immediately follows that $C1 = C2$. Therefore the main point to demonstrate is the reverse implication, namely that if $C1 = C2$ then $a = c$ and $b = d$. To see this, assume $C1 = C2$ and apply the extraction method to $C1$ and $C2$. This returns a first element a from $C1$ and c from $C2$. The two elements returned must be equal, as $C1 = C2$. Then, the method returns a second element, b from $C1$ and d from $C2$, and these too must be equal, given $C1 = C2$.

The above construction of a couple illustrates some important ideas. One in particular is the notion of *encoding*, the representation of a certain type of information – here a couple $\langle a, b\rangle$ – by a certain type of object – in this case the set $\{\{a\}, \{a, b\}\}$.

3.1B Cartesian product

Next we define two new operations on sets, based on the concept of a couple: the cartesian product and the disjoint union of two sets. The cartesian product is used in the definition of relations and functions. The disjoint union is defined in terms of the cartesian product.

Consider any two sets A and B. For any two objects $a\!:\!A$ and $b\!:\!B$, we may form the couple $\langle a, b\rangle$. All the couples which may be constructed in this way make up a certain set called the cartesian product of A and B and denoted by '$A \times B$'. (Recall that '$a\!:\!A$' means 'by definition a is a member of A'.)

Definition 3.1B.1

For any two sets A and B, the *cartesian product* of A and B is the set of all the couples $\langle a, b\rangle$ such that $a\!:\!A$ and $b\!:\!B$. This set is denoted by '$A \times B$'. It is formally defined by

$$A \times B =_{\mathrm{d}} \{x \mid \exists\, a\!:\!A, b\!:\!B \cdot x = \langle a, b\rangle\}$$

This formula is abbreviated as

$$A \times B =_{\mathrm{d}} \{\langle a, b\rangle \mid a\!:\!A \wedge b\!:\!B\}$$ ■

Note that in this definition, the two formulas are entirely equivalent. The second one is a slight innovation. In it, the members of $A \times B$ are not represented by a variable, but directly by the function $\langle a, b\rangle$ of the other variables a and b. This notation is quite natural and it is nothing more than an abbreviation for the 'official' expression.

It is intuitively obvious that for any two sets A and B, $A \times B$ is a set. The proof is left as an exercise for the reader.

Example 3.1B.1

(1) Let $A =_{\mathrm{d}} \{1, 2, 3\}$ and $B =_{\mathrm{d}} \{\mathrm{a}, \mathrm{b}\}$. Then

$$A \times B = \{\langle 1, \mathrm{a}\rangle, \langle 1, \mathrm{b}\rangle, \langle 2, \mathrm{a}\rangle, \langle 2, \mathrm{b}\rangle, \langle 3, \mathrm{a}\rangle, \langle 3, \mathrm{b}\rangle\}$$

(2) Let $A =_{\mathrm{d}} B =_{\mathrm{d}} \mathrm{Nat}$, the set of natural numbers. Then

$$\begin{aligned} A \times B &= \mathrm{Nat} \times \mathrm{Nat} = \{\langle x, y\rangle \mid x, y\!:\!\mathrm{Nat}\} \\ &= \{\langle 0, 0\rangle; \langle 0, 1\rangle, \langle 1, 0\rangle; \langle 0, 2\rangle, \langle 1, 1\rangle, \langle 2, 0\rangle; \\ &\quad \langle 0, 3\rangle, \langle 1, 2\rangle, \langle 2, 1\rangle, \langle 3, 0\rangle; \ldots\} \end{aligned}$$

(3) Let $A =_{\mathrm{d}} \{1, 2, \mathrm{a}\}$ and $B =_{\mathrm{d}} \{2, \mathrm{b}\}$. Then

$$A \times B = \{\langle 1, 2\rangle, \langle 1, \mathrm{b}\rangle, \langle 2, 2\rangle, \langle 2, \mathrm{b}\rangle, \langle \mathrm{a}, 2\rangle, \langle \mathrm{a}, \mathrm{b}\rangle\}$$ ■

In $A \times B$, the two sets A and B may be identical, as in part (2) of this example; and they may be different but with common members, as in part (3).

Example 3.1B.2

Within a given year, a *date* may be defined as consisting of two elements: a day and a month. A day is a number in the range 1 to 31; that is, it belongs to the set

$$\mathrm{Days} =_{\mathrm{d}} \{day\!:\!\mathrm{Nat} \mid 1 \leqslant day \leqslant 31\}$$

Similarly, a month is a member of the set

$$\mathrm{Months} =_{\mathrm{d}} \{\mathrm{January}, \mathrm{February}, \ldots, \mathrm{December}\}$$

Consequently, the set of all possible dates in a given year may be described as the cartesian product Days × Months. Each individual date is a couple $date =_d \langle day, month\rangle$ where day: Days and $month$: Months. This is the same as writing

$$date : \text{Days} \times \text{Months}$$

where Days × Months =

$$\{\langle 1, \text{January}\rangle, \langle 2, \text{January}\rangle, \ldots, \langle 1, \text{February}\rangle, \ldots, \langle 31, \text{December}\rangle\}$$

Note that some members of this set should be ruled out:

$$\{\langle 30, \text{February}\rangle, \langle 31, \text{February}\rangle, \langle 31, \text{April}\rangle, \ldots\}$$

But at least every *valid* date is a member of Days × Months. ■

The cartesian product may be *iterated* – that is, applied repeatedly. Given three sets A, B and C, we may first form $A \times B$. This is a set in its own right. Therefore, it may in turn be combined with C, giving $(A \times B) \times C$. The reader may verify, from Definition 1, that this is exactly the set

$$(A \times B) \times C = \{\langle\langle a, b\rangle, c\rangle \mid a : A \wedge b : B \wedge c : C\}$$

Example 3.1B.3

The concept of date introduced in Example 3.1B.2 may be extended by combining it with the set Years of possible years in, say, this century. Define

$$\text{Years} =_d \{year : \text{Nat} \mid 1900 \leqslant year \leqslant 1999\}$$

Then the set of all possible dates in this century is the cartesian product

$$(\text{Days} \times \text{Months}) \times \text{Years}$$

and each individual date now is a couple $date =_d \langle\langle day, month\rangle, year\rangle$ where $\langle day, month\rangle$: Days × Months and $year$: Years. This is the same as writing

$$date : (\text{Days} \times \text{Months}) \times \text{Years}$$

where (Days × Months) × Years =

$$\{\langle\langle 1, \text{January}\rangle, 1900\rangle, \langle\langle 2, \text{January}\rangle, 1900\rangle, \ldots, \langle\langle 31, \text{December}\rangle, 1999\rangle\}$$

■

Note that given three sets A, B and C, there are two ways of iterating the application of $\times$. We may either form $(A \times B) \times C$, as we have seen above, or $A \times (B \times C)$. The latter is given by

$$A \times (B \times C) = \{\langle a, \langle b, c \rangle \rangle \mid a{:}A \wedge b{:}B \wedge c{:}C\}$$

These two sets are *not* equal, although it should be clear that they are equivalent: from any $\langle \langle a, b \rangle, c \rangle$, we may derive $\langle a, \langle b, c \rangle \rangle$ and vice versa. Section 3.5 gives a definition of the n-ary cartesian product which eliminates this complication.

3.1C Disjoint union

Consider any two sets A and B, as well as $C =_{\mathrm{d}} A \cup B$. If A and B are disjoint – that is, $A \cap B = \varnothing$ – then for any $c{:}C$ we can tell if $c \in C$ by virtue of being a member of A or of B. However if A and B are *not* disjoint then for any $c{:}A \cap B$, we cannot determine whether $c \in C$ on account of being a member of A or of B. Thus in this case, replacing A and B by C results in a certain loss of information which may be important.

Example 3.1C.1

A company makes payments to two groups of people: salaries to employees and pensions to pensioners. Let A be the range of salaries and B the range of pensions paid by the company. Again let $C =_{\mathrm{d}} A \cup B$. If the two ranges do not overlap, $A \cap B = \varnothing$, then we may determine the nature (salary or pension) of any specific payment $p{:}C$ just by determining whether $p \in A$ or $p \in B$. However, if $A \cap B \neq \varnothing$, then for any $p{:}A \cap B$, the nature of p cannot be determined. ∎

The purpose of defining the disjoint union of two sets A and B is to construct a new set C, similar to $A \cup B$, but with the added property that the initial information available, namely the two sets A and B themselves, is not lost in C. In particular, the loss of information illustrated by Example 3.1C.1 is prevented. There is a simple way of defining C. The idea is first to attach a *tag* or *label*, say the number 1, to each member of A, and another tag, say 2, to each member of B. This operation produces two new sets, say A' and B'. These two sets *are* disjoint: $A' \cap B' = \varnothing$, so $A' + B'$ is defined. The result of this last operation, the *disjoint union* of A and B, is denoted by $A \amalg B$.

The key property of $A \amalg B$ is that if $C =_{\mathrm{d}} A \amalg B$, from C alone, we may recover both A and B. In other words, the operation $A \amalg B$ is fully *invertible*. This point is further discussed in the exercises below. The inversion of an operation is treated in Section 3.6E.

How do we 'tag' or 'label' the members of A with 1, and the members of B with 2? The answer is simple: replace each $a{:}A$ by the couple $\langle 1, a \rangle$ and each $b:B$ by $\langle 2, b\rangle$. In other words, let

$$A' =_{\mathrm{d}} \{1\} \times A = \{\langle 1, a\rangle \mid a:A\}$$

and

$$B' =_{\mathrm{d}} \{2\} \times B = \{\langle 2, b\rangle \mid b:B\}$$

It is clear that $A' \cap B' = \varnothing$, as each member of A' differs from each member of B' at least by its tag. Here, we are making use of Property 3.1A.1 of couples, which is crucial.

Definition 3.1C.1

For any two sets A and B, the *disjoint union* of A and B is the set denoted by $A \amalg B$ and given by

$$A \amalg B =_{\mathrm{d}} (\{1\} \times A) + (\{2\} \times B)$$

or, equivalently,

$$A \amalg B =_{\mathrm{d}} \{\langle 1, a\rangle \mid a:A\} + \{\langle 2, b\rangle \mid b:B\}$$ ■

Example 3.1C.2

A company maintains a database of records on various groups of people. In one group G, the income of any member is either a salary or a pension. Salaries may range between £10,000 and £25,000, and pensions between £8,000 and £20,000. The problem is to record the income of each member of G with an indication of its type.

The two types of income may be described as the sets

$$\text{Salaries} =_{\mathrm{d}} \{s:\text{Nat} \mid 10{,}000 \leqslant s \leqslant 25{,}000\}$$

and

$$\text{Pensions} =_{\mathrm{d}} \{p:\text{Nat} \mid 8{,}000 \leqslant p \leqslant 20{,}000\}$$

respectively. As we have seen in Example 3.1C.1, if these two sets were disjoint then for each member of G the value of the corresponding income would indicate whether it is a salary or a pension. However, this condition is not satisfied:

$$\text{Salaries} \cap \text{Pensions} = \{x:\text{Nat} \mid 10{,}000 \leqslant x \leqslant 20{,}000\} \neq \varnothing$$

Therefore, to each income we must add a label to indicate its type. We adopt the following convention: any salary is labelled with 1, and any pension with 2. Thus, any income is now recorded as a member of the disjoint union Salaries ⊔ Pensions. A salary s: Salaries is recorded as $\langle 1, s\rangle$ and a pension p: Pensions as $\langle 2, p\rangle$. When a recorded income is retrieved from the database, it is of the form $\langle t, x\rangle$, where $t \in \{1, 2\}$, and the value of t indicates whether x is a salary or a pension. ■

Remarks

1 The disjoint union ⊔ must not be confused with the union of disjoint sets $+$. $A \sqcup B$ is defined *for all pairs of sets A* and *B*, but it involves tagging their respective elements. $A + B$ is defined *only if A* and *B are disjoint*, and it involves *no* tagging of members.

2 So far, we have used 1 and 2 as tags or labels. In fact there is no need to use these two values: any two different objects will do, and in practice one would prefer to use meaningful names – for example, {Salary, Pension} in Example 3.1C.2. ■

EXERCISES

3.1.1 Let $A =_d \{\text{m, n, p}\}$ and $B =_d \{1, 2\}$. Compute the cartesian products $A \times B$, $B \times A$, $A \times A$, and $B \times B$. What relationship(s) can you identify between $A \times B$ and $B \times A$?

3.1.2 Repeat Exercise **3.1.1** with $A =_d \{\text{m, n, p}\}$ and $B =_d \{\text{k, m}\}$.

3.1.3 There is an obvious but important relationship between Num($A \times B$) (alias Card($A \times B$)), Num(A) and Num(B). What is it?

3.1.4 There is an important difference between the properties of the cartesian product and those of *arithmetic* multiplication (apart from the fact that the former operates on *sets* and the latter on *numbers*). This is obvious from Exercise **3.1.1**. What is it?

3.1.5 Let $A =_d \{\text{a, b, c, d}\}$. Enumerate $\{0\} \times A$. What simple relationship between this product and A can you observe?

3.1.6 Calculate $\varnothing \times A$ for any set A.

3.1.7 Let Nat = {0, 1, 2, 3, . . .} be the set of natural numbers. Enumerate six members of Nat × Nat selected at random.

3.1.8* Consider the following partial enumeration of $\text{Nat}^2 = \text{Nat} \times \text{Nat}$:

$$\text{Nat}^2 = \{\langle 0, 0\rangle; \langle 0, 1\rangle, \langle 1, 0\rangle; \langle 0, 2\rangle, \langle 1, 1\rangle, \langle 2, 0\rangle; \langle 0, 3\rangle, \langle 1, 2\rangle, \langle 2, 1\rangle, \langle 3, 0\rangle; \ldots\}$$

(a) Explain the method used to produce it. Hint: observe that Nat^2 is partitioned into finite subsequences separated by semicolons. First, identify for each subsequence the common property of its members. Then explain (i) how each subsequence is ordered and (ii) the order in which the subsequences are concatenated.
(b) Show this enumeration method is both *nonredundant* (no $\langle x, y\rangle : \text{Nat}^2$ is enumerated more than once) and *complete* (every $\langle x, y\rangle : \text{Nat}^2$ is enumerated).
(c) There are many different ways of enumerating Nat^2 completely and nonredundantly. Devise a few alternatives.

3.1.9 Show that for any sets A, A', B and B', if $A' \subseteq A$ and $B' \subseteq B$ then $(A' \times B') \subseteq (A \times B)$.

3.1.10 Show that for any sets S, A and B,

(a) $(S \cup A) \times B = (S \times B) \cup (A \times B)$
(b) $(S \cap A) \times B = (S \times B) \cap (A \times B)$

3.1.11 Consider two operations *Fst* and *Snd* defined as follows: for any a and b, if $x =_d \langle a, b\rangle$, then $Fst(x) =_d a$ and $Snd(x) =_d b$. Show how any $x =_d \langle a, b\rangle$ may be converted to $y =_d \langle b, a\rangle$ using these two operations.

3.1.12 Show how any $x =_d \langle\langle a, b\rangle c\rangle$ may be converted to $y =_d \langle a,\langle b, c\rangle\rangle$ (and y to x) using *Fst* and *Snd* defined in Exercise **3.1.11**.

3.1.13* Show that for any two sets A and B, $A \times B$ is a set. That is, define $A \times B$ by a formula involving only the basic set operations introduced in Chapter **2**, specifically: pair, union, powerset and forming a set by a subset axiom. Hint: first, construct a set S such that $A \times B \subseteq S$, using the two operations $\cup$ and Pow only. Define S by using what you know about $A \times B$, namely that any $x : A \times B$ must be a set such that there exist $a : A$ and $b : B$ with $x =_d \{\{a\}, \{a, b\}\}$. Second, define $A \times B$ by abstraction as the subset of S whose members x satisfy the property just stated.

3.1.14 In defining the disjoint union $A \amalg B$, it is essential to tag the members of *both* A and B. In general, labelling only one set is not sufficient to discriminate its members from the members of the other set. Illustrate this point by an example. Hint: construct two simple sets A and B such that $(\{1\} \times A) \cap B \neq \emptyset$.

3.1.15 For any sets A and B, show that we may recover A and B from $A \amalg B$. That is, there is a rule or formula which, given $A \amalg B$, returns the set A, and a similar rule returning B. What are these two rules?

3.1.16 Show that in general, given two *disjoint* sets A and B: (a) given $A+B$, we cannot identify A or B; (b) given $A+B$ *and* B, we can identify A; (c) this last property is not shared by the ordinary union $A \cup B$ when $A \cap B \neq \emptyset$.

3.2 Relations

In this section, an informal description of the notion of a relation is first given. Then two variants are defined in set-theoretical terms. The first variant has essentially one feature, namely a set of couples, called the *graph* of the relation. In the second variant, this set is defined as a subset of a cartesian product. Thus, the second variant is an extension of the first.

Next we study several examples of relations, define two secondary features of relations and describe certain important categories of relations. Finally the notion of a class relation, which is a generalization of the strict set-theoretical definition is introduced.

3.2A The concept of a relation

When we write '$x \in S$', we express a property which is either true or false, depending on which object is represented by 'x' and which set is represented by 'S'. We say that '$\in$' denotes a *relation* between objects and sets, specifically the *membership* relation.

Several other examples of relations have already been introduced: the inclusion relation $\subseteq$ between sets; the 'less than' relation $<$ between natural numbers, and other similar relations, such as $\leqslant$, $>$ and $\geqslant$; the equality relation $=$ between sets, or between numbers; and so on.

In every case, the situation is the same. We have a certain property that is true for certain couples $\langle x, y\rangle$ of objects, and false for all others. For instance, '$n < m$' is true for certain couples $\langle n, m\rangle$ of numbers, for example, $\langle 2, 5\rangle$, and false for all others, for example $\langle 8, 7\rangle$ or $\langle 13, 13\rangle$. '$S \subseteq T$' is true for some couples $\langle S, T\rangle$ of sets, for example $\langle\{1, 2\}, \{1, 2, 3\}\rangle$, and false for all others, for example $\langle\{1, 4\}, \{1, 2, 3\}\rangle$. This leads us to our first, informal definition of a relation:

Definition 3.2A.1 (informal)

A relation R is a property which is true for some couples of objects. We write

$$x \, R \, y$$

or sometimes $R(x, y)$, to state that the couple $\langle x, y\rangle$ has the property R.

■

A relation R in this sense is also called a *predicate*, and the name 'R' a *predicate symbol*. The name is often a special symbol, but it may also be a letter or a word. The notion of a relation has already been discussed in Chapter 2. The only new feature of the above informal description is its reference to couples. We now emphasize that a relation is a property of *ordered* pairs. This is necessary because, in general, a certain property may be true for a couple

$\langle x, y\rangle$ and false for $\langle y, x\rangle$. For instance, if n, m:Nat and $n < m$ is true then $m < n$ is false.

A relation R may also be viewed as a *correspondence* between certain objects, as we can say that R *associates* with any x the various objects y such that $x\ R\ y$. Note that x may be associated with no, one or several ys in this way.

First formal definition

In many cases a relation R is such that the couples $\langle x, y\rangle$ for which $x\ R\ y$ is true form a set. In such a case, set theory postulates that the relation R is essentially given by this set. Consequently, a relation is defined formally as follows:

Definition 3.2A.2

A relation is an object R with one feature, namely a *set of couples* of objects. This set is called the *graph* of R and denoted by Gr(R).

This definition is naturally linked to Definition 3.2A.1 as follows. If R is a relation in the first sense and $\{\langle x, y\rangle \mid x\ R\ y\}$ is a set, then formally R is the relation such that

$$\mathrm{Gr}(R) =_{\mathrm{d}} \{\langle x, y\rangle \mid x\ R\ y\}$$

■

Example 3.2A.1

Let R be a relation defined for any $\langle x, y\rangle$ by the statement

$$x\ R\ y \text{ iff } x, y \in \mathrm{Nat} \wedge x < y \leqslant 2$$

The graph of R – that is, the set of all couples $\langle x, y\rangle$ for which $x\ R\ y$ is true – is

$$\begin{aligned}&\mathrm{Gr}(R)\\ &= \{\langle x, y\rangle \mid x, y : \mathrm{Nat} \wedge x < y \leqslant 2\}\\ &= \{\langle 0, 1\rangle, \langle 0, 2\rangle, \langle 1, 2\rangle\}\end{aligned}$$

■

Remarks

1 Definition 3.2A.2 is formal in that it does not rely on the notion of property, which is only intuitive. It is given entirely in terms of the primitive concepts of set theory, namely set and membership.

2 In set theory, it is common to identify a relation R with its graph Gr(R) completely. This means that 'R' is also used instead of 'Gr(R)' to denote the set $\{\langle x, y\rangle \mid x\ R\ y\}$ itself. This leads one to write '$x\ R\ y$ iff $\langle x, y\rangle \in R$', for instance, which may be confusing. The notation 'Gr(R)' is preferred as it is more precise and ties in better with the third definition given below. ■

Second formal definition

In many definitions of a relation R, a natural preliminary step is to fix the sets of the objects x and y for which $x\ R\ y$ may be true. The set from which x may be drawn is called the *domain* of R and is denoted by Dom(R). The set from which y may be taken is called the *codomain* of R and is written Cod(R). Consequently, the graph Gr(R) of the relation must be a subset of the cartesian product Dom(R) × Cod(R). Note that Dom(R) and Cod(R) may intersect or even be equal.

A typical example is the relation $<$. The expression '$n < m$' makes sense only if n and m belong to the same set of numbers, for example Nat. This is why it is customary to require first that n and m be members of (say) Nat if $n < m$ is to be true. In this case, Nat is both the domain and the codomain of the relation $<$.

Accordingly, there is a second set-theoretical definition of a relation, which is as follows:

Definition 3.2A.3

A relation R is an object with three features:

(1) a set called the *domain* of R and written Dom(R)

(2) a set called the *codomain* of R and written Cod(R)

(3) a subset of the cartesian product Dom(R) × Cod(R) called the *graph* of R and denoted by Gr(R) ■

Most of the relations we define in the sequel are in the sense of this definition. Thus by 'relation' we henceforth always mean a relation in this sense unless otherwise stated.

Notation

In order to introduce a relation R, we must specify its domain D and codomain C, where D and C are two predefined sets. We write

(1) $R : D \leftrightarrow C$

to indicate that R is a relation with domain Dom(R) $=_d D$ and codomain Cod(R) $=_d C$, and we say that R is a *relation on* C and D. We regard '$D \leftrightarrow C$' as denoting the *set* of all relations R with Dom(R) $=_d D$ and Cod(R) $=_d C$, and (1) as the *introduction* of R as a member of this set. Note that the arrow '$\leftrightarrow$' connects the two *sets* Dom(R) and Cod(R), *not* members of these sets. ■

3.2B Examples of relations

We now give further examples of relations. These supplement the various instances we have already seen in previous sections.

Example 3.2B.1

(1) Let $D =_d \{1, 2, 3\}$ and $C =_d \{1, 2, 3, 4\}$. The inequality relation $<$ (less than) *restricted to* $D \times C$ is the relation R defined by

$$x \; R \; y \Leftrightarrow_d x : D \wedge y : C \wedge x < y$$

Therefore, R is a relation in the sense of Definition 3.2A.3. Dom(R) = D, Cod(R) = C, and the graph Gr(R) is given by

$$\begin{aligned} &\{\langle x, y\rangle : D \times C \mid x < y\} \\ &= \{\langle 1, 2\rangle, \langle 1, 3\rangle, \langle 1, 4\rangle, \langle 2, 3\rangle, \langle 2, 4\rangle, \langle 3, 4\rangle\} \end{aligned}$$

(2) The relation $<$ defined on the whole of Nat is a relation in the sense of Definition 3.2A.3. Dom($<$) = Cod($<$) = Nat, and the graph Gr($<$) of this relation is

$$\begin{aligned} &\{\langle x, y\rangle : \text{Nat} \times \text{Nat} \mid x < y\} \\ &= \{\langle 0, 1\rangle, \langle 0, 2\rangle, \langle 1, 2\rangle, \langle 0, 3\rangle, \langle 1, 3\rangle, \langle 2, 3\rangle, \ldots\} \end{aligned}$$

This graph is obviously infinite. Explain the method used to generate it.

Note that the two relations R and $<$ *are entirely different.* They have different domains, codomains and graphs. ■

Example 3.2B.2

(1) Let $D =_d$ {Albert, Bernard, Cathy, Dick and Elsa}. Dick and Elsa are the father and mother respectively of Albert, Bernard and Cathy.

Let ParentOf be the relation defined by $\langle x, y\rangle \in$ Gr(ParentOf) iff x is a parent of y:

$$x \text{ ParentOf } y \quad \Leftrightarrow_d \quad x : D \wedge y : D \wedge x \text{ is a parent of } y$$

This is a relation in the sense of Definition 3.2A.3 if we take Dom(ParentOf) = Cod(ParentOf) = D. What is the graph Gr(ParentOf) of this relation?

$$\begin{aligned} \text{Gr(ParentOf)} = \{&\langle \text{Dick, Albert}\rangle, \langle \text{Dick, Bernard}\rangle, \\ &\langle \text{Dick, Cathy}\rangle, \langle \text{Elsa, Albert}\rangle, \\ &\langle \text{Elsa, Bernard}\rangle, \langle \text{Elsa, Cathy}\rangle\} \end{aligned}$$

(2) Define the relation BrotherOf in a similar way. What is the graph Gr(BrotherOf)?

$$\begin{aligned} \text{Gr(BrotherOf)} = \{&\langle \text{Albert, Bernard}\rangle, \langle \text{Albert, Cathy}\rangle, \\ &\langle \text{Bernard, Albert}\rangle, \\ &\langle \text{Bernard, Cathy}\rangle\} \end{aligned}$$

As an exercise, define some further family relationships, such as SisterOf, SiblingOf, etc. ■

Diagrammatic representation of a finite relation

A finite relation R may be depicted by a diagram in which Dom(R) and Cod(R) are represented by two disjoint ovals, their members by points or circles inside the respective ovals and each couple $\langle x, y\rangle$: Gr(R) by a barred arrow '$\mapsto$' from x to y. For instance, if Dom(R) $=_d A =_d \{1, 2, 3, 4\}$, Cod(R) $=_d B =_d \{a, b, c, d, e\}$ and Gr(R) $=_d \{\langle 1, b\rangle, \langle 1, d\rangle, \langle 3, b\rangle, \langle 4, d\rangle, \langle 4, e\rangle\}$, then R is represented as in Figure 3.2B.1.

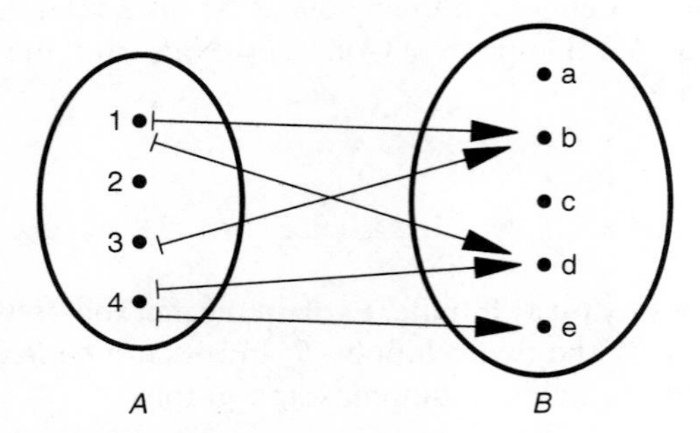

Figure 3.2B.1 Representation of a relation.

3.2C Some derived features of relations

For any relation R, we call Dom(R), Cod(R) and Gr(R) the *primary variable* features of R. The reason for this terminology is as follows. In order to obtain *different* relations R we must *vary* Dom(R), Cod(R) or Gr(R). This, of course, must be done within the constraints (*fixed features*) of Definition 3.2A.3: Dom(R) and Cod(R) may be any sets, but Gr(R) must be a subset of Dom(R) $\times$ Cod(R).

However, once these three features have been fixed, R is *entirely determined, and any other feature which would otherwise vary with R is now fixed.* Consequently, any such variable feature is called *secondary*, *derived* or *implied.* We now define two derived variable features of a relation R which frequently arise in applications.

Definition domain

Let R be any relation in the sense of Definition 3.2A.2 or 3.2A.3. From the graph Gr(R), we may derive the set of elements x such that there exists at least one y with $\langle x, y\rangle \in$ Gr(R). This set is called the definition domain of R.

Definition 3.2C.1

The *definition domain* of a relation R is the set denoted by $\mathrm{Def}(R)$ and given by

$$\mathrm{Def}(R) =_{\mathrm{d}} \{x \mid \exists\, y \cdot \langle x, y\rangle \in \mathrm{Gr}(R)\}$$ ■

Example 3.2C.1

Consider the relation R with

$$\mathrm{Gr}(R) =_{\mathrm{d}} \{\langle 1, \mathrm{b}\rangle, \langle 1, \mathrm{d}\rangle, \langle 3, \mathrm{b}\rangle, \langle 4, \mathrm{d}\rangle, \langle 4, \mathrm{e}\rangle\}$$

The objects x such that there exists a y with $\langle x, y\rangle \in \mathrm{Gr}(R)$ are 1, 3 and 4. Therefore

$$\mathrm{Def}(R) = \{1, 3, 4\}$$ ■

The definition domain $\mathrm{Def}(R)$ is a simple illustration of a derived or secondary variable feature of a relation R. In general $\mathrm{Def}(R)$ varies as we vary R or, more precisely, the graph of R. However, once $\mathrm{Gr}(R)$ is fixed, so is $\mathrm{Def}(R)$, as it is exactly determined by $\mathrm{Gr}(R)$, by Definition 3.2C.1.

Note that if $\mathrm{Dom}(R)$ is defined then $\mathrm{Def}(R) \subseteq \mathrm{Dom}(R)$, as in this case $\mathrm{Gr}(R)$ is a subset of the cartesian product $\mathrm{Dom}(R) \times \mathrm{Cod}(R)$.

Range

For any relation R in the sense of Definition 3.2A.2 or 3.2A.3, we may derive a second set from $\mathrm{Gr}(R)$ called the range of R. This is defined as the set of elements y such that there exists at least one x with $\langle x, y\rangle \in \mathrm{Gr}(R)$. There is an obvious symmetry between this second construction and the definition of $\mathrm{Def}(R)$.

Definition 3.2C.2

The *range* of a relation R is the set denoted by $\mathrm{Ran}(R)$ and given by

$$\mathrm{Ran}(R) =_{\mathrm{d}} \{y \mid \exists\, x \cdot \langle x, y\rangle \in \mathrm{Gr}(R)\}$$ ■

Example 3.2C.2

Consider again the relation R with

$$\mathrm{Gr}(R) =_{\mathrm{d}} \{\langle 1, \mathrm{b}\rangle, \langle 1, \mathrm{d}\rangle, \langle 3, \mathrm{b}\rangle, \langle 4, \mathrm{d}\rangle, \langle 4, \mathrm{e}\rangle\}$$

The objects y such that there exists an x with $\langle x, y\rangle \in \mathrm{Gr}(R)$ are b, d and e. Therefore

$$\mathrm{Ran}(R) = \{\mathrm{b}, \mathrm{d}, \mathrm{e}\}$$ ■

Notice how Definition 3.2C.1 is mirrored by Definition 3.2C.2: the latter is obtained from the former simply by interchanging x and y in appropriate places. We also say that Def(R) and Ran(R) are *dual* concepts. More of this in Section 3.6E. If Cod(R) is defined then $\text{Ran}(R) \subseteq \text{Cod}(R)$, for the same reason that $\text{Def}(R) \subseteq \text{Dom}(R)$.

3.2D Basic categories of relations

Finally, here is a basic taxonomy of relations. Part of this taxonomy is usually defined for functions only. As these are special cases of relations and the categories involved are well defined for all relations, we here extend it to the latter. This taxonomy is illustrated in Figure 3.2D.1.

Definition 3.2D.1

Let R be any relation.

(1) R is *functional* iff for any $x:\text{Def}(R)$, there is *exactly one* y *with* $\langle x, y\rangle \in \text{Gr}(R)$. In this case, we also say that R is a *possibly partial* function.

(2) R is *injective* iff for any $y:\text{Ran}(R)$, there is *exactly one* x *with* $\langle x, y\rangle \in \text{Gr}(R)$.

(3) R is *total* iff for any $x:\text{Dom}(R)$, there is *at least one* y *with* $\langle x, y\rangle \in \text{Gr}(R)$. Equivalently, R is total iff $\text{Def}(R) = \text{Dom}(R)$.

(4) R is *surjective* iff for any $y:\text{Cod}(R)$, there is *at least one* x *with* $\langle x, y\rangle \in \text{Gr}(R)$. Equivalently, R is surjective iff $\text{Ran}(R) = \text{Cod}(R)$. ■

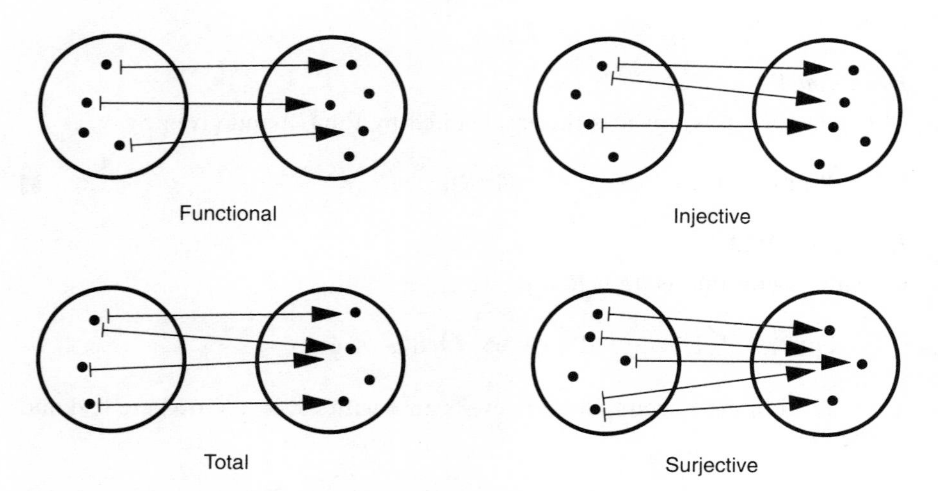

Figure 3.2D.1 Four categories of relations.

The symmetries between these four categories should be apparent. Part (1) of the definition anticipates the definition of a function. Note that in parts (1) and (2) there is no reference to Dom(R) or Cod(R). Consequently, these definitions also apply to relations R which have no specified domain and codomain.

In Definition 3.2D.1, (1) and (2) are expressed informally. In special symbols, a relation R is functional iff

$$\forall x : \mathrm{Def}(R) \cdot \exists 1\ y \cdot \langle x, y \rangle \in \mathrm{Gr}(R)$$

This translation is immediate but uses the special quantifier '$\exists 1\ y$'. A more primitive definition, which does not rely on $\exists 1$, is thus:

> R is functional iff for any $x : \mathrm{Def}(R)$ and any $y, z : \mathrm{Ran}(R)$,
> if $\langle x, y \rangle \in \mathrm{Gr}(R)$ and $\langle x, z \rangle \in \mathrm{Gr}(R)$, then $y = z$.

In special symbols, this condition of functionality reads:

$$\forall x : \mathrm{Def}(R) \cdot \forall y, z : \mathrm{Ran}(R) \cdot [\langle x, y \rangle \in \mathrm{Gr}(R) \wedge \langle x, z \rangle \in \mathrm{Gr}(R)] \Rightarrow y = z$$

Analogous formal definitions of injectiveness are left as an exercise.

Equivalent definitions can be found in various branches of computing. For instance, in systems analysis a functional relation is called *many-to-one*, and an injective relation *one-to-many*. Obviously these categories may be combined in all possible ways. For instance, a relation may be both functional and injective. Such a relation is called *one-to-one*.

3.2E Class relations AT

According to the strict set-theoretical definition of a relation R, its graph must be a set. The same is true of the domain and the codomain of R, if these are defined. This definition therefore excludes many objects which one would naturally regard as relations. Examples are set membership and set inclusion. '$x \in S$' is a property which is true or false for *any* object x, possibly a set, and *any* set S. '$A \subseteq B$' is true or false for any couple $\langle A, B \rangle$ of sets. However, there is no set of all sets, let alone of all objects (which includes sets). Therefore we cannot regard $\in$ and $\subseteq$ as relations in the sense of Definition 3.2A.2 or 3.2A.3, as their respective graphs $\{\langle x, S \rangle \mid x : S\}$ and $\{\langle A, B \rangle \mid A \subseteq B\}$ cannot be regarded as strict sets.

For this reason, we now extend the concepts of cartesian product and relation to account for such cases. We do this simply by allowing the operands A and B of $A \times B$, and the features Dom(R), Cod(R) and Gr(R) of a relation R, to be *classes* – that is, strict sets or proper classes as defined in Section 2.5. In every other respect the definitions remain the same. Thus $\in$, $\subseteq$, etc. are relations and $\cup$, $\cap$, $\setminus$ etc. are functions in this wider sense. They are called *class relations* (or *functions*). Note that if A and B are two proper classes, then so is $A \times B$. For instance, Set $\times$ Set is a subclass of the class Set of all sets, as (under Kuratowski's definition of a couple, for instance) the members of Set $\times$ Set are sets.

EXERCISES

3.2.1 Let $A =_d \{2, 3, 4\}$ and $B =_d \{1, 2, 3\}$. A number of relations R with $\mathrm{Dom}(R) =_d A$ and $\mathrm{Cod}(R) =_d B$ are specified below by expressing their graph $\mathrm{Gr}(R)$ as an abstraction. Enumerate each graph $\mathrm{Gr}(R)$.

R1: $\mathrm{Gr}(R1) =_d \{\langle x, y\rangle \mid x \leqslant y\}$
R2: $\mathrm{Gr}(R2) =_d \{\langle x, y\rangle \mid x > y\}$
R3: $\mathrm{Gr}(R3) =_d \{\langle x, y\rangle \mid x = y\}$
R4: $\mathrm{Gr}(R4) =_d \{\langle x, y\rangle \mid x \neq y\}$
R5: $\mathrm{Gr}(R5) =_d \{\langle x, y\rangle \mid y = [(x+1) \text{ MOD } 3]+1\}$
R6: $\mathrm{Gr}(R6) =_d \{\langle x, y\rangle \mid x \text{ is divisible by } y\}$
R7: $\mathrm{Gr}(R7) =_d \{\langle x, y\rangle \mid y \text{ is divisible by } x\}$

3.2.2 In Exercise **3**.2.1, for which of the seven relations R does $\mathrm{Def}(R)$ differ from $\mathrm{Dom}(R)$? (Hint: $\mathrm{Dom}(R) \neq \mathrm{Def}(R)$ in three cases.)

3.2.3 In Exercise **3**.2.1, for which of the seven relations R does $\mathrm{Ran}(R)$ differ from $\mathrm{Cod}(R)$?

3.2.4 Consider a description of a human family as a set A of people – say four – and a set B of objects – say six – owned by the members of A. Any object may be common property of several members of A. For instance, $A =_d$ {Alfred, Bernard, Cathy, Danny} and $B =_d$ {car, yellow toothbrush, doll, wedding ring 1, wedding ring 2, dog, ...}. For some family (A, B) of your invention, specify a reasonable relation of ownership $Own\colon A \leftrightarrow B$ by enumerating its graph $\mathrm{Gr}(Own)$. In your specification, you should take into account the status of each member (father, mother, and so on), and this should be stated first.

3.2.5 Consider Example **3**.2B.2, in which a relation ParentOf is defined for a family D. Define relations SisterOf, SiblingOf, FatherOf, MotherOf, each with domain and codomain D, by enumerating their respective graphs. Note that names have been chosen so that they can be represented by their first letter.

3.2.6 Add Fred, George and Helen to the family of Example **3**.2B.2. Fred is Dick's father, George is Elsa's brother and Helen is Dick's sister. Define relations UncleOf, AuntOf, GrandparentOf, CousinOf and NieceOf on this extended family, by enumerating their respective graphs.

3.2.7* What relationships (expressed in terms of $\in$, $\subseteq$, $\subset$ and set operations) can you find between the (graphs of the) various relations constructed in Exercises **3**.2.5 and **3**.2.6?

3.2.8 Enumerate Def(ParentOf) and Ran(ParentOf) for the relation ParentOf defined in Example 3.2B.2.

3.2.9 Repeat Exercise 3.2.8 for the relation BrotherOf of Example 3.2B.2, as well as the relations defined in Exercises 3.2.5 and 3.2.6.

3.2.10 Define an injective relation formally (a) using $\exists 1$ and (b) without $\exists 1$. Hint: consider the formal definitions of a functional relation.

3.2.11 Let $A =_{\mathrm{d}} \{n : \mathrm{Nat} \mid 1 \leqslant n \leqslant 4\}$ and $B =_{\mathrm{d}} \{\mathrm{a, b, c, d, e}\}$. Construct relations $R : A \leftrightarrow B$ to illustrate the four special categories defined in Section 3.2D. Represent each graph $\mathrm{Gr}(R)$ by a diagram.

3.2.12 For any relation R, let the *opposite* relation R' be defined by $\mathrm{Dom}(R') =_{\mathrm{d}} \mathrm{Cod}(R)$, $\mathrm{Cod}(R') =_{\mathrm{d}} \mathrm{Dom}(R)$ and $\mathrm{Gr}(R') =_{\mathrm{d}} \{\langle y, x\rangle \mid \langle x, y\rangle : \mathrm{Gr}(R)\}$.

(a) Illustrate R and R' by a simple example. Draw a diagram to represent the two relations.
(b) Show that R is functional iff R' is injective and vice versa.
(c) Show that R is total iff R' is surjective and vice versa.

3.2.13* Given any two sets A and B with $m =_{\mathrm{d}} \mathrm{Num}(A)$ and $n =_{\mathrm{d}} \mathrm{Num}(B)$, determine the number of relations $R : A \leftrightarrow B$. Indicate the method used to arrive at your solution. Hint: recall that for any finite set S of n members, $\mathrm{Num}(\mathrm{Pow}(S)) = 2^n$.

3.2.14* Repeat Exercise 3.2.13 for the following categories of relations $R : A \leftrightarrow B$:

- functional
- total
- injective
- surjective

3.3 Functions

Functions are universal: they arise in all areas of life, even though implicitly in most cases. They are closely linked to relations. As we shall see, they are in fact equivalent: a function is a special type of relation, and a relation may be described as a kind of function. Therefore, the various features of relations described in Section 3.2 apply to, or are *inherited* by, functions. Conversely, functions enable us to describe further features of relations. The concept of a function is first defined. Then we study some examples. Finally, we consider some basic categories of functions.

3.3A The concept of a function

As with relations, we first describe the notion of a function informally. Then we define two variants in set-theoretical terms. These variants closely correspond to Definitions 3.2A.2 and 3.2A.3 of relations, respectively.

Definition 3.3A.1 (informal)

A function F is a rule by which each object in some set or class is assigned another, *unique* object. For any x the object assigned to x, if there is one, is denoted by $F(x)$ or some other similar notation, for example Fx or F_x. We also say that F *sends* x to $F(x)$.

In the expression '$F(x)$', we say that F is *applied* to x and x is called the *argument* of F. $F(x)$ is the *result* of applying F to x. ■

A function is a special type of relation. Recall that a relation R may be viewed as a correspondence which associates with any x the various objects y such that $x \; R \; y$. In the case of a function F, any x is associated with *at most one* y, that is, the object written $F(x)$ if this is defined.

Example 3.3A.1

1 Several family relationships are functions. For instance, any person has exactly one mother. Therefore, 'mother' denotes a function. More precisely, there is a certain correspondence which associates with any person x another person y called 'the mother of x'. This association is defined only for human beings. The English phrase 'mother of x' is equivalent to the formal notation 'mother(x)'; they have *exactly the same meaning*.

2 Similarly, any person has exactly one father. Consequently, 'father' denotes another function. It assigns to any person x another person y called 'father of x'. Again, this last phrase is entirely equivalent to the formal notation 'father(x)'. ■

It is also useful to contrast these examples with human family relationships which are *not* functions. The latter are more numerous. For instance, the word 'parent' represents another relation between people, but it associates *two* persons with any person x, namely the mother and the father of x. Therefore as a human family relation, 'parent' is *not* a function. Likewise, 'child' represents the opposite relation between individuals, but as a person may have several children, this relation is *not* a function. The same remark applies to other family relationships: brother, sister, and so on.

Example 3.3A.2

1 Consider the set of towns in a given country. Each town has exactly one name. Therefore, the rule which associates a name y with each town x is a function. In English, the name assigned to any x is called 'the name of x'. It is equivalent to the formal notation 'name(x)'.

2 This example may be repeated with many other types of object. For instance, in any group of people each individual x is given a proper name, so again name is a function which sends any x to name(x). Likewise, 'name' denotes a function for continents, seas, countries, rivers, mountains, and so on. ■

The naming of a small group of persons as a function is illustrated in Figure **3**.3A.1. This is based on the same conventions as Figure **3**.2B.1.

In the example of Figure **3**.3A.1, the function 'name' sends *P1* to name(*P1*) = John, *P2* to name(*P2*) = Fred and *P3* to name(*P3*) = Fred. The fact that *P2* and *P3* have the same name and that 'Jack' and 'Sven' are nobody's names does not deny 'name' the status of a function.

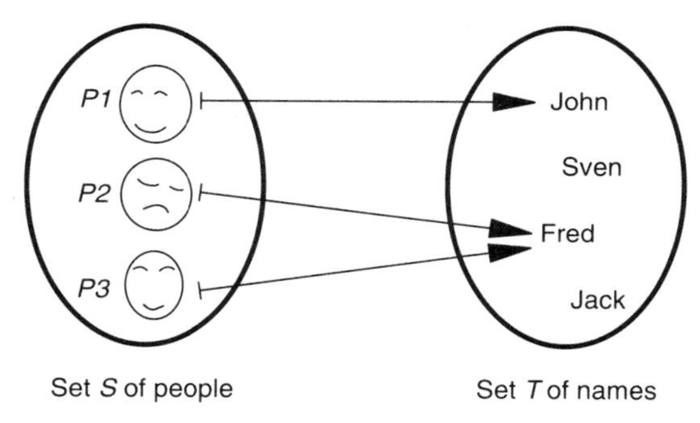

Figure 3.3A.1 Naming of persons.

First formal definition

We now turn to the first set-theoretical definition of a function. Given a function F, we may consider the various couples $\langle x, F(x)\rangle$. If these form a set, then F may be formally described as the relation whose graph $\mathrm{Gr}(F) = \{\langle x, y\rangle \mid y = F(x)\}$. The distinctive feature of F is that any x occurs in at most one couple $\langle x, y\rangle \in \mathrm{Gr}(F)$.

Definition 3.3A.2

A function F is a relation whose graph $\mathrm{Gr}(F)$ satisfies the following condition:

For any x, there is at most one y such that $\langle x, y\rangle \in \mathrm{Gr}(F)$. ■

The remarks on relations following Definition **3**.2A.2 apply *mutatis mutandis* to functions. A function may also be defined succinctly as a *functional relation* in the sense of Definition **3**.2D.1(1). Note that, although we could write '$x\ F\ y$' to indicate that $\langle x, y\rangle \in \mathrm{Gr}(F)$, this is not usually done. Instead, we express this by writing '$y = F(x)$'.

Example 3.3A.3

Let F be the function which assigns $y =_{\mathrm{d}} x + 2$ to every natural number x in the range 1 to 3. Thus

$$\forall x\colon \mathrm{Nat} \text{ with } 1 \leqslant x \leqslant 3 \cdot F(x) =_{\mathrm{d}} x + 2$$

Note that in this definition of F, we have deliberately restricted to $\{1, 2, 3\}$ the set of x for which $F(x)$ is defined. The graph of F is

$$\begin{aligned} \mathrm{Gr}(F) &= \{\langle x, y\rangle \mid x\colon\{1, 2, 3\} \wedge y\colon \mathrm{Nat} \wedge y = x+2\} \\ &= \{\langle 1, 3\rangle, \langle 2, 4\rangle, \langle 3, 5\rangle\} \end{aligned}$$ ■

We can see that in this example no x occurs in more than one couple $\langle x, y\rangle$ in $\mathrm{Gr}(F)$. This is what makes F a *function.*

Second formal definition

The reason which led to the second formal definition of a relation holds for functions as well: it is often natural first to specify two sets of which the argument x and the result $F(x)$ of a function F must be members respectively. These sets are also called the *domain* and the *codomain* of F. Consequently, our second variant is as follows:

Definition 3.3A.3

A function F is an object with three features:

(1) A set called the *domain* of F and denoted by $\mathrm{Dom}(F)$

(2) A set called the *codomain* of F and written $\mathrm{Cod}(F)$

(3) A set called the *graph* of F, denoted by $\mathrm{Gr}(F)$ and such that

$$\mathrm{Gr}(F) \subseteq \mathrm{Dom}(F) \times \mathrm{Cod}(F)$$

The set $\mathrm{Gr}(F)$ is subject to the additional condition of Definition **3**.3A.2, namely:

For any x, there is at most one y such that $\langle x, y\rangle \in \mathrm{Gr}(F)$. ■

Thus in this sense a function is a functional relation in the sense of Definitions **3**.2A.3 combined with **3**.2D.1(1). Henceforward, the term 'function' will always be used in the sense of Definition **3**.3A.3, unless otherwise stated.

Remarks

1 A function F is a special type of relation, inheriting all the properties of a relation. These include the two derived features described in Section **3**.2C, the *definition domain* $\mathrm{Def}(F)$ and the *range* $\mathrm{Ran}(F)$. Likewise, the basic taxonomy of relations given in Section **3**.2D holds for functions, except of course that the distinction between functional and nonfunctional relations is now irrelevant. This taxonomy is restated for functions in Section **3**.3C.

2 As it is defined here, a function may be *partial*. In mathematics, a function is usually understood to be *total* – that is, defined for every member of its domain. We use the more general definition as the functions which arise in computing are frequently partial.

3 Functions in the sense of Definition **3**.3A.3 are often called 'partial'. This is a misnomer, as the qualifier 'partial' logically rules out total functions. The proper way of describing our functions is to call them *possibly partial*, as any function F is either strictly total, if $\mathrm{Def}(F) = \mathrm{Dom}(F)$, or strictly partial, if $\mathrm{Def}(F) \neq \mathrm{Dom}(F)$.

4 It is important to realize the precise meaning of '$F(x)$' for any function F. Given any $x:\mathrm{Dom}(F)$, $F(x)$ denotes *nothing more* than the object associated with x by F. Thus, x itself is *not* included in the information represented by $F(x)$. For instance, in the example of Figure **3**.3A.1, name($P2$) = name($P3$) = Fred. 'Fred' in itself does *not* indicate whether this is the name associated with $P2$ or $P3$. Consequently, if we are told that name(x) = Fred, we cannot infer from this information whether $x = P2$ or $x = P3$. ■

Notation and terminology

1 In order to introduce a function F, we must specify its domain D and codomain C, where D and C are two predefined sets. We write

(1) $\quad F : D \nrightarrow C$

to indicate that F is a (possibly partial) function with domain $\mathrm{Dom}(F) =_{\mathrm{d}} D$ and codomain $\mathrm{Cod}(F) =_{\mathrm{d}} C$. We may interpret '$D \nrightarrow C$' as denoting the *set* of all possibly partial functions F with $\mathrm{Dom}(F) =_{\mathrm{d}} D$ and $\mathrm{Cod}(F) =_{\mathrm{d}} C$, and (1) as the *introduction* of F as a member of this set. Note that the arrow '$\nrightarrow$' connects the two *sets* Dom(F) and Cod(F), *not* members of these sets.

2 We write

(2) $\quad F : D \rightarrow C$

to introduce a *total* function F with domain $D =_{\mathrm{d}} \mathrm{Dom}(F)$ and codomain $C =_{\mathrm{d}} \mathrm{Cod}(F)$. Thus (2) conveys the same information as (1), together with the fact that F is total – that is, $\mathrm{Def}(F) = \mathrm{Dom}(F)$.

3 In order to indicate that a function F *sends* x to $F(x)$, we write

$$x \longmapsto F(x)$$

Note the special barred arrow used for this purpose. It connects *members* of Dom(F) and Cod(F), and must be carefully distinguished from the normal arrows '$\nrightarrow$' and '$\rightarrow$', which link these sets themselves.

4 A function $F : D \rightarrow C$ is also called a *map*, *mapping* or *transformation from D into C*. We also say that F *maps D* into C. ■

3.3B Examples of functions

A substantial list of applications now follows, in order to illustrate the universality of functions and their variety. Preference is given to practical, familiar examples. In each case the emphasis is on the graph of the function, as it forms the 'concrete side' of this concept. Note that in practice the graph Gr(F) of a function F is usually represented as a table, and we mainly use this form. In a table, the couples $\langle x, y\rangle : \text{Gr}(F)$ are represented by listing their components in two adjacent columns. The association between elements x and y is represented by the two-dimensional layout of the table. The effectiveness of this form is a matter of common experience.

Example 3.3B.1 Dictionaries

A dictionary is a function. Essentially, it is a *set* of entries, each of which is a word and an associated piece of information. The term 'dictionary' is used here in a broad, generic sense. It covers many different types of dictionary. The examples set out below are more specific instances.

1 A telephone directory In a telephone directory T, each entry is a couple $\langle x, y\rangle$, where x is the name of a person and y the associated telephone number. The set of entries $\langle x, y\rangle$ forms the graph of T. We may regard the set of all *possible* names as forming the domain Dom(T). The precise definition of Dom(T) is up to the authors of the directory. Likewise, the set of all possible numbers may be taken as the codomain Cod(T), again to be established precisely by the authors. No name x occurs in more than one couple $\langle x, y\rangle \in \text{Gr}(T)$. This makes T a function. This function is *partial* as in general Def(T) is a small finite subset of Dom(T).

Here is a concrete example: the internal directory T of a very small firm. It is assumed that in each entry $\langle x, y\rangle$, x must be just one surname of up to 10 letters, and y a 4-digit number. The graph Gr(T) is

$$\{ \langle \text{Adams}, 4598\rangle, \langle \text{Jones}, 4410\rangle, \langle \text{Peters}, 8822\rangle, \langle \text{Webb}, 6271\rangle \}$$

This is equivalent to the table

Name	Tel. no.
Adams	4598
Jones	4410
Peters	8822
Webb	6271

In this example, Def(T) = {Adams, Jones, Peters, Webb}.

2 A birthday book A birthday book B is essentially a set of entries $\langle x, y\rangle$ in which x is the name of a friend and y is x's birthday. The main difference between this and the previous example is that here y must be a date, so it is appropriate to take as codomain $\text{Cod}(B)$ the set of all possible dates, to be determined precisely by the owner of the book.

Assuming each date must be of the form $d/m/y$, where d, m and y:Nat, an instance of $\text{Gr}(B)$ is

$$\{\ \langle \text{Albert}, 3/4/42\rangle,\ \langle \text{Charles}, 17/10/48\rangle,\ \langle \text{Kate}, 31/7/46\rangle,\ \langle \text{Martin}, 23/1/52\rangle\ \}$$

or, in tabular form,

Name	Birthday
Albert	3/4/42
Charles	17/10/48
Kate	31/7/46
Martin	23/1/52

3 An address book An address book A may be described in the same way with $\text{Cod}(A)$ defined as the set of all possible addresses of an appropriate format.

4 A language dictionary A dictionary D in the narrow, usual sense features a set of couples $\langle x, y\rangle$ where x is a word and y the corresponding definition. As domain $\text{Dom}(D)$ we may take the set of all possible words which may be formed in the language described and as codomain $\text{Cod}(D)$ the set of all possible texts in this language.

Note that in each case the specification of the domain and codomain of the dictionary is a matter of choice, that is, of *modelling*. In Chapter 15 we extend this description of dictionaries by adding operations on them. ■

Example 3.3B.2 Fixed attributes of objects

In any set D of objects, the members of D may have certain *attributes*. Each attribute is a function F which sends each member x:D to a corresponding value $F(x)$ in some set A of attribute values. However, $F(x)$ is often determined for members x of a finite subset S of D only. For instance, S may be a group of people, such as the pupils of a school or the population of a country, and F any attribute of human individuals: height, weight, age, gender, hair colour, and so on. As another example, D may be a certain set of products, such as the set of all cars; S may be a set of particular types of car; and F may be any characteristic of these models: price, petrol consumption, and so on. In each case, F is a partial function with domain $\text{Dom}(F) =_{\text{d}} D$, codomain $\text{Cod}(F) =_{\text{d}} A$ and definition domain $\text{Def}(F) =_{\text{d}} S$. Here are some specific instances.

1 Three attributes of people Four friends, George, Hector, Kevin and Paul, form a circle they call *Club*. They want to know more about each other. They are interested in their age, weight and height. These are described as three partial functions, Age, Weight (kg) and Height (metres), with graphs as in the tables here:

Member	Age
George	23
Hector	27
Kevin	18
Paul	27

Member	Weight
George	68
Hector	72
Kevin	55
Paul	82

Member	Height
George	1.87
Hector	1.55
Kevin	1.48
Paul	1.74

For each function F, we may take the set of all people as the domain $\text{Dom}(F)$, and $\text{Def}(F) = \textit{Club}$. Cod(Age) may be defined as Nat or some subset of it, for example $\{n\text{:Nat} \mid 0 \leqslant n \leqslant 130\}$. Cod(Weight) may be defined similarly, and Cod(Height) as the set of real numbers or some subset.

2 Attributes of car models Some of the main attributes of a car are its price and petrol consumption (miles per gallon). The graphs of these functions for a set of models could be as shown in the accompanying tables.

Model	Price
Rover Metro	£ 8,562
Ford Escort	£10,236
Nissan Sunny	£11,064
BMW 520i	£18,514

Model	Mpg
Rover Metro	37
Ford Escort	35
Nissan Sunny	37
BMW 520i	27

■

Example 3.3B.3 Personnel records

Every organization keeps records of details of its staff. These typically include the following items for each person:

- name
- address
- sex
- marital status
- date of birth
- salary
- social security number

Each of these items is an attribute, very much as in Example **3**.3B.2, even though some of them are liable to change in time. Each attribute may be described as a partial function F from the set of all possible persons to a set of attribute values. For each person x, $F(x)$ is defined iff x is an employee of the organization. ■

Remark

Often in practice all the details of a person are stored in a single record. This is a matter of database organization, which does not contradict the fact that, objectively, each attribute constitutes a separate function in its own right. ■

Example 3.3B.4 Timetables

Any kind of timetable is a function. There are different types of timetable, but in each case there is a functional correspondence between a set of times and a set of planned events. Here are three instances.

1 School timetable A school timetable T for a particular class assigns an activity – lecture, laboratory and so on – to each period during the week. The graph Gr(T) of such a function for one day is as shown in the accompanying table.

Time	Lecture
09.10–10.00	Physics
10.10–11.00	Mathematics
11.10–12.00	Chemistry
13.30–14.20	Computing
14.30–15.20	Philosophy

Note that in this example, for any couple $\langle x, y\rangle : \mathrm{Gr}(T)$, x is a 50-minute period in the day. It is a *single element*, even though it is specified by two time limits.

2 Flight timetable An airline flight timetable assigns a daily departure time to each flight. Therefore, it is a function T from flight numbers to departure times. Specifically, each couple $\langle x, y\rangle : \mathrm{Gr}(T)$ consists of a flight number x and a corresponding departure time y. An example is as follows:

Flight	Departure time
PA 5040	07.00
PA 5180	09.40
PA 5320	11.20
PA 6610	14.50
PA 6340	17.10

Note that here the association is from flights *to* times, the opposite of the previous example.

3 Programme A one-day conference is a set of events: talks, lectures, demonstrations, and so on. A *programme P* for such a conference is a function which assigns a starting time to each such event, very much as in the flight timetable above. ■

Example 3.3B.5 ***Rule systems***

Social relations are governed by numerous rule systems: legal, conventional, linguistic, and so on. Whenever a rule is precisely defined, it determines a function. Here are three instances.

1 Chess The game of chess may be described as a function. With each possible configuration of pieces on the board, of which there is a very large though finite number, the rules of the game associate a *set* of allowed moves. Therefore, these rules determine a total function F from the set *Conf* of all possible configurations. Note that with any configuration x:*Conf*, the object $F(x)$ which F associates with x is a whole *set* of allowed moves. This feature distinguishes this example from the previous ones.

Another important difference is that the graph $\text{Gr}(F)$ is finite but very large. Consequently, it cannot be described by enumeration in practice, and F may only be defined abstractly. Other games may be described as functions in a similar way.

2 Criminal law One purpose of a penal code is to establish a list of offences and associate a precise range of sanctions with each offence. This involves two functions. The first sends each offence, referred to by its name, to its definition, that is, the conditions which must be satisfied for the offence to be realized. The second sends each offence to a corresponding set of possible sanctions.

3 Decision rules In business or government we find many rules or procedures which determine what course of action must be taken when certain conditions are satisfied. Each such rule may be described as a function which associates with every relevant combination of conditions a corresponding course of action. An instance is a stock control rule for a commodity, stating that 'whenever the stock level falls below a certain point L, a quantity Q of the commodity must be reordered'. ■

Example 3.3B.6 ***Formal languages***

The two main aspects of a formal notation, or language, are its syntax and its semantics. Both features are described by functions.

1 Syntax The syntax of a language L is a set of rules which determine (a) its set of basic symbols (alphabet) and (b) which strings of basic symbols are well-formed expressions (wfes), terms or formulas. Each wfe is obtained by applying some function to a list of other, more elementary, wfes. For instance in logic, if 'P' and 'Q' are any two valid formulas, then so is '$(P \wedge Q)$'. The latter is obtained by applying a certain construction rule to '$\langle P, Q\rangle$'. This construction rule is a 'formula-building' operation, or function. The set of all possible wfes forms the 'language' generated by the syntax rules. These ideas are treated fully in Part **3**.

2 Semantics Given the set of all possible wfes making up a formal language L, the semantics of L is a function M which associates with each wfe x a certain object $M(x)$ called the *semantic value* or meaning of x. The manner in which the function M is determined is also treated in Part **3**. ■

Example 3.3B.7 Numeric functions

The previous examples should be sufficient to convince the reader that functions need not be numeric. However, numeric functions are also important. Here is another example, named F, in which the sets Dom(F), Def(F), Cod(F), Ran(F) and Gr(F) are all infinite. We introduce F by

$$F : \text{Nat} \nrightarrow \text{Nat}$$

Recall that this means that F is possibly partial, the domain Dom(F) = Nat, the codomain Cod(F) = Nat and the graph Gr(F) is a subset of Nat × Nat.

We define $F(n)$ for every n:Nat such that $n \geqslant 3$ by the condition

$$F(n) =_{\text{d}} \begin{array}{ll} n - 3 & \text{if } n \text{ is odd} \\ n - 4 & \text{if } n \text{ is even} \end{array}$$

This means that the definition domain Def(F) is different from the domain Dom(F):

$$\text{Def}(F) = \{n : \text{Nat} \mid n \geqslant 3\} = \{3, 4, 5, \dots\}$$

Even though Def(F) is a proper subset of Nat, it is infinite. Therefore we cannot enumerate Gr(F) completely. What we can do is enumerate a small finite subset of Gr(F), sufficient to suggest what the whole graph looks like. This is as follows in tabular form:

n	$F(n)$
3	0
4	0
5	2
6	2
7	4
8	4
...	...

What is the range Ran(F)?

Answer The portion of Gr(F) represented above clearly suggests that Ran(F) is the set of even natural numbers:

$$\text{Ran}(F) = \{n : \text{Nat} \mid n \text{ is divisible by } 2\}$$

Thus Ran(F) is an infinite but proper subset of Cod(F) = Nat.

This example illustrates that in general we may define the same set in different ways. The standard definition of the set of even numbers is

$$\{n : \text{Nat} \mid \exists\, m : \text{Nat} \cdot 2 \times m = n\}$$

Now the present function F gives us an alternative description of this set, namely Ran(F). ■

This completes our list of examples of functions. Many more instances arise in subsequent developments.

Diagrammatic representation of a function

It is useful to represent functions diagrammatically using the conventions introduced in Section **3**.2B for relations in general. For example, consider the function $F : S \to T$ where $S =_d \{\text{a, b, c}\}$ and $T =_d \{1, 3, 7, 15\}$. It is defined by

$$F(\text{a}) =_d 3$$
$$F(\text{b}) =_d 1$$
$$F(\text{c}) =_d 15$$

The diagrammatic representation of F is shown in Figure **3**.3B.1.

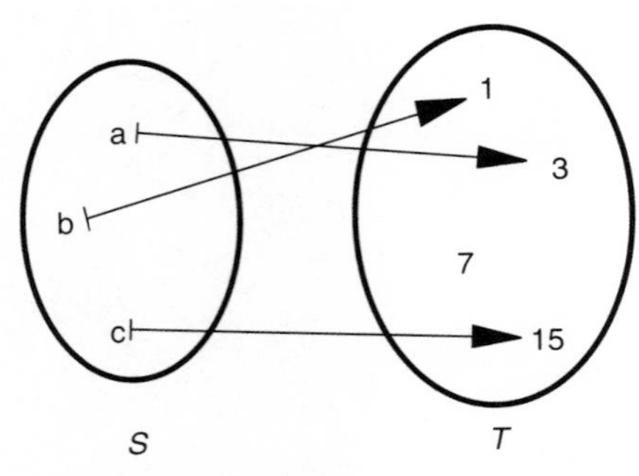

Figure 3.3B.1 Representation of $F : S \to T$.

3.3C Basic categories of functions

The taxonomy of relations set out in Section **3**.2D applies to functions. As it is usually defined for functions only, we restate it here for this special case, with some additional terms.

Definition 3.3C.1

Let F be any function (or functional relation, which is the same).

(1) F is *injective* iff for any y: Ran(F), there is *exactly one* x with $\langle x, y\rangle \in \mathrm{Gr}(F)$. In this case, F is also called an *injection*. The condition of injectiveness is expressed formally as follows:

$$\forall x, y : \mathrm{Def}(F) \cdot F(x) = F(y) \Rightarrow x = y$$

(2) F is *total* iff for any x: Dom(F), there is *at least one* y with $\langle x, y\rangle \in \mathrm{Gr}(F)$. Equivalently, F is total iff $\mathrm{Def}(F) = \mathrm{Dom}(F)$.

(3) F is *surjective* iff for any y: Cod(F), there is *at least one* x with $\langle x, y\rangle \in \mathrm{Gr}(F)$. Equivalently, F is surjective iff $\mathrm{Ran}(F) = \mathrm{Cod}(F)$. In this case, F is also called a *surjection*.

(4) F is *bijective* iff it is *total, injective and surjective*. In this case, F is also called a *bijection*. ■

Alternative terminology An injective relation is also called *single-rooted*. An injection is a *one-to-one* function. A surjection $F : S \leftrightarrow T$ is a function *from S onto T*. A *bijection* is a *one-to-one correspondence*. ■

Example of an injection

An injection has been defined as a function F such that for any elements x, y: Def(F), if $F(x) = F(y)$ then $x = y$. This condition is equivalent to the following alternative, which we shall also use to define an injection:

$$\forall x, y : \mathrm{Def}(F) \cdot x \neq y \Rightarrow F(x) \neq F(y)$$

An injection $F : S \rightarrow T$ is represented in Figure **3**.3C.1. F is an injection as no $y : T$ is at the end of more than one arrow. ■

Example of a surjection

From Definition **3**.3C.1, a function $F : S \leftrightarrow T$ is a surjection iff every $y : T$ is equal to $F(x)$ for some $x : S$. Such a function is represented in Figure **3**.3C.2. We can see it is a surjection as every $y : T$ is at the end of at least one arrow. ■

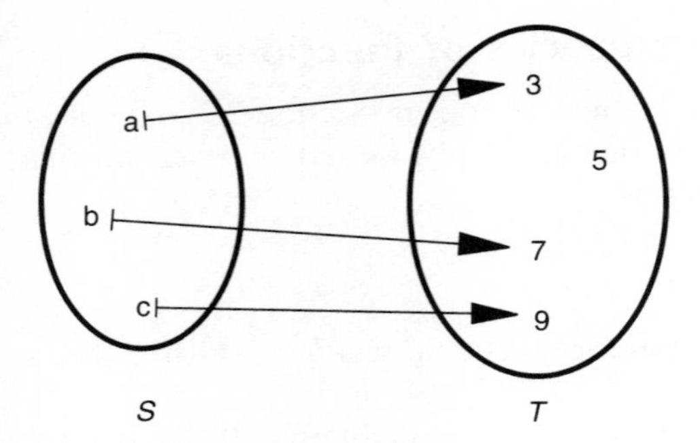

Figure 3.3C.1 An injection $F: S \rightarrow T$.

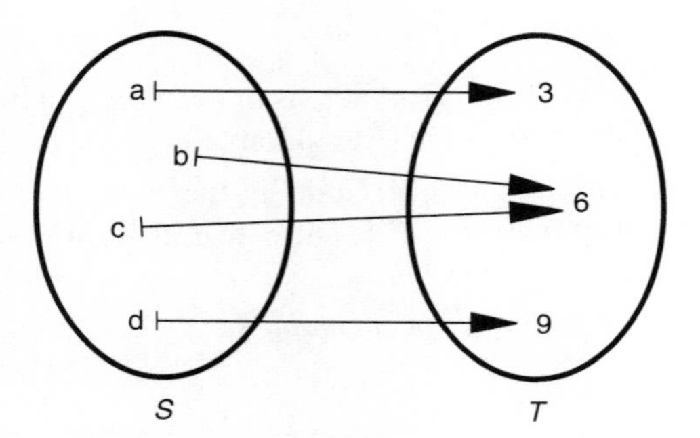

Figure 3.3C.2 A surjection $F: S \rightarrow T$.

Example of a bijection

From Definition 3.3C.1, a bijection is a relation F such that

(1) Every x : Dom(F) is associated with exactly one y : Cod(F), which makes F a *total function.*

(2) Every y : Cod(F) is associated with exactly one x : Dom(F), which makes F *surjective* and *injective.*

We also say that each x : Dom(F) is *matched* with a unique y : Cod(F) and each y : Cod(F) with a unique x : Dom(F).

A bijection $F: S \rightarrow T$ is represented in Figure 3.3C.3. We can verify that every $x : S$ is at the start of *exactly one* arrow and every $y : T$ is at the end of *exactly one* arrow. ■

If S and T are finite in the bijection $F: S \rightarrow T$, then it is obvious that they have the same number of members. Thus, the notion of bijection gives an important method of determining if any two sets S and T have the same cardinality:

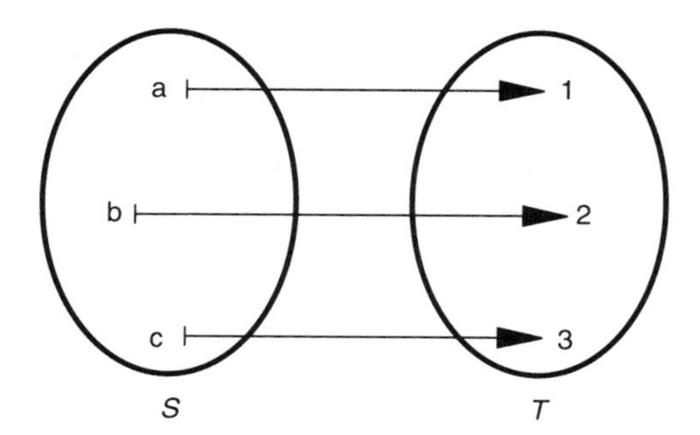

Figure 3.3C.3 A bijection $F: S \to T$.

If we can show that there exists a bijection from S to T, then it follows that S and T have the same cardinality, or number of members.

This is obvious for finite sets. Moreover, this criterion may be used to define the cardinality of infinite sets.

Another obvious and related property is this:

If there is a bijection from a set S to a set T, then (and only then) there is a bijection from T to S.

This too is intuitively obvious. Given a bijection $F: S \to T$, reverse the direction of all the arrows $x \mapsto y$: this gives a bijection from T to S. More on this in Section **3**.6E.

Class functions

Our generalization of set-theoretical relations to class relations (Section **3**.2E) naturally holds for functions, as these are special relations. We use the term '*class function*' to refer to a function F such that Dom(F), Cod(F) and/or Gr(F) may be proper classes.

The various set operations introduced in Section **2**.2 – union, intersection, relative complement and so on – are all class functions, as they send every couple of sets (or other similar operands) to another set.

EXERCISES

3.3.1 Let $S =_{\mathrm{d}} \{\mathrm{a, b, c, d}\}$ and $T =_{\mathrm{d}} \{1, 2, 3, 4, 5\}$. Let $F: S \to T$ be defined by the rules: $F(\mathrm{a}) =_{\mathrm{d}} 3$; $F(\mathrm{b}) =_{\mathrm{d}} 1$; $F(\mathrm{c}) =_{\mathrm{d}} 3$; and $F(\mathrm{d}) =_{\mathrm{d}} 5$. Draw a diagram to represent F, and enumerate Gr(F).

3.3.2 Let $S =_d \{1, 2, 3, 4\}$ and $F: S \rightarrow S$ be defined by $F(x) =_d [(x + 1) \text{ MOD } 4] + 1$ for all $x: S$. Draw a diagram to represent F, and enumerate $\text{Gr}(F)$.

3.3.3 Find three further examples of objects which may be described as dictionaries, hence possibly partial functions, as in Example **3**.3B.1. In each case specify the domain and codomain of the function carefully and give a small sample of members of its graph in tabular form.

3.3.4 Find three further examples of functions each sending the members of some domain to some set of attribute values (codomain), as in Example **3**.3B.2.

3.3.5 Let F and G be two total functions from a common domain A, $F: A \rightarrow B$ and $G: A \rightarrow C$. Show that these two functions may be combined in an obvious way into a single function $H: A \rightarrow B \times C$. Define H completely and illustrate this construction with examples similar to those of Exercise **3**.3.4.

3.3.6 Give further examples of 'rule systems' which may be described as functions or sets of functions, as in Example **3**.3B.5.

3.3.7 Consider the two formal definitions of an injection. Show that the conditions used there are equivalent. Recall that these are:

$$\forall x, y: \text{Def}(F) \cdot F(x) = F(y) \Rightarrow x = y$$

and

$$\forall x, y: \text{Def}(F) \cdot x \neq y \Rightarrow F(x) \neq F(y)$$

This equivalence is based on a tautology called *contraposition*. Tautologies are treated in Chapter **6** on propositional logic.

3.3.8 Which of the following functions $F: \text{Nat} \rightarrow \text{Nat}$ are (a) injections, (b) surjections and (c) bijections? Each function F is defined by an equation which holds for all $x: \text{Nat}$. For each function F, draw a diagram representing the first six couples of $\text{Gr}(F)$ in the natural order $\langle 0, F(0) \rangle, \ldots, \langle 5, F(5) \rangle$.

(1) $F(x) =_d \quad x$
(2) $F(x) =_d \quad x + 3$
(3) $F(x) =_d \quad x - 3$ if $x > 3$, 0 otherwise
(4) $F(x) =_d \quad 2 \times x$
(5) $F(x) =_d \quad x \text{ DIV } 2$
(6) $F(x) =_d \quad x + 2$ if $x \text{ MOD } 3 = 0$;
$\qquad x$ if $x \text{ MOD } 3 = 1$;
$\qquad x - 2$ if $x \text{ MOD } 3 = 2$

3.3.9 For each application of functions given in Section **3**.3B or required in Exercises **3**.3.3 to **3**.3.6, determine whether it should normally, or necessarily, be a special case – that is, total, injective and/or surjective.

3.3.10 Using the sets S and T of Exercise **3**.3.1, construct two different total injections F and $G: S \to T$ and two different total surjections H and $K: T \to S$. (Note the interchange of domain and codomain.)

3.3.11 Using the sets S and T of Exercise **3**.3.1, show that it is impossible to construct a total injection $F: T \to S$ and a surjection $G: S \to T$.

3.3.12* Repeat Exercise **3**.3.10 with $S =_{\mathrm{d}} \{\mathrm{a, b, c, d}\}$ and $T =_{\mathrm{d}} \{1, 2, 3, 4\}$. What can you observe about the four functions F, G, H and K in this case? On the basis of your observations, formulate a general law on total injections, total surjections and bijections between *finite sets* S and T.

3.3.13 Consider the operations *Fst* and *Snd* introduced in Exercise **3**.1.11. Give a full definition of these two operations as functions in the sense of Definition **3**.3A.3 – that is, specify their domain, codomain and graph.

3.3.14 For any set A, let $F: A \to \{0\} \times A$ be the function sending each $a: A$ to $\langle 0, a \rangle$. Show that F is a bijection. From this fact, we may conclude that A and $\{0\} \times A$ are *equivalent* or *isomorphic*, and F is a description of this equivalence. Hint: you must show that F is both injective and surjective, using the functions *Fst* and *Snd* of Exercise **3**.3.13.

3.3.15 For any two sets A and B, show that the correspondence between members of $A \times B$ and $B \times A$ defined in Exercise **3**.1.11 is a bijection $G: A \times B \to B \times A$. Draw conclusions as in Exercise **3**.3.14.

3.3.16* Repeat Exercise **3**.3.15 with the correspondence defined in Exercise **3**.1.12. Hint: make sure you specify the domain and codomain of the bijection properly.

3.3.17 (a) For any set A, there is *exactly one* function $F1: \varnothing \leftrightarrow A$. Define $F1$ precisely. Is $F1$ partial or total?

(b) There is only one set A which admits a *total* function $F2: A \to \varnothing$. Define A *and* $F2$.

(c) For any singleton T, say $\{0\}$, and any set A, there is just one *total* function $F3: A \to T$. Define $F3$.

3.4 Fundamental applications of functions

Many fundamental concepts may be described as special types of function. This is further evidence of the centrality of this notion. In this section we describe some of these applications. This section may be skipped on first reading.

3.4A Characteristic functions of subsets and relations

Let U be any set, which we now consider fixed. We may suppose that U is our 'universe of discourse', in the sense that any object we may be interested in belongs to U (apart from U itself). Consider any subset $S \subseteq_d U$. Our concern here is to develop an important alternative means of describing, or characterizing, S. This means is the *characteristic function* of S (relative to U).

Before considering this function, recall the various means already available to describe a set S in practice. These are:

(1) enumerating the members of S (provided S is finite);

(2) defining S by an abstraction – that is, by

$$S =_d \{x : U \mid — x —\}$$

where '$— x —$' is a formula in which 'x' may, and normally does, occur;

(3) defining S as the result of an operation on other subsets of U, for example $S =_d A \cup B$.

The characteristic function is a fourth means of describing S. It is denoted by the Greek letter χ.

Now recall that by the principle of extensionality, a set $S \subseteq_d U$ is entirely determined by the membership relation. We know S iff for any object $x : U$, we know whether '$x \in S$' is true or false. This immediately suggests that we may describe S by the function χ which sends each $x : U$ to true if $x \in S$, and to false if $x \notin S$. Clearly, the function χ is well defined for all members $x : U$, as for any such x, either $\chi(x) = \text{true}$ or $\chi(x) = \text{false}$.

There remains to specify the domain and the codomain of χ. Dom(χ) must include the whole of U, as Def(χ) = U. As there is no need to consider a larger set, we take Dom(χ) $=_d U$. This makes χ a total function. Similarly, as codomain Cod(χ) we need a set including {true, false}. As no further values are needed as members of Cod(χ), we define Cod(χ) $=_d$ {true, false}. The set {true, false} is commonly named Bool, after the mathematician and logician George Boole (1815–1864). Therefore, Cod(χ) = Bool. This completes our description of χ, the characteristic function of S.

Definition 3.4A.1

Let Bool be the set defined by

$$\text{Bool} =_d \{\text{true}, \text{false}\}$$

For any subset $S \subseteq_d U$, the *characteristic function* of S (relative to U) is the total function

$$\chi : U \to \text{Bool}$$

defined by

$$\chi(x) =_{\mathrm{d}} \text{true} \quad \text{if } x \in S$$
$$\chi(x) =_{\mathrm{d}} \text{false} \quad \text{if } x \notin S$$

for any $x : U$. ■

Example 3.4A.1

Let $U =_{\mathrm{d}} \{\mathrm{a, b, c}\}$. We define the characteristic functions of various subsets $S \subseteq_{\mathrm{d}} U$, using the abbreviations T for true and F for false.

(1) Let $S =_{\mathrm{d}} \{\mathrm{a, c}\}$. Then for this set, χ is defined by

$$\chi(\mathrm{a}) = \mathrm{T}$$
$$\chi(\mathrm{b}) = \mathrm{F}$$
$$\chi(\mathrm{c}) = \mathrm{T}$$

or, in tabular form

x	$\chi(x)$
a	T
b	F
c	T

(2) Let $S =_{\mathrm{d}} \{\mathrm{b}\}$. Then for this set χ is defined in tabular form by

x	$\chi(x)$
a	F
b	T
c	F

(3) Let $S =_{\mathrm{d}} \varnothing$. For this set, χ is given by

x	$\chi(x)$
a	F
b	F
c	F

that is, $\chi(x)$ is false everywhere on U.

(4) Let $S =_d U$. For this set, χ is given by

x	$\chi(x)$
a	T
b	T
c	T

that is, $\chi(x)$ is true everywhere on U. ■

Remarks

1 The most natural codomain to use in the definition of the characteristic function is Bool = {true, false}. However, any other set with exactly two members would do. In particular, the set {0, 1} is often used instead of Bool, with 0 corresponding to false and 1 to true:

$$0 \mapsto \text{false}$$
$$1 \mapsto \text{true}$$

Under this correspondence (bijection) between {0, 1} and Bool, it is clear that the function $\chi' : U \to \{0, 1\}$ defined by

$$\chi'(x) =_d 1 \quad \text{if } x \in S$$
$$\chi'(x) =_d 0 \quad \text{if } x \notin S$$

is equivalent to the function χ of Definition 3.4A.1.

2 *Each subset* $S \subseteq_d U$ has its own characteristic function. In other words there is a one-to-one correspondence between all the various subsets S of U and all the possible characteristic functions on U. This is clearly illustrated by Example 3.4A.1 above. If necessary, we write χ_S to denote the characteristic function of the set S – that is, if this must be distinguished from other characteristic functions on U. ■

Characteristic function of a relation

Any relation R, in the sense of Definition 3.2A.3, is a subset of a certain set: the cartesian product $D \times C$, where $D =_d \text{Dom}(R)$ and $C =_d \text{Cod}(R)$, to be precise. Therefore, Gr(R) may be described by its characteristic function relative to $D \times C$.

Example 3.4A.2

Consider the relation R with $D =_{\text{d}} \text{Dom}(R) =_{\text{d}} \{3, 4\}$ and $C =_{\text{d}} \text{Cod}(R) =_{\text{d}} \{3, 4, 5\}$. Let $\text{Gr}(R) \subseteq D \times C$ be defined by

$$\text{Gr}(R) =_{\text{d}} \{\langle x, y\rangle : D \times C \mid x < y\} = \{\langle 3, 4\rangle, \langle 3, 5\rangle, \langle 4, 5\rangle\}$$

The characteristic function of $\text{Gr}(R)$ is the function $\chi : D \times C \to \text{Bool}$ defined in tabular form by

$\langle x, y\rangle$	$\chi(\langle x, y\rangle)$
$\langle 3, 3\rangle$	F
$\langle 3, 4\rangle$	T
$\langle 3, 5\rangle$	T
$\langle 4, 3\rangle$	F
$\langle 4, 4\rangle$	F
$\langle 4, 5\rangle$	T

■

Remark

This example gives us an opportunity to appreciate the significance of specifying the domain and the codomain of a relation R. *It is precisely because Dom(R) and Cod(R) are defined that we are able to represent Gr(R) by its characteristic function.* ■

3.4B Equivalence between relations and functions

As already mentioned, the two concepts of function and relation are equivalent. On the one hand, a function is a special type of relation – it is a functional relation. On the other hand, any relation R may be described as a certain function, and this in a very natural way. We now consider this representation.

Consider any relation R. For any $x : \text{Dom}(R)$, there is a set of elements $y : \text{Cod}(R)$ such that $\langle x, y\rangle \in \text{Gr}(R)$. Let $A(x)$ denote this set:

$$A(x) =_{\text{d}} \{y : \text{Cod}(R) \mid \langle x, y\rangle \in \text{Gr}(R)\}$$

Clearly $A(x)$ is a function of x – it varies as we vary x over $\text{Dom}(R)$. This is the function corresponding to the relation R.

Example 3.4B.1

Consider the relation given by

(1) $\text{Dom}(R) =_{\text{d}} \{1, 2, 3, 4\}$

(2) $\text{Cod}(R) =_{\text{d}} \{\text{a, b, c, d, e}\}$

(3) $\text{Gr}(R) =_{\text{d}} \{\langle 1, \text{b}\rangle, \langle 1, \text{d}\rangle, \langle 3, \text{b}\rangle, \langle 4, \text{d}\rangle, \langle 4, \text{e}\rangle\}$

For any $x:\mathrm{Dom}(R)$, the corresponding set $A(x)$ is set out in the following table:

x	$A(x)$
1	{b, d}
2	$\varnothing$
3	{b}
4	{d, e}

■

For any $x:\mathrm{Dom}(R)$, $A(x)$ is the set of elements *associated* with x by R, as defined in Section 3.2A. Clearly A is a total function

$$A:\mathrm{Dom}(R) \to \mathrm{Pow}(\mathrm{Cod}(R))$$

Moreover given R, the function A is entirely determined and vice versa. This is why A and R are said to be equivalent: they contain the same information.

Image

For any relation R, the corresponding function A as defined above may be generalized. Instead of sending a *member* $x:\mathrm{Dom}(R)$ to its associated elements $y:\mathrm{Cod}(R)$, we may send a *subset* $S \subseteq_{\mathrm{d}} \mathrm{Dom}(R)$ to the subset $T \subseteq_{\mathrm{d}} \mathrm{Cod}(R)$ of associated elements. This subset T is called the *image* of S and is denoted by $\mathrm{Im}_R(S)$

For any $S \subseteq_{\mathrm{d}} \mathrm{Dom}(R)$, the associated set $\mathrm{Im}_R(S) \subseteq \mathrm{Cod}(R)$ may be described informally as follows: any y is a member of $\mathrm{Im}_R(S)$ iff there exists at least one $x:S$ such that y is associated with x – that is, $y \in A(x)$. This is expressed formally as follows:

Definition 3.4B.1

Let R be any relation. For any $S \subseteq_{\mathrm{d}} \mathrm{Dom}(R)$, the *image* of S *under* R is the set $\mathrm{Im}_R(S)$ defined by

$$\mathrm{Im}_R(S) =_{\mathrm{d}} \cup \{A(x) | x:S\}$$

where for all $x:\mathrm{Dom}(R)$, $A(x) =_{\mathrm{d}} \{y:\mathrm{Cod}(R) \mid \langle x, y\rangle \in \mathrm{Gr}(R)\}$ as above. ■

3.4C Families and bags

We now return to an old problem of ours. Suppose we want to define an object F which is like a set, except that somehow *any member may occur several times in F*, rather than just once. For instance, we want to define the set of words making up a sentence, but in the sense that different *occurrences* of the same word in the sentence are regarded as distinct – recall the example of Section **2**.1E, Answer 1. We shall see how this problem can be solved in general using a certain type of function.

Let us start with a strict set V of elements that we shall call 'values'. Our aim is to construct a new object F which is like V, except that for any member v of V, there may be several instances of v in F. How do we define F?

The answer is to take an arbitrary set I, and define F as a *total function* from I to V:

$$F : I \rightarrow V$$

Consider the graph $\mathrm{Gr}(F)$. It is a set of couples $\langle i, v \rangle$, where $i : I$ and $v : V$. The various members of $\mathrm{Gr}(F)$ are all distinct from one another *at least by their first component i*. Consequently, for any $v : V$, we may represent *several* instances of v in F as couples $\langle i, v \rangle \in \mathrm{Gr}(F)$ with different first components i but the same second component v. These different instances are *distinct in F*: we have achieved our goal. The same idea was used in the definition of the disjoint union of two sets (Section **3**.1C).

The function F is called a *family*. The distinctive feature of a family is that in general the set I is arbitrary. In themselves, its members are of no or little relevance. They have only one role, to distinguish multiple instances of the various members of V. The members of I are often called *indexes*, and I an *index set*. This type of function is very frequent.

Example 3.4C.1

Consider again Answer 1 in the example of Section **2**.1E. In order to distinguish the various occurrences of words in a sentence, we marked each occurrence with its position in the sentence. The result was as follows:

{(1, 'Every'), (2, 'human'), (3, 'is'), (4, 'mortal'), (5, 'but'), (6, 'not'), (7, 'every'), (8, 'mortal'), (9, 'is'), (10, 'human')}

This operation was simply the construction of the graph of a total function F from the index set $I =_d \{1, 2, 3, \ldots, 9, 10\}$ to the set of words 'proper' – that is, the set {'every', 'human', 'is', 'mortal', 'but', 'not'} as defined in Answer 2. ■

Example 3.4C.2

Families are often used to establish a correspondence between two sets. A familiar example is as follows. When a person deposits a garment in a cloakroom, the attendant typically affixes a ticket bearing a number i to the garment, and issues a counterfoil bearing the same number to the owner of the garment. The number i is arbitrary. The only constraint imposed on the tickets used is that they bear different numbers. This situation may be modelled by *two* total functions $F1$ and $F2$ from a common index set I. The index set I is the set of numbers of issued tickets. The two functions $F1$ and $F2$ are defined as follows.

1 The first function, $F1$, is determined by the set of tickets affixed to garments. Dom($F1$) $=_d I$, and Cod($F1$) is the set of all possible garments. For any $i:I$, $F1(i)$ is the deposited garment bearing the ticket with number i. Ran($F1$) is the subset of deposited garments. $F1$ is an injection: different deposited garments bear different numbers – that is, for any two indexes i and $j:I$, if $i \neq j$ then $F1(i) \neq F1(j)$.

2 The second function, $F2$, is given by the set of counterfoils issued to the owners of the garments. Dom($F2$) $=_d I$, and Cod($F2$) is the set of all possible garment owners, namely all people. For any $i:I$, $F2(i)$ is the owner of the deposited garment $F1(i)$. Ran($F2$) is the subset of owners of deposited garments. Unlike $F1$, $F2$ need *not be* injective: the same person may deposit several garments, and thus receive several counterfoils. Hence for any indexes i and $j:I$, we may have $i \neq j$ and $F2(i) = F2(j)$.

We can see how each index $i:I$ establishes a correspondence between $F1(i)$ and $F2(i)$. This is depicted in Figure 3.4C.1. This coordinating role of functions with common (definition) domains is typical. ■

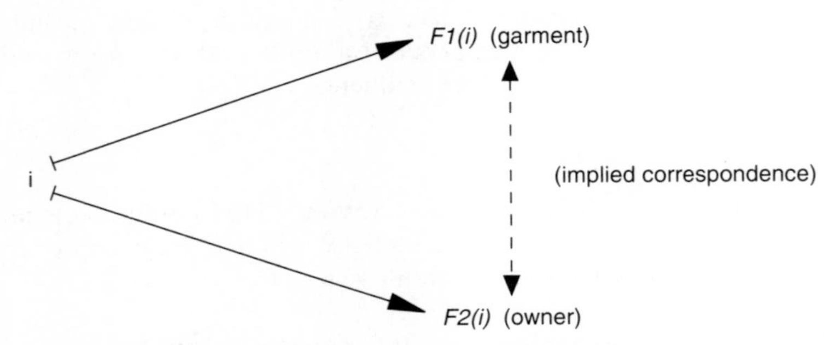

Figure 3.4C.1 Connection between $F1(i)$ and $F2(i)$ for any $i:I$.

To sum up, families are defined as follows:

Definition 3.4C.1

A family is a total function $F:I \rightarrow V$ where I is a set of indexes. It is also denoted by

$$(F_i | i:I)$$

Indexes are elements with no other essential properties than to be distinct from one another. Often I is the set $\{1, 2, \ldots, n\}$ where n is any positive natural number, or the whole of Nat.

When $I =_d \{1, 2, \ldots, n\}$ and n is small, we also represent F simply by listing its elements:

$$(F_1, F_2, \ldots, F_n)$$ ■

The notation $(F_i | i : I)$ is similar to the notation used for sets. It emphasizes the purpose of F, which is to represent a set which may contain multiple instances of the same object, *regarded as distinct*. It is important to distinguish this notation from $\{F_i | i : I\}$. In the latter, the distinction between different instances of the same value are ignored: $\{F_i | i : I\}$ is just the range $\text{Ran}(F)$.

Bags

Bags are related to families. They share their key purpose, which is to represent multiple instances of members of a set. A *bag* is defined as a set S, together with a function which associates a positive natural number $m(x)$ with every element $x : S$. The aim of $m(x)$ is to indicate the number of distinct instances of x occurring in the bag. This is expressed formally as follows:

Definition 3.4C.2

Let $\text{Pos} =_d \text{Nat} - \{0\}$ be the set of positive natural numbers. A *bag* is an object B with two features: a set S, and a function

$$m : S \rightarrow \text{Pos}$$

For any $x : S$, $m(x)$ is called the *multiplicity* of x in B. ■

Remarks

1 A bag is a generalization of a set. A set S is equivalent to a bag given by $m : S \rightarrow \text{Pos}$, where $m(x) = 1$ for all $x : S$.

2 Any bag may be represented as a family $F = (F_i | i : I)$. For instance, consider the bag B for which $S =_d \{\text{a, b, c}\}$ and the multiplicity function m is given in the table below.

$x : S$	$m(x)$
a	2
b	3
c	1

Let $I =_d \{1, 2, 3, 4, 5, 6\}$ and $F = (F_i | \, i : I)$ be defined by

$i : I$	F_i
1	a
2	a
3	b
4	b
5	b
6	c

Then it is clear that the bag B may be reconstructed from F. Which of the two representations is more appropriate depends on the application. The concept of a family, as defined above, seems preferable, as it is more natural than a bag in the sense of Definition 3.4C.2. The term 'bag' is presumably derived from the physical model of a set of balls contained in an actual bag, each 'painted' with some colour or value v from some set V. The only relevant property of the balls is to be distinct from one another. Thus, the natural description of the physical model is that the balls form an index set I, and the values painted on them a function $I \to V$. ■

3.4D Families of sets and partitions

Many functions F which arise in practice associate a *set* with each element in their definition domain. Often such functions are families F of sets, that is, their domain is an index set I. Any family $(F_i | i : I)$ of sets is essentially a collection in which each member F_i is a set labelled with the index i; any two sets F_i and F_j may be equal, even if $i \neq j$.

Operations on families of sets

Given any family $(F_i | i : I)$ of sets, we may apply to its members all the set operations described in previous sections. In particular, we may take the union or the intersection of any two members F_i and F_j, or perform various comparisons: for example, $F_i \subseteq F_j$, $F_i \subset F_j$, $F_i = F_j$ or even $F_i \in F_j$ (recall that a set may be a *member* of another set).

We may also apply any set operation to $(F_i | i : I)$ as a whole. In particular, the following two operations are defined:

- Union $\cup (F_i | i : I)$
- Intersection $\cap (F_i | i : I)$

These operations are defined in the obvious way. $\cup (F_i | i : I)$ is the set of elements x each of which belongs to at least one F_i, and $\cap (F_i | i : I)$ is the set of elements which belong to every set F_i. In other words, these sets are equal to $\cup \{F_i | i : I\}$ and $\cap \{F_i | i : I\}$, respectively. For these two operations, both notations may be used interchangeably.

Partitions

A special kind of family of sets is particularly important. It is called a *partition.* In a first sense, a partition is a family of sets which are *pairwise disjoint.* In a second sense, a partition is defined relative to a *predefined set S.* Given such a set, a partition of S is a family of pairwise disjoint sets whose union equals S. We only consider partitions in this second sense.

Example 3.4D.1

Let $S =_{\mathrm{d}} \{n : \mathrm{Nat} | n \leqslant 9\}$. The following are partitions of S:

(1) $(\{1, 5, 6\}, \{2\}, \{3, 7, 8, 9\}, \{0, 4\})$

(2) $(\{9\}, \{7, 8\}, \{4, 5, 6\}, \{2, 3\}, \{1\}, \{0\})$

(3) $(\varnothing, \{0, 1, 2\}, \varnothing, \{3, 4\}, \{5, 6, 7, 8\}, \varnothing, \varnothing, \{9\})$

(4) $(\{0, 1, 2, 3, 4, 5, 6, 7, 8, 9\})$

(5) $(\{0\}, \{1\}, \{2\}, \{3\}, \{4\}, \{5\}, \{6\}, \{7\}, \{8\}, \{9\})$ ■

In each of these cases, the reader may verify that (a) the members of the family are pairwise disjoint and (b) their union is equal to S. The first two partitions are random. The last three are special cases.

In (3), several members are instances of the empty set. This is allowed by the above definition of a partition. As (3) is a family, these various instances of $\varnothing$ are regarded as distinct. Below we introduce a second variant of a partition, in which empty members are disallowed.

The last two partitions in Example **3**.4D.1 are the two extreme cases in which $\varnothing$ is not allowed. (4) is the smallest partition. It has just one member, necessarily S itself. (5) is the largest partition with no empty members. Each member is a singleton.

Example 3.4D.2

Let $S =_{\mathrm{d}} \{n : \mathrm{Nat} | n \leqslant 9\}$ again. This time, we define partitions of S using the method of abstraction.

(1) $(\{n | n \text{ is odd and } n \leqslant 9\}, \{n | n \text{ is even and } n \leqslant 9\})$

(2) $(\{n | 0 \leqslant n \leqslant 3\}, \{n | 7 \leqslant n \leqslant 9\}, \{n | 4 \leqslant n \leqslant 6\})$ ■

We now give two variants of a partition of a set S. Recall that by Definition **2**.2E.1, a set A of sets is *pairwise disjoint* iff for any two *different* members S and T of A, $S \cap T = \varnothing$. We first introduce a predicate expressing this property both for a set of sets and for a family of sets.

Definition 3.4D.1

(1) Let A be any set of sets. We write

IsDisjointPairwise(A)

to express that A is pairwise disjoint – that is, for any two *different* members S and T of A, $S \cap T = \varnothing$.

(2) Let F be a family $(F_i | i : I)$ of sets. Then

IsDisjointPairwise(F)

means that F is pairwise disjoint – that is, $\forall i, j : I$, if $i \neq j$ then $F_i \cap F_j = \varnothing$. ∎

The two variants of a partition follow.

Definition 3.4D.2

Let S be any set. A *partition* of S is a family $(F_i | i : I)$ of sets satisfying the following two conditions:

(1) IsDisjointPairwise$(F_i | i : I)$

(2) $S = \cup (F_i | i : I)$ ∎

Definition 3.4D.3

Let S be any set. A *partition* of S is a family $(F_i | i : I)$ of sets satisfying the following conditions:

(1) IsDisjointPairwise$(F_i | i : I)$

(2) $S = \cup (F_i | i : I)$

(3) $\forall i : I \cdot F_i \neq \varnothing$ ∎

There is a close correspondence between the various partitions $F =_d (F_i | i : I)$ of a set S and a certain category of relations $R : S \leftrightarrow S$ called *equivalences* on S. The latter are treated in Section 3.6F. On account of this correspondence, the sets F_i of F are also often called *equivalence classes.*

3.4E Distributed functions

In some applications, we need a function F such that for each x : Def(F), $F(x)$ is a member of a set which is itself a function of x. This concept generalizes the notion of a function. We call it a *distributed function* and define it as follows:

Definition 3.4E.1

A *distributed function* is a function F with an auxiliary set function C satisfying the following conditions:

(1) Def(C) = Def(F)

(2) $\forall x : \mathrm{Def}(F) \cdot F(x) \in C(x)$ ∎

Condition (2) of this definition implies that for all $x:\text{Def}(F)$, $C(x) \neq \varnothing$. To keep Definition 3.4E.1 simple, we have not explicitly specified the domains and codomains of F and C. These can always be added if necessary. In particular a reasonable way of specifying Cod(F) is

$$\text{Cod}(F) =_{\text{d}} \cup \{C(x) \mid x:\text{Def}(F)\}$$

This ensures that $F(x) \in \text{Cod}(F)$ for all $x:\text{Def}(F)$.

Notation

Suppose Def(F) is some set I, possibly of indexes. A convenient alternative way of denoting F is the following extension of the family notation:

(1) $F = (F(x):C(x)|x:I)$

This clearly indicates the source $C(x)$ of each $F(x)$, itself a function of x. ■

Example 3.4E.1

In Section 3.5, we introduce n-tuples and n-ary relations and functions, where n:Nat. An n-tuple is in itself a small distributed function normally with domain (index set) $I =_{\text{d}} \{1, 2, \ldots, n\}$. ■

Distributed functions arise in various fields, logic and type theory in particular. See, for instance, Nordström *et al.* (1990).

EXERCISES

3.4.1 Let $U =_{\text{d}} \{1, 2, 3, 4\}$. Tabulate the characteristic functions of the following subsets of U:

(a) $S1 =_{\text{d}} \varnothing$ (b) $S2 =_{\text{d}} U$
(c) $S3 =_{\text{d}} \{2, 4\}$ (d) $S4 =_{\text{d}} \{3\}$
(e) $S5 =_{\text{d}} \{1, 2, 4\}$

3.4.2 Let $U =_{\text{d}} \{\text{a, b, c, d, e, f}\}$, $A =_{\text{d}} \{\text{b, c, d}\}$ and $B =_{\text{d}} \{\text{a, c, d, f}\}$. Tabulate the characteristic functions of the following subsets of U:

(a) A (b) B (c) $U - A$
(d) $U - B$ (e) $A \backslash B$ (*f*) $B \backslash A$
(g) $A \cup B$ (h) $A \cap B$

3.4.3 Let $S =_d \{3, 4, 5\}$ and $T =_d \{3, 5\}$. Tabulate the characteristic functions of the relations $R : S \leftrightarrow T$ whose graphs are set out below:

(a) $\mathrm{Gr}(R1) =_d \{\langle x, y\rangle \mid x = y\}$ (b) $\mathrm{Gr}(R2) =_d \{\langle x, y\rangle \mid x \neq y\}$
(c) $\mathrm{Gr}(R3) =_d \{\langle x, y\rangle \mid x < y\}$ (d) $\mathrm{Gr}(R4) =_d \{\langle x, y\rangle \mid x \geqslant y\}$

Hint: the heading and first two lines for *R1* should be

$\langle x, y\rangle : S \times T$	$\chi(\langle x, y\rangle)$
$\langle 3, 3\rangle$	T
$\langle 3, 5\rangle$	F
...	...

3.4.4 Let U be any set. With each subset S of U, there is a corresponding characteristic function $\chi_S : U \to \mathrm{Bool}$. Show that this correspondence is a bijection $\chi : \mathrm{Pow}(U) \to (U \to \mathrm{Bool})$. (Recall that '$U \to \mathrm{Bool}$' denotes the set of all total functions from U to Bool.)

3.4.5 Attempt to formulate a general law that describes the relationship between each of the set operations $\cup$, $\cap$, $\setminus$ and $-$ on subsets of a given set U, and the corresponding characteristic function as illustrated in Exercise **3**.4.2. For instance: given the characteristic functions of A and $B \subseteq_d U$, what is the characteristic function of $A \cup B$, and so on?

3.4.6 Let $S =_d \{1, 2, 3, 4\}$, $T =_d \{1, 3, 5\}$ and $R : S \leftrightarrow T$ be defined by $x \mathrel{R} y$ iff $x < y$ for all $x : S$ and $y : T$. Tabulate the function $A : S \to \mathrm{Pow}(T)$ equivalent to R – that is, defined by $A(x) =_d \{y : T \mid x \mathrel{R} y\}$ for all $x : S$, as in Section **3**.4B.

3.4.7 Show that for any two sets S and T, the equivalence sending each $R : S \leftrightarrow T$ to the corresponding function $A : S \to \mathrm{Pow}(T)$ as defined in Section **3**.4B is a bijection E. Note: take care to define $\mathrm{Dom}(E)$ and $\mathrm{Cod}(E)$ properly.

3.4.8 Let $I =_d \{n : \mathrm{Nat} \mid 1 \leqslant n \leqslant 10\}$ and let the family $F = (F_i \mid i : I)$ be defined by the following tabulated graph:

i	F_i
1	Madrid
2	Rome
3	Paris
4	Rome
5	Moscow

i	F_i
6	Paris
7	Moscow
8	Rome
9	Bonn
10	Madrid

Represent this family as a bag.

3.4.9 Consider the following bag B, with set S and multiplicity function m given by the table below:

$x:S$	$m(x)$
Arnold	2
Beth	1
Charles	3
Diana	2

Represent this bag by a family $G = (G_i | i:I)$ where $I =_{\mathrm{d}} \{1, 2, \ldots, 8\}$.

3.4.10 Repeat Exercise 3.4.9(a) with a different index set, say $I =_{\mathrm{d}} \{\mathrm{a}, \mathrm{b}, \ldots, \mathrm{h}\}$, and (b) with the original index set $I =_{\mathrm{d}} \{1, 2, \ldots, 8\}$ but associated differently with the members of S. From this exercise, we may conclude that the same bag has many different representations as families. However, all these representations are clearly equivalent. We also say they are *isomorphic*; see Exercise 3.4.17 below.

3.4.11 Let $A =_{\mathrm{d}} \{\mathrm{a}, \mathrm{b}, \mathrm{c}\}$. Enumerate the various partitions of A in the sense of Definition 3.4D.3 (no empty members allowed).

3.4.12 Consider any function $f: S \to V$. Show that f induces a partition $P =_{\mathrm{d}} (P_i | i:I)$ of S with no empty member sets (Definition 3.4D.3), by the rule: any two $x, y:S$ belong to the same subset P_i iff $f(x) = f(y)$. Define P precisely.

3.4.13 Consider the relation $Eq4: \mathrm{Nat} \leftrightarrow \mathrm{Nat}$ defined by

$$x \; Eq4 \; y \text{ iff } (x \text{ MOD } 4) = (y \text{ MOD } 4)$$

for all $x, y:\mathrm{Nat}$. This relation induces a partition $P = (P_i | i:I)$ of Nat with $I =_{\mathrm{d}} \{0, 1, 2, 3\}$ and no empty member sets, such that any two $x, y:\mathrm{Nat}$ are in the same set P_i iff $x \; Eq4 \; y$. Define this partition and enumerate the first six members of each set P_i. Hint: There is a natural way of defining each P_i using the MOD operator.

3.4.14* Devise a method of systematically enumerating the set of partitions of a finite set S without empty members (Definition 3.4D.3). Hint: solve the problem for sets of the form $\{1, 2, \ldots, n\}$ with $n =_{\mathrm{d}} 0, 1, \ldots$. For each $n:\mathrm{Nat}$, derive the partitions of $\{1, \ldots, n, n+1\}$ from those of $\{1, \ldots, n\}$.

3.4.15 Show that a couple $\langle a, b \rangle$ with $a:A$ and $b:B$ may be represented as a distributed total function with domain $I =_{\mathrm{d}} \{1, 2\}$.

3.4.16 Redefine the cartesian product $A \times B$ using the representation of couples of Exercise 3.4.15.

3.4.17* *Isomorphism of families.* Given two families $F = (F_i | i : I)$ and $G = (G_j | j : J)$, we say that F and G are *equivalent* or *isomorphic* iff they satisfy the following condition: there exists a *bijection* $Iso : I \to J$ such that for all $i : I$, $F_i = G(Iso(i))$. This bijection is called an *isomorphism* (of families). We say that *Iso preserves* the values F_i in G.

(a) Show that the two families $F = (F_i | i : I)$ and $G = (G_j | j : J)$ below with $I =_{\mathrm{d}} \{1, 2, \ldots, 6\}$ and $J =_{\mathrm{d}} \{\mathrm{a, b}, \ldots, \mathrm{f}\}$ are isomorphic by constructing an isomorphism $Iso : I \to J$ in tabular form.

$i : I$	F_i
1	A
2	B
3	A
4	C
5	A
6	C

$j : J$	G_j
a	C
b	A
c	A
d	B
e	C
f	A

(b) Give a full formal definition of the condition which two families must satisfy in order to be isomorphic.

3.5 n-ary relations and functions

The humble couple $\langle a, b \rangle$ is the seed of the various constructions described in the previous sections: cartesian product, disjoint union, relations, functions and the various applications we have seen. A couple is an ordered set of exactly two elements. We now generalize this notion to an ordered set of n elements, where n is any positive natural number. This is called an n-tuple. More to the point, the various constructions based on couples are generalized accordingly.

Table 3.5.1 Generalization from couples to n-tuples.

	Couple $\langle a, b \rangle$	n-tuple
Basic object	Couple $\langle a, b \rangle$ *equivalent* to (a_1, a_2)	n-tuple $(a_1, a_2, \ldots, a_n)$
Cartesian product	Standard or *binary* product $A \times B$ or $A_1 \times A_2$	n-ary product $A_1 \times A_2 \times \cdots \times A_n$
Disjoint union	Standard or *binary* disjoint union $A \amalg B$ or $A_1 \amalg A_2$	n-ary disjoint union $A_1 \amalg A_2 \amalg \cdots \amalg A_n$
Relation	Standard or *binary* relation $R \subseteq A_1 \times A_2$	n-ary relation $R \subseteq A_1 \times A_2 \times \cdots \times A_n$
Function	Standard or *unary* function $F : A_1 \leftrightarrow A_2$	n-ary function $F : A_1 \times \cdots \times A_n \leftrightarrow A_{n+1}$

This process of generalization is described by the taxonomy set out in Table 3.5.1.

This section first defines an n-tuple precisely, and the related notions of n-ary cartesian product and disjoint union. Then n-ary relations are described and illustrated. Finally, n-ary functions are described. As we often use strictly positive natural numbers, we denote their set by Pos. Thus, $\text{Pos} =_{\text{d}} \{n:\text{Nat} \mid n > 0\}$.

3.5A n-tuples

A couple $\langle a, b\rangle$ has been informally defined as an ordered pair of elements a and b, and formally established in set-theoretical terms. We now introduce a second formal definition based on the notion of function. This variant directly captures the idea that in a couple $\langle a, b\rangle$, a is *first* and b *second.* Consequently, it generalizes easily to the concept of an n-tuple, where $n \geqslant 1$.

Definition 3.5A.1

A couple (of elements a and b) is a function with graph

$$1 \mapsto a$$
$$2 \mapsto b$$

Defined in this way, a couple is written (a, b). ■

This is a *new* definition of a couple, which is why a new notation is introduced. (a, b) and $\langle a, b\rangle$ are *not equal* but *equivalent*: they are two different representations of the intuitive notion of an ordered pair. We say that (a, b) and $\langle a, b\rangle$ are equivalent because any $\langle a, b\rangle$ may be converted to (a, b) in a unique way and vice versa. The way to perform this conversion is obvious.

Defining n-tuples

We may now proceed to generalize couples to n-tuples. Essentially, an n-tuple is a function a from the index set $I =_{\text{d}} \{1, 2, \ldots, n\}$, where n is a given, fixed positive number. As I is an index set, we may also say that an n-tuple is a family. We write a by enumerating its elements in parentheses, as with families:

$$a = (a_1, a_2, \ldots, a_n)$$

This definition is not complete yet. There remains to specify the set or sets from which the elements a_i must come. As for couples $\langle a, b\rangle$, we stipulate that each element a_i must be a member of a predefined set A_i, for all $i:I$. As these sets A_i may differ, an n-tuple is precisely described as a *distributed function* in the sense of Definition 3.4E.1.

Definition 3.5A.2

Let n be a positive number and $I =_d \{1, 2, \ldots, n\}$ (index set). An n-tuple is a function a from I and is denoted by

(1) $a = (a_1, a_2, \ldots, a_n)$

It is subject to the condition that there are given sets $A_1, A_2, \ldots, A_n$ and for each $i : I$, $a_i \in A_i$. (Thus, a is a distributed function.)

The following alternative family notation is also used:

(2) $a = (a_i | i : I)$

and more specifically

(3) $a = (a_i : A_i | i : I)$

Exceptionally and unless otherwise stated, for the special case $n = 1$, we define a tuple of *one* element b as b itself: $(b) =_d b$. ■

Remark

The definition of a 1-tuple requires an explanation. If we applied the general rule, a 1-tuple would be defined as a function with graph $\{\langle 1, b \rangle\}$ and written (b), where b is any element. Clearly, this function is equivalent to b on its own: given b, $\{\langle 1, b \rangle\}$ is entirely determined and vice versa. Thus, we may define the 1-tuple (b) in either way. The option chosen, to identify (b) with b as a rule, turns out to be quite convenient in practice. ■

3.5B n-ary cartesian product

The n-ary cartesian product follows naturally from the definition of an n-tuple. Recall that, given any two sets A and B, the standard cartesian product $A \times B$ is the set of all couples $\langle a, b \rangle$ such that $a : A$ and $b : B$. By analogy, the n-ary cartesian product is an operation on n sets $A_1, A_2, \ldots, A_n$. It is defined as the set of all n-tuples $a = (a_1, a_2, \ldots, a_n)$, where each element $a_i : A_i$.

Definition 3.5B.1

Let n be a positive number and $I =_d \{1, 2, \ldots, n\}$. Given n sets $A_1, A_2, \ldots, A_n$, the n-ary cartesian product

(1) $A_1 \times A_2 \times \ldots \times A_n$

is the set of all *n*-tuples $a = (a_1, a_2, \ldots, a_n)$ such that for all $i:I$, $a_i:\mathrm{A}_i$. The number *n* is called the *arity* of (1). This product is also denoted by

(2) $\Pi(A_i | i:I)$

or

(3) $\Pi_{i:I}\, A_i$ ■

Example 3.5B.1

Consider again Example 3.1B.3, in which a date was defined as a couple $\langle\langle day, month\rangle, year\rangle$, where $\langle day, month\rangle$: Days × Months, *year*: Years and

$$\begin{aligned}&\text{Days} =_{\mathrm{d}} \{day:\text{Nat} \mid 1 \leqslant day \leqslant 31\}\\&\text{Months} =_{\mathrm{d}} \{\text{January, February}, \ldots, \text{December}\}\\&\text{Years} =_{\mathrm{d}} \{year:\text{Nat} \mid 1900 \leqslant year \leqslant 1999\}\end{aligned}$$

Thus, a date in this sense is a variable

$$date:(\text{Days} \times \text{Months}) \times \text{Years}$$

This description is somewhat artificial: there is no *a priori* reason for grouping *day* and *month* before combining these elements with *year* in *date*. Therefore, a more natural definition of a date is that it is a 3-tuple (or *triple*) *date* = (*day*, *month*, *year*) where *day*: Days, *month*: Months and *year*: Years. This is the same as writing

$$date:\text{Days} \times \text{Months} \times \text{Years}$$

where Days × Months × Years = Π(Days, Months, Years) =

$$\{(1, \text{January}, 1900), (2, \text{January}, 1900), \ldots, (31, \text{December}, 1999)\}$$ ■

Remarks

1 There is a slight ambiguity in the notation (1) of Definition 3.5B.1, in the case $n = 2$. '$A_1 \times A_2$' means both the set of couples $\langle a_1, a_2\rangle$, and the set of couples (a_1, a_2), where $a_1:\mathrm{A}_1$ and $a_2:\mathrm{A}_2$. These are equivalent but not identical, as already pointed out. We shall just live with this little ambiguity. If necessary, we may always specify which type of couple is meant in a given context.

2 What is a 1-ary or *unary* cartesian product? We can see that by Definition 3.5B.1 with $n = 1$, it is the set of all 1-tuples (b) such that $b:A$ for some set A. By the same definition, this set of 1-tuples (b) is simply denoted by A. We can now reap a first small benefit from our specification of a 1-tuple (b) in Definition 3.5A.2, namely $(b) =_{\mathrm{d}} b$: no ambiguity is caused by the fact that

'A' denotes both a certain set and the corresponding unary product, as these two objects are equal by our definition of a 1-tuple. If (b) had been defined as the function with graph $\{\langle 1, \mathrm{b}\rangle\}$, then A would be slightly ambiguous.

3 In the cartesian product $\Pi(A_i \mid i \in I)$, the n sets $A_1, A_2, \ldots, A_n$ themselves form a family, namely $(A_i \mid i \in I)$ precisely. It is an n-tuple (of sets) in its own right.

4 Henceforth, we use the terms 'tuple' to mean any n-tuple and 'general cartesian product' to mean any n-ary product, where n is any number. A 2-ary product is also called *binary*, and a 1-ary product *unary*. ■

Using any index set I

In our definition of tuples and general cartesian products, we have used as domain I an index set $\{1, 2, \ldots, n\}$. In fact, there is no absolute necessity to use this type of set – any set I with the appropriate cardinality will do in most applications.

Indeed, an alternative frequently used in practice is to use a set of meaningful names. Examples will be given later. The point is that in all the definitions above we may substitute any non-empty set I for $\{1, 2, \ldots, n\}$ without essentially altering the concepts described.

n-ary cartesian product of identical sets

In order to denote the cartesian product of n *identical* sets $A_1, A_2, \ldots, A_n$, we generally use a simpler notation. If these sets are all equal to the set A, then their product is denoted by A^n.

Definition 3.5B.2

The cartesian product $A \times A \times \ldots \times A$, where A occurs n times, is written A^n. Thus,

$$A^n =_{\mathrm{d}} A \times A \times \ldots \times A$$ ■

3.5C n-ary disjoint union

The generalization of the disjoint union $A \sqcup B$ is immediate. Given n sets $A_1, A_2, \ldots, A_n$ where n:Pos, the disjoint union $A_1 \sqcup A_2 \sqcup \ldots \sqcup A_n$ is the set obtained as in the binary case. First, for each set A_i, replace each element $a_i \in A_i$ by its tagged version $\langle i, a_i\rangle$. Then take the union of these new sets. In this definition, n is the *arity* of the disjoint union.

Definition 3.5C.1

Let n:Pos and $I =_{\mathrm{d}} \{1, 2, \ldots, n\}$. Given n sets $A_1, A_2, \ldots, A_n$, the n-ary disjoint union

(1) $A_1 \sqcup A_2 \sqcup \ldots \sqcup A_n$

also written

(2) $\amalg(A_i | i : I)$

is the set defined by

$$\amalg(A_i | i : I) =_{\mathrm{d}} \Sigma(\{i\} \times A_i | i : I)$$

where for any $i : I$,

$$\{i\} \times A_i = \{\langle i, a_i \rangle | a_i : A_i\}$$

An alternative notation for $\amalg(A_i | i : I)$ is

(3) $\amalg_{i:I} A_i$

If all the sets A_i are equal to A, their disjoint union $A \amalg A \amalg \ldots \amalg A$ is written as

$$n \times A$$

■

Recall that in Definition 3.5C.1, Σ is the union of *disjoint sets*. The various sets ($\{i\} \times A_i$) are indeed pairwise disjoint. Henceforth, we use the term 'general disjoint union' to mean any n-ary disjoint union, where n is any number. The remarks of Section 3.1C on the binary disjoint union extend to the general case.

As for the general cartesian product, there is no necessity to use $I = \{1, 2, \ldots, n\}$ as the index set in a disjoint union. Any set of appropriate cardinality, for example any set of names, will do.

3.5D n-ary relations

A standard or binary relation has been defined as follows in Section 3.2A. By Definitions 3.2A.1 and 3.2A.2, a relation R is intuitively a property of couples, and formally an object with one feature, namely the graph $\mathrm{Gr}(R)$. This feature is a set of couples $\langle x, y \rangle$. By Definition 3.2A.3, a relation is an object R with three features: a domain $\mathrm{Dom}(R)$, a codomain $\mathrm{Cod}(R)$ and a graph $\mathrm{Gr}(R)$, where $\mathrm{Gr}(R)$ is a subset of $\mathrm{Dom}(R) \times \mathrm{Cod}(R)$.

We define an n-ary relation R by generalizing these definitions in the obvious way. In the first sense, an n-ary relation R is intuitively a property of certain n-tuples $(a_1, a_2, \ldots, a_n)$. In the second sense, it is an object with one feature, its graph $\mathrm{Gr}(R)$. This is defined as a set of n-tuples $(a_1, a_2, \ldots, a_n)$. In the third sense, an n-ary relation R is an object with the following features: first, a family of n sets called domains of R, and second, a subset of the n-ary cartesian product of these sets, the graph of R. The following definitions correspond to Definitions **3**.2A.1, **3**.2A.2 and **3**.2A.3, respectively.

Definition 3.5D.1 (informal)

Let n: Pos and $I =_{\mathrm{d}} \{1, 2, \ldots, n\}$. Intuitively, an n-ary *relation* R is a property which is true for some n-tuples $(a_1, a_2, \ldots, a_n)$ and false for all other n-tuples. We write

$$R(a_1, a_2, \ldots, a_n)$$

to state that R is true for $(a_1, a_2, \ldots, a_n)$. ■

Definition 3.5D.2

Let n: Pos and $I =_{\mathrm{d}} \{1, 2, \ldots, n\}$. Formally, an n-ary *relation* is an object R with one feature, the *graph* Gr(R). This feature is a *set of n-tuples*.

This definition is linked to Definition **3**.5D.1 as follows. If R is a relation in the first sense and $\{(a_1, a_2, \ldots, a_n) \mid R(a_1, a_2, \ldots, a_n)\}$ is a set, then formally R is the relation such that

$$\mathrm{Gr}(R) =_{\mathrm{d}} \{(a_1, a_2, \ldots, a_n) \mid R(a_1, a_2, \ldots, a_n)\}$$ ■

Definition 3.5D.3

Let n: Pos and $I =_{\mathrm{d}} \{1, 2, \ldots, n\}$. An n-ary *relation* is an object R with the following features:

(1) A family of sets

$$(\mathrm{Dom}_i(R) \mid i : I)$$

(2) A subset

$$\mathrm{Gr}(R) \subseteq_{\mathrm{d}} \mathrm{Dom}_1(R) \times \mathrm{Dom}_2(R) \times \ldots \times \mathrm{Dom}_n(R)$$

Each set $\mathrm{Dom}_i(R)$ is called the ith domain of R, and Gr(R) is called the graph of R. ■

In these definitions, n is the *arity* of the relation. In the sequel, an 'n-ary relation' is understood in the sense of Definition **3**.5D.3, unless otherwise stated. A general relation means any n-ary relation, with n unspecified.

Unary relations

What is a 1-ary, or unary relation? From Definition **3**.5D.3, it is a relation R whose graph is a subset of a unary cartesian product. As we have seen in the remark following Example 3.5B.1, the unary product of a set A is just A itself. Consequently, Gr(R) is just *a subset of a given set A*. Typically, it is a subset of members of A satisfying some specified property.

3.5E Examples of n-ary relations

General relations are central in several areas of computing and mathematics. In database theory for instance, one of the most popular forms of data organization is the *relational model.* In this model, data is represented as a collection of finite n-ary relations of various arities. The available operations on these relations are directly derived from the set-theoretical functions we have described so far: union, intersection, cartesian product, taking a subset satisfying a certain property, and so on. The reason for the popularity of the relational model in practice appears to be its flexibility combined with its high descriptive power.

In logic, too, n-ary relations play a central role, more precisely in the specification of the semantics of well-formed formulas. In general, predicates are interpreted as n-ary relations on a predefined set U (for 'universe'), and functions as n-ary functions on U. As n-ary functions are special cases of $(n + 1)$-ary relations, we can say that ultimately, 'everything' is described as a general relation.

In this section, several examples of n-ary relations are given.

Example 3.5E.1 Dates

The 3-ary or ternary cartesian product

$$\text{Dates} =_{\text{d}} \text{Days} \times \text{Months} \times \text{Years}$$

presented in Example 3.5B.1 contains some invalid dates – for example, (30, February, 1900). If we eliminate these invalid dates, we obtain a subset of Dates. This is the graph of a ternary relation, say DatesValid:

$$\text{Gr(DatesValid)} \subseteq_{\text{d}} \text{Dates}$$ ■

Example 3.5E.2 Personnel records

Consider again Example 3.3B.3. In practice, the various details of employees kept by an organization are typically recorded as a set of n-tuples. This is a finite n-ary relation R. In such an application, it is natural to refer to each domain of R by a meaningful name rather than a number.

Here is a concrete example. The index set I consists of a set of identifiers

$$I =_{\text{d}} \{\text{Name, Sex, MaritalStatus, Birthday, Salary}\}$$

For each of these identifiers, there is an associated domain or set of *possible* values. For instance

$$\text{Dom}_{\text{Name}}(R) =_{\text{d}} \text{Names} =_{\text{d}} \{\text{Adam, Andrews, \ldots, Zaleski}\}$$
$$\text{Dom}_{\text{Sex}}(R) =_{\text{d}} \text{Sexes} =_{\text{d}} \{\text{Male, Female}\}$$
$$\text{Dom}_{\text{Marital Status}}(R) =_{\text{d}} \text{MarStats} =_{\text{d}} \{\text{Single, Married, Divorced}\}$$
$$\text{Dom}_{\text{Birthday}}(R) =_{\text{d}} \text{Dates} =_{\text{d}} \text{Days} \times \text{Months} \times \text{Years}$$
$$\text{Dom}_{\text{Salary}}(R) =_{\text{d}} \text{Salaries} =_{\text{d}} \{n : \pounds\text{Nat} \mid \pounds 5{,}000 \leqslant n \leqslant \pounds 45{,}000\}$$

The graph Gr(R) is a finite subset of

$$\text{Names} \times \text{Sexes} \times \text{MarStats} \times \text{Dates} \times \text{Salaries}$$

that is, it is a finite set of 5-tuples such as

(Adam, Male, Married, (3, April, 1962), £19,000)

one per employee. In computing, such tuples are usually called *records*. As with binary relations, the graph of a finite n-ary relation R is commonly represented by a table, in which each column corresponds to one of the domains $\text{Dom}_i(R)$ and each row is one of the tuples that are members of Gr(R). Typically each column is headed with the identifier of the corresponding domain. Table **3**.5E.1 shows an example.

■

Table 3.5E.1 Graph of a relation of employee details.

Name	*Sex*	*Marital Status*	*Birthday*	*Salary*
Adam	Male	Married	(3, April, 1962)	£19,000
Charles	Female	Single	(15, June, 1965)	£19,000
North	Male	Divorced	(7, October, 1958)	£21,500
Smith	Female	Married	(23, May, 1960)	£20,000

Example 3.5E.3 Numeric relation

The following ternary (3-ary) relation R is the set of triples (x, y, z): Nat^3 satisfying the following conditions:

(1) $1 \leqslant x \leqslant 2$

(2) $1 \leqslant y$

(3) $x + y + z = 5$

The graph Gr(*R*) is defined by the abstraction

$$\text{Gr}(R) =_{\text{d}} \{(x, y, z) : \text{Nat}^3 \mid 1 \leqslant x \leqslant 2 \wedge 1 \leqslant y \wedge x + y + z = 5\}$$

It is given by the following table:

x	y	z
1	1	3
1	2	2
1	3	1
1	4	0
2	1	2
2	2	1
2	3	0

■

Example 3.5E.4 League table

A small company has decided to organize a charitable marathon in which its employees are invited to take part. Each participant undertakes to run from his or her house to the company's offices. Any sponsor of a participant promises to make a cash donation based on (a) the participant's age and (b) the distance run by the participant.

The participants are classed into two leagues: *Red*, for the physically fit, and *Green* for the others. Each league is partitioned into three age groups, and for each age group there is a corresponding distance range which a person must run to be in this league.

The various groups making up the two leagues may be described by one relation *M* for *Marathon*, whose graph is tabulated in *summary form* in Table 3.5E.2.

Table 3.5E.2 Graph of marathon relation (summary form).

League	*Age range* $a : Age$	*Distance range* $d : Distance$
Red	$20 < a \leqslant 30$	$16 < d \leqslant 20$
Red	$30 < a \leqslant 45$	$12 < d \leqslant 16$
Red	$45 < a \leqslant 65$	$8 < d \leqslant 12$
Green	$20 < a \leqslant 30$	$9 < d \leqslant 12$
Green	$30 < a \leqslant 45$	$6 < d \leqslant 9$
Green	$45 < a \leqslant 65$	$3 < d \leqslant 6$

In Table 3.5E.2, we take the two sets Age and Distance as given – they can be defined as Nat, for instance. This table differs somewhat from previous examples in that it does not describe M directly. Each row represents a triple (L, A, D) where L:{Red, Green}, A is an age *interval*, that is, a certain *subset* of Age, and D a distance *interval*. Thus, what Table 3.5E.2 directly represents is a relation M' which 'summarizes' M. It is the relation whose graph $\mathrm{Gr}(M')$ consists of six members: the six triples (L, A, D) just described.

In turn, M' represents the main relation M whose graph $\mathrm{Gr}(M)$ is as follows. Each member in it is a triple (l, a, d), where for some (L, A, D): $\mathrm{Gr}(M')$,

$$l =_{\mathrm{d}} L,\ a : A \text{ and } d : D$$

For instance, $(\text{Red}, 25, 17) \in \mathrm{Gr}(M)$ because it is a member of the group described by the first row (L, A, D) of $\mathrm{Gr}(M')$.

To sum up, Table 3.5E.2 is an enumeration of the members of $\mathrm{Gr}(M')$. In turn, each member (L, A, D): $\mathrm{Gr}(M')$ describes (by abstraction) a certain *subset* of $\mathrm{Gr}(M)$. ■

3.5F n-ary functions

Recall that a function is a rule which associates with any element a at most one object, written $F(a)$. Essentially, an n-ary function is such that the objects a to which a value $F(a)$ is assigned are n-tuples $(a_1, a_2, \ldots, a_n)$. In other words, an n-ary function is a rule which sends n-tuples $(a_1, a_2, \ldots, a_n)$ to corresponding values $F(a_1, a_2, \ldots, a_n)$. There are essentially two ways of formalizing this description. We present these two approaches in turn.

Definition 3.5F.1

Let n be any positive number. An n-ary function is a (possibly partial) function F whose domain $\mathrm{Dom}(F)$ is an n-ary cartesian product. It is introduced by

$$F: A_1 \times A_2 \times \ldots \times A_n \nrightarrow A_{n+1}$$

where $A_1, A_2, \ldots, A_{n+1}$ are given sets. Thus in this definition, $\mathrm{Dom}(F) = A_1 \times A_2 \times \ldots \times A_n$ and $\mathrm{Cod}(F) = A_{n+1}$. ■

This definition is conceptually simple, directly based as it is on the original notion of a function. The second variant describes an n-ary function as a special case of $(n + 1)$-ary relation. The advantage of this alternative is that all the theory of $(n + 1)$-ary relations immediately applies to n-ary functions, a significant advantage. This is why we make it our 'official' definition.

A standard (unary) function has been formally defined in Section 3.3 as a special (binary) relation F such that for any x there is *at most one* y with $\langle x, y\rangle \in \mathrm{Gr}(F)$. The second definition is a generalization of this idea.

Definition 3.5F.2

An n-ary function F is a special type of $(n + 1)$-ary relation where $n \geqslant 0$. It is such that

> for any n-tuple $(a_1, a_2, \ldots, a_n)$, there is at most one element b with $(a_1, a_2, \ldots, a_n, b) \in \mathrm{Gr}(F)$.

The set of n-tuples $(a_1, a_2, \ldots, a_n)$ such that there exists an element b with $(a_1, a_2, \ldots a_n, b) \in \mathrm{Gr}(F)$ is the *definition domain of* F and is denoted by $\mathrm{Def}(F)$. For any $(a_1, \ldots, a_n) : \mathrm{Def}(F)$, the unique element b such that $(a_1, \ldots, a_n, b) \in \mathrm{Gr}(F)$ is written $F(a_1, \ldots, a_n)$. The elements a_i are the *arguments* of F, and b the *result* (of applying F to $(a_1, \ldots, a_n)$). ■

Definition 3.5F.2 is as simple as possible. It automatically yields two types of n-ary function F, depending on which kind of relation it qualifies. The first type has only one feature, namely the graph $\mathrm{Gr}(F)$. The second has two features: a family $(\mathrm{Dom}_i(F) \mid i : I)$ of domains, where $I =_{\mathrm{d}} \{1, \ldots, n+1\}$ and a graph $\mathrm{Gr}(F) \subseteq_{\mathrm{d}} \Pi(\mathrm{Dom}_i(F) \mid i : I)$. Clearly Definitions 3.5F.1 and 3.5F.2 are equivalent. For the reason given, an n-ary function F is understood in the sense of Definition 3.5F.2 unless otherwise stated.

Notation

An n-ary function F has *two* arities. As a relation, F has arity $n+1$, but as a function, F has arity n. Whenever necessary, we call the former *relation arity* and the latter *function arity* of F. A function F with specified domains $A_1, \ldots, A_n, A_{n+1}$ is introduced by

$$F : A_1 \times A_2 \times \ldots \times A_n \nrightarrow A_{n+1}$$

as in Definition 3.5F.1. This states that F is a relation with $\mathrm{Dom}_i(F) =_{\mathrm{d}} A_i$ for all $i =_{\mathrm{d}} 1, 2, \ldots, n + 1$. As in Section 3.3A, we represent the association of a tuple $(a_1, \ldots, a_n)$ with $F(a_1, \ldots, a_n)$, if it is defined, by

$$(a_1, \ldots, a_n) \mapsto F(a_1, \ldots, a_n)$$

■

Example 3.5F.1

Consider the following binary function F. The graph $\mathrm{Gr}(F)$ is defined as a subset of $A_1 \times A_2 \times A_3$ where $A_1 =_{\mathrm{d}} A_2 =_{\mathrm{d}} \{1, 2, 3\}$ and $A_3 =_{\mathrm{d}} \{1, 2, 3, 4\}$. It is given by

$$\begin{aligned} \mathrm{Gr}(F) =_{\mathrm{d}} \{ \ &(1, \ 1, \ 2), \\ &(1, \ 2, \ 3), \\ &(1, \ 3, \ 4), \\ &(2, \ 1, \ 3), \\ &(2, \ 2, \ 4), \\ &(3, \ 1, \ 4) \ \} \end{aligned}$$

No couple $(a_1, a_2): A_1 \times A_2$ occurs in more than one triple (a_1, a_2, a_3): Gr(F). This confirms that F is a binary or 2-ary function. It is a *partial* function, as some couples $(a_1, a_2): A_1 \times A_2$ are absent from Gr(F), namely (2, 3), (3, 2) and (3, 3). The alert reader will have noticed that for each (a_1, a_2) for which $a_3 =_d F(a_1, a_2)$ is defined, $a_3 = a_1 + a_2$. F is the addition operation *restricted* to $A_1 \times A_2 \times A_3$. (Function restrictions are covered in Section **3**.6C.) ■

Derived features

An n-ary function F has derived or implied features analogous to those of simple functions. We have already introduced the definition domain Def(F) above, which is determined by Gr(F). Formally:

$$\text{Def}(F) =_d \{(a_1, \ldots, a_n) \mid \exists\, b \cdot (a_1, \ldots, a_n, b) \in \text{Gr}(F)\}$$

The dual feature is the range of F, written Ran(F). This is defined as the set of elements b such that there is a tuple $(a_1, \ldots, a_n, b) \in \text{Gr}(F)$:

$$\text{Ran}(F) =_d \{b \mid \exists\,(a_1, \ldots, a_n) \cdot (a_1, \ldots, a_n, b) \in \text{Gr}(F)\}$$

Also if $(\text{Dom}_i(F) \mid i{:}I)$ is defined, where $I =_d \{1, \ldots, n+1\}$, then we let $\text{Dom}(F) =_d \text{Dom}_1(F) \times \ldots \times \text{Dom}_n(F)$ and $\text{Cod}(F) =_d \text{Dom}_{n+1}(F)$. Thus if Dom($F$) is defined then $\text{Def}(F) \subseteq \text{Dom}(F)$ and if Cod(F) is defined, $\text{Ran}(F) \subseteq \text{Cod}(F)$.

Special functions

The remaining definition is a generalization of Definition **3**.3C.1.

Definition 3.5F.3

Let F be any n-ary function with $n \geqslant 1$.

(1) F is *injective* or an *injection* iff for any $b \in \text{Ran}(F)$ there is exactly one tuple $(a_1, \ldots, a_n)$ such that $(a_1, \ldots, a_n, b) \in \text{Gr}(F)$.

(2) If Dom(F) is defined, then F is *total* iff Def(F) = Dom(F); otherwise, F is *partial.* A total function F is introduced by writing

$$F: A_1 \times A_2 \times \ldots \times A_n \to A_{n+1}$$

(3) If Cod(F) is defined then F is *surjective* or a *surjection* iff Ran(F) = Cod(F).

(4) F is bijective or a *bijection* iff it is total, injective and surjective. ■

3.5G Examples of n-ary functions

Example 3.5G.1 ***Arithmetic operations on Nat***

Addition, subtraction, multiplication and division on the set Nat of natural numbers are all examples of binary functions Nat × Nat → Nat. Addition and multiplication are total. Subtraction and division are *partial functions* on Nat. $m - n$ is defined iff $m \geqslant n$, and division by 0 is not defined. In particular addition on Nat is a function

(1) $\quad + : \text{Nat}^2 \to \text{Nat}$

Indeed, when we add two numbers x and y:Nat, we associate the result $x + y$:Nat with the couple $(x, y) \in \text{Nat} \times \text{Nat}$. For example, addition sends the couple (3, 5) to $3 + 5 = 8$. The traditional notation for the result is *infix*: the function symbol '+' is placed between its arguments x and y. We could write $+(x, y)$ instead, for example $+(3, 5) = 8$. The graph Gr(+) is defined by the abstraction

$$\text{Gr}(+) =_{\text{d}} \{(x, y, z) : \text{Nat}^3 \mid z = x + y\}$$

A partial enumeration of Gr(+) is as follows:

$$\begin{aligned}\text{Gr}(+) = \{\; &(0,\ 0,\ 0),\\ &(0,\ 1,\ 1),\\ &(1,\ 0,\ 1),\\ &(1,\ 1,\ 2),\\ &(0,\ 2,\ 2),\\ &\ldots \qquad \}\end{aligned}$$

Other arithmetic operations may be described in a similar way. ■

Example 3.5G.2 ***Logical connectives***

Let P and Q be two propositions. Thus, P may take the truth value true (T) or false (F), and likewise for Q. We may combine these two propositions into a new one, for instance $P \wedge Q$. This compound proposition has a truth value determined by the truth value of its components P and Q, according to the relevant table of Section **2**.4C, reproduced here.

P	Q	$P \wedge Q$
T	T	T
T	F	F
F	T	F
F	F	F

This is the graph of a binary function which we call AND and use in Part **3**. It is a total function

$$\text{AND}: \text{Bool} \times \text{Bool} \to \text{Bool}$$

where $\text{Bool} = \{\text{true}, \text{false}\}$. AND sends each couple $(x, y): \text{Bool} \times \text{Bool}$ to a third value $\text{AND}(x, y): \text{Bool}$ as indicated in the above table. For instance, $\text{AND}(\text{T}, \text{T}) = \text{T}$. Note that the *function* AND must not be confused with the logical connective 'and' alias '$\wedge$', which is just a *symbol*. The former represents the meaning of the latter. The meaning of the other logical connective symbols may be described in the same way. ■

Example 3.5G.3 Timetables

Timetables are often more general than illustrated in Example **3**.3B.4.

(1) For instance, a school timetable T for a given class assigns an activity to each period of the week. This can be described as a *binary* function sending couples (*day*, *time*) to activities, say lectures. The members of the graph $\text{Gr}(T)$ are triples (*day*, *time*, *lecture*); for example:

(Monday, 09.10–10.00, Physics)

(Recall that '09.10–10.00' is just a name for a period, that is, a single element. Alternatively, it may be regarded as a couple in its own right.) A partial enumeration of the graph $\text{Gr}(T)$ in tabular form is as in Table **3**.5G.1.

(2) There is one such timetable for each class. Therefore, the totality of the timetables for the whole school may be described globally as a ternary function T' that sends triples (*class*, *day*, *time*) to lectures. The members of $\text{Gr}(T')$ are 4-tuples (*class*, *day*, *time*, *lecture*); for example:

(Class 1, Monday, 09.10–10.00, Physics)

The graph $\text{Gr}(T')$ is very similar to $\text{Gr}(T)$. ■

Table 3.5G.1 Partial enumeration of the graph of a school timetable.

Day	*Time*	*Lecture*
Monday	09.10–10.00	Physics
Monday	10.10–11.00	Mathematics
Monday	11.10–12.00	Chemistry
Tuesday	09.10–10.00	English
Tuesday	10.10–11.00	Philosophy
Tuesday	11.10–12.00	French

Example 3.5G.4 Forming work teams

Delegates from three nations A, B and C are to be grouped into work teams. Each team must consist of three persons, one from each nation. Each nation speaks its own language, different from the other two. The languages are also referred to by A, B and C. The members of each team must speak a common language if possible. The set of nations is named N:

$$N =_{\mathrm{d}} \{A, B, C\}$$

This also denotes the set of the nations' languages.

Each nation is represented by four delegates. Any delegate is referred to as (n, i), where $n : N$ and $i : I =_{\mathrm{d}} \{1, 2, 3, 4\}$. Thus, delegate (n, i) is the ith representative of nation n, and the total set *Dels* of delegates is the cartesian product

$$Dels =_{\mathrm{d}} N \times I$$

The set of languages spoken by each delegate is known. It is a total function *Sp* from *Dels* to *subsets* of N, that is, to Pow(N):

$$Sp : Dels \rightarrow \mathrm{Pow}(N)$$

As *Dels* is a binary cartesian product, *Sp* is a binary function. The graph Gr(*Sp*) is given in Table 3.5G.2.

From the function *Sp*, we may determine the common language(s) of each possible three-delegate team. The delegates from nation A form the set

$$\{(A, i) \mid i : I\}$$

Table 3.5G.2 The graph Gr(*Sp*).

Delegate		*Languages spoken*
$n \in N$	$i \in I$	$Sp(n, i)$
A	1	$\{A, B\}$
A	2	$\{A\}$
A	3	$\{A, C\}$
A	4	$\{A, B, C\}$
B	1	$\{A, B\}$
B	2	$\{B\}$
B	3	$\{B\}$
B	4	$\{B, C\}$
C	1	$\{A, C\}$
C	2	$\{B, C\}$
C	3	$\{C\}$
C	4	$\{A, B, C\}$

where $I =_d \{1, 2, 3, 4\}$, and similarly for nations B and C. Consequently, a team is a triple (of couples!)

$$((A, i), (B, j), (C, k))$$

where i, j and $k:I$. The set of all possible work teams is the cartesian product

$$Teams =_d \{(A, i) \mid i:I\} \times \{(B, j) \mid j:I\} \times \{(C, k) \mid k:I\}$$

There are $4^3 = 64$ different possible teams.

For each team, the set of common languages spoken by its members is well defined. For instance, for $((A, 1), (B, 1), (C, 1))$, this is

$$\begin{aligned} & Sp(A, 1) \cap Sp(B, 1) \cap Sp(C, 1) \\ = & \{A, B\} \cap \{A, B\} \cap \{A, C\} \\ = & \{A\} \end{aligned}$$

We denote by $Com((A, i), (B, j), (C, k))$ the set of common languages spoken by any team $((A, i), (B, j), (C, k))$. This set is a subset of $N = \{A, B, C\}$. Therefore, Com is a total function

$$Com: Teams \rightarrow \text{Pow}(N)$$

It is a *ternary* function and the members of Gr(Com) are 4-tuples. Seven of these members are given in Table 3.5G.3. These have been listed in a systematic order, but recall that as Gr(Com) is a *set*, this order is not essential. We leave the general definition of Com as an exercise.

From this table, we may (perhaps) select four teams whose sets of common languages are nonempty. Of course, the selected teams must be pairwise disjoint. ■

Table 3.5G.3 Initial and final members of Gr(Com).

(A, i)	(B, j)	(C, k)	$Com((A, i), (B, j), (C, k))$
$(A, 1)$	$(B, 1)$	$(C, 1)$	$\{A\}$
$(A, 1)$	$(B, 1)$	$(C, 2)$	$\{B\}$
$(A, 1)$	$(B, 1)$	$(C, 3)$	$\varnothing$
$(A, 1)$	$(B, 1)$	$(C, 4)$	$\{A, B\}$
$(A, 1)$	$(B, 2)$	$(C, 1)$	$\varnothing$
...			
$(A, 4)$	$(B, 4)$	$(C, 3)$	$\{C\}$
$(A, 4)$	$(B, 4)$	$(C, 4)$	$\{B, C\}$

3.5H Nullary functions and n-ary operations

Nullary functions

An n-ary function F has been defined for any $n \geqslant 0$. We now discuss the special case where $n = 0$. In this case, F is a *nullary function*. The question is: what exactly is a nullary function?

Consider any n-ary function F, where n is any number $n \geqslant 0$. The graph $\mathrm{Gr}(F)$ is a set of $(n+1)$-tuples

(1) $(a_1, a_2, \ldots a_n, b)$

As F is a *function*, if all the predecessors $a_1, a_2, \ldots, a_n$ of b in (1) are *fixed*, then so is b and, consequently, the whole of (1). In other words, the only way to vary (1) over $\mathrm{Gr}(F)$ is to vary at least one of the predecessors $a_1, a_2, \ldots, a_n$ of b. Now in the case where $n = 0$, any member of $\mathrm{Gr}(F)$ must be a 1-tuple

(1′) (b)

– that is, b has *no* predecessors in (1′). Consequently (b) *cannot vary* in $\mathrm{Gr}(F)$, as the only way (1′) could be made to vary is by varying some predecessors of b. We conclude:

Property 3.5H.1

A *nullary function* F is a function whose graph $\mathrm{Gr}(F)$ is a set with at most one member, which is a 1-tuple $(b) = b$:

$$\mathrm{Gr}(F) = \{b\} \quad \text{or} \quad \mathrm{Gr}(F) = \varnothing$$

Consequently, F is equivalent to a *constant*: the element b of the unique 1-tuple $(b) = b : \mathrm{Gr}(F)$, if b exists.

Conversely, any element b is equivalent to a nullary function with graph equal to $\{b\}$. ∎

For any n-ary function F with $n \geqslant 0$, the element b associated with any n-tuple $(a_1, a_2, \ldots, a_n)$ is denoted by $F(a_1, a_2, \ldots a_n)$. When $n = 0$, this becomes $F() = b$ or simply $F = b$. This again confirms that in the nullary case, F is just a constant. Furthermore, if a codomain $\mathrm{Cod}(F)$ is defined then F is a constant member of $\mathrm{Cod}(F)$, that is, $F \in \mathrm{Cod}(F)$. For the record:

Notation

Let F be a nullary function. Then unless otherwise stated, the symbol 'F' is used to denote both the function as a whole and the unique element $b : \mathrm{Gr}(F)$. ∎

n-ary operations

The term 'operation' is often used instead of 'function'. In the broad sense, '(*n*-ary) operation' is synonymous with '(*n*-ary) function'. In a stricter sense, an *n*-ary operation is a function

$$F: A_1 \times A_2 \times \ldots \times A_n \leftrightarrow A_{n+1}$$

in which all the sets A_i are identical. In other words it is a function

$$F: A^n \leftrightarrow A$$

We use the term in the broader sense.

3.5I n-ary class relations and functions AT

As we have done for standard (that is, binary) relations, we generalize set-theoretical *n*-ary relations to *class* relations. We do this as usual by allowing the operands A_i of a cartesian product $A_1 \times A_2 \times \ldots \times A_n$ to be sets or proper classes. This generalization naturally covers the special case of *n*-ary functions.

Example 3.5I.1 Set-theoretic operations
The three set operations of union, intersection and relative complement are binary class operations Set × Set → Set, where Set is the proper class of all sets. For instance, union is a function which sends *any* couple (A, B) of sets to a third set, $A \cup B$:

$$(A, B) \mapsto A \cup B.$$

Some elements of the graph Gr(∪) are

({1, 2}, {2, 3, 4}, {1, 2, 3, 4})
({a, 5, 'rr'}, {a, 6, 'bb', 'rr'}, {a, 5, 6, 'bb', 'rr'})
({*n*:Nat | *n* is even}, {*n*:Nat | *n* is odd}, Nat)

Other set operations are similarly *n*-ary class functions. ■

EXERCISES

3.5.1 Let $A =_d \{a, b\}$, $B =_d \{1, 2, 3\}$ and $C =_d \{v, w\}$. Enumerate the cartesian products $S =_d A \times B \times C$ and $T =_d C \times A \times B$.

3.5.2 A training centre runs various short courses. It employs 20 teachers and owns 8 classrooms, 10 overhead projectors and 4 video recorders. (a) Describe the set of all possible combinations of these resources as a 4-ary cartesian product. (b) Calculate the cardinality of this product.

3.5.3 For any sets A, B and C, let S and T be defined as in Exercise 3.5.1. (a) Construct a natural bijection $F : S \to T$, and prove that F is indeed bijective. (b) Enumerate five members of the graph $\mathrm{Gr}(F)$ for the specific sets A, B, C of Exercise 3.5.1.

3.5.4 A company makes payments of four types: salaries, pensions, fees and expenses. Each type of payment must be within a certain range, and the four ranges partly overlap. Describe the set of all possible payments such that the type of each payment may be determined. Hint: express this set as a disjoint union of four sets and use meaningful tags.

3.5.5 Let $A =_{\mathrm{d}} \{1, 2, 3\}$, $B =_{\mathrm{d}} \{2, 4\}$ and $C =_{\mathrm{d}} \{1, 4\}$. Enumerate the graphs of the relations $R1$ and $R2$ defined by

$$\mathrm{Gr}(R1) =_{\mathrm{d}} \{(x, y, z) : A \times B \times C \mid x + y - z = 2\}$$
$$\mathrm{Gr}(R2) =_{\mathrm{d}} \{(x, y, z) : A \times B \times C \mid x + y - z = 3\}$$

3.5.6 (a) There is a simple relationship between the relations $R1$ and $R2$ defined in Exercise 3.5.5. What is it? (b) How does this relationship generalize to the set of all relations R such that

$$\mathrm{Gr}(R) =_{\mathrm{d}} \{(x, y, z) : A \times B \times C \mid x + y - z = n\}$$

where n is any natural number? (c) Describe this general relationship as a partition of $A \times B \times C$ with no empty sets.

3.5.7 Describe the set of all possible results of a throw of two *distinct* six-face dice as a cartesian product. Assume the six faces are numbered 1 to 6. Also assume one die is white and the other black, to emphasize their distinction. Repeat with three such *distinct* dice. In each case, give the cardinality of the cartesian product.

3.5.8 (a) Consider the set of all possible results of a throw of three *distinct* six-face dice satisfying a certain property. Describe this set as a ternary (3-ary) relation R. (b) In particular, define by abstraction the relation $R1$ in which the three face values add up to a number *less than* 6, and enumerate $\mathrm{Gr}(R1)$. (c) Similarly describe the relation $R2$ whose defining property is that the three components of the result must add up to a number *greater than* 15, and enumerate $\mathrm{Gr}(R2)$.

3.5.9* There is a natural bijection between $\mathrm{Gr}(R1)$ and $\mathrm{Gr}(R2)$ of Exercise 3.5.8. Define this bijection. Hint: let $I =_{\mathrm{d}} \{1, 2, 3, 4, 5, 6\}$ and use the bijection $f : I \to I$ defined by $f(i) =_{\mathrm{d}} 7 - i$ for all $i : I$.

3.5.10 Give three examples of *functions* from some of the cartesian products defined in the above exercises to codomains of your choice.

3.5.11 Let $S =_d \{1, 2, 3\}$. Show that the expression $[(x \times y) \text{ MOD } 3] + 1$ defines a binary function $f: S \times S \to S$. Tabulate this function.

3.5.12 Let $S =_d \{1, 2, 3\}$. Show that the expression $[(x \times y) + z \text{ MOD } 3] + 1$ defines a ternary function $f: S^3 \to S$. Tabulate the first 10 values of this function, starting at $(x\ y, z) = (1, 1, 1)$ and varying z fastest and x slowest.

3.5.13 Describe the multiplication of natural numbers as a total *binary function* $\times: \text{Nat}^2 \to \text{Nat}$ and as a *ternary relation* on Nat. Tabulate this function for the following arguments: (0, 0); (0, 1), (1, 0); (0, 2), (1, 1), (2, 0); (0, 3), (1, 2), (2, 1), (3, 0).

3.5.14 Describe the subtraction of natural numbers as a *partial binary function* $-: \text{Nat}^2 \nrightarrow \text{Nat}$ and as a *ternary relation* on Nat. Tabulate this function for the correct subset of the arguments specified in Exercise 3.5.13.

3.5.15 Consider the definition of the logical connectives given in Section 2.4C. (a) Show that the semantics of $\neg$ (not) is given by a total unary function NOT: Bool $\to$ Bool. Define this function precisely. (b) Repeat for the other logical connectives: $\vee$ (or), $\Rightarrow$ (if ... then) and $\Leftrightarrow$ (iff).

3.5.16 Consider Example 3.5G.4. (a) Give the full definition of the function *Com*: *Teams* $\to$ Pow(N). (b) Define a function *Lans*, similar to *Com*, which for each team returns the set of languages spoken by *at least one* member.

3.5.17 The general definition of an n-tuple may be used for the case $n = 0$. Give this definition precisely, and show that there is exactly one 0-tuple, which we shall denote by ε. Note that ε is *not* the same as the empty set, although the two concepts are closely related. Explain this difference.

3.5.18 Let A^1 be the set of 1-tuples described as functions $\{1\} \to A$, as in the general definition of an n-tuple. Let $A^0 =_d \{\varepsilon\}$, the unique set with ε as unique member. Thus A^n is now defined for all n: Nat in a uniform manner, and these various sets are pairwise disjoint.

(a) Justify the assertion that the sets $A^0, A^1, A^2, \ldots$ are pairwise disjoint.
(b) Let A^* be the set of all n-tuples, $n =_d 0, 1, 2, \ldots$. Give two formal definitions of A^*, one direct and the other in terms of the union Σ of pairwise disjoint sets.

3.6 Operations on relations and functions AT

One of the strengths of set theory is that its basic constructions may be applied repeatedly, and thus naturally lead to objects of rapidly growing complexity. These form a rich variety of models from which we may hope to draw adequate representations of any kind of real phenomena, however complex. The value of these models does not lie so much in their complexity as in the simplicity of the methods by which they are constructed.

Specifically, the members of a set may be any objects. In particular, they may be other sets, or relations, or functions. In other words, we may construct sets of sets, relations, functions, and so on. Likewise, we may build relations and functions whose domain and/or codomain elements are simpler sets, relations or functions.

We have already availed ourselves several times of this fundamental feature of set theory. Here are some examples. (a) The power set Pow(S) of a set S is a set of sets. (b) A couple has been defined as a set $\{\{a\}, \{a, b\}\}$, that is, a set of sets (and a or b themselves may be sets or relations). (c) Relations are essentially described by their graphs, which are sets of couples. (d) We have defined an n-tuple as a function a from $I =_{\mathrm{d}} \{1, 2, \ldots, n\}$; therefore the graph of an n-ary relation is a set of such functions a, and each of these functions has a graph that is a set of couples. This list could be extended.

Two points emerge from these examples. First, the ability to define sets of sets and so on has yielded a useful technique for defining new concepts. In fact, in pure set theory, it is the only method ever used! This naturally suggests that we should continue using this technique in order to define further concepts, and indeed this is exactly what we do in this section and the remainder of this book. Second, by elevating the building of sets of sets and so on to a systematic 'construction strategy', we are led to define a complete *hierarchy* of objects, with those at higher levels involving sets of objects from lower levels. We do not define this hierarchy precisely; this is done in books on set theory, such as Enderton (1977). What matters is to bear the principle in mind, and to recognize when an object is a component of a more complex one.

In this section we focus primarily on relations, bearing in mind that everything stated about them holds for functions as special cases. By 'element of a relation' is meant a member of its domain or codomain (or of any of its n domains in the case of an n-ary relation). The term 'higher-order' is used to categorize sets or relations whose elements are themselves more elementary sets or relations. Our main aim now is to define operations on relations and functions, that is, higher-order operations. Operations on functions are treated primarily as operations on relations, suitably qualified, if necessary, when applied to functions. Note that operations include relations as these may be described by their characteristic functions (see Section 3.4A). Note also that some operations are 'class functions' in the sense that their domains or codomains are proper classes.

3.6A Operations returning sets of relations

We begin with a few examples of sets of relations encountered in previous sections. We show that these may be regarded as the results of operations on such sets. Recall that for any two given sets A and B, we write

$$F : A \to B$$

to introduce F as a total function from A to B – that is, with graph $\mathrm{Gr}(F) \subseteq A \times B$. This means that the notation '$A \to B$' is intended to represent the *set* of all total functions with domain A and codomain B, and F is introduced as a member of this set. (Recall that ':' is to be read 'by definition a member of'.)

Example 3.6A.1

Let $A =_d \{0, 1\}$ and $B =_d \{\mathrm{a}, \mathrm{b}, \mathrm{c}\}$. Then $A \to B$ consists of the $3^2 = 9$ total functions whose graphs are as follows:

$\{(0, \mathrm{a}), (1, \mathrm{a})\}$	$\{(0, \mathrm{a}), (1, \mathrm{b})\}$	$\{(0, \mathrm{a}), (1, \mathrm{c})\}$
$\{(0, \mathrm{b}), (1, \mathrm{a})\}$	$\{(0, \mathrm{b}), (1, \mathrm{b})\}$	$\{(0, \mathrm{b}), (1, \mathrm{c})\}$
$\{(0, \mathrm{c}), (1, \mathrm{a})\}$	$\{(0, \mathrm{c}), (1, \mathrm{b})\}$	$\{(0, \mathrm{c}), (1, \mathrm{c})\}$

On the other hand, the set $B \to A$ consists of $2^3 = 8$ total functions from B to A. The reader should write down their graphs. ■

Now by varying A and B, we obtain different sets $A \to B$ of total functions. The arrow $\to$ may therefore be regarded as denoting a binary operation sending any pair (A, B) of sets to a new set, namely the set $A \to B$. This is an operation similar to the union of sets or the cartesian product of two sets. It is a proper class operation.

Likewise, $A \leftrightarrow B$ is the set of all relations with domain A and codomain B, and $A \nrightarrow B$ is the set of all (possibly partial) functions from A to B. These may also be regarded as functions of (A, B). Moreover, the three sets $A \leftrightarrow B$, $A \nrightarrow B$ and $A \to B$ are obviously linked by the relation

$$A \to B \subseteq A \nrightarrow B \subseteq A \leftrightarrow B$$

which says that any total function from A to B is a function from A to B, and any function from A to B is a relation with domain A and codomain B. Here, the inclusion relation $\subseteq$ is applied to sets of relations.

Further similar sets of relations may be constructed and operated on. For instance, for any two sets A and B, let $\mathrm{Inj}(A, B)$ be the set of total injections from A to B, and $\mathrm{Sur}(A, B)$ the set of total surjections from A to

B. These again are higher-order functions of A and B. Moreover, we have

$$\text{Inj}(A, B) \subseteq A \to B$$

and

$$\text{Sur}(A, B) \subseteq A \to B$$

Finally, let Bij(A, B) be the set of bijections from A to B. We may *define* this set as the intersection

$$\text{Bij}(A, B) =_{\text{d}} \text{Inj}(A, B) \cap \text{Sur}(A, B)$$

This further illustrates how higher-order operations may be used to define concepts elegantly.

3.6B Composition of relations and functions

Next, we define an important operation on relations, called *composition.* Consider three sets A, B and C, and two relations $R1$ and $R2$, such that Dom($R1$) $=_{\text{d}} A$, Cod($R1$) $=_{\text{d}}$ Dom($R2$) $=_{\text{d}} B$ and Cod($R2$) $=_{\text{d}} C$; an example is given in Figure 3.6B.1.

It is clear from this figure that from $R1$ and $R2$ we may derive a third relation R', with domain Dom(R') $=_{\text{d}} A$ and codomain Cod(R') $=_{\text{d}} C$, and defined as follows: for any $x : A$ and any $z : C$, $x\ R'\ z$ iff *there exists* $y : B$ such that $x\ R1\ y$ and $y\ R2\ z$. For instance in Figure 3.6B.1, $a\ R'\ c$ because B contains an element b such that $a\ R1\ b$ and $b\ R2\ c$. However we do not have $a'\ R'\ c'$, because there is no intermediate point b' such that $a'\ R1\ b'$ and $b'\ R2\ c'$. The

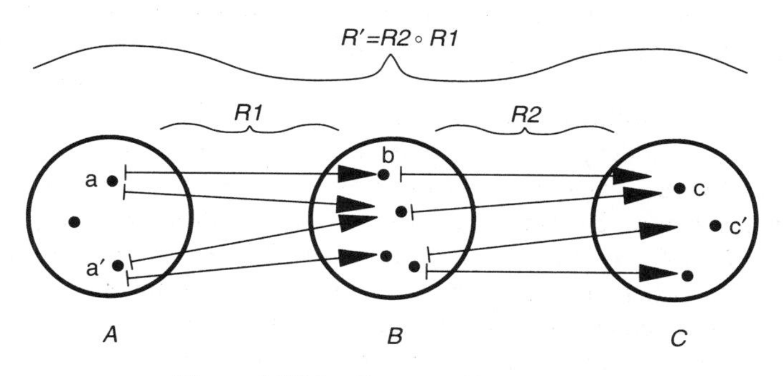

Figure 3.6B.1 Composable relations.

new relation, R', is denoted by $R2 \circ R1$. (Note the order of the operands!) For the record:

Definition 3.6B.1

Let $R1$ and $R2$ be two relations such that $\mathrm{Cod}(R1) = \mathrm{Dom}(R2)$. The *composition* of $R1$ and $R2$ is the relation

$$R' = R2 \circ R1$$

with $\mathrm{Dom}(R') =_{\mathrm{d}} \mathrm{Dom}(R1)$ and $\mathrm{Cod}(R') =_{\mathrm{d}} \mathrm{Cod}(R2)$, and defined as follows. Let $A =_{\mathrm{d}} \mathrm{Dom}(R1)$, $B =_{\mathrm{d}} \mathrm{Cod}(R1) = \mathrm{Dom}(R2)$ and $C =_{\mathrm{d}} \mathrm{Cod}(R2)$.

$$\forall\, x\!:\!A, z\!:\!C \cdot x\; R'\; z \Leftrightarrow_{\mathrm{d}} (\exists\, y\!:\!B \cdot x\; R1\; y \wedge y\; R2\; z)$$

Equivalently, in terms of the graphs $\mathrm{Gr}(R1)$ and so on,

$$\forall\, x\!:\!A, z\!:\!C \cdot (x, z) \in \mathrm{Gr}(R') \Leftrightarrow_{\mathrm{d}}$$
$$(\exists\, y\!:\!B \cdot (x, y) \in \mathrm{Gr}(R1) \wedge (y, z) \in \mathrm{Gr}(R2))$$

The relation $R' = R2 \circ R1$ is also called the *composite* of $R1$ and $R2$. ■

This is the basic definition of the composition of two relations. Note that composition is a *partial* operation. It is defined for any two relations $R1$ and $R2$ iff $\mathrm{Cod}(R1) = \mathrm{Dom}(R2)$. The reader should establish the definition domain $\mathrm{Def}(R2 \circ R1)$ and the range $\mathrm{Ran}(R2 \circ R1)$.

Next, consider two *functions* F and G, possibly partial. As these are relations, they have a composite $F' =_{\mathrm{d}} G \circ F$ determined by Definition **3**.6B.1, provided $\mathrm{Cod}(F) = \mathrm{Dom}(G)$. We know this composite is a relation; what else can we say about it?

The answer is that as both F and G are functional, F' itself is a function. This should be clear on reflection. In outline, the proof is as follows. We must show that for any $x\!:\!\mathrm{Dom}(F')$, there is at most one $z\!:\!\mathrm{Cod}(F')$ such that $(x, z) \in \mathrm{Gr}(F')$. This follows from the fact that as F and G are functions, there is at most one $y\!:\!\mathrm{Cod}(F) = \mathrm{Dom}(G)$ with $(x, y) \in \mathrm{Gr}(F)$ and for this y at most one $z\!:\!\mathrm{Cod}(G)$ with $(y, z) \in \mathrm{Gr}(G)$. Draw a diagram like Figure **3**.6B.1.

This result may be strengthened if the two functions F and G are *total*. In this case, $F' = G \circ F$ is itself a total function. To prove this, simply replace 'at most' by 'at least' in the previous proof! Further similar results may be obtained (by symmetry) about other special types of relation, such as injective or surjective ones. This is left to the reader as an exercise.

In the case of functions F and G, there is an alternative way of defining their composite $F' = G \circ F$:

Definition 3.6B.2

Let F and G be two functions with $\mathrm{Cod}(F) = \mathrm{Dom}(G)$. For all $x:\mathrm{Dom}(F)$, $(G \circ F)(x)$ is defined iff $x \in \mathrm{Def}(F)$ and $F(x) \in \mathrm{Def}(G)$. In this case, $(G \circ F)(x) =_{\mathrm{d}} G(F(x))$. ■

The reader should verify that Definitions 3.6B.1 (for functions) and 3.6B.2 are equivalent – that is, they assign the same meaning to $(G \circ F)$.

3.6C Restrictions and overriding

Consider any relation $R: A \leftrightarrow B$, as illustrated in Figure 3.6C.1. Note that in general, A and B need not be disjoint; they may even be equal. Let S be some proper subset of A, for example $S =_{\mathrm{d}} A - \{a, b\}$. Considering the figure, it is intuitively clear that S *naturally* determines a certain new relation $R': S \leftrightarrow B$. This is the relation obtained from R by removing all the couples (x, y) which cannot possibly be members of $\mathrm{Gr}(R')$, simply because $x \notin S$. Clearly R' is uniquely determined. We call it the (domain) restriction of R induced by S, and denote it by $S \langle R$. Note that in the general definition which follows, S need not be a subset of A.

Definition 3.6C.1

Given a set S and a relation R (which could be a function), $S \langle R$ is the relation R' such that

(1) $\mathrm{Dom}(R') =_{\mathrm{d}} S \cap \mathrm{Dom}(R)$

(2) $\mathrm{Cod}(R') =_{\mathrm{d}} \mathrm{Cod}(R)$

(3) $\mathrm{Gr}(R') =_{\mathrm{d}} (S \times \mathrm{Cod}(R)) \cap \mathrm{Gr}(R)$

Condition (3) states that $\mathrm{Gr}(R')$ is the set of members (x, y) of $\mathrm{Gr}(R)$ such that $x \in S$. ■

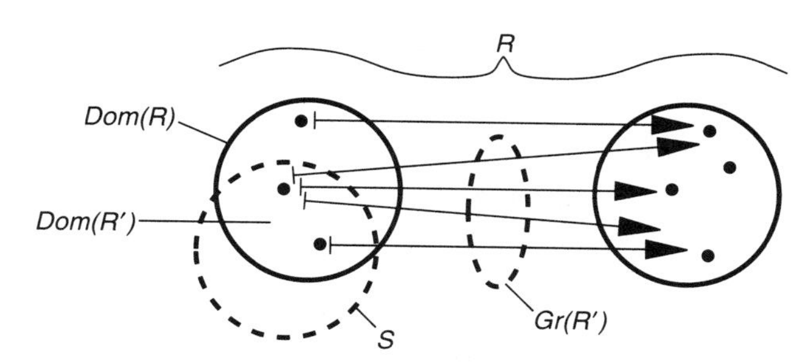

Figure 3.6C.1 Domain restriction R' of R induced by S.

Note that the domain restriction operation $\langle$ is a binary operation which sends any couple (S, R), where S is a set and R a relation, to a new relation R'. Also, there are other, equivalent, ways of defining $\mathrm{Gr}(R')$, such as

$$\mathrm{Gr}(R') =_{\mathrm{d}} (\mathrm{Dom}(R') \times \mathrm{Cod}(R')) \cap \mathrm{Gr}(R)$$

We have chosen the simplest expression. The reader should prove the equivalence of these two definitions and look for further alternatives.

The *codomain* restriction of a relation R induced by a set T is denoted by $T \langle\cdot R$ and defined symmetrically:

Definition 3.6C.2

Given a set T and a relation R, $T \langle\cdot R$ is the relation R' such that

(1) $\mathrm{Dom}(R') =_{\mathrm{d}} \mathrm{Dom}(R)$
(2) $\mathrm{Cod}(R') =_{\mathrm{d}} T \cap \mathrm{Cod}(R)$
(3) $\mathrm{Gr}(R') =_{\mathrm{d}} (\mathrm{Dom}(R) \times T) \cap \mathrm{Gr}(R)$

Condition (3) states that $\mathrm{Gr}(R')$ is the set of members (x, y) of $\mathrm{Gr}(R)$ such that $y \in T$. ■

Finally, we need an operation which restricts both the domain and the codomain of a relation. This arises mainly when these two sets are equal. Consequently we establish this third operation by

Definition 3.6C.3

Given a set S and a relation R, $S \diamond R$ is the relation R' such that

(1) $\mathrm{Dom}(R') =_{\mathrm{d}} S \cap \mathrm{Dom}(R)$
(2) $\mathrm{Cod}(R') =_{\mathrm{d}} S \cap \mathrm{Cod}(R)$
(3) $\mathrm{Gr}(R') =_{\mathrm{d}} (S \times S) \cap \mathrm{Gr}(R)$

Condition (3) states that $\mathrm{Gr}(R')$ is the set of members (x, y) of $\mathrm{Gr}(R)$ such that both x and y are members of S. ■

Function overriding

Various other similar operations on relations may be defined. We need only one such operation. This is defined on functions, and is a special case of 'functional overriding' in the sense of, for example, Spivey (1989). The principle is as follows. Given a (possibly partial) function F, any $x{:}\mathrm{Dom}(F)$ and any $y{:}\mathrm{Cod}(F)$, the operation returns a new function F'. This is identical with F except that $F'(x)$ is defined and equal to y. In other words, the value $F(x)$, if it exists, is replaced by y. The new function F' is denoted by $(F \mid x \mapsto y)$. Note that $F(x)$ itself may be equal to y, in which case $F' = F$.

Definition 3.6C.4

Given a function F, $x:\text{Dom}(F)$ and $y:\text{Cod}(F)$, $(F \mid x \mapsto y)$ is the function F' such that

(1) $\text{Dom}(F') =_d \text{Dom}(F)$

(2) $\text{Cod}(F') =_d \text{Cod}(F)$

(3) $\text{Def}(F') =_d \text{Def}(F) \cup \{x\}$

(4) $\forall x' : \text{Def}(F') \cdot F'(x') =_d \begin{cases} F(x') & \text{if } x' \neq x; \\ y & \text{otherwise} \end{cases}$ ■

Alternatively, $F' = (F|x \mapsto y)$ may be defined in terms of its graph $\text{Gr}(F')$: remove the old couple $(x, F(x))$, if any, and insert the new couple (x, y). Thus:

$$\text{Gr}(F') =_d [\text{Gr}(F) \setminus \{(x, F(x))\}] + \{(x, y)\}$$

Note how '$\cup$' in Definition **3**.6C.4 alerts us to the fact that x may already belong to the definition domain of F. Likewise, in the definition of $\text{Gr}(F')$, '$\setminus$' emphasizes that $(x, F(x))$ need not be a member of $\text{Gr}(F)$ (if $F(x)$ is undefined) and '$+$' emphasizes that, once $(x, F(x))$ has been removed, (x, y) is necessarily a new couple.

3.6D Identity and inclusion functions

Consider any set S. We may associate with it a certain total function $\text{Id}_S : S \to S$ called the *identity function* of S. This function is uniquely defined by the rule

$$\forall x : S \cdot \text{Id}_S(x) =_d x$$

We may describe Id_S as the function that 'changes nothing': each element x of S is sent to itself. Note that *each* set S has its own identity function – that is, the latter is itself a function of S – hence the subscript in 'Id_S'. For instance, for $S =_d \{1, 2, 3\}$, Id_S is given in tabular form by

$x:S$	$\text{Id}_S(x)$
1	1
2	2
3	3

whereas for $S' =_d \{\mathrm{m, n, p, q}\}$, $\mathrm{Id}_{S'}$ is given by

$x:S'$	$\mathrm{Id}_{S'}(x)$
m	m
n	n
p	p
q	q

The identity function may seem irrelevant, but it is not. Its significance becomes apparent when considered in context. For instance, one key property is that it is the *right and left identity for composition*, in the following sense:

Property 3.6D.1
Consider any relation $R:S \leftrightarrow T$. Then

$$R \circ \mathrm{Id}_S = R = \mathrm{Id}_T \circ R \qquad \blacksquare$$

This is immediate. Thus, Id behaves with respect to composition in the same way as 0 does with respect to addition: for any integer n, $n + 0 = n = 0 + n$. These two analogous properties are quite important. Note that Property 3.6D.1 is usually described for the special case where R is a function. The more general statement does no harm.

Inclusion functions

Given any set S, an *inclusion function on* S is a (possibly partial) function $F:S \nrightarrow S$ such that

$$\mathrm{Gr}(F) \subseteq_d \mathrm{Gr}(\mathrm{Id}_S)$$

Thus, it is obtained by deleting 0 or more couples (x, y) from $\mathrm{Gr}(\mathrm{Id}_S)$. For instance if $S =_d \{\mathrm{m, n, p, q}\}$ then $F:S \nrightarrow S$ with graph

$$\mathrm{Gr}(F) =_d \{(\mathrm{m, m}), (\mathrm{p, p})\}$$

is an inclusion function on S.

Clearly an inclusion function $F:S \nrightarrow S$ is entirely determined by *two* sets: S and the subset $S' =_d \mathrm{Def}(F) \subseteq S$. Therefore we denote it by

$$\mathrm{Inc}_{S'}:S \nrightarrow S$$

This introduction indicates the set S on which $\mathrm{Inc}_{S'}$ is defined. An identity function is an inclusion function which is total. An inclusion function may also be defined using the function restriction $\diamond$ operation. This alternative is left as an exercise.

3.6E Opposites and inverses

We now introduce two related concepts, the *opposite* and the *inverse* of a relation, and discuss their connection. Inverses of functions are particularly important. They are extensively used in Parts **4** and **5**. We begin with the opposite of a relation.

Consider any relation $R: A \leftrightarrow B$, as illustrated in Figure 3.6E.1(a). It is obvious that we may transform R into a new relation $R': B \leftrightarrow A$, by (a) interchanging the domain and codomain of R and (b) replacing each couple $(x, y): \mathrm{Gr}(R)$ by (y, x). The new relation R' is called the *opposite* or *dual* of R. We denote it by $\mathrm{Opp}(R)$, following Mac Lane and Birkhoff (1979). Opp is a unary class operation sending relations to relations.

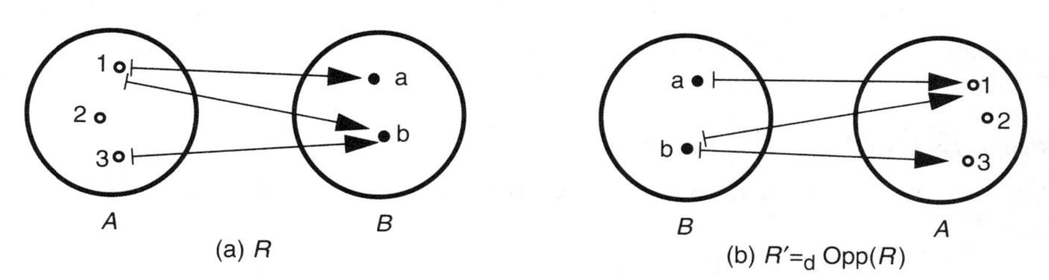

Figure 3.6E.1 A relation R and its opposite $R' =_{\mathrm{d}} \mathrm{Opp}(R)$.

Definition 3.6E.1

For any relation R, the *opposite* of R is the relation $R' = \mathrm{Opp}(R)$ such that

(1) $\mathrm{Dom}(R') =_{\mathrm{d}} \mathrm{Cod}(R)$

(2) $\mathrm{Cod}(R') =_{\mathrm{d}} \mathrm{Dom}(R)$

(3) $\mathrm{Gr}(R') =_{\mathrm{d}} \{(y, x) \mid (x, y): \mathrm{Gr}(R)\}$

$\mathrm{Opp}(R)$ is also called the *dual* of R. ■

The term 'dual' is used to emphasize the symmetry which exists between R and $\mathrm{Opp}(R)$. This symmetry is highlighted in Figure 3.6E.1.

Two properties of Opp

The opposite operation enjoys various properties. Here are two important ones. First, for any relation R, consider the opposite of $\mathrm{Opp}(R)$. It is obvious that this is R again:

Property 3.6E.1
For any relation R,

$$\mathrm{Opp}(\mathrm{Opp}(R)) = R \qquad \blacksquare$$

From this property, it immediately follows that *any relation entirely determines, and is entirely determined by, its opposite*. Therefore, instead of specifying, say, R, we may give Opp(R), from which R may then be derived exactly. Moreover, it is clear that every property of R gives rise to a corresponding property of Opp(R), called the *dual* property. This fact, called the *principle of duality*, is exploited in some applications of Parts **4** and **5**. The principle is established formally in Mac Lane (1971).

Second, consider any two relations $R1$ and $R2$ such that $\mathrm{Cod}(R1) =_{\mathrm{d}} \mathrm{Dom}(R2)$. Their composite $R' =_{\mathrm{d}} R2 \circ R1$ is defined. It is also easy to see that the opposite of R' is equal to the composition of Opp($R1$) and Opp($R2$) *but in reverse order*, $\mathrm{Opp}(R1) \circ \mathrm{Opp}(R2)$. This is intuitively obvious, considering Figure 3.6E.2.

Property 3.6E.2
For any two relations $R1$ and $R2$ such that $\mathrm{Cod}(R1) = \mathrm{Dom}(R2)$,

$$\mathrm{Opp}(R2 \circ R1) = \mathrm{Opp}(R1) \circ \mathrm{Opp}(R2) \qquad \blacksquare$$

The reader should seek to prove this property in outline, using Figure 3.6E.2 as a guide.

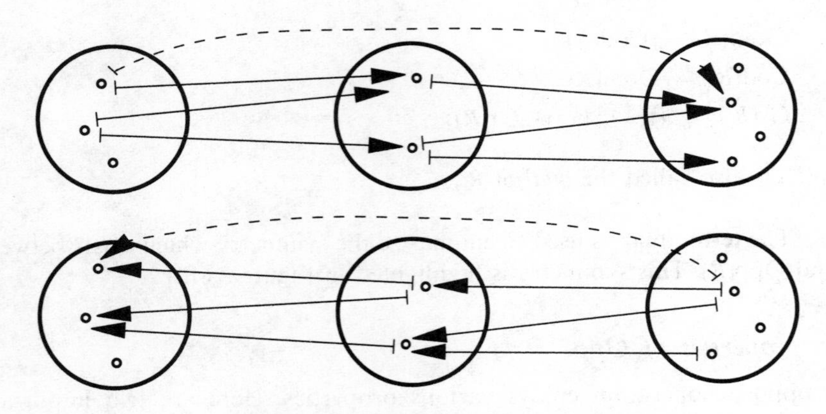

Figure 3.6E.2 Opposite of a composite relation.

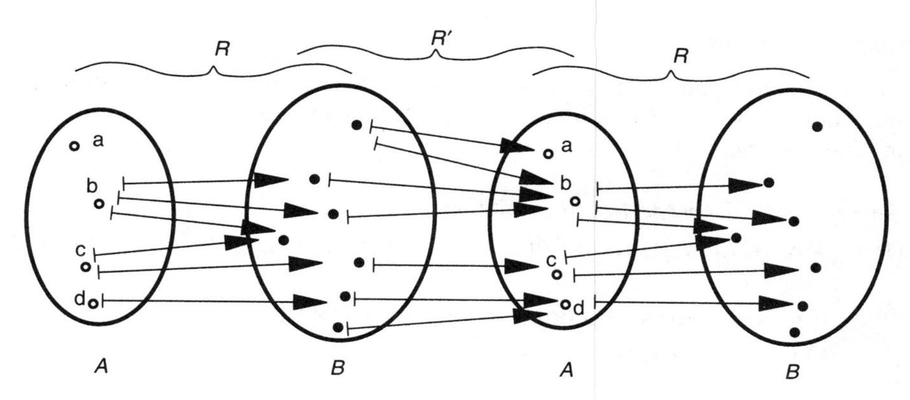

Figure 3.6E.3 The two compositions of R and R'.

Inverses

Next, we define three notions connected with the operation Opp. Consider any two relations R and R' such that $\mathrm{Dom}(R') =_{\mathrm{d}} \mathrm{Cod}(R)$ and $\mathrm{Cod}(R') =_{\mathrm{d}} \mathrm{Dom}(R)$. It follows that both $R' \circ R$ and $R \circ R'$ are defined. Moreover $R' \circ R$ is a relation from Dom(R) to Dom(R), whereas $R \circ R'$ is a relation from Cod(R) to Cod(R); see Figure 3.6E.3. Note that a special case is where $R' =_{\mathrm{d}} \mathrm{Opp}(R)$.

Definition 3.6E.2

Let R and R' be two relations such that $\mathrm{Dom}(R') =_{\mathrm{d}} \mathrm{Cod}(R)$ and $\mathrm{Cod}(R') =_{\mathrm{d}} \mathrm{Dom}(R)$. Let $A =_{\mathrm{d}} \mathrm{Dom}(R)$ and $B =_{\mathrm{d}} \mathrm{Cod}(R)$.

(1) If $R' \circ R$ is an *inclusion function on A with* $\mathrm{Def}(R' \circ R) = \mathrm{Def}(R)$, then R' is called *a left inverse of R*.

(2) If $R \circ R'$ is an *inclusion function on B with* $\mathrm{Def}(R \circ R') = \mathrm{Def}(R')$, then R' is called *a right inverse of R*.

(3) If R and R' satisfy both conditions, then R' is both a left and a right inverse of R. In this case, R' is uniquely determined by R; it is called *the inverse* of R and denoted by Inv(R). We may call it the *full inverse* to emphasize that it is both a left and a right inverse. Also, we may call a left or right inverse which is *not necessarily* a full inverse a *semi-inverse*. ■

Note that in general a relation R may have several left inverses and several right inverses, but at most one full inverse. In Figure 3.6E.3 R' is a left inverse of R (and R is a *right* inverse of R'), but R is *not* a left inverse of R'.

Opp versus Inv

There are important connections between opposites and inverses, although these notions must be carefully distinguished. Here are some key facts, considering full inverses first:

Theorem 3.6E.3 (properties of full inverses)

(1) Any relation R has a full inverse $\mathrm{Inv}(R)$ iff R is both functional and injective.

(2) If it exists, $\mathrm{Inv}(R)$ is unique and equal to $\mathrm{Opp}(R)$.

(3) Let $R' =_{\mathrm{d}} \mathrm{Inv}(R)$, assuming it exists. Then

$$\mathrm{Def}(R) = \mathrm{Ran}(R')$$
$$\mathrm{Ran}(R) = \mathrm{Def}(R')$$

■

This theorem shows that to have a full inverse, a relation R must satisfy strong conditions. These in turn imply the connection – identity, in fact – between $\mathrm{Opp}(R)$ and the full inverse of R. However, a relation R may have a left inverse R' even if R is neither functional nor injective. Dually, a relation R may have a right inverse even if it is neither functional nor injective. Moreover, a semi-inverse of a relation R may differ from $\mathrm{Opp}(R)$. All these observations are illustrated in Figure 3.6E.3.

Inverses are usually defined for total functions only. However, it is interesting to know that *semi-inverses* need to be neither functional nor injective. As for full inverses, their generalization to partial functions is also useful. In Parts **4** and **5**, we resort to a strategy of modelling based on the systematic construction of *partial* operations with full inverses. This yields several significant benefits, as we shall see. The importance of partial functions is also apparent from Manes and Arbib (1986), where they play a central role.

Notation

As a relation has a full inverse only if it is a function F, the inverse of F is traditionally denoted by F^{-1}. We also use this notation. ■

Inverse of a composition

Recall that an injection is an injective *function*. Consider two injections F and G, possibly partial. By Theorem **3**.6E.3, each of them has an inverse. Using Property **3**.6E.2, we obtain

Property 3.6E.4

The composition $G \circ F$ of two injections F and G has a full inverse, given by

$$(G \circ F)^{-1} = F^{-1} \circ G^{-1}$$

■

3.6F Special types of relation

We conclude this chapter with a brief description of some fundamental types of relation. All the relations R we consider are such that $\text{Dom}(R) = \text{Cod}(R)$. A relation R of this type is sometimes said to be *defined on the set* $S = \text{Dom}(R)$.

Definition 3.6F.1

Consider any (binary) relation R on a set S, that is, such that $\text{Dom}(R) = \text{Cod}(R) = S$.

(1) R is *reflexive* iff

$$\forall x : S \cdot x \; R \; x$$

(2) R is *symmetric* iff

$$\forall x, y : S \cdot x \; R \; y \Rightarrow y \; R \; x$$

(3) R is *transitive* iff

$$\forall x, y, z : S \cdot (x \; R \; y \wedge y \; R \; z) \Rightarrow x \; R \; z$$

■

We may also need to consider relations in which any of these properties is 'strongly negated' in the sense that for all x, y and $z : S$ the consequence of the original condition is negated (or 'quasi-negated'). In particular:

Definition 3.6F.2

Let R be any (binary) relation on a set S.

(1) R is *antireflexive* iff

$$\forall x : S \cdot \neg(x \; R \; x)$$

(2) R is *antisymmetric* iff

$$\forall x, y : S \cdot (x \; R \; y \wedge y \; R \; x) \Rightarrow x = y$$

■

Note that the strong negation of reflexivity is often named 'irreflexivity'. This is a misnomer, as the simple negation of reflexivity only means that *there exists* an $x : S$ such that $x \; R \; x$ is false.

Definition 3.6F.3

A relation which is reflexive, symmetric and transitive is an *equivalence*. ■

An example of equivalence is as follows. Consider the set Nat of natural numbers. Define the relation *Eq4* by

$$\forall n, m : \text{Nat} \cdot n \; Eq4 \; m \Leftrightarrow_{\text{d}} (n \text{ MOD } 4) = (m \text{ MOD } 4)$$

where n MOD 4 is the remainder of the integer division of n by 4 (see Exercise 2.1.3). Thus, *Eq4* is a relation on Nat. It is easy to see that it is an equivalence, as the reader is invited to verify.

Equality ($=$) on any set S is another equivalence. It is the only antisymmetric equivalence on S.

It can be shown that any equivalence *Eq* on a set S partitions S into so-called *equivalence classes*, where a partition is as defined in Section 3.4D. Conversely, any partition of a set S defines an equivalence *Eq* on S: simply state that for any $x, y\!:\!S$, x *Eq* y iff x and y belong to the same partition class.

In the above example of *Eq4*, there are four partition classes:

$$\{0, 4, 8, \ldots\} = \{n\!:\!\text{Nat} \mid n \text{ MOD } 4 = 0\}$$
$$\{1, 5, 9, \ldots\} = \{n\!:\!\text{Nat} \mid n \text{ MOD } 4 = 1\}$$
$$\{2, 6, 10, \ldots\} = \{n\!:\!\text{Nat} \mid n \text{ MOD } 4 = 2\}$$
$$\{3, 7, 11, \ldots\} = \{n\!:\!\text{Nat} \mid n \text{ MOD } 4 = 3\}$$

In general, each class is

$$\{n\!:\!\text{Nat} \mid n \text{ MOD } 4 = r\}$$

where $0 \leqslant r < 4$.

Further *order* concepts are defined in terms of the above definitions.

Definition 3.6F.4

(1) A relation R on a set S is a *preorder* iff R is *reflexive* and *transitive*.

(2) A relation R on a set S is a *partial order* iff R is an *antisymmetric* preorder. A set S together with a partial order R on it is called a *partially ordered set*, or *poset*. Note that 'partial' should be read as '*possibly partial*'.

(3) A *total order* R on S is a partial order such that for all $x, y\!:\!S$, $x\ R\ y$ or $y\ R\ x$. A total order is also called *linear*.

(4) A relation R on a set S is a *strict partial order* iff R is *antireflexive* and *transitive*. ■

The relation $\leqslant$ on the set Nat is a total order. It is also a 'partial order', even though this is a misnomer in this case. The inclusion relation $\subseteq$ on the class of sets is a properly partial order. The same holds for this relation, but restricted to the powerset Pow(S) of any given set S.

Note that a strict order is *not* a special case of a partial order. However, there is a one–one correspondence between these two types of order: for any partial order, the corresponding strict order is obtained by removing all the couples (x, x) from its graph, and vice versa. A strict order may be total; this is defined by analogy with our definition of total order.

EXERCISES

3.6.1 Enumerate the graph Gr(F) of each of the $2^3 = 8$ functions $F:B \to A$ with $A =_d \{0, 1\}$ and $B =_d \{a, b, c\}$.

3.6.2 Show that for any two sets A and B, the set Bij(A, B) of bijections $F:B \to A$ is equal to Inj(A, B) $\cap$ Sur(A, B) as claimed in Section **3.6A**.

3.6.3 Let $A =_d \{a, b, c, d\}$, $B =_d \{1, 2, 3\}$ and $C =_d \{k, m, n, p\}$. Construct two relations $R1 : A \leftrightarrow B$ and $R2 : B \leftrightarrow C$ of your choice and represent them by a diagram. Then enumerate the graph Gr($R2 \circ R1$) and represent it by a diagram.

3.6.4 Let $R1 : A \leftrightarrow B$ and $R2 : B \leftrightarrow C$, where A, B and C are any sets. Formally establish (a) the definition domain Def($R2 \circ R1$) and (b) the range Ran($R2 \circ R1$).

3.6.5 Consider the expression $[(x \times 2) + 3] \times 5$. It defines a function F: Nat $\to$ Nat, sending any x: Nat to the corresponding value of the expression. Express the function F as the composition of three more elementary functions f, g and h: Nat $\to$ Nat. Draw a diagram with five values of x and the corresponding values $f(x)$, $g(f(x))$ and $h(g(f(x)))$.

3.6.6 Let $R1$ and $R2$ be defined as in Exercise **3.6.4**. Prove the following:

(1) If $R1$ and $R2$ are injective, then so is $R2 \circ R1$.
(2) If $R1$ and $R2$ are surjective, then so is $R2 \circ R1$.

3.6.7 Let $R1$ and $R2$ be defined as in Exercise **3.6.4**. Construct simple counter-examples to show that if *only* $R1$, or *only* $R2$ is functional (injective, total or surjective) then $R2 \circ R1$ *may* fail to be functional (injective, total or surjective, respectively).

3.6.8 Verify that Definition **3.6B.2** is equivalent to Definition **3.6B.1** where both $R1$ and $R2$ are functions.

3.6.9 Let $A =_d \{1, 2, 3, 4, 5\}$, $B =_d \{a, b, c, d, e, f\}$ and $R : A \leftrightarrow B$ be defined by

$$\text{Gr}(R) =_d \{(1, a), (1, d), (2, a), (3, a), (3, c), (3, f), (4, b), (4, c), (5, a), (5, d), (5, f)\}$$

Let $S1 =_d \{2, 4, 5, 6\}$, $S2 =_d \{a, c, d, f, p, r\}$ and $S3 =_d \{1, 2, 5, 8, a, b, e, m\}$. Enumerate the domains, codomains and graphs of the following restrictions of R:

(1) $R1 =_d \quad S1 \langle R$
(2) $R2 =_d \quad S2 \langle\cdot R$
(3) $R3 =_d \quad S3 \diamond R$

3.6.10 Verify that in each of the Definitions **3.6C.1**, **3.6C.2** and **3.6C.3**, $\text{Gr}(R') \subseteq \text{Dom}(R') \times \text{Cod}(R')$.

3.6.11 Let A and B be defined as in Exercise 3.6.9, and $F: A \nrightarrow B$ be given by

x	$F(x)$
2	a
3	f
5	e

Tabulate the graphs of $F1 =_{\mathrm{d}} (F \mid 2 \mapsto \mathrm{b})$, $F2 =_{\mathrm{d}} (F \mid 1 \mapsto \mathrm{c})$ and $F3 =_{\mathrm{d}} (F2 \mid 4 \mapsto \mathrm{f})$.

3.6.12 Consider Definition 3.6C.4. Show that the function-overriding operation which sends any function F to $F' =_{\mathrm{d}} (F \mid x \mapsto y)$ is well defined, that is, (a) $\mathrm{Def}(F') \subseteq \mathrm{Dom}(F')$; (b) $\mathrm{Ran}(F') \subseteq \mathrm{Cod}(F')$; and (c) for all $x' : \mathrm{Def}(F')$, $F'(x')$ is defined in exactly one way.

3.6.13 Verify Property 3.6D.1 with the help of a diagram.

3.6.14 Let S and S' be two sets with $S' \subseteq S$. Define the inclusion function $\mathrm{Inc}_{S'} : S \nrightarrow S$ using the restriction operation $\diamond$ and the identity function $\mathrm{Id}_{S'} : S' \to S'$.

3.6.15 Let R be defined as in Exercise 3.6.9 and $R' =_{\mathrm{d}} \mathrm{Opp}(R)$. Define $\mathrm{Dom}(R')$ and $\mathrm{Cod}(R')$, and enumerate $\mathrm{Gr}(R')$.

3.6.16 Prove Property 3.6E.1.

3.6.17 Prove that for any relation $R : A \leftrightarrow B$:

(a) R is functional iff $\mathrm{Opp}(R)$ is injective.
(b) R is total iff $\mathrm{Opp}(R)$ is surjective.
(c) $\mathrm{Def}(R) = \mathrm{Ran}(\mathrm{Opp}(R))$.

3.6.18 Prove Property 3.6E.2 with the help of a diagram.

3.6.19 Verify that for any relation $R : A \leftrightarrow B$, if R' is both left and right inverse of R, then R' is uniquely determined, and derive $\mathrm{Gr}(R')$ from $\mathrm{Gr}(R)$.

3.6.20 Prove Theorem 3.6E.3 with the help of a diagram.

3.6.21 Prove Property 3.6E.4 with the help of a diagram.

3.6.22 Let $P = (P_i \mid i : I)$ be a partition of a set A. Show that it induces an equivalence relation Eq on A. Define Eq precisely.

3.6.23 Verify that any relation R which is a strict partial order (that is, antireflexive and transitive) is antisymmetric.

3.6.24 Prove that any strict partial order R' may be derived from a *unique* partial order R by letting $\text{Dom}(R') =_{\text{d}} \text{Dom}(R)$ and $\text{Gr}(R') =_{\text{d}} \text{Gr}(R) - \{(x, x) \mid x : \text{Dom}(R)\}$. Conversely, R may be derived from R' by letting $\text{Gr}(R) =_{\text{d}} \text{Gr}(R') + \{(x, x) \mid x : \text{Dom}(R')\}$. We may conclude that there is a one-to-one correspondence between these two types of relation.

4 Induction and Recursion

It was pointed out in Section **1**.3A that induction and recursion are two other notions of fundamental importance in computing, mathematics and related sciences. We refer to these two concepts generically as *inductive constructions*. Recall that induction refers to a certain method of defining a set, which is then said to be *inductively generated*, whereas recursion refers to a method of constructing a *function* on an inductively generated set (acting as the domain of the function). Moreover, such a function is in general well defined only if its domain is *freely* generated – that is, if each domain element is 'generated in just one way'. This in essence is the *recursion theorem*, a result of fundamental importance.

Recall also that our aims are first to enable the reader to recognize inductive constructions when they arise, as they are often implicit, and second to be aware of the conditions which an inductive construction must satisfy to be correct. In the case of recursion, these are relatively complex.

This chapter lays the theoretical foundations of inductive constructions. Several initial examples are given at this stage. However, many more applications arise in subsequent chapters, especially in Part **3**. It is only by the end of this part that the reader should have acquired a good 'feel' for the practical significance of these constructions.

In Section 4.1, we describe a first instance of an inductive construction, arguably the simplest and also the most important. This is the construction of the natural numbers. They are defined in set-theoretical terms by five rules known as *Peano's postulates* or *axioms*, after the Italian mathematician who published them in 1889, although he himself attributed them to the German mathematician Dedekind. Thus, this section serves a double purpose: (a) to give a first major example of an inductive construction; and (b) to provide a rigorous description of the natural numbers which supplements the intuitive notion we have so far relied on. The natural numbers play a major role in subsequent chapters, but mainly through the properties described by Peano's postulates.

Section 4.2 is devoted to proofs by induction based on Peano's definition of the natural numbers. Note that they are *not* recursive constructions: they are inductive constructions of the simpler kind, and depend on only three out of five of Peano's postulates. In Section 4.3 we introduce simple recursion. By this we mean the construction of a recursive function on the set of natural numbers, based on their structure. This now relies on all five of Peano's axioms, that is, on the fact that natural numbers are *freely* generated by these postulates.

Section 4.4 is devoted to a generalization of induction called *structural induction*. This generalization is first introduced by an example; it is so straightforward that one could almost dispense with the general definition. It is accompanied with two related concepts, namely *parse trees* and *construction sequences*. A parse tree is a key *representation* of (one of) the way(s) in which any element is inductively generated; such trees are widely used in practice. A construction sequence is more complicated to describe and mainly of theoretical interest. In Section 4.5, we describe the construction of a recursive function based on structural induction. This generalizes simple recursion.

Perhaps the most important application of structural induction and recursion is the definition of formal languages, which is particularly relevant to computing scientists. In particular, these two concepts find a major application in the definition of logic as a formal language in Part 3: induction for syntax and formal deduction, and recursion for semantics.

Some of the material in this chapter is more difficult than that presented in previous chapters. However, the main results it contains, proofs by induction or the recursion theorem for instance, are essential and should be known by every student of computing. This is why this chapter is not flagged as 'advanced'. Nevertheless, the reader is advised to study the general ideas as outlined and skip the details on first reading, if these appear too demanding.

4.1 Peano's postulates for the natural numbers

We begin this chapter with a description of the set Nat of natural numbers. This is done for two main reasons. First, a precise description of the natural numbers is at least appropriate, given the frequency with which they are being used. Second, and more importantly, these numbers have fundamental properties which play a major role in inductive constructions.

As for the approach we follow in defining Nat, recall the remarks of Section **3**.1A on the fundamental property of couples. It was mentioned that in general there are two main ways of describing a concept or a class of objects: the *concrete approach*, which focuses on the 'anatomy' of any member of the class, considered in isolation, and the *abstract approach*, which focuses on the relations that exist between members of the class. We meet this distinction again here. Our main aim is to develop an abstract description of the natural numbers. Specifically, we describe Nat as a set whose members satisfy various essential relations between them, without stating what each individual member actually is. We concentrate on these global properties because they are the dominant considerations, very much as Property **3**.1A.1 is 'what really matters' about couples. These properties are Peano's postulates, mentioned above. A concrete definition of the natural numbers is also given subsequently, but this is almost incidental.

4.1A Deriving Peano's postulates

A *postulate* is a property which is required of an object. Thus, it is *specified*, that is, used as a means of defining the object, rather than implied. Five postulates characterize the natural numbers. Instead of presenting these properties as a *fait accompli*, we *identify* them progressively – one might say dialectically – by analysing what would happen if any one of them were not satisfied. This is another illustration of the nature of concept establishment, combining specification and analysis interactively.

We start with the natural numbers as we know them intuitively. These form an ordered set Nat whose initial elements are

$$0, 1, 2, 3, 4, \ldots$$

This display suggests two features of Nat.

(1) Nat has a member named 0, which is the first of the set.

(2) Each number n: Nat has an immediate *successor* – exactly one:

0 is followed by 1;

1 is followed by 2;

2 is followed by 3;

and so on. We can express this precisely by saying that there is a certain *total function* which sends each n to another number, the *successor* of n. This function is called the *successor function* of Nat and is denoted by S. A partial enumeration of the graph Gr(S) is

$$\mathrm{Gr}(S) =_{\mathrm{d}} \{ \langle 0, 1\rangle, \langle 1, 2\rangle, \langle 2, 3\rangle, \langle 3, 4\rangle, \langle 4, 5\rangle, \ldots \}$$

Thus the successor function is a total, unary function

$$S : \mathrm{Nat} \to \mathrm{Nat}$$

These two features of Nat are summarized in Definition **4**.1A.P1. It is stressed that this is only an *approximate* definition.

Definition 4.1A.P1 (approximate)

The natural numbers consist of a set Nat of elements together with two additional features:

(1) A constant element, namely $0 : \mathrm{Nat}$. This is also regarded as a *nullary function* to Nat.

(2) A *unary* function

$$S : \mathrm{Nat} \to \mathrm{Nat}$$

called the *successor function* of Nat. ■

Altogether, the set Nat with the constant $0 : \mathrm{Nat}$ and the function $S : \mathrm{Nat} \to \mathrm{Nat}$ is referred to as the *system* (Nat, 0, S).

This definition is inadequate and needs strengthening. What is wrong with it? The answer is that it is too liberal, allowing features which are clearly inconsistent with our intuitive understanding of Nat.

First, we have not formally expressed the fact that 0 is not the successor of any other member of Nat. Consequently, Definition **4**.1A.P1 allows, for example, the following system (Nat, 0, S), which contains a circuit. The set $\mathrm{Nat} =_{\mathrm{d}} \{0, \mathrm{a}, \mathrm{b}, \mathrm{c}, \mathrm{d}\}$, and S is given by

$$\mathrm{Gr}(S) =_{\mathrm{d}} \{ \langle 0, \mathrm{a}\rangle, \langle \mathrm{a}, \mathrm{b}\rangle, \langle \mathrm{b}, \mathrm{c}\rangle, \langle \mathrm{c}, \mathrm{d}\rangle, \langle \mathrm{d}, 0\rangle \}$$

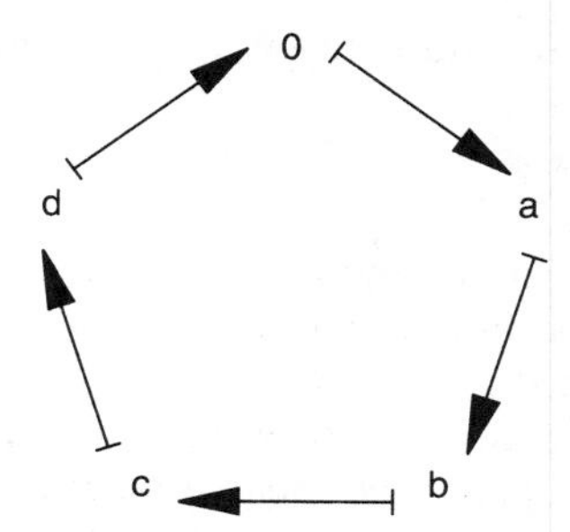

Figure 4.1A.1 A system (Nat, 0, S) forming a circuit.

S is also depicted in Figure 4.1A.1. Note that here and in the remainder of this chapter, we use letters to denote members of the tentative set Nat to avoid any confusion with actual natural numbers. It is understood that *different letters represent different elements.*

The presence of a circuit in (Nat, 0, S) is clearly at variance with our intuitive understanding of the natural numbers. In particular, it implies that Nat is *finite*, which cannot be right. We make good this deficiency by adding the rule:

For all x: Nat, $S(x) \neq 0$.

In other words, $0 \notin \text{Ran}(S)$. This makes 0 the 'first' element of Nat.

Second, even with this new rule the system (Nat, 0, S) may still contain circuits. The following is an example. Nat is as before. S is given by

$$\begin{aligned}\text{Gr}(S) =_d \{ & \langle 0, \text{a} \rangle, \\ & \langle \text{a}, \text{b} \rangle, \\ & \langle \text{b}, \text{c} \rangle, \\ & \langle \text{c}, \text{d} \rangle, \\ & \langle \text{d}, \text{a} \rangle \ \}\end{aligned}$$

and is pictured in Figure 4.1A.2.

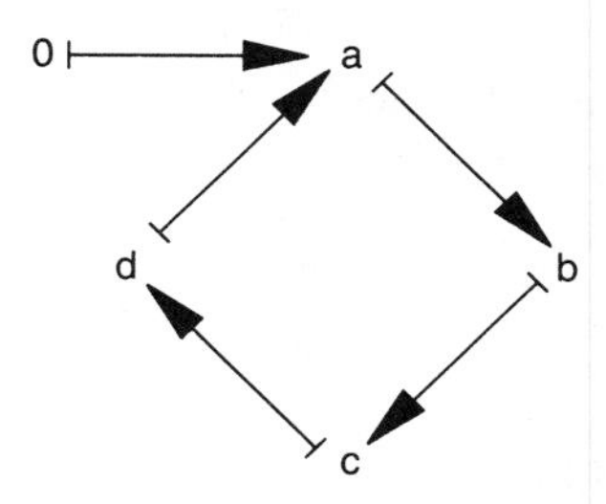

Figure 4.1A.2 A system (Nat, 0, S) containing a circuit.

We make good this second deficiency by imposing:

For all $x, y\colon \text{Nat}$, if $x \neq y$ then $S(x) \neq S(y)$.

In other words, the successor function S is an injection (Section **3**.3C). This condition is satisfied by the first system (Nat, 0, S), but not by the second, in which $S(0) = S(\text{d}) = \text{a}$ even though $\text{d} \neq 0$.

Third, even supplemented with these last two rules, Definition **4**.1A.P1 is still inadequate, because *it allows more elements than expected.* In addition to the expected set

$0 \mapsto \text{a} \mapsto \text{b} \mapsto \text{c} \mapsto \ldots$

Nat may include any number of pairwise disjoint infinite 'chains', such as $(\text{a}' \mapsto \text{b}' \mapsto \text{c}' \mapsto \ldots)$ with a starting point a′, or $(\ldots \mapsto \text{a}'' \mapsto \text{b}'' \mapsto \text{c}'' \mapsto \ldots)$ with no starting point – that is, 'infinite in both directions'. It may also contain any number of finite circuits similar to the one illustrated in Figure **4**.1A.1, but disjoint from one another and from the infinite chains. Such 'unwanted elements' are sometimes called 'junk'. This point is further developed in the exercises.

To remedy this last deficiency we add the rule

For any subset $A \subseteq_{\text{d}} \text{Nat}$, if $0 \in A$ and for all $x\colon A$, $S(x) \in A$,
then $A = \text{Nat}$.

This last rule is called the *induction principle*. With it, the system (Nat, 0, S) is properly defined.

Collecting these rules into one definition we obtain, using special symbols for variety:

Definition 4.1A.1

The natural numbers consist of a set Nat of elements with the following five properties (Peano's postulates):

(1) There is a constant element $0\colon \text{Nat}$. This is also regarded as a *nullary function* to Nat.

(2) There exists a *total unary* function

$$S\colon \text{Nat} \to \text{Nat}$$

called the *successor function* of Nat.

(3) $\forall x\colon \text{Nat} \cdot S(x) \neq 0$

In other words, $0 \notin \text{Ran}(S)$.

(4) $\forall x, y : \text{Nat} \cdot x \neq y \Rightarrow S(x) \neq S(y)$

In other words, the successor function S is an *injection*. Recall that an equivalent formulation is:

$$\forall x, y : \text{Nat} \cdot S(x) = S(y) \Rightarrow x = y$$

(5) *Induction principle*

$$\forall A \subseteq_d \text{Nat} \cdot [0 \in A \wedge (\forall x : A \cdot S(x) \in A)] \Rightarrow A = \text{Nat}$$

The set Nat together with the constant $0 : \text{Nat}$ and the function $S : \text{Nat} \rightarrow \text{Nat}$ are referred to as the *Peano system* (Nat, 0, S). ■

4.1B Significance of Peano's postulates

1 The definition of (Nat, 0, S) is given entirely in terms of well-defined primitive set-theoretic concepts: sets, functions and so on. For instance, we have *not* defined the successor function S by the rule '$S(x) =_d x + 1$ for all $x : \text{Nat}$' as one might be tempted to do. Addition must be *defined* in terms of (Nat, 0, S), not the other way round. Likewise the term 'first' is not used in the definition because, however intuitively clear, this term has never been defined rigorously.

2 If we regard 0 as a *nullary* operation, we may say that Nat is *generated* by two operations: (a) the nullary operation 0, which produces $0 : \text{Nat}$ precisely, and (b) the *unary* operation $S : \text{Nat} \rightarrow \text{Nat}$, which produces $S(x)$ for every $x : \text{Nat}$. We say that Nat is *the set inductively generated by* 0 *and* S.

3 The import of Peano's postulates (3) and (4) is this: *they ensure that each* $x : \text{Nat}$ *is generated in just one way*. 0 is generated by the nullary operation of the same name and in no other way, as no application of S to any $x : \text{Nat}$ produces 0, by postulate (3). For any other $y : \text{Nat}$, y is generated by applying S to some *unique* $x : \text{Nat}$, as the application of S to any x' different from x produces a result $S(x')$ different from y, by postulate (4). Because of this property, Nat is said to be *freely generated* by 0 and S.

4 There is an alternative view of the natural numbers. This is to say that they are all the objects constructed in the following way: First, produce 0. Then generate $S\,0$, $S\,S\,0$, $S\,S\,S\,0, \ldots$ by *repeatedly applying* S to the last x obtained. The purpose of Peano's postulate (5), the induction principle, is to assert that *every member* of Nat is an object obtained in this way. The key feature of the induction principle is to make this assertion *without using the term 'repeatedly'*, which is not formally defined.

To elaborate on this last point, how do we define the concept of repetition – for example, 'do this 3 times' or 'this type of object 17 times' or 'for ever'? The answer is: we can do this precisely *only by reference to the natural numbers*. Indeed, the only way rigorously to define an object or an action repeated n

times is to say that it is a *function* a: $\{1, 2, \ldots, n\} \to A$, where each a_i is the ith instance of the repeated object or action for $i =_{\mathrm{d}} 1, 2, \ldots, n$. Likewise an *infinite* repetition may only be defined precisely as a function a: Nat $\to A$, giving the infinite sequence $(a_0, a_1, \ldots)$ of instances a_i of the repeated object or action. In conclusion, repetition must be *defined* in terms of the natural numbers rather than the other way round. The main point of the induction principle is to provide a basis for a rigorous definition of this concept.

4.1C Sets inductive with respect to 0 and S

The first two properties of Nat we pointed out are (a) 0: Nat and (b) for any x: Nat, $S(x) \in$ Nat. Hence we say that Nat is *closed* under the two operations 0 (nullary) and S (unary). In practice, it is often convenient to consider these two properties separately from the induction principle. This leads us to the definition of a set that is *inductive* with respect to 0 and S, which is *any* set closed under 0 and S. This concept proves to be very useful in subsequent developments.

In particular, we may now define Nat in two stages. First, Nat is required to be an inductive set (with respect to 0 and S). In addition, Nat must satisfy the induction principle. Moreover, this is now easier to formulate. It is that any inductive subset $A \subseteq$ Nat must be equal to Nat; or, equivalently, that Nat *is the smallest of all inductive sets.* Consequently, an inductive set must contain every member of Nat, but it may also contain other elements.

Definition 4.1C.1

A set A is *inductive with respect to* 0 and S if A satisfies the following two conditions:

(1) $0 \in A$
(2) for all x: A, if $S(x)$ is defined then $S(x) \in A$

We also say that A is *closed under the two operations* 0 and S. ■

We are using as general a definition as possible here: an object x may be in A even if $x \notin \mathrm{Def}(S)$. Also we stress 'with respect to 0 and S' as we shall later define other inductive sets using 'generators' different from 0 and S. For the moment the only inductive sets we consider are with respect to 0 and S.

We may now consider various applications of this concept. First, as mentioned above, the induction principle may be restated in terms of inductive sets as follows:

Induction principle (restatement) For any subset $A \subseteq_{\mathrm{d}}$ Nat, if A is inductive (with respect to 0 and S) then $A =$ Nat. ■

Second, we may assert that the set Nat itself is inductive. Note that this is due to Peano's postulates (1) and (2) only, *not* to the induction principle.

Third, we may verify the following property of Nat, which results from the induction principle:

Theorem 4.1C.1

The set Nat is the intersection of all inductive sets:

$$\text{Nat} = \cap \{A \mid A \text{ is inductive with respect to 0 and } S\}$$ ■

In a nutshell, this theorem states that Nat is the *smallest* of all inductive sets, for it contains every element which is a member of *all* inductive sets *and nothing else*. To put it another way: any *other* inductive set A must contain all the members of Nat, *plus* some additional elements.

Assuming Peano's postulates (1) and (2), Theorem **4**.1C.1 is implied by the induction principle. The converse is true: the theorem also *implies* the induction principle. For the condition Nat $= \cap \{A \mid A$ is inductive$\}$ implies that for any inductive set A (with respect to 0 and S), Nat $\subseteq A$. Moreover, by the extensionality principle, Nat $\subseteq A$ and $A \subseteq$ Nat implies $A =$ Nat. In conclusion, the induction principle and Theorem **4**.1C.1 are equivalent, and the theorem may be regarded as an alternative formulation of the induction principle.

4.1D A concrete definition of the natural numbers AT

Definition **4**.1A.1 specifies the properties of a system (Nat, 0, S), but this does not determine (Nat, 0, S) uniquely. As it is defined, (Nat, 0, S) is just a set with two associated operations on its elements satisfying certain conditions. It is easy to construct many different such systems. These are called *Peano systems*. Fortunately, all these systems are *equivalent* in a certain sense, so we could say that what we denote by (Nat, 0, S) is *any one* of them, chosen once for all, and leave things at that. We also say that any two Peano systems are *isomorphic*. This is developed in the exercises.

This approach is not entirely satisfactory, because it does not give us any concrete example of a Peano system. It would be nice to see at least one specific system, if only to confirm our belief that such objects do exist. We now construct such a concrete system. This is the standard definition of natural numbers in set-theoretical terms and it is due to the mathematician John von Neumann (1903–1957). It is given by the following rules:

(1) Each natural number x is a *set*.

(2) The number 0 is defined as the empty set, that is $\varnothing$.

(3) For any natural number x, the successor $S(x)$ is defined by

$$S(x) =_{\text{d}} x \cup \{x\}$$

The first 4 numbers are therefore:

$$
\begin{aligned}
0 &=_{d} && \varnothing\\
1 &=_{d} \varnothing \cup \{\varnothing\} = && \{\varnothing\}\\
2 &=_{d} \{\varnothing\} \cup \{\{\varnothing\}\} = && \{\varnothing, \{\varnothing\}\}\\
3 &=_{d} \{\varnothing, \{\varnothing\}\} \cup \{\{\varnothing, \{\varnothing\}\}\} = && \{\varnothing, \{\varnothing\}, \{\varnothing, \{\varnothing\}\}\}
\end{aligned}
$$

From these examples, it can be seen that the above rules may be expressed concisely as follows:

Each number n is defined as the set of its predecessors:

$$n =_{d} \{0, 1, \ldots, n-1\}$$

Therefore: $0 =_{d} \varnothing$; $1 =_{d} \{0\}$; $2 =_{d} \{0, 1\}$; $3 =_{d} \{0, 1, 2\}$; etc.

Remarks

1 These 'set-theoretic numbers' should be regarded as *representations* of the natural numbers in set theory. There are other representations: any Peano system will do.

2 The set of numbers defined by the above rules is specifically denoted by the Greek omega, 'ω'. For any set x, $x \cup \{x\}$ is denoted by x^{+}. Thus, x^{+} represents the successor $S(x)$ for all $x : \omega$. We continue using 'Nat' for the set of natural numbers when we do not wish to assume any particular representation. Note that S is the *restriction* of the function $x \mapsto x^{+}$ to ω.

3 In a complete axiomatic treatment of set theory we cannot *prove* with the axioms adopted so far that there exists a *set* ω containing *all* the natural numbers: $\varnothing$, $\{\varnothing\}$, $\{\varnothing, \{\varnothing\}\}, \ldots$. Consequently, we must introduce a further axiom, the so-called *infinity axiom*. This asserts that there exists at least one set which is inductive with respect to $\varnothing$ (as nullary function) and the function $x \mapsto x^{+}$. Thence, ω is defined as the intersection of all such inductive sets. ω is properly defined in this way, by a subset axiom, and so its existence is proved. For further details, see Enderton (1977).

4 The fact that $(\omega, \varnothing, S)$ with $S(x) =_{d} x^{+}$ is a Peano system must be proved. For this proof, the reader is referred to Enderton (1977) or Halmos (1974). ■

EXERCISES

4.1.1 Consider Definition **4**.1A.1. We may *define* any Peano system (P, e, F) by substituting P, e and F for Nat, 0 and S respectively in this definition. This makes P a set, e a certain member of P and F a function $P \to P$, all satisfying the conditions stated in the definition, namely Peano's postulates (1) to (5).

Alternatively, we may specify (P, e, F) in some other way and then seek to *prove* that (P, e, F) is a Peano system, by demonstrating that all the conditions of Definition **4**.1A.1 are satisfied (when P, e and F are substituted for Nat, 0 and S). In this second case, the conditions of Definition **4**.1A.1 are *implied* by the specification of (P, e, F).

Let $(P1, e1, F1)$ be a (demonstrably Peano) system defined by

(1) $P1 =_{\mathrm{d}} \{n : \mathrm{Nat} \mid n \text{ is odd}\}$

(2) $e1 =_{\mathrm{d}} 1$

(3) $F1 : P1 \to P1$ and $\forall n : P1 \cdot F1(n) = n + 2$

(a) Give a formal definition of $P1$ using MOD, and redefine $F1$ using the successor function S of (Nat, 0, S).

(b) Draw a diagram representing the part of the graph $\mathrm{Gr}(F1)$ containing the first six members of $P1$.

(c) Verify that $(P1, e1, F1)$ satisfies Peano's postulates (1) to (4) in the sense explained above.

Note Exercise **4**.2.3 is to demonstrate that $(P1, e1, F1)$ also satisfies postulate (5), the induction principle. This will be an application of proof by induction, which is presented in Section **4**.2. It will complete the proof that $(P1, e1, F1)$ is a Peano system.

4.1.2 Let $(P2, e2, F2)$ be defined like $(P1, e1, F1)$ except that $P2 =_{\mathrm{d}} \mathrm{Nat}$. Thus:

(1) $P2 =_{\mathrm{d}} \mathrm{Nat}$

(2) $e1 =_{\mathrm{d}} 1$

(3) $F2 : P2 \to P2$ and $\forall n : P2 \cdot F2(n) =_{\mathrm{d}} n + 2$

Thus, both $P2$ *and* $F2$ are affected by the new definitions of $P2$. Draw a diagram representing the graph of $F2$ for about 10 initial values of $P2$. From this diagram, conclude that although inductive with respect to $e2$ and $F2$, $P2$ does *not* satisfy the induction principle. Indicate which inductive proper subset of $P2$ does satisfy the induction principle, and what is the 'junk'.

4.1.3 Let (P, e, F) be any Peano system. Let (P', e', F') be the system defined informally by removing e from P, setting $e' =_{\mathrm{d}} F(e)$ and adapting F in the obvious way to give F'.

(a) Draw a diagram representing $\mathrm{Gr}(F)$ for a few initial members of P, and mark the part representing $\mathrm{Gr}(F')$ in the diagram.

(b) Derive (P', e', F') formally from (P, e, F), with and without the function restriction operation $\diamond$.

4.1.4* Verify that the system (P', e', F') defined in Exercise **4**.1.3 is a Peano system.

4.1.5 Using Exercises **4**.1.3 and **4**.1.4, show that for any Peano system (P, e, F), we may construct an infinite number of different Peano systems.

4.1.6 Let $(P3, e3, F3)$ be the (demonstrably Peano) system defined as follows:

(1) $P3 =_{\mathrm{d}} \{n\!:\!\mathrm{Nat} \mid n \text{ is a power of } 2\}$
(2) $e3 =_{\mathrm{d}} 1$
(3) $F3\!:\!P3 \rightarrow P3$ and $\forall n\!:\!P3 \cdot F3(n) =_{\mathrm{d}} n \times 2$

(a) Define $P3$ formally.
(b) Draw a diagram representing the part of the graph $\mathrm{Gr}(F3)$ containing the first six members of $P3$.
(c) Verify that $(P3, e3, F3)$ satisfies Peano's postulates (1) to (4) in the sense explained in Exercise **4**.1.1. (The proof of postulate (5) is left to Section **4**.2.)

4.1.7* In this exercise, we embed $(P3, e3, F3)$ into a larger system $(P4, e4, F4)$ which does *not* satisfy Peano's postulates. Here is a partial specification of $(P4, e4, F4)$:

(1) $P4 =_{\mathrm{d}} \mathrm{Nat}$
(2) $e4 =_{\mathrm{d}} e3 = 1$
(3) $F4\!:\!P4 \rightarrow P4$

The definition of $F4$ is completed below. The aim of this exercise is to illustrate the following points. First, $P3$ is the smallest inductive subset of $P4 = \mathrm{Nat}$, with respect to $e4$ and $F4$. Thus, as Nat is larger than $P3$, it fails to satisfy the induction principle. Second, $F4$ has none of the properties expected of a Peano system. It contains at least one circuit. Moreover, there are several elements y, including members of $P3$, each of which has several predecessors, i.e. values x with $F4(x) =_{\mathrm{d}} y$, so $F4$ is *not* injective. Third, the restriction $P3 \diamond F4$ is $F3$ itself. Therefore, *F4 restricted to P3* satisfies all the conditions of Definition **4**.1A.1 as $(P3, e3, F3)$ is a Peano system. Consequently, the subset inductively generated by $e4$ and $F4$, namely $P3$, has the right linear structure, but within $F4$ as a whole all the desired properties of a Peano system are destroyed by the junk elements.

We now define two preliminary functions and $F4$ itself. For any $n\!:\!\mathrm{Nat}$, let

(1) $LD(n) =_{\mathrm{d}}$ the least divisor of n greater than 2
(2) $p(n) =_{\mathrm{d}}$ 0 if $n = 0$ or n is a power of 2
$\qquad LD(n) - 2$ otherwise
(3) $F4(n) =_{\mathrm{d}} 2 \times (n - p(n))$

Note (i) 1 is a power of 2, being 2^0. (ii) LD is a partial function $\mathrm{Nat} \nrightarrow \mathrm{Nat}$ as $LD(n)$ is defined iff n is *not* a power of 2.

(a) Define the functions LD and p formally.
(b) Tabulate n, $LD(n)$, $p(n)$ and $F4(n)$ for all $n:I$, where $I =_d \{1, 2, \ldots, 20\}$.
(c) Draw a diagram representing the part of Gr($F4$) containing the members x of I and their values $F4(x)$, and describe how this diagram illustrates the points made above.
(d) Prove that $F4(n)$ is defined for all n: Nat.

4.1.8 Prove Theorem **4.1C.1** – that is, demonstrate that it is implied by Peano's postulates (Definition **4.1A.1**).

4.1.9* Consider the system (P, e, F) *partially* defined by

(1) $P =_d \{1, 2\} \times \text{Nat}$
(2) $e =_d (1, 0)$
(3) $\forall n: \text{Nat} \cdot F(1, n) =_d (1, S\ n)$

where S is the successor function of (Nat, 0, S). Let $P1 =_d \{1\} \times \text{Nat}$ and $P2 =_d \{2\} \times \text{Nat}$. Note that $P = P1 + P2$ as $P1 \cap P2 = \varnothing$. Thus F so far is defined over $P1$, but for any $x: P2$, $F(x)$ is still undefined.

(a) Prove that $P1$ is inductive with respect to e and F. This implies that P itself, though inductive with respect to e and F, does *not* satisfy the induction principle.
(b) Verify that the subsystem $(P1, e, P1 \diamond F)$ satisfies Peano's postulates (1) to (4). This subsystem also satisfies postulate (5); the proof is left to Section **4.2**. Consequently, $P1$ is the set inductively generated by e and F, and it is a Peano system regardless of the way F is defined over $P2$.
(c) Extend the initial definition of F by specifying some values $F(x)$ for members x of $P2$, and represent Gr(F) by a diagram. Choose your extension in such a way that F satisfies Peano's postulates (1) to (4) *yet contains finite circuits involving* elements from $P2$. This will illustrate that the absence of circuits in a Peano system results from the conjunction of all the conditions of Definition **4.1A.1**.
(d) Carry out further experiments similar to (c).

4.2 Proof by induction

We now describe a first major practical implication of the induction principle. This is to give a means of proving that a proposition about a natural number n is true *for all possible values of n*. This type of proof is called *proof by mathematical induction* and is widely used in both computing and mathematics.

4.2A Proposition $P(n)$; example

In the present Section **4**.2, we consider any proposition involving (or 'about') any n: Nat. We denote this proposition by $P(n)$ to indicate that it depends on n. Thus, it may be true for some values of n and false for all other values.

An example of a proposition $P(n)$ is

(1) $(n \neq S\ n)$

That is, $P(n)$ states that 'the number n is different from its successor $S\ n$'. This is a function of n: it is a predicate, in principle true for some values of n and false for others. We shall in fact prove that it is true for all n: Nat, but until this has been done we cannot rule out the possibility of $P(n)$ failing for some n.

Two instantiations of $P(n)$ – simply replacing n by any number in (1) – are as follows.

$P(0)$: $(0 \neq S\ 0)$

This is true by Peano's postulate (3), Definition **4**.1A.1, which states that for all x: Nat, $0 \neq S\ x$. This inequality holds in particular for $x = 0$.

$P(1)$: $(1 \neq S\ 1)$

This is also true, as we shall prove.

We come back to this example in Section **4**.2C, where we derive the full proof by induction that this particular proposition $P(n)$ is true for all n: Nat.

4.2B Proof by induction: theorem and method

We now consider again any proposition $P(n)$. Note that $P(n)$ is about a *particular* number n, *assumed fixed before* $P(n)$ *is asserted.* Our concern now is to verify that $P(n)$ is true for all n: Nat, if possible. That is, we want to prove

$\forall\ n: \text{Nat} \cdot P(n)$

for instance

$\forall\ n: \text{Nat} \cdot (n \neq S\ n)$

This is quite different from $P(n)$ on its own.

The induction principle gives us one way of providing such a proof. In outline, this is as follows. Suppose we can prove

(1) $P(0)$

(2) $\forall\ n: \text{Nat} \cdot P(n) \Rightarrow P(S\ n)$

Then it must follow that

(3) $\forall\, n\!:\!\mathrm{Nat} \cdot P(n)$

We can see this intuitively as follows:

> $P(0)$ is true by (1);
> hence $P(1)$ is true, as $P(0) \Rightarrow P(1)$ by (2);
> hence $P(2)$ is true, as $P(1) \Rightarrow P(2)$ by (2);
> and so on.

We have a chain of implications, and this must reach every n:Nat. Therefore, $P(n)$ must be true for all n, precisely on account of the induction principle. We conclude:

Theorem 4.2B.1

Let $P(n)$ be any proposition depending on n:Nat. Suppose the following conditions are true:

(1) $P(0)$

(2) $\forall\, n\!:\!\mathrm{Nat} \cdot P(n) \Rightarrow P(S\ n)$

Then $P(n)$ is true for all n:Nat; that is,

(3) $\forall\, n\!:\!\mathrm{Nat} \cdot P(n)$ ■

Method 4.2B.1 The import of Theorem **4**.2B.1 is that it gives us a practical method of proving that a proposition $P(n)$ is true for all n. This is:

> Seek to demonstrate (1) and (2). If this can be done then conclude (3), namely that for all n:Nat, $P(n)$ is true.

The proof of (1) is called the *induction basis* and the proof of (2) the *induction step*. In the induction step, $P(n)$ is the *induction hypothesis*. ■

Proof of Theorem 4.2B.1 The theorem follows from the induction principle. Consider the set A of all n:Nat such that $P(n)$ is true:

$$A =_{\mathrm{d}} \{n\!:\!\mathrm{Nat} \mid P(n)\}$$

Assume that conditions (1) and (2) of Theorem **4**.2B.1 are satisfied. They imply that A is inductive with respect to 0 and S:

(1′) $0 \in A$ by (1)

(2′) For all n:Nat, if $n \in A$ then $S\ n \in A$ by (2).

Consequently, as A is inductive then $A = \text{Nat}$ by the induction principle. This is the same as saying that $P(n)$ is true for all $n : \text{Nat}$. ■

4.2C Example of a proof by induction

Consider again the proposition $P(n)$ given by

$$P(n): \quad (n \neq S\ n)$$

Intuitively, it is obvious that this must be true for every natural number n. But the question is: can we *prove* this, using only the postulates stated in Definition 4.1A.1? This is our goal here. More specifically, we want to prove that

$$\forall\, n : \text{Nat} \cdot (n \neq S\ n)$$

using Method 4.2B.1.

Induction basis We must prove $P(0)$, that is, $0 \neq S\ 0$. As already stated in Section 4.2A, this is true by Peano's postulate (3), Definition 4.1A.1, which reads as follows:

$$\forall\, x : \text{Nat} \cdot S(x) \neq 0$$

If we *substitute* 0 for x in this rule, we obtain $S(0) \neq 0$, which is $P(0)$.

Induction step It remains to be proved that:

$$\forall\, n : \text{Nat} \cdot P(n) \Rightarrow P(S\ n)$$

or in this particular case

$$\forall\, n : \text{Nat} \cdot (n \neq S\ n) \Rightarrow (S\ n \neq S\ S\ n)$$

Note that $P(S\ n)$ is obtained *mechanically* by substituting $S\ n$ for n in the definition of $P(n)$, namely $(n \neq S\ n)$.

Consider any $n : \text{Nat}$. Assume $P(n)$ is true. Then $P(S\ n)$ must be true by Peano's postulate (4), which reads:

$$\forall\, x, y : \text{Nat} \cdot x \neq y \Rightarrow S(x) \neq S(y)$$

If we substitute n for x and $S\ n$ for y in this rule, we obtain

$$n \neq S\ n \Rightarrow S\ n \neq S\ S\ n$$

which is precisely

$$P(n) \Rightarrow P(S\ n)$$

Therefore if $P(n)$ is true then so is $P(S\ n)$, and the proof is complete.

4.2D Alternative application of the induction principle

Instead of using Theorem **4**.2B.1, we may reason directly in terms of the set A used in the proof of this theorem. Given any proposition $P(n)$, define A by

$$A =_{\mathrm{d}} \{n : \mathrm{Nat} \mid P(n)\}$$

and seek to show that A is inductive. If this can be done then conclude that $P(n)$ holds for all n : Nat by the induction principle, for this states that $A = \mathrm{Nat}$.

It is emphasized that this method is entirely equivalent to Method **4**.2B.1. It is preferred in practice, as it justifies the conclusion – namely, that $P(n)$ is true for all n – directly from the induction principle. Thus it is somewhat simpler and clearer.

Example 4.2D.1

For any n : Nat, if $n \neq 0$ then there exists m : Nat such that $n = S(m)$. We prove this fact by induction, using the direct method just outlined. Thus we want to prove that the proposition

(1) $\quad P(n)\colon \quad (n \neq 0) \Rightarrow (\exists\, m : \mathrm{Nat} \cdot n = S\ m)$

is true for all n : Nat.

Let A be the set of numbers n : Nat such that $P(n)$ is true:

$$A =_{\mathrm{d}} \{n : \mathrm{Nat} \mid P(n)\}$$

We must show that A is inductive.

Induction basis We must show that $0 \in A$, or that $P(0)$ is true, which is the same. $P(0)$ is the proposition

$$(0 \neq 0) \Rightarrow (\exists\, m : \mathrm{Nat} \cdot 0 = S\ m)$$

and this *is* true because $(0 \neq 0)$ is false, even though there is no m with $0 = S\ m$. See the definition of $\Rightarrow$ in Section **2**.4C.

Induction step Consider any $n{:}A$ – that is, such that $P(n)$ is true. We must show that $P(S\ n)$ is also true, implying $S\ n \in A$. $P(S\ n)$ is the proposition defined by

$$P(S\ n): \qquad (S\ n \neq 0) \Rightarrow (\exists\ m{:}\text{Nat} \cdot S\ n = S\ m)$$

Again, this is obtained mechanically by substituting $S\ n$ for n in (1). Now we must show that if $S\ n \neq 0$ then there exists a number m such that $S\ n = S\ m$. This is true: n is a natural number, so we may take $m = n$. Actually, the existence of m such that $S\ n = S\ m$ does *not* depend on $S\ n \neq 0$ or on $P(n)$, but this does not matter; the important thing is to prove that m exists. This example is a special case in this respect.

In conclusion, A is inductive. Therefore, by the induction principle $A = \text{Nat}$, which means that $P(n)$ is true for all $n{:}\text{Nat}$. ■

4.2E Second induction principle

There is a second induction principle, which immediately follows from the first, and a related proof method. Consider a set $A \subseteq_{\text{d}} \text{Nat}$ satisfying the following conditions:

(1) $0 \in A$

(2) $\forall\ n{:}\text{Nat} \cdot \{0, 1, \ldots, n\} \subseteq A \Rightarrow S(n) \in A$

Then it is easy to see that $A = \text{Nat}$. We can prove this fact by induction (*first* principle!). Let proposition $P(n)$ be defined for all $n{:}\text{Nat}$ by

$$P(n): \quad \{0, 1, \ldots, n\} \subseteq A$$

We must prove that $P(n)$ is true for all n, as this is clearly equivalent to $A = \text{Nat}$. For the induction basis, $P(0)$, namely $\{0\} \subseteq A$, is true by (1). The induction step is to prove that for all $n{:}\text{Nat}$, $P(n) \Rightarrow P(S\ n)$. This is immediate: by (2), $P(n)$ implies $S(n) \in A$ and consequently $\{0, 1, \ldots, n, S(n)\} \subseteq A$, which is $P(S\ n)$. In conclusion, $P(n)$ is true for all n, which implies $n \in A$ for all $n{:}\text{Nat}$.

This second induction principle yields a corresponding second proof by induction. For any proposition $P(n)$, in order to prove $P(n)$ for all $n{:}\text{Nat}$, proceed as follows: prove

(1) $P(0)$

(2) $\forall\ n{:}\text{Nat} \cdot (\forall\ k{:}\{0, 1, \ldots, n\} \cdot P(k)) \Rightarrow P(S\ n)$

It is sometimes easier to prove (2) than to show that $P(n) \Rightarrow P(S\ n)$ for all $n{:}\text{Nat}$.

EXERCISES

4.2.1 Let $f:\text{Nat} \to \text{Nat}$ be defined by

(a) $f(0) =_{d} 0$

(b) $\forall n:\text{Nat} \cdot f(S\,n) =_{d} \begin{cases} 1 & \text{if } f(n) = 0 \\ 0 & \text{if } f(n) = 1 \end{cases}$

Prove by induction that for all n: Nat, $f(n) = n$ MOD 2. Hint: recall the definition of MOD. $f(n) = n$ MOD 2 means that $0 \leqslant f(n) < 2$ and there exists q:Nat such that $2 \times q + f(n) = n$. This definition must be used in the proof. Note: the definition of f is *recursive*. Recursive functions are developed and justified in Section **4**.3, and so are the other recursive functions introduced in the next exercises.

4.2.2 Let $f:\text{Nat} \to \text{Nat}$ be defined by

(1) $f(0) =_{d} 0$

(2) $\forall n:\text{Nat} \cdot f(S\,n) =_{d} \begin{cases} S(f\,n) & \text{if } f(n) < k - 1 \\ 0 & \text{if } f(n) = k - 1 \end{cases}$

for any $k > 1$. Prove by induction that for all n: Nat, $f(n) = n$ MOD k.

4.2.3 Let $(P1, e1, F1)$ be the Peano system defined in Exercise **4**.1.1. Prove by induction that this system satisfies the induction principle.

4.2.4 Repeat Exercise **4**.2.3 for the following systems:

(a) $(P3, e3, F3)$ of Exercise **4**.1.6

(b) $(P1, e, P1 \diamond F)$ of Exercise **4**.1.9(b).

4.2.5 Let $A:\text{Nat} \to \text{Pow(Nat)}$ be defined by $A_n =_{d} \{m \mid 0 \leqslant m < n\}$. Prove that for all n: Nat, $\text{Num}(\text{Pow}(A_n)) = 2^n$. Hint: recall that for any n: Nat, $\text{Pow}(A_n) =_{d} \{B \mid B \subseteq A_n\}$ and observe that if $n > 0$, $\text{Pow}(A_n)$ is given by

$$\text{Pow}(A_n) = \text{Pow}(A_{n-1}) + \{C \mid \exists B \subseteq_{d} A_{n-1} \cdot C = B + \{n\}\}$$

(See Exercise **2**.2.9.) Also, observe that $A_0 = \varnothing$ as there is no $m < 0$. Note that the property to be proved in this exercise holds for any finite set T with $n =_{d} \text{Num}(T)$. Each set A_n we are using here should be regarded as representative of any set of cardinality n.

4.2.6 Let $f(n)$ be the sum of the first n natural numbers:

$$f(n) =_{d} 0 + 1 + 2 + \cdots + n$$

We may define f recursively by

(a) $f(0) =_{d} 0$

(b) $\forall\, n : \text{Nat} \cdot f(S\, n) =_{d} f(n) + S\, n$

Verify that $[n \times (n + 1)]/2$ is a natural number for all n: Nat. Then prove by induction that for all n: Nat, $f(n) = [n \times (n + 1)]/2$.

4.3 Simple recursion

The method of proof by induction is a first major consequence of Peano's postulates. We now describe a second key implication of these postulates. This is that they give us a method of defining an important class of functions

$$h : \text{Nat} \to V$$

that is, from the natural numbers to any given set V. These functions are called *recursive*. They occur very frequently in both computing and mathematics, although their importance is not always recognized as they often arise implicitly rather than explicitly.

The purpose of what follows is twofold. First, it is to introduce the concept of a recursive function and to enable the reader to recognize such functions when they occur. Second, it is to explain why these functions are well defined, and to emphasize the conditions which they must satisfy in order to be well defined.

The definition of a recursive function is usually called an *inductive* or *recursive definition*. The functions we consider in this section are called more specifically *simply recursive*, to distinguish them from more general recursive functions, some of which are described in subsequent sections.

Note that the proof by induction described in Section **4**.2 depends only on Peano's postulates (1), (2) and (5) (Definition **4**.1A.1), whereas recursive functions depend on all five postulates. In particular, postulates (3) and (4) are essential conditions of well-definedness of a recursive function.

The approach of this section is mainly intuitive. It first gives an example of a recursive function. Then it presents the theorem which guarantees that such a function is well defined and explains the key fact justifying this theorem. This is followed by further examples. Finally, we review the common features of inductive *definitions* and inductive *proofs*, collectively called *inductive constructions*, and we show that these two types of construction are closely linked in practice.

4.3A Example of a simply recursive function

Recall that so far we have not formally defined *addition* on the natural numbers. Our first example is the construction of a recursive function h which paves the way towards such a definition.

Suppose that a certain number k:Nat is given, say $k =_d 4$. The function h which we define is very simple: it is the function which adds k to any number n:Nat. In other words, h sends every n:Nat to $h(n) =_d k + n$. This, of course, is only a statement of intent, *not* a definition, as we have not rigorously defined the addition operation yet. Addition is *derived* from the construction of h rather than h being derived from addition.

To start with, let us tabulate a few initial values of $h(n)$, assuming $k =_d 4$. The table is a (very) partial enumeration of the graph Gr(h).

n	$h(n)$
0	4
1	5
2	6
3	7
...	...

Two features emerge from this table:

1 $h(0) = k$. Here, this is 4. Thus for $n =_d 0$, $h(n)$ is *directly* given.

2 Any *other* number n:Nat is the successor of some m:Nat, i.e. $n =_d S(m)$, and $h(n)$ is derived from $h(m)$ by the simple rule

$$h(n) =_d S(h(m))$$

or, equivalently,

$$h(S(m)) =_d S(h(m))$$

For instance:

$$h(0) = 4$$
$$h(1) = h(S(0)) = S\,4 = 5$$
$$h(2) = h(S(1)) = S\,5 = 6$$
$$h(3) = h(S(2)) = S\,6 = 7$$

and so on.

We may represent this by the following diagram.

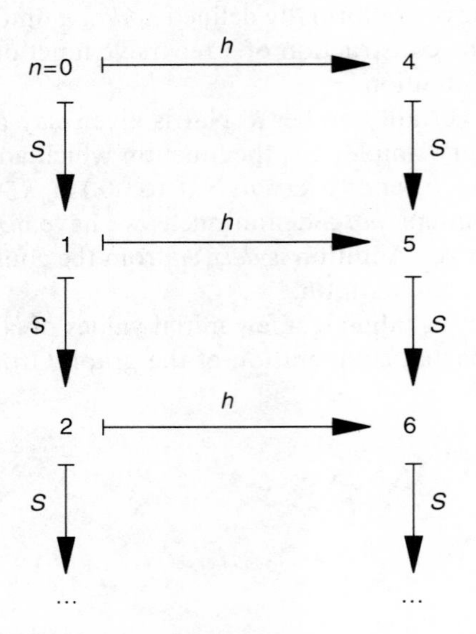

This diagram becomes in general:

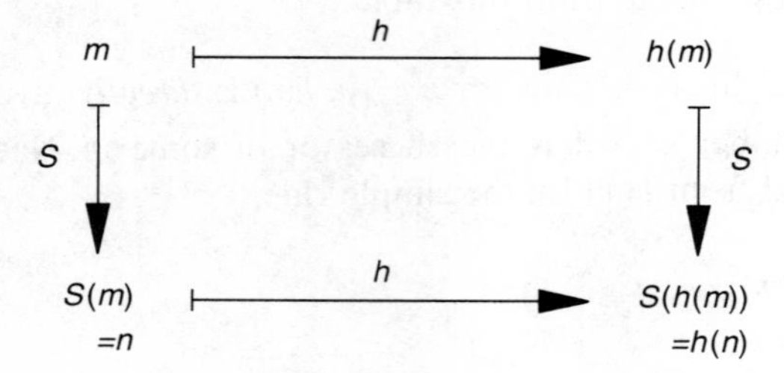

The general diagram says that for any m, if we go from m to $n = S(m)$ and then from n to $h(n)$, we reach the same result as by going first from m to $h(m)$ and then from $h(m)$ to its successor $S(h(m))$. This is just another way of stating the equation $h(S(m)) = S(h(m))$, which must hold for all m: Nat. Because of this equality of results obtained by following different paths from m, the above diagrams are called *commutative*.

To sum up, we have defined a (putative) function h by the two conditions

(1) $h(0) =_d k$

(2) $\forall\, m : \text{Nat} \cdot h(S(m)) =_d S(h(m))$

For $n =_{\mathrm{d}} 0$, $h(n)$ is directly given by (1). Any other n:Nat is the successor of some m, and $h(n) =_{\mathrm{d}} h(S(m))$ is derived from $h(m)$ as indicated by (2). It remains to be proved that h is indeed a function.

4.3B Simple recursion theorem

We have defined a rule which associates a certain value $h(n)$ with every n:Nat. Now we must answer the following question: does this rule define a *total function*

$$h:\mathrm{Nat} \rightarrow \mathrm{Nat}$$

and if so, is this function unique?

More precisely:

(1) Is $h(n)$ *uniquely defined* for any n:Nat?

(2) Is $h(n)$ defined *for all* n:Nat?

(3) Is there *only one* function h satisfying conditions (1) and (2) of Section 4.3A?

These three questions are crucial. It would be a serious mistake to answer 'obviously yes' – a mistake too often made in only slightly more complex cases. This answer must be proved.

The practical significance of Peano's postulates is to guarantee that these three questions may be answered affirmatively – that h is a well-defined *total function* from Nat to Nat, and that it is *unique*. This guarantee is formulated as the next theorem.

Theorem 4.3B.1

Given any k:Nat, let $h:\mathrm{Nat} \rightarrow \mathrm{Nat}$ be defined by

(1) $h(0) =_{\mathrm{d}} k$

(2) $\forall\, m:\mathrm{Nat} \cdot h(S(m)) =_{\mathrm{d}} S(h(m))$

Then h is a well-defined total function: that is, for each n:Nat there is a unique value $h(n)$:Nat. Moreover, h is unique: no other function satisfies conditions (1) and (2). ■

Outline justification

A partial and intuitive justification of this result follows. Above all, it shows why the existence of h as a total function depends on *all five* of Peano's postulates.

The *uniqueness* of h is easy to prove by induction. We ignore this aspect here, and concentrate on the *existence* of h as a total function. Our aim is to explain how for successive values n: Nat, $h(n)$ is defined in *exactly one way* by conditions (1) and (2) of Theorem **4**.3B.1. Our explanation rests on the assumption that for no m: Nat is $h(m)$ determined *from* $h(S(m))$ by condition (2). This assumption turns out to be true, but it has to be proved!

1 Consider first $n =_d 0$. $h(0)$ is defined (as equal to k) by condition (1). The only other way $h(0)$ could be defined is by condition (2). However, there is no m such that $0 = S(m)$, by Peano's postulate (3) (Definition **4**.1A.1). Consequently $h(0)$ is uniquely defined.

2 Next, consider any $n \neq 0$. $h(n)$ can only be determined by condition (2). There is at most one m with $S(m) = n$, by Peano's postulate (4). Therefore, $h(n)$ can only be determined by $h(m)$, through condition (2), and if $h(m)$ is defined and unique, then so is $h(n)$. Thus:

- $h(0)$ is uniquely determined from k;
- hence, as $1 = S(0)$, $h(1)$ is uniquely determined from $h(0)$;
- hence, as $2 = S(1)$, $h(2)$ is uniquely determined from $h(1)$; and so on.

We see that for each m: Nat such that $h(m)$ is uniquely defined, $h(S(m))$ is also uniquely defined on account of condition (2) and so $h(n)$ is uniquely defined for each n: Nat by the induction principle, Peano's postulate (5).

This description is *not* a proof of Theorem **4**.3B.1, but it sheds light on the 'process' by which h is defined and on the role of Peano's postulates. Suppose, for instance, that postulate (3) did *not* hold. Then 0 would also be the successor of some m: Nat, and $h(0)$ would be determined by both conditions (1) and (2). If $S(h(m))$ were different from k, which we could not rule out, $h(0)$ would be given at least two different values.

Likewise, suppose that postulate (4) did not hold. Then there would be an n: Nat with $n = S(m1)$ and $n = S(m2)$ for two different numbers $m1$ and $m2$: Nat. If $S(h(m1))$ were different from $S(h(m2))$ then again $h(n)$ would be given at least two different values.

Finally, if the induction principle did not hold – that is, if Nat contained elements in excess of the minimum needed to make it inductive – $h(n)$ would not be defined for any such element n.

To sum up:

(1) Recall that on account of postulates (3) and (4), Nat is said to be *freely generated* by 0 and S. This essentially means that each n: Nat is generated in just one way. Now it is this property that ensures that *for each* n: Nat, $h(n)$ *itself is uniquely defined*, that is, h is a function.

(2) Nat is the smallest inductive set by the induction principle, postulate (5), and it is this property that ensures that $h(n)$ *is defined for all* n: Nat, that is, h is total.

These are the key facts about recursive functions, or inductive definitions. Note that Theorem **4**.3B.1 is about a function h defined by specific conditions.

We focused on this case to keep matters as simple and concrete as possible. However, it is easy to generalize this theorem to any function $h\colon \text{Nat} \to V$ defined by similar conditions. The result is the simple recursion theorem, which follows. In turn, this result is further generalized in Section **4**.5C, following structural induction. It is emphasized that these generalizations are straightforward, and all the essential ideas about recursion have by now been presented.

General theorem

In Theorem **4**.3B.1, the function $h\colon \text{Nat} \to \text{Nat}$ is determined by two rules: condition (1), which defines $h(0)$ as a constant $k\colon \text{Nat}$, and condition (2), which determines $h(S(m))\colon \text{Nat}$ for any m by applying the function $S\colon \text{Nat} \to \text{Nat}$ to $h(m) \in \text{Nat}$. This construction can be generalized as follows.

(1) Instead of Nat, take any nonempty set V as codomain of h. The aim now is to define a total function $h\colon \text{Nat} \to V$.

(2) Instead of $k\colon \text{Nat}$, select any element $a\colon V$ for $h(0)$.

(3) Instead of $S\colon \text{Nat} \to \text{Nat}$, take any function $F\colon V \to V$ to determine $h(S(m))$ from $h(m)$, for any $m\colon \text{Nat}$.

Theorem **4**.3B.1 now becomes:

Theorem 4.3B.2 (simple recursion theorem, variant 1)

Let V be any nonempty set, a any member of V, and F any total function $V \to V$. There exists a total function

$$h\colon \text{Nat} \to V$$

which satisfies the following conditions:

(1) $h(0) =_{\text{d}} a \in V$

(2) $\forall\, m\colon \text{Nat} \cdot h(S(m)) =_{\text{d}} F(h(m)) \in V$

Moreover, this function is unique: there exists no other function $h'\colon \text{Nat} \to V$ satisfying conditions (1) and (2). ■

Everything that has been stated above about Theorem **4**.3B.1 holds under these more general conditions. This is true in particular of the commutative diagrams. The general diagram becomes:

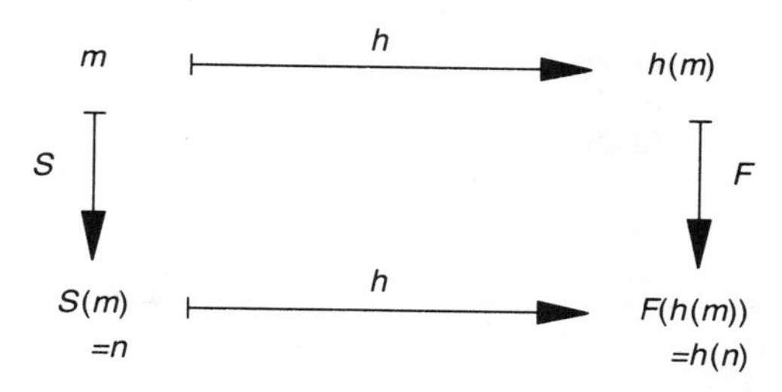

Here is an example of another recursive function, this time to a codomain V different from Nat.

Example 4.3B.1

Let V be the set of squares on a chessboard, $a: V$ the bottom left square and $F: V \to V$ a function describing how a piece may be moved from any square $v: V$ to another point $F(v): V$.

Suppose F is given by the rules set out below. Each square $v: V$ is described as a couple $(v_1, v_2): I^2$ where $I =_d \{0, 1, \ldots, 7\}$, and for any $v: V$ we denote $F(v)$, the next square, by $w = (w_1, w_2)$. In particular, $a = (0, 0)$. We need a special operation, addition modulo 8. This is denoted by $+_8$. It is defined for all $x, y: I$ by

$$x +_8 y =_d \begin{cases} x + y & \text{if } x + y \leqslant 7; \\ x + y - 8 & \text{otherwise} \end{cases}$$

The aim of $+_8$ is to ensure that for any $x, y: I$, $x +_8 y \in I$.

(1) If $(v_1 + 1) \times (v_2 + 1) - 1$ is a prime number then

$$w_1 =_d v_2 +_8 1 \text{ and } w_2 =_d v_1 +_8 3$$

(2) else if $(v_1 + 1) \times (v_2 + 1) - 1$ is divisible by 2 then

$$(w_1, w_2) =_d (v_1, v_2 +_8 2)$$

(3) else $(w_1, w_2) =_d (v_1 +_8 1, v_2)$

It is clear that these three rules define a total function $F: V \to V$. Therefore, we have all the ingredients necessary to define a total function $h: \text{Nat} \to V$ by

Table 4.3B.1 Partial enumeration of the graph Gr(h).

n	$h(n) = (v_1, v_2)$	$(v_1 + 1) \times (v_2 + 1) - 1$
0	(0, 0) ($= a$)	0
1	(0, 2)	2
2	(3, 3)	15
3	(4, 3)	19
4	(4, 7)	39
5	(5, 7)	47
6	(0, 0)	0
7	(0, 2)	2
...	...	...

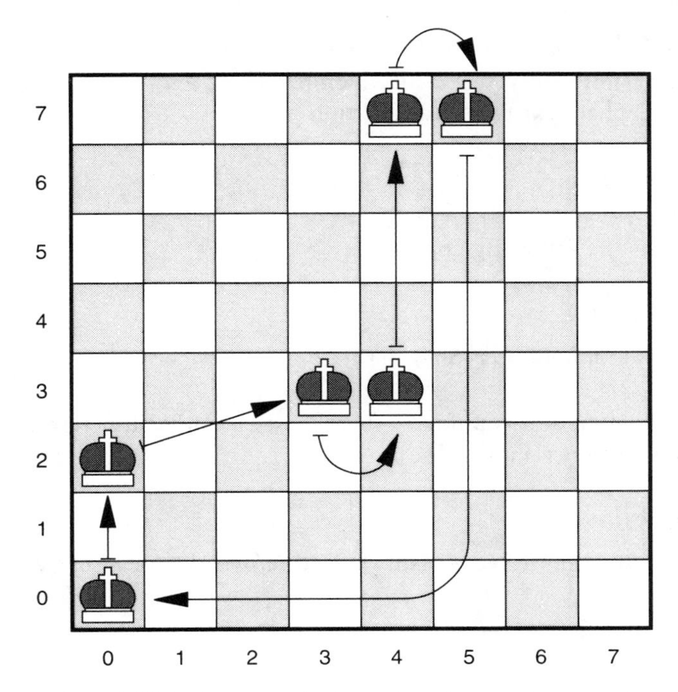

Figure 4.3B.1 Recursively defined path on a chessboard.

applying rules (1) and (2) of the simple recursion theorem. This function defines a path on the chessboard, starting at $a =_{\mathrm{d}} (0, 0)$. The first eight positions on this path are tabulated in Table **4**.3B.1. This tabulation is a partial enumeration of the graph Gr(h). Recall that 0 and 1 are *not* prime numbers.

It can be seen that h starts cycling after five moves. This simply means that h is not an injection. Cycling is bound to occur with any similar function, as Def(h) = Nat is infinite but Cod(h) = $V = I^2$ is finite. The reader may enjoy tabulating h for other starting positions a – preferably not in Ran(h) of the above function h! ■

4.3C A second variant of the simple recursion theorem

In some applications, the following variant of the simple recursion theorem is more appropriate. The principle is to define any $h(S(m))$ as a function not only of $h(m)$, but also of $S(m)$ itself. This means that F must be a function from Nat × V to V rather than from V to V. The proof of this variant is essentially the same as that of the original one.

Theorem 4.3C.1 (simple recursion theorem, variant 2)

Let V be any nonempty set, a any member of V, and F any total function $\text{Nat} \times V \to V$. There exists a total function

$$h : \text{Nat} \to V$$

which satisfies the following conditions:

(1) $h(0) =_{\text{d}} a \in V$

(2) $\forall\, m : \text{Nat} \cdot h(S(m)) =_{\text{d}} F(S(m), h(m)) \in V$

Moreover, this function is unique – there exists no other function $h' : \text{Nat} \to V$ satisfying conditions (1) and (2). ■

Example 4.3C.1

Consider the function $h : \text{Nat} \to \text{Nat}$ defined *informally* for all n by

(1) $h(n) =_{\text{d}} 1 + 2 + \cdots + n$

(Here we are still relying on our informal understanding of addition.) How can we define the function h exactly? The problem is to get rid of the ellipsis (...), which is an informal (though effective) way of conveying the idea of repetition. We do this by expressing $h(n)$ recursively as follows:

(2) (a) $h(0) =_{\text{d}} 0$

(b) $\forall\, m : \text{Nat} \cdot h(S(m)) =_{\text{d}} h(m) + S(m)$

A portion of the graph $\text{Gr}(h)$ is tabulated here, to help the reader see that (2) is the correct inductive rendering of (1).

n	$h(n)$
0	0
1	1
2	3
3	6
4	10

What is the function F in this case? The answer is: for all n, $x : \text{Nat}$,

$$F(n, x) = x + n$$

as the reader should verify. This shows that F must be a function

$$F: \text{Nat} \times V \to V$$

where $V = \text{Nat}$ here. ■

4.3D Inductive constructions

There is a close connection between a proof by induction and an inductive definition, that is, the definition of a recursive function. On the one hand, both constructions have a similar structure. On the other hand, inductive proofs and inductive definitions often depend on one another – they are 'interactive'. We now briefly discuss these two aspects. The observations made below readily extend to structural induction. The term '*inductive construction*' is used generically to mean three things: (a) the *system* (Nat, 0, S) itself; (b) any inductive *proof* based on (Nat, 0, S); and (c) any inductive *definition* based on (Nat, 0, S).

Common features of inductive constructions

A proof by induction involves a proposition $P(n)$, where n: Nat. An inductive definition is the construction of a function h: Nat → V. We refer to the case of an inductive *proof* as 'case 1' and that of an inductive *definition* as 'case 2'. The ultimate goal in case 1 is to demonstrate the generalization $\forall n: \text{Nat} \cdot P(n)$. In case 2, it is to define the function h as a whole. Both cases involve certain activities: the application of certain symbol manipulation rules or calculational processes. These activities have common features, which may be outlined as follows.

1 In both cases, the starting point is the Peano system (Nat, 0, S). This system forms the underlying structure of the inductive construction.

2 In both cases, we associate a certain object with each n: Nat. In the case of an inductive proof, this is the proposition $P(n)$. In the case of an inductive definition of a function h, the associated object is $h(n)$. Note that it is not so much $P(n)$ which corresponds to $h(n)$ as the proof of $P(n)$.

3 In both cases, there is a certain rule associated with 0. This rule is a *proof* that $P(0)$ is true in case 1, and a definition of $h(0)$ in case 2.

4 In both cases, there is a certain rule associated with each couple $(m, S(m))$. In case 1, this rule is a proof that if $P(m)$ is true then $P(S(m))$ is also true. In case 2, the rule indicates how to derive $h(S(m))$ from $h(m)$. In other words, the proof that $\forall m: \text{Nat} \cdot P(m) \Rightarrow P(S(m))$ corresponds to the function $F: V \to V$ in the definition of h. These common features are depicted in Figure **4**.3D.1.

Recall that there is also one important difference between proofs by induction and recursive functions. The latter depend on the fact that Nat is *freely* generated by 0 and S (Peano's postulates (3) and (4)), whereas the former do not.

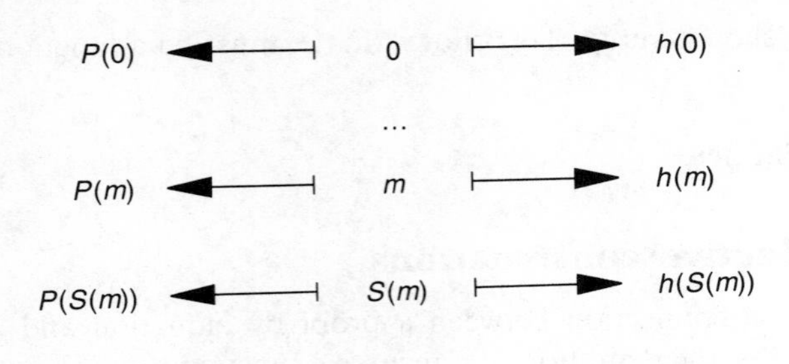

Figure 4.3D.1 Common features of inductive constructions.

Interaction between inductive proofs and definitions

Inductive proofs and definitions often arise simultaneously, because they are frequently interdependent. There are several reasons for that.

1 Whenever we define a function f, we must verify that f is indeed a function, that is, for each x: Def(f) the associated value $f(x)$ is uniquely determined. In the case of a recursive function, this is precisely the proof of the simple recursion theorem, and this proof is by induction – in fact, it involves several inductions.

2 Any proof by induction is about a certain proposition $P(n)$. Often the formulation of $P(n)$ involves one or more recursive functions. We may then expect that the inductive proof of $\forall n : \text{Nat} \cdot P(n)$ follows the same pattern as the inductive definition of the functions on which $P(n)$ is based.

3 Often we start with a main class of objects defined by induction, that is, as a recursive function, and we seek to identify and prove various properties of these objects. In this case, it is common for the proof of each property to be by induction and to follow the inductive definition of the main objects.

To sum up, inductive proofs and definitions often depend on one another and have a common or closely related structure. This interdependence is further evidence of the interactive nature of specification (definition) and analysis (proof) in establishment. There are many instances of related inductive definitions and proofs in subsequent developments.

4.3E Defining arithmetic operations in Nat AT

It was stated in Section **4**.3A that the recursive function h introduced there is the basis of the definition of addition in Nat. We now complete the inductive construction of this operation.

Recall that h was defined informally as the function that adds a value k: Nat to any n: Nat. The formal definition of h is

(A1) $h(0) =_{\text{d}} k$

(A2) $\forall\, m : \text{Nat} \cdot h(S(m)) =_{\text{d}} S(h(m))$

Now so far we have assumed k to be a fixed number, given once for all. However it is clear that a different function h is described by (A1) and (A2) for *each* k:Nat. This means that we may regard h *as a whole* as a function of k. Accordingly, we write h as Add_k to indicate that it is a function of k.

We must be specific about what we are doing here. We are introducing a new function *Add*. This function sends any k:Nat to another object, Add_k, and *this itself is a function* Nat → Nat, the function which adds k to its argument n. *Add* is a total function with domain Dom(*Add*) = Nat. The codomain Cod(*Add*) is the set of all total functions from Nat to Nat. In general this set is denoted by Nat → Nat. To sum up:

(1) For any k:Nat, Add_k:Nat → Nat is defined by

(A1′) $Add_k(0) =_d k$

(A2′) $\forall\, m:\text{Nat} \cdot Add_k(S(m)) =_d S(Add_k(m))$

(2) Dom(*Add*) = Nat and Cod(*Add*) = Nat → Nat.

Consequently *Add* is a unary function

$$Add:\text{Nat} \rightarrow (\text{Nat} \rightarrow \text{Nat})$$

There remains to define the standard operation + in terms of *Add*. These are *not* the same. + is a *binary* function

$$+:\text{Nat} \times \text{Nat} \rightarrow \text{Nat}$$

It sends any *couple* $(k, n):\text{Nat}^2$ to $k + n \in \text{Nat}$ – for example, (3, 5) to 8. *Add* is a *unary* function. It sends any k:Nat to the function Add_k:Nat → Nat. But we may define + in terms of *Add*. What we must do is indicate how $k + n$ is computed for each $(k, n):\text{Nat}^2$. This is given by the rule

$$\forall\, (k, n):\text{Nat}^2 \cdot k + n =_d Add_k(n)$$

which completes our definition of addition.

The other operations of multiplication and exponentiation in Nat are constructed in the same way. For multiplication (×), we first define for any k:Nat the function Mul_k:Nat → Nat which is to send each n:Nat to $k \times n$. This is given inductively by

(M1) $Mul_k(0) =_d 0$

(M2) $\forall\, m:\text{Nat} \cdot Mul_k(S(m)) =_d k + (Mul_k(m))$

(At this point we are using the inductive definition of +.) Mul_k is itself a function of k, so *Mul* is, like *Add*, a unary function

$$Mul:\text{Nat} \rightarrow (\text{Nat} \rightarrow \text{Nat})$$

The standard multiplication function

$$\times : \text{Nat}^2 \to \text{Nat}$$

is derived like + by the rule

$$\forall (k, n): \text{Nat}^2 \cdot k \times n =_{\text{d}} Mul_k(n)$$

Exponentiation is defined in the same way. All the basic properties of arithmetic operations – commutativity, associativity, distributivity and so on – may be formally proved from these definitions. The proofs are by induction in most cases.

EXERCISES

4.3.1 The factorial function is defined as the function $f: \text{Nat} \to \text{Nat}$ sending each n: Nat to $f(n) =_{\text{d}} 1 \times 2 \ldots \times n$. It is usually denoted by $n!$. For $n =_{\text{d}} 0$, $f(n) = 0! =_{\text{d}} 1$. Define f recursively.

4.3.2 Verify that the functions specified in exercises **4**.2.1, **4**.2.2 and **4**.2.6 have been properly defined recursively.

4.3.3 This and subsequent exercises are concerned with *enumerating* some infinite set M. This means constructing a rule selecting the members of M as elements E_0, E_1, $E_2, \ldots$ such that each member of M is selected exactly once. In other words the enumeration must be *complete* and *nonredundant*. Clearly such a rule is a bijection $E: \text{Nat} \to M$. The problem is to define E and to show that it is bijective – that is, both injective (nonredundancy constraint) and surjective (completeness constraint). A common strategy is to seek to define E recursively.

The problem is further complicated by the fact that some infinite sets M cannot be enumerated – there exists no bijection $E: \text{Nat} \to M$. An example is the set of real numbers; see also Exercise **4**.3.8 below. We say that a set M is *countable* iff it can be enumerated, that is, iff it admits a bijection $E: \text{Nat} \to M$. Often the sole purpose of constructing such a bijection E is to demonstrate that M is countable.

Let $M =_{\text{d}} \{1, 2\} \times \text{Nat}$. Construct a bijection $E: \text{Nat} \to M$. Hint: clearly $M = (\{1\} \times \text{Nat}) + (\{2\} \times \text{Nat})$. However, it would not do to try to enumerate all the members of $(\{1\} \times \text{Nat})$ first, and *then* all those of $(\{2\} \times \text{Nat})$: the latter would never be 'reached'. In selecting successive elements, we must somehow alternate between these two sets. There is a very simple method of attacking this problem: (a) first, tabulate a few values $E(n)$, for $n =_{\text{d}} 0, 1, 2, \ldots$; (b) then specify E; (c) finally show that E is injective and surjective.

4.3.4 Define bijections $E1: \text{Nat} \to M1$, $E2: \text{Nat} \to M2$ and $E3: \text{Nat} \to M3$ for the sets defined below. In each case, redefine the set formally as a preliminary step, if necessary.

(a) $M1 =_{\text{d}} \{n: \text{Nat} \mid n > 4\}$
(b) $M2 =_{\text{d}} \{n: \text{Nat} \mid n \text{ is even}\}$
(c) $M3 =_{\text{d}} \{n: \text{Nat} \mid n \text{ is odd}\}$

Hint: an alternative method for $M3$ is to construct an auxiliary bijection $F: M2 \to M3$ and then to define $E3$ by composition. For the proof that $E3$ is a bijection in that case, see Exercise **3**.6.6.

4.3.5* Enumerate $\text{Nat}^2 = \text{Nat} \times \text{Nat}$. Hint: partition Nat^2 into *finite* sets $P_0, P_1, P_2,$ and so on such that each P_i is defined by a simple property of its members (x, y) – for example, $\max(x, y) = i$ or $x + y = i$. Then, for each P_i, enumerate its elements – that is, construct a bijection $f_i: \{1, \ldots, n_i\} \to P_i$ where $n_i =_{\text{d}} \text{Num}(P_i)$. Finally, combine these successive f_i into a single function $E: \text{Nat} \to \text{Nat}^2$.

4.3.6* Enumerate $\text{Nat}^* =_{\text{d}} \text{Nat}^0 + \text{Nat}^1 + \text{Nat}^2 + \ldots$ where Nat^0 is the set with one member, the 0-tuple ( ). Hint: this requires a strategy similar to that suggested in Exercise **4**.3.4. As a preliminary step, verify that the various sets Nat^n are pairwise disjoint.

4.3.7* Enumerate Powf(Nat) using a strategy similar to that of Exercise **4**.3.6. (Recall that Powf(Nat) is the set of *finite* subsets of Nat.)

4.3.8* The set Pow(Nat), which contains many infinite subsets of Nat, is *uncountable*: there is no bijection $E: \text{Nat} \to \text{Pow(Nat)}$. Demonstrate this fact. Hint: let E be any function $\text{Nat} \to \text{Pow(Nat)}$. Clearly for any $n: \text{Nat}$, either $n \in E(n)$ or $n \notin E(n)$. Therefore, there is a set W of all $n: \text{Nat}$ such that $n \notin E(n)$. Show that W itself cannot be counted by E, that is, there is no $m: \text{Nat}$ such that $E(m) = W$, for otherwise we would have a contradiction. Consequently, E cannot be surjective, and therefore no function $E: \text{Nat} \to \text{Pow(Nat)}$ can be a bijection. Compare this line of reasoning with Russell's paradox, described in Section **2**.5A: there is an interesting similarity of structure.

It can be shown that there is a bijection between the set of real numbers and Pow(Nat). Thence, we may conclude that the set of real numbers is uncountable. The proof of the latter is the famous diagonal argument due to Cantor (1845–1918). This argument is similar to that required in this exercise.

4.3.9 Let M be any infinite subset of Nat. Enumerate M. Hint: M is ordered by $<$ in the same way that Nat is; the aim is to enumerate M in this order. Consider two successive elements $E(n), E(S\,n): M$. They delimit a finite subset $I_n =_{\text{d}} \{k \mid E(n) \leqslant k < E(S\,n)\}$ for any $n: \text{Nat}$, and $(I_n \mid n: \text{Nat})$ is a partition of

Nat without empty members. Define $E(n)$ using the successive sums of the cardinalities of these sets I_n.

From this exercise we may conclude that Nat is no 'larger' than any infinite subset of Nat! Thus, when it comes to infinite sets, the part may be as large as the whole.

4.3.10 Show that the successor function S of (Nat, 0, S) has a partial inverse P: Nat $\nrightarrow$ Nat. Define P precisely.

4.3.11 *Definition of* $<$ So far, we have used the relation $<$ without formally defining it. (a) Recursively define the function Anc: Nat $\rightarrow$ Powf(Nat) which sends each n: Nat to the set $Anc(n) =_d \{m : \text{Nat} \mid m < n\}$; that is, construct *Anc without reference* to $<$. (b) Define $<$ using the function *Anc*.

4.3.12 Prove by induction that for all n: Nat, $n \notin Anc(n)$. This implies that $<$ is antireflexive.

4.3.13 Prove by induction that the relation $<$, as defined by Exercise **4**.3.10 is transitive.

4.3.14* *Trichotomy law of* $<$ Prove by induction that for all n, m: Nat, exactly one of the following is true: (a) $n < m$; (b) $n = m$; (c) $m < n$. Hint: this requires a double induction.

4.3.15 Let (P, e, F) and (P', e', F') be any two Peano systems. Show that they are equivalent, or *isomorphic*, in the sense that there exists a bijection $Iso : P \rightarrow P'$ with the following properties:

(1) $Iso(e) =_d e'$
(2) $\forall\, x : P \cdot Iso(F\ x) =_d F'(Iso\ x)$

We also say that *Iso preserves e* and *F* in (P', e', F'), and that this function is an *isomorphism* (of Peano systems). Note that *Iso* is *unique*. This last property is *not* shared in general by isomorphisms of other types of object, such as families.

4.3.16 Show that the isomorphism relation between Peano systems is an equivalence – that is, a relation which is reflexive, symmetric and transitive. Note that any type of isomorphism shares this property.

4.3.17 Let exp: $\text{Nat}^2 \rightarrow$ Nat be the exponentiation function informally defined by

$$\exp(n, m) =_d n^m =_d n \times n \times \cdots \times n \text{ (m operands)}$$

Define exp recursively in the same way that $+$ and $\times$ have been constructed.

4.4 Structural induction

The various inductive constructions we have defined so far are all based on the same underlying system, (Nat, 0, S). This system consists of a certain set Nat inductively generated by two functions: $0 : \text{Nat}$ (nullary) and $S : \text{Nat} \rightarrow \text{Nat}$ (unary). Moreover as functions, these are special cases of general relations. As an operation, 0 is a *unary* relation whose graph is the singleton

$$\text{Gr}(0) = \{0\}$$

and S is a *binary* relation with graph

$$\text{Gr}(S) = \{(0, 1), (1, 2), (2, 3), (3, 4), \ldots\}$$

Now the system (Nat, 0, S) may be generalized as follows. Instead of 0 and S, we may use *any number of relations R of any arities*. These relations are used to generate a certain set C inductively *exactly* as Nat is generated by 0 and S. First, we define the class of *inductive sets*, or sets closed under the various relations considered. Then C is defined as the smallest of all these – as their intersection, to be precise. The inductive construction of (Nat, 0, S) is just a special case.

The relations used to define C are called (C-) *generators* and we often name them G_i. They *may* but *need not* be functions, total or partial. They may be of any arities – we may simultaneously use unary, binary, ternary relations, and so on, as C-generators. In the examples of this chapter and of Part **3** they are mainly functions, sometimes partial, but in Part **4** we use nonfunctional generators to define trees.

Given the set C generated by the selected relations, we may then establish proofs and definitions by induction based on the structure of C. It is emphasized again that these are constructed *exactly as we have done so far on the basis of* (Nat, 0, S).

We begin with an example illustrating the inductive construction of a set C. There follow the general definitions of an inductive set with respect to a set of C-generators, of C itself, and of a *parse tree*, which pictures the way in which any element of C is generated. Finally, the notion of a *construction sequence*, an alternative means of describing the generation of C, is introduced.

4.4A Example of a structural inductive construction

The set C we construct is a subset of the lowercase alphabet $Alph =_{\text{d}} \{\text{a}, \text{b}, \ldots, \text{z}\}$. Also recall that for a unary relation G with unique domain $Alph$, the graph $\text{Gr}(G)$ is a subset of $Alph$.

Consider the following family $\boldsymbol{G} =_{\text{d}} (G_1, G_2, G_3)$ of relations. G_1 is a unary relation given by

$$\text{Gr}(G_1) =_{\text{d}} \{\text{a}, \text{e}, \text{i}, \text{o}\} \subseteq Alph$$

Table 4.4A.1 Graph of the binary relation G_2.

a	b
a	a
a	c
a	o
c	k
n	b
n	t
q	g
q	i

Table 4.4A.2 Graph of the ternary relation G_3.

a	b	c
a	f	m
a	f	u
d	b	e
d	q	z
g	c	s
k	i	a
i	k	q
m	m	m
m	s	g
m	s	s
s	o	m

G_2 is a binary relation whose graph $\mathrm{Gr}(G_2)$ (set of couples $(a, b): Alph^2$) is given in Table 4.4A.1. G_3 is a ternary relation with graph $\mathrm{Gr}(G_3) \subseteq_d Alph^3$ given in Table 4.4A.2.

Any set A is *inductive with respect to* $\boldsymbol{G} = (G_1, G_2, G_3)$, or *closed* under $\boldsymbol{G}$, if it satisfies the following conditions:

(I1) For any $a: Alph$, if $a \in \mathrm{Gr}(G_1)$ then $a \in A$. In other words, $\mathrm{Gr}(G_1) \subseteq A$.

(I2) For any $a: A$ and $b: Alph$, if $(a, b) \in \mathrm{Gr}(G_2)$ then $b \in A$.

(I3) For any $a: A$, $b: A$ and $c: Alph$, if $(a, b, c) \in \mathrm{Gr}(G_3)$ then $c \in A$.

In the remainder of this section, by 'inductive' we mean 'inductive with respect to $\boldsymbol{G} = (G_1, G_2, G_3)$'. An example of an inductive set is *Alph* itself. Likewise, any set including *Alph*, such as $Alph + \{A, B, 3\}$, is inductive. Each of these sets satisfies conditions (I1), (I2) and (I3) but is not the *smallest* inductive set.

Table 4.4A.3 Members of the set C.

$x{:}C$	First cause of $x \in C$ (given the subset of C identified so far)
a	$\mathrm{a} \in \mathrm{Gr}(G_1)$
e	$\mathrm{e} \in \mathrm{Gr}(G_1)$
i	$\mathrm{i} \in \mathrm{Gr}(G_1)$
o	$\mathrm{o} \in \mathrm{Gr}(G_1)$
c	$(\mathrm{a}, \mathrm{c}) \in \mathrm{Gr}(G_2)$
k	$(\mathrm{c}, \mathrm{k}) \in \mathrm{Gr}(G_2)$
q	$(\mathrm{i}, \mathrm{k}, \mathrm{q}) \in \mathrm{Gr}(G_3)$
g	$(\mathrm{q}, \mathrm{g}) \in \mathrm{Gr}(G_2)$
s	$(\mathrm{g}, \mathrm{c}, \mathrm{s}) \in \mathrm{Gr}(G_3)$
m	$(\mathrm{s}, \mathrm{o}, \mathrm{m}) \in \mathrm{Gr}(G_3)$

The set C *inductively generated by* $\boldsymbol{G} = (G_1, G_2, G_3)$ is defined as the intersection of all inductive sets. It turns out to be the following subset of *Alph*:

$$C = \{\mathrm{a, c, e, g, i, k, m, o, q, s}\}$$

It is obtained as follows: a, e, i and o are the members of $\mathrm{Gr}(G_1)$ and therefore of C, by condition (I1). In order to determine the remaining members of C we must use G_2 and G_3 repeatedly until all members of C have been traced. Table 4.4A.3 indicates how each member of C is identified.

Remarks

1 In this example, none of the relations G_i is a function: G_1 because $\mathrm{Gr}(G_1)$ has several members; G_2 because each of a, n and q is the first element of several couples $(a, b){:}\mathrm{Gr}(G_2)$; and G_3, because each of (a, f) and (m, s) occurs as (a, b) in several triples $(a, b, c){:}\mathrm{Gr}(G_3)$. These nonfunctional relations were chosen deliberately to show that C-generators need not be functions.

2 We must verify that all the members of C have been identified. We do this by checking that C is inductive with respect to (G_1, G_2, G_3), that is, that

(I1′) any $a{:}\mathrm{Gr}(G_1)$ is a member of C;

(I2′) for any $a{:}C$ and $b{:}Alph$, if $(a, b) \in \mathrm{Gr}(G_2)$ then $b \in C$;

(I3′) for any $(a, b){:}C \times C$ and $c{:}Alph$, if $(a, b, c) \in \mathrm{Gr}(G_3)$ then $c \in C$.

This can be done elementwise as C and all the sets $\mathrm{Gr}(G_i)$ are finite. This task is left to the reader.

3 It is clear that any $x:C$ is a member of any set inductive with respect to (G_1, G_2, G_3). In other words, C is a subset of every inductive set and, as C itself is inductive, it is the intersection of all inductive sets.

4 The members of C have been identified in a certain systematic order based on the order in which each graph $\mathrm{Gr}(G_i)$ has been enumerated. This order is convenient for calculation purposes but not essential, as C and the graphs $\mathrm{Gr}(G_i)$ are just sets.

5 Some members of C are generated in several ways. For instance, $a \in C$ by virtue of $a \in \mathrm{Gr}(G_1)$, $(\mathrm{a, a}) \in \mathrm{Gr}(G_2)$ and $(\mathrm{k, i, a}) \in \mathrm{Gr}(G_3)$; $\mathrm{o} \in C$ on account of $\mathrm{o} \in \mathrm{Gr}(G_1)$ and $(\mathrm{a, o}) \in \mathrm{Gr}(G_2)$; $\mathrm{m} \in C$ by virtue of $(\mathrm{s, o, m}) \in \mathrm{Gr}(G_3)$ and $(\mathrm{m, m, m}) \in \mathrm{Gr}(G_3)$; and so on. For these reasons C is *not* freely generated by (G_1, G_2, G_3). (The concept of free generation will be defined as for (Nat, 0, S).)

6 Some members of $\mathrm{Gr}(G_2)$ and $\mathrm{Gr}(G_3)$ are not active in the determination of C. For instance, (n, b) and $(\mathrm{n, t}) \in \mathrm{Gr}(G_2)$ are 'inactive', as n itself is not a member of C. Consequently, neither b nor t belongs to C. Likewise (a, f, m) and (a, f, u) play no role in this definition as f is not a member of C. Consequently, u is not a member of C. However, the fact that (a, f, m) is inactive does *not* imply $\mathrm{m} \notin C$, because m belongs to C on account of (s, o, m), for instance. ■

4.4B General definition of structural induction

From the above example of structural induction, as well as the definition of (Nat, 0, S), the general definition of a set C generated inductively may now be given. The starting point is a family of generators (relations)

$$\boldsymbol{G} = (G_i \mid i:I)$$

where I is any index set. Each relation G_i has an arity which we denote by $arity(G_i)$. Different relations G_i may have different arities and, for any i, $arity(G_i) \geqslant 1$. We first define an inductive set with respect to $\boldsymbol{G}$. Then we define *the* set C inductively generated by $\boldsymbol{G}$.

Definition 4.4B.1

Let $\boldsymbol{G} = (G_i \mid i:I)$ be a family of relations (generators). For any $i:I$, let $arity(G_i) \geqslant 1$ denote the arity of the relation G_i. A set A is *inductive with respect to* $\boldsymbol{G}$ iff the following condition is satisfied.

For any relation G_i and any $n-1$ members $a_1, a_2, \ldots, a_{n-1}$ of A, where $n =_{\mathrm{d}} \mathrm{arity}(G_i)$, if there exists an element a_n such that

$$(a_1, a_2, \ldots, a_{n-1}, a_n) \in \mathrm{Gr}(G_i)$$

then a_n is a member of A.

In the case of $n = 1$, this statement reduces to the condition that any $a:\mathrm{Gr}(G_i)$ is a member of A, that is, $\mathrm{Gr}(G_i) \subseteq A$. ■

For instance, consider the relations (G_1, G_2, G_3) in the example of Section **4**.4A, and any set A. This set is inductive with respect to (G_1, G_2, G_3) iff the following conditions hold. For G_1, $arity(G_1) = 1$ so $\mathrm{Gr}(G_1)$ must be included in A. For G_2, $arity(G_2) = 2$. If $\mathrm{a} \in A$ then a, c and o must belong to A because (a, a), (a, c) and (a, o) $\in \mathrm{Gr}(G_2)$, and so on. For G_3, $arity(G_3) = 3$. If a and f belong to A then both m and u must belong to A because (a, f, m) and (a, f, u) $\in \mathrm{Gr}(G_3)$; if d and b belong to A then e must belong to A because (d, b, e) $\in \mathrm{Gr}(G_3)$, and so on.

Note that this example is just a precise application of the general condition of inductiveness stated above, and not a definition of the *smallest* inductive set. In particular, we are not saying that *every* inductive set must contain f, for instance – indeed, f is not in C. But we are saying that *if* f is a member of A *then* A must also contain m and u in order for A to be inductive.

Given $\boldsymbol{G} = (G_i \mid i : I)$, an inductive set A with respect to $\boldsymbol{G}$ is also said to be *closed* under $\boldsymbol{G}$ or by $\boldsymbol{G}$. We introduce a predicate ClosedBy to express this property.

Definition 4.4B.2

Given a family $\boldsymbol{G} = (G_i \mid i : I)$ of relations and any set A, we write

A ClosedBy $\boldsymbol{G}$

to express the fact that A is inductive with respect to $\boldsymbol{G}$ in the sense of Definition **4**.4B.1. ■

The next step is to define the (unique) set C generated by a family $\boldsymbol{G} = (G_i \mid i : I)$ of relations. This is done exactly as for (Nat, 0, S).

Definition 4.4B.3 Structural induction principle

Given a family $\boldsymbol{G} = (G_i \mid i : I)$ of relations, the set (*inductively*) *generated by* $\boldsymbol{G}$ is the set C defined by the following conditions:

(1) C is inductive with respect to $\boldsymbol{G}$.

(2) For any set $A \subseteq_{\mathrm{d}} C$, if A is inductive with respect to $\boldsymbol{G}$, then $A = C$. ■

Example 4.4B.1

If we take as family $\boldsymbol{G}$ the two operations $0 : \mathrm{Nat}$ and $S : \mathrm{Nat} \to \mathrm{Nat}$ in Definition **4**.4B.3, then we obtain the induction principle for the set Nat of natural numbers (Peano's postulate (5), Definition **4**.1A.1). Indeed, Peano's postulate (5) states that Nat is the set inductively generated by $\boldsymbol{G} =_{\mathrm{d}} (0, S)$. ■

The remarks made about the induction principle for Nat hold for the set C generated by any family $\boldsymbol{G} = (G_i \mid i : I)$ of relations. In particular, C may be described as the smallest of all inductive sets (with respect to $\boldsymbol{G}$), or as the intersection of all these sets. Thus, Theorem **4**.1C.1 generalizes to

Theorem 4.4B.1

The set C inductively generated by a family $\boldsymbol{G} = (G_i | i : I)$ of relations is the intersection of all inductive sets with respect to $\boldsymbol{G}$, i.e.

$$C = \cap \{A | A \text{ ClosedBy } \boldsymbol{G}\}$$

■

Remarks

1 As in the special case of Nat, Theorem **4**.4B.1 is equivalent to Definition **4**.4B.3 and could be used as an alternative definition of the structural induction principle.

2 In Definitions **4**.4B.1–3, there is no reference to the domains $\text{Dom}_j(G_i)$ of the generators. Thus the definition of C holds with relations G_i of either type, without or with specified domains (Definition **3**.5D.2 or **3**.5D.3). In fact, domains $\text{Dom}_j(G_i)$ are usually specified and they are often all equal to some universe U. If for each generator G_i the graph $\text{Gr}(G_i)$ is a set, then it is clear that C itself is a set. As we only consider this case, we ignore that in which $\text{Gr}(G_i)$ is a proper class for some relations G_i. ■

4.4C Parse trees

Let $\boldsymbol{G}$ be a family $(G_i | i : I)$ of relations, C the set inductively generated by $\boldsymbol{G}$, and c any element of C. A *parse tree* for c is a description of one of the ways in which c is generated by the relations G_i. Note that in general an element $c : C$ may be generated in several ways, as was illustrated in the example of Section **4**.4A, unless C is freely generated. *Each way is described by a different parse tree.* This is allowed for in the definition below.

Informally, a tree T is a diagram of points and lines or arrows connecting points. A connection between two points x and y is made to indicate that x is the parent of y. The key property of T is that exactly *one* point called the *root* of T has no parent, and every other point has exactly one parent. Moreover, any point x may be reached from the root by tracing successive lines, said to form a path from the root to x. A tree is finite iff it has a finite set of points. Trees are treated in Chapter **12**.

We begin with a preliminary definition.

Definition 4.4C.1

Let $\boldsymbol{G} = (G_i | i : I)$ and C be the set inductively generated by $\boldsymbol{G}$. For any c, if there is a generator G_i with arity n and an n-tuple $(a_1, \ldots, a_{n-1}, c) : \text{Gr}(G_i)$ with $a_j \in C$ for $j =_{\text{d}} 1, \ldots, n-1$, then $(G_i, a_1, \ldots, a_{n-1})$ is called an *immediate generator* of c (and c of course is in C). ■

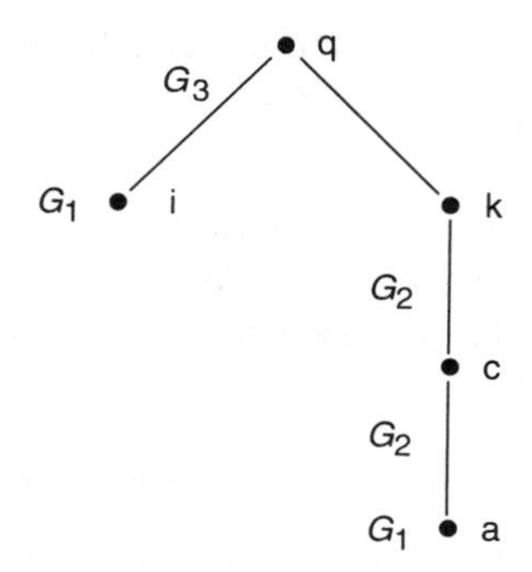

Figure 4.4C.1 Parse tree for q.

Definition 4.4C.2 (parse tree)

Let $\boldsymbol{G} = (G_i | i : I)$ and the set C be defined as in Definition **4**.4C.1. For any $c : C$, a parse tree T for c is constructed by the following rules:

(1) If c is generated by a unary relation G_i, that is, $c \in C$ by virtue of being a member of $\mathrm{Gr}(G_i)$, then T (for *this* generator) consists of a single point labelled with G_i on the left and c on the right:

$G_i \cdot c$

(2) Otherwise, c has an immediate generator $(G_i, a_1, \ldots, a_{n-1})$, with $n > 1$. In this case T (for this generator) is obtained as follows:

(a) Draw a point labelled with c on the right; this is the root of T.

(b) Draw a parse tree T_j for each a_j, $j =_{\mathrm{d}} 1, 2, \ldots, n-1$, underneath the root of T.

(c) Connect the root of T to the root of each T_j by a line and label these lines collectively with G_i on the left. ■

An example of a parse tree is given in Figure **4**.4C.1. It is one of the trees for the letter q in the example of Section **4**.4A.

4.4D Second example

One of the main applications of structural induction in computing is the definition of formal languages for various purposes: computer programming, data or rule declaration. Logic provides an important group of such languages. They are treated systematically in Part **3**. In this section this type of application is introduced by means of a very simple and arbitrary example. It is just a little game with letters.

Consider the following set of letters, which we call an alphabet:

$$Al =_{\mathrm{d}} \{\mathrm{R, D, a, b, c, d, e}\}$$

A *string* on Al is a finite sequence of letters from Al, for example 'R', 'Da', 'bbb', 'edcca'. We include the *empty string* or sequence of 0 letters. This is denoted by ε and must not be confused with the empty set $\varnothing$. Also, let Al^* be the set of all strings on Al:

$$Al^* =_{\mathrm{d}} \{\varepsilon, \text{'R'}, \text{'D'}, \text{'a'}, \text{'b'}, \text{'c'}, \text{'d'}, \text{'e'}, \text{'RR'}, \text{'RD'}, \text{'Ra'}, \ldots\}$$

Our purpose is to define a certain subset C of Al^* by certain rules. C is called a *language* (on the alphabet Al). We use the Greek letters $\alpha, \beta, \ldots$ to denote any strings on Al; that is, they are variables ranging over Al^*.

First, we introduce a unary relation G_1 and two operations G_2 and G_3 on Al^*. These are the *generators* of C. They are defined as follows:

(1) $\mathrm{Gr}(G_1) =_{\mathrm{d}} \{\text{'a'}, \text{'b'}, \text{'c'}, \text{'d'}, \text{'e'}\} \subseteq Al^*$

(2) $G_2 : Al^* \to Al^*$ is defined by

$$G_2(\alpha) =_{\mathrm{d}} \text{'R}\alpha\text{'}$$

for all $\alpha : Al^*$. For instance, $G_2(\text{'a'}) = \text{'Ra'}$; $G_2(\text{'Rbb'}) = \text{'RRbb'}$; $G_2(\text{'edDD'}) = \text{'RedDD'}$; and so on.

(3) $G_3 : Al^* \times Al^* \to Al^*$ is defined by

$$G_3(\alpha, \beta) =_{\mathrm{d}} \text{'D}\alpha\beta\text{'}$$

for all α and $\beta : Al^*$. For instance, $G_3(\text{'a'}, \text{'Rbb'}) = \text{'DaRbb'}$; $G_3(\text{'Rc'}, \text{'de'}) = \text{'DRcde'}$; $G_3(\text{'Rb'}, \text{'Dbe'}) = \text{'DRbDbe'}$; and so on.

We may now specify C semiformally as follows:

(1′) $\mathrm{Gr}(G_1) \subseteq C$. In words, every member of $\mathrm{Gr}(G_1)$ belongs to C.

(2′) For any $\alpha : C$, $G_2(\alpha) = \text{'R}\alpha\text{'} \in C$. Thus if a string α is a member of C, then so is 'Rα'.

(3′) For any $(\alpha, \beta) : C \times C$, $G_3(\alpha, \beta) = \text{'D}\alpha\beta\text{'} \in C$. In words, if two strings α and β are members of C, then so is 'D$\alpha\beta$'.

(4′) No string belongs to C if it is not accounted for by one of the previous rules.

Here are some examples of members of C, generated 'from the bottom up': that is, each group is generated by application of a generator to members of previous groups.

Generated by G_1: 'a', 'b', 'c', 'd', 'e'.
Generated by G_2: 'Ra', 'Rb', etc.

Generated by G_3: 'Daa', 'Dab', 'DaRa', 'DRaa', 'DRaRb', etc.
Generated by G_2: 'RRa', 'RRb', 'RDaa', 'RDab', 'RDaRa', etc.

It is easy to see that C is a strict subset of Al^*. Several previous examples of strings are clearly not members of C, such as 'Rbb' or 'edDD'. Note that G_2 and G_3 are total operations on the whole of Al^*, not just C. 'edDD' is not in C because it is not a member of $\mathrm{Gr}(G_1)$ and is not the result of an application of G_2 or G_3. 'Rbb' is the result of applying G_2 to another string, namely 'bb', but it does not belong to C, because 'bb' itself is not in C.

Remarks

1 A string of n letters on Al may be defined rigorously as an n-tuple; this is left as an exercise. In the case $n = 0$ it is the empty string ε defined in Exercise 3.5.17.

2 Note that $\mathrm{Gr}(G_1) \subseteq Al$ *and* $\mathrm{Gr}(G_1) \subseteq Al^*$. Each element of $\mathrm{Gr}(G_1)$ is also regarded as a string of one letter. ■

Formal description

We now turn to the formal definition of C. This follows closely the semiformal one. First, G_1, G_2 and G_3 are three relations on Al^*, unary, binary and ternary respectively. So we have a family $\boldsymbol{G} = (G_1, G_2, G_3)$ of generators.

Second, an inductive set with respect to $\boldsymbol{G}$ is a set A closed under these three relations; that is, it is any set that satisfies the three rules (1′), (2′) and (3′) above, where 'A' is substituted for 'C'. So all that remains to do is to formalize rule (4′). We express it as the induction principle:

For any set $A \subseteq_{\mathrm{d}} C$, if A is inductive with respect to $\boldsymbol{G}$ then $A = C$.

In other words, C is defined as *the* set inductively generated by $\boldsymbol{G}$. This completes our formal definition of C.

A parse tree for a random $\alpha : C$ is given in Figure 4.4D.1.

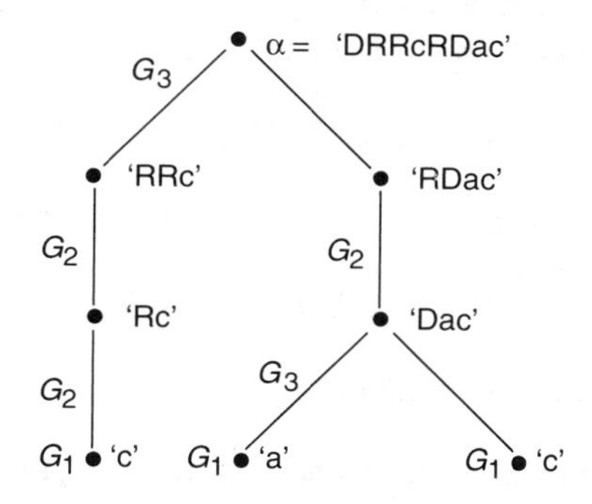

Figure 4.4D.1 Parse tree for $\alpha : C$.

4.4E Construction sequences

Let C be the set generated by any family $\mathbf{G} = (G_i | i : I)$ of relations. We now define an alternative means of demonstrating that an element c is a member of C, similar to a parse tree for c. This is a so-called *construction sequence* for c, and it is defined as follows:

Definition 4.4E.1

Given a family $\mathbf{G} = (G_i | i : I)$ of relations, the set C generated by $\mathbf{G}$ and any element $c : C$, a *construction sequence for* c is a (finite) sequence

(C1) $S =_{\mathrm{d}} (c_1, c_2, \ldots, c_p)$

with the following properties:

(1) Each element c_j is a member of C for $j =_{\mathrm{d}} 1, 2, \ldots, p$.

(2) $c_p =_{\mathrm{d}} c$.

(3) Any c_j in S is generated by some relation G_i of $\mathbf{G}$ of arity $n =_{\mathrm{d}} arity(G_i)$ from $n - 1$ elements occurring in S *before* c_j. More precisely, there exists an n-tuple $(a_1, a_2, \ldots, a_{n-1}, a_n)$: $\mathrm{Gr}(G_i)$ such that $a_n =_{\mathrm{d}} c_j$ and every a_k occurs before c_j in S (that is, $a_k =_{\mathrm{d}} c_h$ for some $h < j$). ■

One method of obtaining a construction sequence for an element c is to 'flatten' or 'linearize' a parse tree for c.

Example 4.4E.1

Consider the example of Section **4**.4A. A construction sequence for 'q' is

$S = (\mathrm{i, a, c, k, q})$

This sequence is obtained by 'flattening' the parse tree of Figure **4**.4C.1 in the obvious way. ■

Example 4.4E.2

Consider the example of Section **4**.4D, and the parse tree of Figure **4**.4D.1. Here is a construction sequence for α = 'DRRcRDac' obtained as in Example **4**.4E.1:

S = ('c', 'Rc', 'RRc', 'a', 'c', 'Dac', 'RDac', 'DRRcRDac')

Note that this sequence is slightly redundant; it may be reduced to:

S' = ('c', 'Rc', 'RRc', 'a', 'Dac', 'RDac', 'DRRcRDac')

by deleting the second occurrence of 'c'. ■

Construction sequences are closely related to parse trees. For any $c : C$, a parse tree T and a construction sequence S for c describe essentially the same thing. Both of them may be regarded either as a description of the way c is generated by the relations G_i, or as a demonstration that c is a member of C. The advantage of a parse tree is that it describes the generation of c more accurately and clearly.

Finally, the concepts of parse tree and construction sequence provide an alternative way of characterizing the set C. It can be shown that the set C (as defined by Definition **4**.4B.3) has the following property:

Theorem 4.4E.1

Let C be the set generated by a family $\boldsymbol{G} = (G_i | i : I)$ of relations. Any object c is a member of C iff there exists a parse tree for c or, equivalently, iff there exists a construction sequence for c. ∎

Thus we could also *define* C as the set of objects for which there is a parse tree or a construction sequence. Theorem **4**.4E.1 is intuitively clear. A proof of it may be found in Enderton (1977).

4.4F Proof by structural induction

In Section **4**.3D, it was pointed out that the system (Nat, 0, S) forms the underlying structure of simple inductive *proofs* on the one hand, and simple inductive *definitions* (recursive functions) on the other. (Nat, 0, S), inductive proofs and inductive definitions were generically called *inductive constructions.*

These ideas may be extended to any family $\boldsymbol{G} = (G_i | i : I)$ of generators. Thus, if C is the set inductively generated by $\boldsymbol{G}$, we may describe $(C, \boldsymbol{G})$ as a system of which (Nat, 0, S) is just a special case. Then we may construct proofs by induction based on $(C, \boldsymbol{G})$. Finally, we may define the conditions which $\boldsymbol{G}$ must satisfy for C to be freely generated, and if these conditions are met then we may construct inductive definitions based on $(C, \boldsymbol{G})$ – that is, recursive functions $h : C \to V$. We call these three types of construction (*structural*) *inductive constructions*. They are defined *exactly as in the special case of* (Nat, 0, S). We now briefly describe proofs by structural induction. Structural recursive functions are developed in Section **4**.5.

Consider any family $\boldsymbol{G} = (G_i | i : I)$ of relations and the set C inductively generated by $\boldsymbol{G}$. A proof by structural induction over C is a generalization of a proof by simple induction as described in Section **4**.2. We are given a proposition $P(a)$, where $a : C$. The purpose of the proof is to show that $P(a)$ is true for all $a : C$, that is:

$$\forall\, a : C \cdot P(a)$$

The method is based on the following generalization of Theorem **4**.2B.1.

Theorem 4.4F.1

Let $\boldsymbol{G}$ be any family $(G_i | i : I)$ of relations and C the set inductively generated by $\boldsymbol{G}$. Let $P(a)$ be any proposition depending on $a : C$. Suppose for each G_i and each n-tuple $(a_1, a_2, \ldots, a_{n-1}, a_n)\colon \mathrm{Gr}(G_i)$, where $n =_\mathrm{d} arity(G_i)$, the following condition is satisfied:

(1) $P(a_n)$ if $n = 1$

(2) $(P(a_1) \wedge \ldots \wedge P(a_{n-1})) \Rightarrow P(a_n)$ otherwise

Then:

$$\forall\, a\colon C \cdot P(a)$$ ■

Proof outline As in the case of Theorem **4**.2B.1, let

$$A =_\mathrm{d} \{a\colon C \mid P(a)\}$$

All we have to do is show that A is inductive with respect to $\boldsymbol{G}$. This follows immediately from Definition **4**.4B.1. Then, by the definition of C, $C = A$ and consequently $P(a)$ for all $a\colon C$. ■

From this theorem, the demonstration that $\forall\, a\colon C \cdot P(a)$ by structural induction is clear. It involves establishing that for each generator G_i and each n-tuple $(a_1, a_2, \ldots, a_{n-1}, a_n)\colon \mathrm{Gr}(G_i)$, where $n =_\mathrm{d} arity(G_i)$, the following condition is satisfied: if $P(a_j)$ is true for each $j =_\mathrm{d} 1, 2, \ldots, n-1$, then so is $P(a_n)$. In the case $n = 1$, this reduces to proving $P(a)$ for all $a\colon \mathrm{Gr}(G_i)$. If this proof can be given, $P(a)$ must be true for all $a\colon C$.

This method generalizes the proof by simple induction given in Section **4**.2B. The related definitions may be generalized accordingly. The *induction basis* is the proof of (1) for each unary relation G_i and each $a_n\colon \mathrm{Gr}(G_i)$. The *induction step* is the proof of (2) for each G_i with $arity(G_i) = n > 1$ and each $(a_1, \ldots, a_{n-1}, a_n)\colon \mathrm{Gr}(G_i)$. $P(a_1) \wedge \ldots \wedge P(a_{n-1})$ is the *induction hypothesis.*

Some theorems of Chapter 8 are proved by structural induction. Note that Theorem **4**.4F.1 does *not* require that C be freely generated by $\boldsymbol{G}$. However, the property P often involves one or more functions recursively defined on C in the sense of Section **4**.5. In this case C must be freely generated on account of these functions.

The second induction principle could be similarly generalized, though we shall not pursue this matter here.

EXERCISES

4.4.1 The purpose of this exercise is to verify that the set C constructed in Section **4**.4A is inductive with respect to $\boldsymbol{G} = (G_1, G_2, G_3)$. (a) Make a copy of the graphs $\mathrm{Gr}(G_1)$, $\mathrm{Gr}(G_2)$ and $\mathrm{Gr}(G_3)$. (b) Check that $\mathrm{Gr}(G_1) \subseteq C$. (c) Underline on your copy the couples $(x, y) : \mathrm{Gr}(G_2)$ such that $x \in C$ and check that $y \in C$. (d) Underline the triples $(x, y, z) : \mathrm{Gr}(G_3)$ such that $(x, y) \in C^2$ – that is, with both $x \in C$ and $y \in C$ – and check that $z \in C$. (e) Finally, check that for every couple $(x, y) : \mathrm{Gr}(G_2)$ *not* underlined, $x \notin C$, and for every triple $(x, y, z) : \mathrm{Gr}(G_3)$ *not* underlined, $(x, y) \notin C^2$ – that is, $x \notin C$ or $y \notin C$.

4.4.2 Show informally that the set C constructed in Section **4**.4A is the intersection of all inductive sets. Hint: take the members of C in the order in which they have been identified in Table **4**.4A.3. For each of them, argue that it must necessarily belong to every inductive set because all its predecessors in the generation sequence do so.

4.4.3 Let *Alph* and $\boldsymbol{G}$ be defined as in Section **4**.4A. Construct other subsets $A \subseteq_d Alph$ that are inductive with respect to $\boldsymbol{G}$, in particular the set $C1$ inductively generated by (G_1, G_2, G_3, G_4), where G_4 is a unary relation with graph $\mathrm{Gr}(G_4) =_d \{a, d, n\}$. Notice that such larger inductive sets are not simply obtained by adding any elements to C. We must ensure that, with the new elements, the larger set is *closed* under all the generating relations; that is, it continues to satisfy the definition of an inductive set with respect to $\boldsymbol{G}$.

4.4.4 Let $\boldsymbol{G} = (G_1, G_2, G_3)$ be the family of generators defined in Section **4**.4A. Draw four different parse trees for members of the set C generated by this family, two for ‘a’ and two for ‘m’.

4.4.5* Let $\boldsymbol{G}$ be as in Exercise **4**.4.4. (a) Show that there is an infinite set of parse trees for ‘a’. Attempt to describe this set; more precisely, to show how it could be generated systematically. (b) Repeat this exercise with ‘m’.

4.4.6 Let *Al* be defined as in Section **4**.4D. (a) Formally define a string α of n letters from *Al* as an n-tuple. (b) Define Al^* formally, using (a). Hint: refer to Exercise **3**.5.18.

4.4.7 Let *Al* and C be defined as in Section **4**.4D. The list below contains various strings $\alpha : Al^*$. For each α, determine whether α is a member of C or not, and justify your conclusion precisely.

(a) ‘RDbd’
(b) ‘DRaa’
(c) ‘RaDa’
(d) ‘c’
(e) ‘DRDedc’
(f) ‘bc’
(g) ‘RDRDbRca’
(h) ‘RDRDbRcbe’

4.4.8 Let C be defined as in Exercise 4.4.7. Draw the parse trees of the following strings $\alpha : C$:

(a) ‘c’
(b) ‘Ra’
(c) ‘DRbc’
(d) ‘RDRaDRbc’
(e) ‘DDReDecRDbRe’
(f) ‘DDDRRaRRRbbDcRe’

4.4.9 Derive construction sequences for the strings listed in Exercise 4.4.8 from the parse trees asked for in this exercise.

4.4.10 For any inductively generated set C, define a precise rule for converting any parse tree to a construction sequence in a unique way. Hint: in outline, for any $c : C$ with immediate generator $(G_i, a_1, \ldots, a_{n-1})$, a construction sequence for c is obtained by concatenating construction sequences for $a_1, a_2, \ldots, a_{n-1}$ and appending c. In general, the result is redundant, but redundant elements may then be eliminated in the appropriate order. Fill in the details. Note that this construction is an example of structural recursion (Section 4.5).

4.4.11 Consider the set C defined in Section 4.4D. Prove the following facts by structural induction:

(a) The empty string ε is *not* a member of C.
(b) For any $c : C$, either c consists of a single letter from $\mathrm{Gr}(G_1)$, or it is a string of several letters starting with ‘R’ or with ‘D’.
(c) For any $c : C$, the length of c, the number of letters making it up, is greater than twice the number of occurrences of ‘D’ in c.

4.5 Free inductive sets; general recursion theorem

The reason why it is possible to define recursive functions $h : \mathrm{Nat} \to V$ is that in addition to the induction principle, Peano's postulate (5), the system (Nat, 0, S) also satisfies postulates (3) and (4) (Definition 4.1A.1). We now describe the corresponding condition for the general case of any inductive set C. If this condition is satisfied, then C is said to be freely generated. This is the topic of Section 4.5A.

Not every inductive set C is freely generated, but if it is, then it is possible to define functions $h: C \to V$ recursively, just as in the special case of (Nat, 0, S). Any such function is total and unique. This fact is referred to as the (*structural*) *recursion theorem*; it generalizes the two variants of the simple recursion theorem of Section **4**.3B. In Section **4**.5B, we give an example of a structural recursive function. In Section **4**.5C, we present a first variant of the recursion theorem and conclude with comments on the theoretical and practical significance of this theorem. A second variant is given in Section **4**.5D.

4.5A Free inductive sets

In a nutshell, Peano's postulates (3) and (4) mean that the generators of Nat (0: Nat and S: Nat $\to$ Nat) produce each n: Nat *in exactly one way*. This is why Nat is said to be freely generated. This definition of free generation holds exactly as stated in the general case. It remains to examine what this means precisely.

Consider any family $\boldsymbol{G} = (G_i | i : I)$ of relations and the set C generated by $\boldsymbol{G}$. Recall that for any $c : C$ there exists *at least one* relation G_i, together with an n-tuple $(a_1, a_2, \ldots, a_{n-1}, c)$: Gr$(G_i)$ where $n =_{\mathrm{d}} arity(G_i)$ and such that each $a_j \in C$. We say that c is generated by G_i from $(a_1, a_2, \ldots, a_{n-1})$. It is now easy to define when C is *freely* generated by $\boldsymbol{G}$. The condition is simply that for each $c : C$, there exists *exactly one* relation G_i and *one* n-tuple $(a_1, a_2, \ldots, a_{n-1}, c)$: Gr$(G_i)$ such that each $a_j \in C$.

This condition sums up Peano's postulates (3) and (4) in the case of $\boldsymbol{G} = (0, S)$. 0 is generated by the operation of the same name, and this is a unary relation with graph Gr$(0) = \{0\}$. Postulate (3) states that 0 is not generated in any other way, that is, that Gr(S) does not contain a couple $\langle x, 0 \rangle$. For any other y: Nat, y is obviously not in Gr(0) as $y \neq 0$, and by postulate (4), there is exactly one couple $\langle x, y \rangle \in$ Gr(S).

Definition 4.5A.1 (freely generated inductive set)

Let C be the set inductively generated by a family $\boldsymbol{G} = (G_i | i : I)$ of relations. C is said to be *freely generated by* **G**, or a *free inductive set*, if the following condition is satisfied by $\boldsymbol{G}$:

> For any $c : C$, there exists exactly one relation G_i, and one *n-tuple* $(a_1, a_2, \ldots, a_{n-1}, c)$: Gr$(G_i)$ where $n =_{\mathrm{d}} arity(G_i)$ and such that $a_j \in C$ for $j =_{\mathrm{d}} 1, 2, \ldots, n-1$. ■

Remarks

1 The condition stated in Definition **4**.5A.1 is imposed primarily on *the family* $\boldsymbol{G} = (G_i | i : I)$ *of generators*, not on C. Of course, it is also a property of C, but by implication.

2 This condition can also be stated in terms of immediate generators thus: '*Any* $c:C$ *has just one immediate generator* $(G_i, a_1, a_2, \ldots, a_{n-1})$ *such that* $a_j \in C$ for $j =_d 1, 2, \ldots, n-1$'.

3 There is a third way of expressing the condition of Definition **4**.5A.1, probably the most useful in practice. This is:

There is exactly one parse tree for each $c:C$.

This property is clearly equivalent to the original condition: if any $c:C$ has a unique immediate generator $(G_i, a_1, a_2, \ldots, a_{n-1})$ and each a_j has a unique parse tree, then c itself can have only one parse tree. (This is in fact a consequence of the recursion theorem; see Exercise **4**.5.1.)

4 The definition of an inductive set C is often made only for the case in which the generators consist of (a) a unary relation G_1 (essentially a set) and (b) a number of operations $G_2, G_3, \ldots$ of various arities greater than 0. In that case, the condition of Definition **4**.5A.1 is stated as follows: (1) the ranges of $G_2, G_3, \ldots$ must be pairwise disjoint and disjoint from $\mathrm{Gr}(G_1)$; (2) each function $G_2, G_3, \ldots$ must be an injection. This condition may be relaxed by applying it only to the restrictions $C \diamond G_i$; it is this last formulation which corresponds to Definition **4**.5A.1. ■

Example 4.5A.1

The set Nat is freely generated by $(0, S)$. The unique parse tree of 0 is

0 • 0

where 0 on the left is the nullary operation, and for any other n, say 2, the unique parse tree is

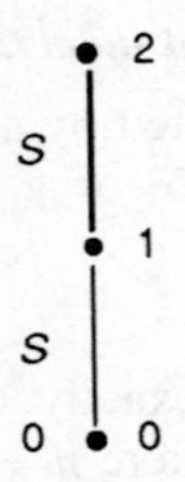

■

Example 4.5A.2 (counterexample)

The inductive set C constructed in Section **4**.4A is *not* freely generated by (G_1, G_2, G_3), as pointed out in Remark 5, Section **4**.4A. For instance 'a' has three different immediate generators: (G_1), (G_2, a) and $(G_3, \mathrm{k}, \mathrm{i})$. Consequently 'a' has the parse trees shown in Figure **4**.5A.1 (and infinitely many others!).

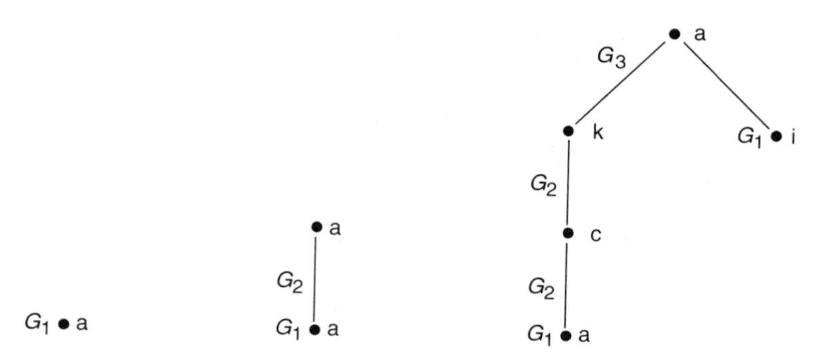

Figure 4.5A.1 Parse trees of 'a' $\in C$.

This counterexample is quite instructive. For any $c:C$, the proliferation of parse trees for c owing to the 'non-freeness' of C reveals how difficult it would be to define recursive *functions* on this set. ■

Example 4.5A.3

The inductive set C of Section **4**.4D is freely generated, as may be proved by simple induction. Therefore, each well-formed formula has a unique parse tree. It is this property that makes it possible to define a recursive function h from C to any set V. An example is given in Section **4**.5B. ■

These examples suggest that freeness in inductive constructions is a fundamental property, both theoretically and practically. The key condition is *for each member of the inductive set C to have a single parse tree*. If this condition is satisfied then recursive functions may be defined on C, as is illustrated in the next section. Note that there are many cases of useful inductive sets C which are *not* freely generated. Therefore, freeness is *not* a universal requirement. In particular, it is not required in order to construct a *proof* by induction (unless the proposition to be proved itself depends on recursive functions on C). It is only when we need to define recursive functions on the inductive set that freeness becomes essential.

4.5B Structural recursion: example

We now introduce the construction of a recursive function $h:C \to V$ based on an inductive set C. We do so by means of a simple example.

Consider the family $\boldsymbol{G} = (G_1, G_2, G_3)$ of generators defined in Section **4**.4D, and the set C inductively generated by $\boldsymbol{G}$. The intention is to regard C as a language representing a certain subset of Nat and certain operations on Nat. More precisely, each member (string) of C is viewed as a formula denoting either a certain natural number of the result (in Nat) of applying some operation to other number(s). Consequently, the recursive function we aim to define is a

Table 4.5B.1 The function m.

α	$m(\alpha)$
'a'	0
'b'	2
'c'	2
'd'	3
'e'	5

function $h: C \to V$, where $V =_d$ Nat (here!). In a language application, for each string $\alpha : C$, $h(\alpha)$ is often called the *value denoted by* α, or the *meaning* of α.

First, we must specify the subset and operations which G_1, G_2 and G_3 are intended to denote. These are entirely arbitrary: they are given only for the sake of illustration.

(1) As $\mathrm{Gr}(G_1)$ is a set, it is intended to represent the subset of V mentioned. This is done by introducing the function $m : \mathrm{Gr}(G_1) \to V$ defined by Table 4.5B.1. The subset of Nat represented is $\{0, 2, 3, 5\}$, with 2 denoted by two different members of $\mathrm{Gr}(G_1)$.

(2) G_2 is a unary function $Al^* \to Al^*$. Thus it is meant to represent a certain unary operation on V, which we introduce as the function $H_2 : V \to V$ defined by

$$H_2(n) =_d 2 \times n + 3$$

for all $n : V$.

(3) G_3 is a binary function $(Al^*)^2 \to Al^*$. It must therefore represent a binary operation $H_3 : V^2 \to V$, which we define by

$$H_3(m, n) =_d m \times n + 5$$

for all $m, n : V$.

Second, we define the function $h : C \to V$ itself. This is done by three rules corresponding to the three generators.

(1) For each $\alpha : \mathrm{Gr}(G_1)$

(R1) $h(\alpha) =_d m(\alpha)$

(2) For each $\alpha : C$, $h(G_2(\alpha)) = h(\text{‘R}\alpha\text{’})$ is derived from $h(\alpha)$ by

(R2) $h(G_2(\alpha)) =_d H_2(h(\alpha))$

(3) For each $\alpha, \beta : C$, $h(G_3(\alpha, \beta)) = h(\text{‘D}\alpha\beta\text{’})$ is derived from $h(\alpha)$ and $h(\beta)$ by

(R3) $h(G_3(\alpha, \beta)) =_d H_3(h(\alpha), h(\beta))$

Now the recursive function h is completely specified, but is it well defined – that is, are we guaranteed that $h(\alpha)$ is *uniquely* defined *for all* $\alpha : C$? The answer is 'yes', because the set C of wffs is freely generated by $\boldsymbol{G} = (G_1, G_2, G_3)$. The import of the recursion theorem is precisely to provide this guarantee.

Example 4.5B.1

Consider again the parse tree of Figure **4**.4D.1. It is reproduced here as Figure **4**.5B.1 with the values $h(\alpha')$ corresponding to the original entries α' indicated in square brackets.

The values $h(\alpha')$ entered in the figure are justified as follows:

(1) $h(\text{'c'}) = m(\text{'c'}) = 2$, as 'c' is generated by G_1.

(2) $h(\text{'Rc'}) = H_2(h(\text{'c'})) = H_2(2) = 7$, as 'Rc' is generated by G_2.

(3) $h(\text{'RRc'}) = H_2(h(\text{'Rc'})) = H_2(7) = 17$.

(4) $h(\text{'a'}) = m(\text{'a'}) = 0$, as 'a' is generated by G_1.

(5) $h(\text{'Dac'}) = H_3(h(\text{'a'}), h(\text{'c'})) = H_3(0, 2) = 5$, as 'Dac' is generated by G_3.

(6) $h(\text{'RDac'}) = H_2(h(\text{'Dac'})) = H_2(5) = 13$.

(7) $h(\text{'DRRcRDac'}) = H_3(h(\text{'RRc'}), h(\text{'RDac'})) = H_3(17, 13) = 226$. ■

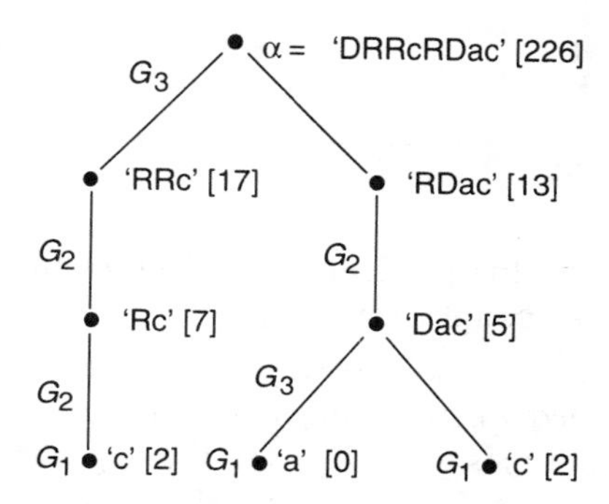

Figure 4.5B.1 Parse tree for $\alpha : C$.

Remarks

1 Consider the parse tree of Figure **4**.4D.1, which we now name T. We call the result of entering values $h(\alpha')$ into T, as we have done in Figure **4**.5B.1, an *augmented parse tree*. The (non-augmented) parse tree T is unique. Therefore, it is clear that given m, each point in T (string α') is assigned a unique value $h(\alpha')$. If α' is elementary then $h(\alpha')$ is determined by m, otherwise $h(\alpha')$ is determined by applying H_2 or H_3 to the values of the 'children' of α'. The parse tree is a vivid illustration of the fact that h is well defined.

2 Often in language applications we vary the function m while keeping the functions H_2 and H_3 (or equivalent) constant. Obviously for each function m we get a different but well-defined recursive function h.

3 The computation rule for strings generated by G_2 may be represented by the commutative diagram

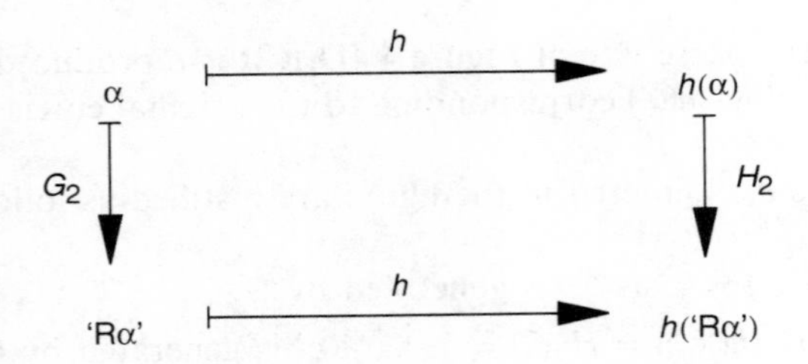

and the rule for strings generated by G_3 by the commutative diagram

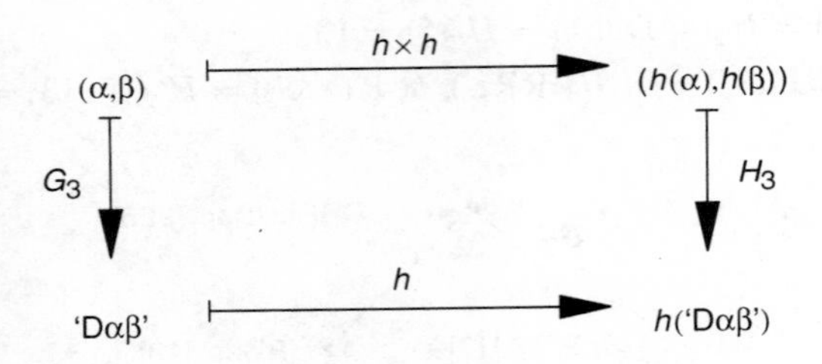

(In this second diagram, the product $h \times h$ denotes the function which sends each couple (α, β) to the couple $(h(\alpha), h(\beta))$.)

4 For any wff $\alpha : C$, consider (a) the way α is generated and (b) the manner in which $h(\alpha)$ is determined: there is an important correspondence between the two. If $\alpha \in \text{Gr}(G_1)$ then $h(\alpha)$ is given by $m(\alpha)$. If α is generated by G_2, which is a unary function, then $h(\alpha)$ is determined by H_2, also a unary function. Finally, if α is generated by G_3, a binary function, then $h(\alpha)$ is determined by the binary function H_3. Thus, *each function G_i has a corresponding function H_i of the same arity*. These correspondences have already been mentioned in the case of simple recursion, for example between $S : \text{Nat} \to \text{Nat}$ and $F : V \to V$. They are essential to the definition of recursive functions. ■

4.5C General recursion theorem

The example of Section 4.5B illustrates the construction of a recursive function h on a freely generated inductive set C other than Nat. We terminate this chapter with the presentation of the general recursion theorem, which justifies this construction. This theorem states that for any inductive set C, if C is *freely* generated then we may construct recursive functions h on C, provided some additional information is given.

We now present a first variant of the theorem, which addresses the special (but usual) case in which C is generated by a unary relation G_1 and functions $G_2, G_3, \ldots$ of various arities. The theorem is developed in two stages. First, we specify the information needed, in addition to C and its generators, to determine a recursive function h on C completely. Second, we indicate how h is determined by this additional information.

The first version of the theorem may be generalized to address the case in which the generators may be any family $\boldsymbol{G}$ of relations. This second variant is presented in Section **4**.5D.

Let $\boldsymbol{G} = (G_1, G_2, G_3, \ldots)$ be a family made up of a unary relation G_1 and various functions $G_2, G_3, \ldots$ of various positive arities. Let C be the set inductively generated by $\boldsymbol{G}$ and assume that C is freely generated by $\boldsymbol{G}$. In the example of Section **4**.5B, we have seen that in order to define a recursive function h on the set C produced by the specific family (G_1, G_2, G_3), we needed a set V and three functions: $m: \mathrm{Gr}(G_1) \to V$, $H_2: V \to V$ and $H_3: V^2 \to V$. These correspond to G_1, G_2, and G_3 respectively, and the arities of corresponding functions correspond.

This example illustrates the information required in general in order to construct a recursive function h on C. This consists of:

- a nonempty set V
- a total function $m: \mathrm{Gr}(G_1) \to V$
- for each function G_i, a total function $H_i: V^n \to V$, where n is the function arity of G_i ($n =_{\mathrm{d}} \mathit{FunArity}(G_i)$)

If these requirements are met, h is defined as a total function $h: C \to V$. We may now see how h is completely determined:

Theorem 4.5C.1 (general recursion theorem, variant 1)

Let $\boldsymbol{G} = (G_1, G_2, G_3, \ldots)$, C, V, m and $(H_2, H_3, \ldots)$ be defined as above. If C is freely generated by $\boldsymbol{G}$ then there exists a total function $h: C \to V$ determined by the following conditions:

(1) For any $c: \mathrm{Gr}(G_1)$, $h(c) =_{\mathrm{d}} m(c)$;

(2) For any function G_i and any $a_1, a_2, \ldots, a_n: C$,

$$h(G_i\,(a_1, a_2, \ldots, a_n)) =_{\mathrm{d}} H_i\,(h(a_1), h(a_2), \ldots, h(a_n))$$

where $n =_{\mathrm{d}} \mathit{FunArity}(G_i)$. Moreover, this function is unique – there exist no other functions $h': C \to V$ with the same property. ■

This theorem should be intuitively clear, considering the example of Section **4**.5B. The proof is fairly advanced and will not be given here. The reader is referred to Enderton (1972) or (1977). A somewhat different proof may be found in Halmos (1974).

On the practical significance of the recursion theorem

The recursion theorem describes one of the most fundamental constructions of computing. Whenever we seek to define a formal language, we must specify its syntax and its semantics. The syntax is the collection of rules defining the various symbol strings of the language – the well-formed expressions or terms, or well-formed formulas as they are usually called. These rules are similar to the generators G_i specified in the example of Section **4**.5B. Moreover, to define the semantics of any language C means to specify a recursive function $h: C \to V$. This holds for *all* formal languages, regardless of their purposes: procedural and declarative programming languages, data description languages, logic languages, and so on.

What the recursion theorem implies in practice is that a formal language should ideally be *freely generated.* If it is, each construct (well-formed expression or formula) may be given a single meaning: that is, there cannot be any *ambiguities* in the language. In practice this is an invaluable property and language designers strive to define languages which are 'as free as possible'.

This phrase has been used because for practical reasons, languages are often only 'nearly free'. A language is nearly free if most of its syntactic constructs (its well-formed expressions) have a single parse tree, while a few constructs have several parse trees. The recursion theorem indirectly tells us what to do in this case: for each construct admitting several parse trees, introduce additional rules to select *one* parse tree as the 'official' one. With these additional rules, the language is as good as free and so a unique semantic function h may be defined without ambiguity. This approach is common in computing. It is the method language designers use in order to simplify the notation of the language or to retain traditional constructs. All these points are further illustrated in Part **3**, where logic is developed as a family of completely formal languages.

4.5D Second variant of the general recursion theorem AT

The first variant of the recursion theorem has been given for the case of a family $\mathbf{G} = (G_i | i: \{1, 2, \ldots\})$ in which G_1 is a unary relation and the other relations are all functions of arity greater than 0. However, we have defined the concept of an inductively generated set C for *any* family $\mathbf{G} = (G_i | i: I)$ of relations. Thus we may wonder whether the first variant of the general recursion theorem naturally generalizes to the latter case, and how. This section presents a possible solution. This could be refined in various ways; what seems to be the simplest version has been selected. The theorem should be intuitively clear, and is given without proof. The variant of the simple recursion theorem given in Section **4**.3C is a special case of this result.

Let $\boldsymbol{G} = (G_i | i : I)$ be any family of relations such that the associated inductive set C is freely generated by $\boldsymbol{G}$. We must now allow for the fact that any G_i may be a general relation – that is, it may be of any arity and need not be functional. This we do by requiring for each G_i a function $H_i : C \times V^n \rightarrow V$, where $n + 1 =_{\mathrm{d}} arity(G_i)$. These functions account for both the function m and the functions $H_2, H_3, \ldots$ of the first variant. Given this information, the function h is exactly determined as follows:

Theorem 4.5D.1 (general recursion theorem, variant 2)

Let C be an inductive set freely generated by a family $\boldsymbol{G} = (G_i | i : I)$ of relations. Let V be any nonempty set and $(H_i | i : I)$ be a family of functions meeting the following condition: for each $i : I$, H_i is a total function

$$H_i : C \times V^n \rightarrow V$$

where $n + 1 =_{\mathrm{d}} arity(G_i)$. Then there exists a total function

$$h : C \rightarrow V$$

with the following property: for any $c : C$, let $(G_i, a_1, a_2, \ldots, a_n)$ be the immediate generator of c. Then

$$h(c) =_{\mathrm{d}} H_i(c, h(a_1), h(a_2), \ldots, h(a_n))$$

Moreover, this function is unique – that is, there exists no other function $h' : C \rightarrow V$ with the same property. ■

This second variant accounts for the first one as follows. Note that $\mathrm{Gr}(G_1) \subseteq C$. The function m is represented by a function $H_1 : C \rightarrow V$, which is any arbitrary extension of m – that is, for any $c : C - \mathrm{Gr}(G_1)$, $H_1(c)$ is an arbitrary member of V. As for the functions H_2, H_3 and so on of the first variant, replace each $H_i : V^n \rightarrow V$ by a new operation $H_i' : C \times V^n \rightarrow V$ with $H_i'(c, x_1, x_2, \ldots, x_n) = H_i(x_1, x_2, \ldots, x_n)$ for all c, x_1, x_2, $\ldots$, x_n. Thus $H_i'(c, x_1, x_2, \ldots, x_n)$ is independent of c – that is, c is treated as a dummy argument in H_i'.

This theorem could be refined. For instance, for each function H_i we could replace C by an appropriate subset dependent on i – for example, $\mathrm{Gr}(G_1)$ for H_1. However, we shall not pursue this matter any further.

EXERCISES

4.5.1 Outline the proof by structural induction that for any set C freely generated by a family $\mathbf{G}$ of relations, each $c : C$ has *exactly one* parse tree T. Note that this means there is a function which sends each $c : C$ to its corresponding parse tree $T(c)$. This function is just the construction of a parse tree given (somewhat informally, but precisely) in Definition **4**.4C.2. This definition is indeed structurally recursive. Therefore, the fact that it produces a function *when C is freely generated* is a consequence of the recursion theorem. The purpose of this exercise is to illustrate one important consequence of this theorem.

4.5.2 Consider the recursive function $h : C \to V$ defined in Section **4**.5B. Let $\alpha =_d$ 'DaRDRbRDed'.

(a) Draw the parse tree T for α and thereby verify that $\alpha \in C$.

(b) Working from the bottom up, compute $h(\alpha')$ for each string α' occurring in T. For each value $h(\alpha')$, give the full justification of its derivation. For instance, for α' = 'e', the full derivation of h('e') is

$$h(\text{'e'}) = m(\text{'e'}) = 5$$

For α' = 'd', the full derivation of h('d') is: "h('d') = m('d') = 3". For α' = 'Ded', the full derivation of h('Ded') is:

$$h(\text{'Ded'}) = H_3(h(\text{'e'}), h(\text{'d'})) = H_3(5, 3) = 20$$

and so on.

You may find it convenient to represent strings by names like α_1, α_2, and so on in your calculations.

4.5.3 Repeat Exercise **4**.5.2 with the function $m : \text{Gr}(G_1) \to V$ defined by

α	$m(\alpha)$
'a'	1
'b'	0
'c'	2
'd'	0
'e'	1

4.5.4 Show that the variant of the simple recursion theorem, Theorem **4**.3C.1, is a special case of Theorem **4**.5D.1.

4.5.5* Prove by induction that the set C defined in Section **4**.4D is freely generated. Proceed as follows.

(a) For any string $\alpha : Al^*$, we call '*length* of α' the number of letters making it up and '*prefix* of α' any initial substring α' of α. For instance, the length of 'acdb' is 4 and 'acd' is one of its prefixes. A prefix α' of α is called *proper* iff $\alpha' \neq \alpha$. An essential property of C is that for any $\alpha : C$, *no other member of C is a proper prefix of α*. It is easy to see that an equivalent property is: *for any string $\alpha : Al^*$, at most one prefix α' of α is a member of C*. Prove this by simple induction on the length of α. That is: (i) show it is true if α is the empty string; (ii) show that if it is true for all strings α of length $\leqslant n$, then it is true for all strings of length $n + 1$, for any $n : \mathrm{Nat}$.

(b) Using (a), show that there is a recursive procedure which for any string $\alpha : Al^*$ identifies the unique prefix α' *of* α belonging to C, if it exists. This procedure generates the unique parse tree of α' as a by-product.

Part 3

Symbolic Logic

5 Introduction to Symbolic Logic

5.1 Knowledge and deductive reasoning

5.1A Two features of scientific knowledge

When we ask the question: 'What are the key features of scientific knowledge?', we are led to the following observations.

First, any form of scientific knowledge is *expressed in symbols*: words, sentences, and so on. An idea can be recorded and communicated only if it is represented by symbols. Whether these are written or verbal does not matter. Thus, knowledge is *bound* to the symbols which represent it. Moreover, any access to knowledge is always necessarily gained through the medium of the symbols that represent it. Consequently, a study of knowledge and how it is obtained, recorded and communicated must include a study of (a) the symbols used to express it, (b) the rules that determine their construction and (c) the relationships between symbols and the ideas they represent. Note that we call 'symbols', not only elementary ones like '2' but also combinations of more elementary ones, like '3 + 4', a sentence or a paragraph.

Second, scientific knowledge is the *product of a process*, namely *reasoning*. Thus, a study of knowledge should also seek to determine the rules that govern this process. Philosophers have identified five main methods of scientific reasoning: *analysis*, *synthesis*, *induction* (deriving general laws from specific instances, *not* to be confused with mathematical induction), *deduction* and *analogy*. Of these, deduction plays a major role in mathematics and related disciplines such as computing. Mathematics is almost exclusively concerned with facts which can be *proved*, and a proof is always obtained by *deductive reasoning*. Now the purpose of logic is precisely to study deductive reasoning as a method of scientific knowledge. As Enderton (1972) states in *A Mathematical Introduction to Logic*: 'Symbolic logic is a mathematical model of *deductive thought*.'

5.1B The nature of deductive reasoning

What are the elements of a deduction? First, we find a collection of sentences. Each sentence is an assembly of symbols (and we regard a sentence itself as a compound symbol). We may roughly analyse a sentence at *two levels*. At the lower level we find the more elementary symbolic components. These represent *objects* in certain sets or classes, some possibly *functions* of others. At the higher level we find *statements* expressing *relations* between the objects represented at the lower level. A statement thus asserts a property of one or several objects, which is either *true* or *false* depending on these. Elementary statements are combined into more complex ones and ultimately into the sentence as a whole. While the truth of an elementary statement depends on the objects it involves, the truth of a compound statement depends on the truth of the more elementary statements of which it is composed.

For instance the sentence 'Britain is an island' is an elementary statement. It is either true or false. The truth of the statement depends on two objects, 'Britain' and 'island'. The statement 'If Britain is an island then it can be circumnavigated' is a compound statement. Its components are (a) 'Britain is an island' and (b) 'It (Britain) can be circumnavigated'. The overall sentence asserts that if the first elementary statement is true then so is the second. The overall statement is either true or false. If we think that Britain is an island but Britain cannot be circumnavigated then we must conclude that the overall statement is false.

Second, in general a deduction involves not one but a collection of sentences which are linked – by *logical implication* precisely – in the following sense: they form a chain and, according to certain rules, the truth of each sentence is either 'taken for granted' or *implied* by the truth of the previous ones.

Here is an example:

S1: 'Every island can be circumnavigated.'

S2: 'Britain is an island.'

'Therefore,'

S3: 'Britain can be circumnavigated.'

This deduction contains three sentences. If the first two sentences are true, then so is the third.

Now there is a fundamental difference between our reasons for believing 'Britain is an island' and our belief that *if* S1 and S2 are both true *then* S3 is true. 'Britain is an island' is an empirical fact. In order to decide whether it is true or not we must know what Britain is as a physical object, we must know the physical characteristics of an island and we must establish that the object 'Britain' has these characteristics. All this is a matter of empirical perception of the physical world. Moreover, if the symbol 'Britain' were used to name another object – for example, an aeroplane – the statement might be false.

The same observation may be made of the other sentence: 'Every island can be circumnavigated'. It is an empirical fact. But now consider our belief that if S1 and S2 are true then S3 is true. This belief is based on totally different reasons, which have nothing to do with physical properties of objects like Britain or an island. In fact our reasons have nothing to do with the very *meaning* of these words! Our belief in the truth of the deduction is entirely based on its *form*: on certain key symbols like 'every', 'is', or 'therefore', and on the fact that some symbols representing objects occur in certain places in the sentences. Thus we would know that the deduction is true even if we did not know the meaning of symbols like 'Britain', 'island' and 'circumnavigate'. To see this, consider another deduction with the same symbolic structure:

S1′: 'Every alef can nev.'

S2′: 'Ela is an alef.'

'Therefore,'

S3′: 'Ela can nev.'

Here the meanings of the names involved are not even known – they could be *anything*! Yet we still believe that if S1′ and S2′ are true then S3′ is also true, for the same reason as we believe the previous deduction. Let us be quite clear about this second deduction. To believe in its truth means exactly this: *whatever meaning* is assigned to the words 'alef', 'nev' and 'Ela', we think that *whenever* a selected meaning makes S1′ and S2′ true, S3′ is also true. Note that our belief in the previous deduction is for exactly the same reason: we regard it as correct *independently of the meaning* of 'Britain', 'island' and 'circumnavigate'.

These two examples illustrate the distinctive feature of deductive reasoning: the validity of a deduction depends on its *form* only, and not on the meaning of the words occurring in it. Consequently, whether a deduction is correct or not may be established by applying purely symbolic rules, that is, rules determining the construction and manipulation of symbols independently of their meaning. As we shall see, such rules may be defined with complete rigour and accuracy.

Naturally, deductive reasoning is not the only source of knowledge. In general the latter is obtained by combining deductive reasoning with other sources, empirical observation in particular. What is important in any enquiry is to *separate* the elements of information obtained by deductive reasoning from the others. Another key feature of deductive reasoning is that this too can be done completely.

The precise definition of the rules of deductive reasoning, and its separation from other sources of knowledge, is the task of logic. Therefore, we may now turn our attention to this discipline.

5.2 Logic

5.2A Purpose of logic

The special nature of deduction as a reasoning process suggests that this process may well be governed by exact and universal rules. Thus, we can already guess that these rules will be solely concerned *with the arrangement of symbols regardless of their meaning.* The purpose of logic is, precisely, to establish what these rules are, in order to obtain an exact description of deductive reasoning. This enterprise has been pursued at least since Greek antiquity and the works of Aristotle (384–322 BC) in particular. But it is only in the last century and this one that it has met with complete success, with the works of Frege, Russell, Whitehead, Tarski and Gödel, to mention but a few.

Logic is *not* concerned with all methods of scientific reasoning. It is concerned with *one* of them, namely deductive reasoning. The distinctive characteristics of logic are entirely due to the special nature of deduction as a reasoning process. The examples of the previous section illustrate this special nature and how deduction differs from other sources of knowledge. The reader is urged to study these examples carefully in order to understand the purpose of logic.

5.2B Logic versus symbolic logic

For centuries no special efforts were made by logicians to regulate the *notation* of sentences – the primary objects of their investigations. Logicians would analyse sentences as expressed in natural language (Latin, English, and so on). The drawback of this approach is that it is bound to be impaired by the numerous complexities and ambiguities of natural languages.

A decisive step was taken when the need for a well-defined and simple notation to express our ideas *unambiguously* was recognized. Instead of working in natural language, the logician would first express ideas as *well-formed formulas* in an artificial or *formal language*. Thus, the definition of an appropriate formal language became a central concern of logic, in addition to its more traditional objectives. In this enterprise, logicians met the same fundamental problems as the designers of any other formal notations – programming languages in particular. Consequently, much can be learnt about theoretical and practical problems of formal language design from the experience of logicians in this respect.

The introduction of a formal language is what distinguishes *symbolic logic*, or *mathematical logic*, from traditional logic. The German mathematician Gottlob Frege (1848–1925) is credited with pioneering symbolic logic. In 1879 he published a booklet in which he presented a notational system to formulate propositions and proofs. Frege called his language 'Begriffsschrift', which means, approximately, '*concept notation*'. This language, developed with great care and due emphasis on form, is the close ancestor of modern predicate logic.

Today, the term 'logic' is used almost exclusively in the sense of *symbolic* logic by scientists, a convention adopted in this book. This is a natural consequence of logic's primary concern with the symbolic expressions representing ideas. All the modern logician is asking for is a regular, disciplined notation for these expressions.

5.2C Propositional logic versus predicate logic

In the section on the nature of deductive reasoning, it was pointed out that a sentence may be decomposed at two levels. At the higher level, we have compound and elementary statements, which may be either true or false. At the lower level, we have symbols representing objects or totalities of objects, such as 'all islands'.

This distinction is reflected in the way in which logic is usually organized and taught. First, we concentrate on the higher level. At this level, a statement is decomposed only if all its immediate components are themselves statements, that is, symbolic expressions which may be either true or false. When the immediate components of a statement *S* include symbols which denote objects in certain sets or classes, we do not analyse *S* itself but treat it as an *elementary* or *atomic unit* ('atomic' means: which cannot be decomposed).

For instance, the statement 'If Britain is an island then Britain can be circumnavigated' can be decomposed into two more elementary statements connected by 'if' . . . 'then':

S1: 'Britain is an island.'

S2: 'Britain can be circumnavigated.'

Neither S1 nor S2 may be further decomposed without separating symbols like 'Britain' or 'island'. These are not meant to express facts which may be true or false but objects in certain sets. Consequently we regard S1 and S2 as elementary or atomic units. (This is why it makes sense to regard 'Britain is an island' as a *single* symbol even though it *looks* like an assembly of more elementary symbols: its decomposition is provisionally suspended.)

A statement which is subjected to this limited amount of analysis only is called a *proposition*. Thus in the strict sense, a proposition is any symbol meant to denote a fact which may be true or false, and nothing else. It can be *compound* or *elementary*. If compound, its components themselves are propositions. They are symbolically linked by the propositional connective symbols introduced in Section **2**.4C and redefined in the next chapter. From this limited point of view, an elementary proposition may just as well be represented by a name like 'A', 'S1' or 'S2'. The compound proposition

'If S1 then S2'

is just as good as

'If Britain is an island then Britain can be circumnavigated.'

at this level of analysis.

Because of its emphasis on propositions as defined above, this first type of logic is called *propositional* or *sentential logic*. Now propositional logic quickly turns out to be too limited as a model of deductive reasoning in many applications. We need to extend the analysis to the lower-level components of ordinary sentences. This means we must be able to represent and handle individual objects from various sets or classes, functions and relations. This extended analysis is the object of the second stage of logic, called *first-order predicate logic* or simply *first-order logic*.

Other types of logic have been devised: higher-order predicate, intuitionistic or non-classical, and modal logic for instance. However, the propositional and first-order variants are traditionally the most important ones, and they are sufficient to meet all our requirements (as a basis for axiomatic set theory in particular). Therefore, the other variants will not be described in this book.

First-order logic is more complex than propositional logic. Moreover, the former may be regarded as an extension of the latter. For these two reasons we shall first study propositional logic and then first-order logic. The former is the topic of Chapter **6**. The latter is treated in Chapters **7** and **8**, and further illustrated in Chapter **9** with the definition of a fully axiomatic form of set theory as an application.

EXERCISES

5.2.1 Revise the propositional connective symbols introduced in Section **2**.4C. Then consider the following English statements:

S1: 'If it rains, then I take my umbrella.'

S2: 'Alfred is not happy but Beth is.'

S3: 'Charles is at home or he is not.'

S4: 'If Albert is French then Deby is not.'

(a) For each statement, list its elementary constituent propositions and name them P_1, P_2, P_3, and so on.
(b) Rewrite each statement by combining their elementary constituent propositions with propositional connectives. Use special symbols to represent the connectives. Note that: (i) In English, we seek to avoid repeating words and phrases if this can be done without affecting the meaning of sentences. Part of this exercise is to re-establish the full intended text. For instance, the full text for S2 is 'Alfred is not happy but Beth is *happy*'. (ii) Some English connectives must be converted: for example, 'but' must be rewritten as 'and', and so on.
(c) Repeat (b) using the names P_1, P_2, P_3, and so on, instead of the full text of the elementary propositions.
(d) Represent the structure of each statement by a parse tree.

5.2.2 Give five examples of simple facts in English, similar to those of Exercise 5.2.1. Determine whether they are elementary or compound propositions, and analyse the compound ones as in Exercise 5.2.1.

5.2.3 Consider the following deduction:

S1: 'If Albert is French then Deby is not.'
'Therefore,'
S2: 'If Deby is French then Albert is not.'

(a) Repeat Exercise 5.2.1 for S2.
(b) Seek to explain why the above deduction is valid. This deduction can be justified in propositional logic.

5.2.4* Consider the following deduction:

S1: 'Every French person speaks French.'
S2: 'Two persons may communicate iff they speak the same language.'
S3: 'Albert and Deby cannot communicate.'
'Therefore,'
S4: 'If Albert is French then Deby is not.'

(a) Repeat Exercise 5.2.1 for each statement.
(b) Seek to explain why the above deduction is valid. Note that this deduction can only be justified in first-order logic.

5.2.5* Give three examples of deductions expressed in English and repeat Exercise 5.2.4 for each of them.

Propositional Logic

Propositional or sentential logic is first of all a *language*. Like any formal language it has two facets: (a) a *syntax*, which is the set of rules defining the various symbolic constructs (well-formed expressions) of the language; (b) a *semantics*, which maps symbolic constructs into a certain set of values in a coherent way.

This chapter describes these two facets in turn. Note that '*the* language of propositional logic' is a slight misnomer, as we may construct many different languages meeting our aims. However, in a certain sense, all these languages are essentially equivalent. So we may take any one as representative of all of them and regard it as *the* language of propositional logic.

Note also that the term '*formal language*' is often used in a restrictive sense to mean only the collection of symbolic constructs generated by its syntax. We adopt this convention as a rule and use the term '*interpreted language*' to refer to a formal language together with a semantics or interpretation attached to its symbolic constructs.

A first example of formal language has been given in Section 4.4D. The reader should revise it before proceeding, as the language of propositional logic is constructed in a very similar way. Likewise, the construction in Section 4.5B of the structurally recursive function h for this initial example illustrates the definition of a language semantics. This too should be revised before the semantics of propositional logic is studied.

In Section **6**.1, the syntax of propositional logic is described. Section **6**.2 is devoted to the semantics of the language. Section **6**.3, introduces the notion of tautological implication, which models deductive reasoning at the 'propositional level', and also introduces the related notion of tautology. Section **6**.4 contains a list of basic tautologies and two theorems which define families of tautologies. This section also includes an analysis of variants of the language and two applications of tautologies as means of proof.

6.1 Syntax of propositional logic

6.1A Alphabet

The first step in defining a formal language is to select an alphabet, or set of basic symbols. As in the example of Section **4**.4D, we denote the chosen set by *Al*. The symbols are also called *atomic*, as they are the most elementary members of the language to be defined.

The alphabet *Al* of propositional logic consists of the following disjoint sets of symbols:

(1) *Parentheses*

(	Left parenthesis
)	Right parenthesis

(2) *Propositional connective symbols*

Form 1	*Form 2*	
$\neg$	not	Negation symbol
$\wedge$	and	Conjunction symbol
$\vee$	or	Disjunction symbol
$\Rightarrow$	if ... then	Conditional symbol
$\Leftrightarrow$	iff	Equivalence symbol

(3) *Proposition symbols*

$p, q,$

$p_1, p_2, p_3, \ldots,$

$q_1, q_2, q_3, \ldots$

The parentheses and the propositional connective symbols (or simply 'connectives') together form the *logical symbols*. Their semantics will be constant. The proposition symbols $p, q, p_1, p_2, p_3, \ldots, q_1, q_2, q_3, \ldots$ are also called *nonlogical symbols* or *parameters*. Their semantics will *not* be constant but vary from application to application. They are also denoted generically by the letter π. Each proposition symbol π is meant to represent an elementary proposition as defined in the introduction. We allow an infinite number of such symbols, and denote their subset by *Props*:

$$Props =_d \{p, q, p_1, p_2, p_3, \ldots, q_1, q_2, q_3, \ldots\}$$

The symbols of propositional logic are not new. They are part of the notation introduced in Section **2.4**.

6.1B Informal definition of well-formed formulas

Expressions or strings

From the alphabet *Al*, we derive the set $U =_d Al^*$ of all *strings* (finite sequences) of symbols from *Al*. The definition of a string was given in Section **4.4D**; see also Exercise **4.4.6**. A string is also called an *expression*. We enclose compound expressions in quotes to distinguish them from the main text whenever necessary. Expressions are denoted generically by Greek lowercase letters as before.

Examples of expressions are

$($

$(p_1 \vee q_3)$

$p_2\, q_4$

$(\neg\, p)$

$)) \vee (\wedge (($

$(\neg\, (p_1 \vee (\neg\, q)))$

(In this list, well-formed expressions alternate with ill-formed ones.)

Well-formed formulas

Given the alphabet *Al* and the associated set $U = Al^*$ of strings, recall that a language on *Al* is a subset $C \subseteq_d U$. In general the members of C are called *well-formed expressions* (*wfes*). In propositional logic, all the members of C are called *well-formed formulas* (*wffs*) more specifically. Accordingly, the set C is also denoted by *Wffs*. Our next step is to define this set – that is, to specify the rules which distinguish the wffs from all other strings. As in Section **4.4D**, these rules are first described informally. Then we show that they may be regarded as operations by which $C = Wffs$ is generated inductively.

Definition 6.1B.1 (informal)

Intuitively, $C \subseteq_{\mathrm{d}} U$ is the set defined by the following rules:

(1) Every proposition symbol $\pi : Props$ (regarded as a one-symbol *string*) is a member of C.

(2) For any string $\alpha : C$, the following is a member of C:

$$(\neg\ \alpha)$$

(3) For any two strings $\alpha, \beta : C$, the following strings are members of C:

(a) $(\alpha \wedge \beta)$
(b) $(\alpha \vee \beta)$
(c) $(\alpha \Rightarrow \beta)$
(d) $(\alpha \Leftrightarrow \beta)$

(4) C does not contain any string not defined by rules (1)–(3) ■

Example

Here are some examples of members of C, that is, wffs. They are again built systematically, each by application of a construction rule of Definition **6**.1B.1 to preceding ones.

By (1) $p, q, p_1, p_2, q_1, q_2, q_3$
By (2) '$(\neg\ p)$', '$(\neg\ q)$', '$(\neg\ p_1)$'
By (3) '$(p \wedge p)$', '$(p \vee q)$', '$(p_1 \Rightarrow (\neg\ p))$', '$((\neg\ p_1) \Leftrightarrow q_3)$'
By (2) '$(\neg\ (p \wedge p))$', '$(\neg\ (p_1 \Rightarrow (\neg\ p)))$', '$(\neg\ ((\neg\ p_1) \Leftrightarrow q_3))$'
By (3) '$((\neg\ (p_1 \Rightarrow (\neg\ p))) \vee (\neg\ ((\neg\ p_1) \Leftrightarrow q_3)))$'
...

■

6.1C Formal definition of well-formed formulas AT

The above generation rules for $C = Wffs$ may be described as a family $\boldsymbol{G}$ of relations and C as the set *inductively generated by* $\boldsymbol{G}$. Instead of denoting each generator by G_i with $i =_{\mathrm{d}} 1, 2, \ldots$ as in Section **4**.4, we use the following more meaningful indexed names:

$$\boldsymbol{G} =_{\mathrm{d}} (G_\pi, G_\neg, G_\wedge, G_\vee, G_\Rightarrow, G_\Leftrightarrow)$$

The generators G_i are defined as follows:

1 G_π is the generator of proposition symbols. It is the unary relation whose graph $\mathrm{Gr}(G_\pi) \subset U$ is the set *Props* of proposition symbols belonging to *Al* and regarded as one-symbol strings:

$$\mathrm{Gr}(G_\pi) =_{\mathrm{d}} Props = \{p, q, p_1, p_2, p_3, \ldots, q_1, q_2, q_3, \ldots\}$$

2 $G_{\neg}$ is the total unary function (binary relation) $G_{\neg}: U \to U$ which sends any string $\alpha: U$ to the string '$(\neg\ \alpha)$' $\in U$:

$$\alpha \mapsto \text{`}(\neg\ \alpha)\text{'}$$

Rule (2) of Definition **6**.1B.1 may be described as the application of $G_{\neg}$ to any $\alpha: C$.

3 $G_{\wedge}$ is the total binary function (ternary relation) $G_{\wedge}: U^2 \to U$ which sends any couple $(\alpha, \beta): U^2$ of strings to the string '$(\alpha \wedge \beta)$' $\in U$:

(a) $(\alpha, \beta) \mapsto \text{`}(\alpha \wedge \beta)\text{'}$

Rule (3)(a) may be viewed as the application of $G_{\wedge}$ to any couple (α, β) of strings $\alpha, \beta: C$.

The remaining generators $G_{\vee}$, $G_{\Rightarrow}$ and $G_{\Leftrightarrow}$ are described in the same way as $G_{\wedge}$. Each is an operation $U^2 \to U$ which sends any couple $(\alpha, \beta): U^2$ of strings to the string indicated below:

$$G_{\vee}: \quad (\alpha, \beta) \mapsto \text{`}(\alpha \vee \beta)\text{'}$$
$$G_{\Rightarrow}: \quad (\alpha, \beta) \mapsto \text{`}(\alpha \Rightarrow \beta)\text{'}$$
$$G_{\Leftrightarrow}: \quad (\alpha, \beta) \mapsto \text{`}(\alpha \Leftrightarrow \beta)\text{'}$$

Each one of the rules (3)(b)–(d) may be regarded as the application of $G_{\vee}$, $G_{\Rightarrow}$, or $G_{\Leftrightarrow}$ respectively to any couple (α, β) of strings $\alpha, \beta: C$.

4 Finally, rule (4) corresponds to the statement that C is the set inductively generated by $\boldsymbol{G}$.

The five functions $G_{\neg}$, $G_{\wedge}$, $G_{\vee}$, $G_{\Rightarrow}$ and $G_{\Leftrightarrow}$ are called *formula-building operations*. C may also be described as the smallest set of strings $\alpha: U$ which includes the set $Props = \mathrm{Gr}(G_{\pi})$ of proposition symbols, and which is closed under these five operations.

It turns out that $C = Wffs$ is *freely generated* by the formula-building operations – that is, each wff $\alpha: C$ has a unique parse tree. This implies that C enjoys the important advantages of this property discussed in Section **4**.5C. The proof that C is freely generated is left as an exercise; it is given in Enderton (1972).

Henceforth we consider only propositions expressed as wffs, that is, according to the rules defined above. However, we take some liberties with the notation for formulas, in order to improve their readability. For instance, we may drop outer parentheses or use a mixture of parentheses and brackets. This is acceptable *as long as the exact formula may be readily reconstructed from its simplified version.*

A parse tree for a wff $\alpha: C$ is given in Figure **6**.1C.1.

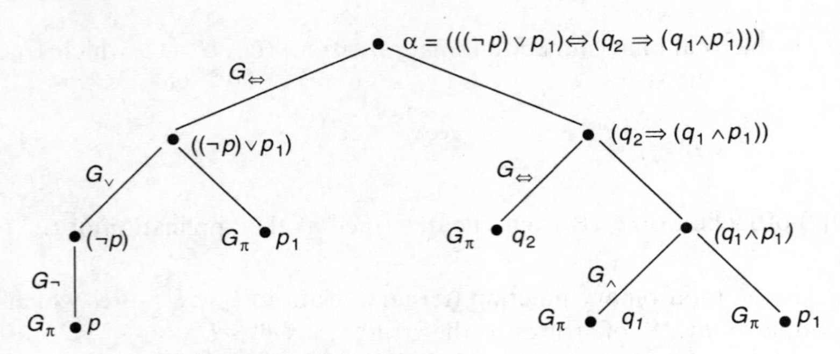

Figure 6.1C.1 Parse tree for a wff $\alpha : C$.

EXERCISES

6.1.1 Consider the following wff $\alpha =_d$ '$((\neg\, p) \wedge (q \Rightarrow p_1))$'. Draw a parse tree for α.

6.1.2 Consider the following sequence of wffs:

$$\begin{aligned}
\alpha_1 &=_d (\neg\, p) \\
\alpha_2 &=_d (q \vee \alpha_1) \\
\alpha_3 &=_d (\neg\, \alpha_2) \\
\alpha_4 &=_d (\alpha_1 \Rightarrow \alpha_1) \\
\alpha_5 &=_d (\alpha_4 \wedge \alpha_3) \\
\alpha_6 &=_d (\neg\, \alpha_5)
\end{aligned}$$

(a) Build the parse tree of α_6 using $\alpha_1, \alpha_2, \ldots$ to refer to its components in the tree. For instance, the point in the tree representing the compound wff α_2 should be labelled '$\alpha_2 = (q \vee \alpha_1)$'.

(b) Write out α_6 in full.

6.1.3 Construct the parse tree of the following formula:

$$\alpha =_d (((p_1 \wedge q_1) \Rightarrow (\neg\, q_1)) \Leftrightarrow ((p_2 \vee q_1) \wedge (p_1 \Rightarrow q_2)))$$

Use α_1, α_2, etc. to represent the various compound subwffs of α, as illustrated in Exercise **6**.1.2. The order of numbering should be reasonably systematic – for example, from the bottom up. Naming intermediate wffs in this way proves to be very convenient in many applications.

6.1.4 What is the set-theoretical relation between the two sets *Al** and *Wffs*?

6.1.5 Let $\alpha =_d$ '$(\neg\, (p_1 \wedge p_2))$'. Construct a new wff β by *simultaneously* substituting

$\gamma_1 =_d$ '$(q_1 \Rightarrow p_2)$' for p_1 and $\gamma_2 =_d$ '$(q_2 \wedge (\neg p_3))$' for p_2 in α. Draw the parse trees of α and β.

6.1.6 Repeat Exercise **6**.1.5 except that this time the substitutions of γ_1 for p_1 and γ_2 for p_2 must not be done simultaneously but in two successive stages. More precisely, first replace p_1 in α, giving β_1, then replace p_2 in β_1, giving β_2. How does β_2 differ from β of Exercise **6**.1.5?

6.1.7 Consider the sequence $(\alpha_1, \alpha_2, \ldots, \alpha_6)$ in Exercise **6**.1.2. Verify that it is a *construction* sequence as defined in Section **4**.4E.

6.1.8 Consider the parse tree of α in Exercise **6**.1.3. Turn this tree into a construction sequence (a) with redundancy and (b) without.

6.1.9 For any string $\alpha: Al^*$, let $LP(\alpha)$ be the number of occurrences of '(' and $RP(\alpha)$ the number of occurrences of ')' in α. Prove by (structural) induction that for any wff α: *Wffs*, $LP(\alpha) = RP(\alpha)$. Hint: Consider three cases of α: (i) α is a proposition symbol; (ii) $\alpha =_d$ '$(\neg \beta)$' where β: *Wffs*; and (iii) $\alpha =_d$ '$(\beta * \gamma)$', where β and γ: *Wffs* and $*$ is any binary propositional connective symbol ($\wedge$, $\vee$, and so on). Carefully state the induction hypothesis in particular.

6.1.10 For any string $\alpha: Al^*$, let $B(\alpha)$ be the number of occurrences of *binary* connectives in α, and $Pr(\alpha)$ the number of occurrences of proposition symbols. Prove by induction that in any wff α: *Wffs*, $Pr(\alpha) = B(\alpha) + 1$.

6.1.11* Let LP and RP be defined as in Exercise **6**.1.9. Prove by induction that for any wff α: *Wffs* and any nonempty proper prefix α' of α, $LP(\alpha') > RP(\alpha')$. See Exercise **4**.5.5 for the definition of a prefix and so on. Hint: Consider the three cases of α defined in Exercise **6**.1.9. For each case, consider the various possible subcases of prefixes α' of α. For instance, there are four subcases to consider if $\alpha =$ '$(\neg \beta)$'. Note that the proof uses the result of Exercise **6**.1.9.

6.1.12* (a) Prove by induction that for any α: *Wffs*, no proper prefix of α is a member of *Wffs*. Hint: Use Exercises **6**.1.9 and **6**.1.11. Recall that any string is its own (improper) prefix.

(b) Show that consequently, for any string $\alpha: Al^*$, there is at most one α': *Wffs* which is a prefix of α.

(c) Likewise, show that for any string $\alpha: Al^*$, there is a unique prefix α'' of α with the following property: (i) α'' is the prefix of a member of *Wffs*; (ii) any greater prefix of α, if any, cannot be the prefix of any member of *Wffs*. (Note that α'' may be empty or equal to α.)

6.1.13* *Unique readability of wffs* Prove that any α: *Wffs* has exactly one parse tree. In other words, the set *Wffs* is freely generated by $G_\pi, \ldots, G_\Leftrightarrow$. Hint: Any α: *Wffs* may be generated in one of six ways. For each case, show that α has exactly one immediate generator in the sense of Definition **4**.4C.1. For instance, if $\alpha =$ '$(\beta \wedge \gamma)$', its immediate generator is $(G_\wedge, \beta, \gamma)$. If $\alpha =$ '$(\beta' * \gamma')$' where $*$ is any binary connective, show that necessarily $\beta = \beta'$, '$*$'='$\wedge$' and $\gamma = \gamma'$, using Exercise **6**.1.12. Show that for similar reasons α cannot be generated by G_π or $G_\neg$. Handle the other five cases in the same way.

6.1.14* Building on Exercises **6**.1.12 and **6**.1.13, devise a precise method, or algorithm, to construct the parse tree of any α: *Wffs* by scanning the symbol occurrences of α in their order in α. Actually the aim of the method should be slightly more general. When applied to any string α: *Al**, it should identify the prefix α'' of α defined in Exercise **6**.1.12(c) and return the parse tree of α'' as a by-product if $\alpha'' \in$ *Wffs*.

6.2 Semantics of propositional logic

In propositional logic, a wff represents a proposition – a statement which is either true or false. Consequently, our next step is to define the semantics of the language $C =$ *Wffs*. This is done as in the example of Section **4**.5B, by constructing a total recursive function on C. We now denote this function by $\boldsymbol{M}$ (for 'meaning'); it is introduced by

$$\boldsymbol{M}: C \to \text{Bool}$$

where Bool $=_\text{d}$ {true, false}, and is established like the recursive function $h: C \to V$ defined in Section **4**.5B. For each wff $\alpha: C$, $\boldsymbol{M}(\alpha) \in$ Bool is the *truth value* (or *boolean* value) of α. The function $\boldsymbol{M}$ is defined so as to agree with the way we understand propositions, that is, build and use them in practice. In what follows we abbreviate 'true' as 'T' and 'false' as 'F'.

6.2A Recursive definition of the semantic function $\boldsymbol{M}$

The semantic function $\boldsymbol{M}$ is established by the following rules.

1 Recall that a wff is *elementary* if it consists of a single proposition symbol, such as p or q_1, and *compound* otherwise. Therefore, the set of elementary wffs is *Props* $= \{p, p_1, \ldots, q, q_1, \ldots\}$. The truth value of elementary wffs is assumed given by a preliminary function

$$m: Props \to \text{Bool}$$

This function is called a *truth assignment*, as it assigns an initial truth value $m(\alpha)$ to each elementary wff α: *Props*.

Given m, the value $\boldsymbol{M}(\alpha) \in \text{Bool}$ is defined for each elementary wff $\alpha : \textit{Props}$ by

(R1) $\boldsymbol{M}(\alpha) =_{\mathrm{d}} m(\alpha)$

2 The remaining rules are as stated in the notation review of Section **2**.4C, except that they are now expressed in terms of *named* operations on Bool.

(a) *Negation* To establish the semantics of any wff '$(\neg\ \beta)$' we introduce the function NOT : Bool → Bool given by

x	NOT (x)
T	F
F	T

Thence, for any wff $\beta : C$, the truth value of '$(\neg\ \beta)$' is derived from $\boldsymbol{M}(\beta)$ by the definition

(R2a) $\boldsymbol{M}(\text{`}(\neg\ \beta)\text{'}) =_{\mathrm{d}} \text{NOT}(\boldsymbol{M}(\beta))$

(b) *Conjunction* To establish the semantics of any wff '$(\beta \wedge \gamma)$', we introduce the function AND : Bool^2 → Bool defined by

x	y	AND (x, y)
T	T	T
T	F	F
F	T	F
F	F	F

Thence, the truth value of '$(\beta \wedge \gamma)$' is determined by

(R2b) $\boldsymbol{M}(\text{`}(\beta \wedge \gamma)\text{'}) =_{\mathrm{d}} \text{AND}(\boldsymbol{M}(\beta), \boldsymbol{M}(\gamma))$

The semantics of the remaining wffs is defined in the same way.

(c) *Disjunction* For wffs '$(\beta \vee \gamma)$', we introduce the function OR : Bool^2 → Bool defined by

x	y	OR (x, y)
T	T	T
T	F	T
F	T	T
F	F	F

Thence,

(R2c) $M(`(\beta \vee \gamma)') =_d \text{OR}(M(\beta), M(\gamma))$

(d) *Conditional* The semantics of wffs '$(\beta \Rightarrow \gamma)$' is specified by the function IF : $\text{Bool}^2 \to \text{Bool}$ defined by

x	y	IF (x, y)
T	T	T
T	F	F
F	T	T
F	F	T

Thence,

(R2d) $M(`(\beta \Rightarrow \gamma)') =_d \text{IF}(M(\beta), M(\gamma))$

(e) *Equivalence* For wffs '$(\beta \Leftrightarrow \gamma)$', we introduce the function IFF : $\text{Bool}^2 \to \text{Bool}$ defined by

x	y	IFF (x, y)
T	T	T
T	F	F
F	T	F
F	F	T

Thence,

(R2e) $M(`(\beta \Leftrightarrow \gamma)') =_d \text{IFF}(M(\beta), M(\gamma))$

This completes the recursive definition of the semantic function $M: C \to \text{Bool}$. To sum up, $M: C \to \text{Bool}$ is determined by six functions: m, which assigns an initial truth value $m(\alpha)$ to each *elementary* wff α; NOT : Bool → Bool, which determines the truth value of any wff '$(\neg\, \beta)$'; and the four operations AND, OR, IF and IFF : $\text{Bool}^2 \to \text{Bool}$, which determine the truth value of wffs '$(\beta \wedge \gamma)$', '$(\beta \vee \gamma)$', '$(\beta \Rightarrow \gamma)$' and '$(\beta \Leftrightarrow \gamma)$' respectively.

6.2B Example

Consider the parse tree of Figure **6**.1C.1. We compute the function M for the various wffs occurring in this tree, and for two different truth assignments m.

As a preliminary step, we denote each compound wff by α_i, $i = 1, 2, \ldots, 5$, for reference purposes. Moreover, we express each α_i in terms of its immediate constituents. The result is shown in Figure **6**.2B.1.

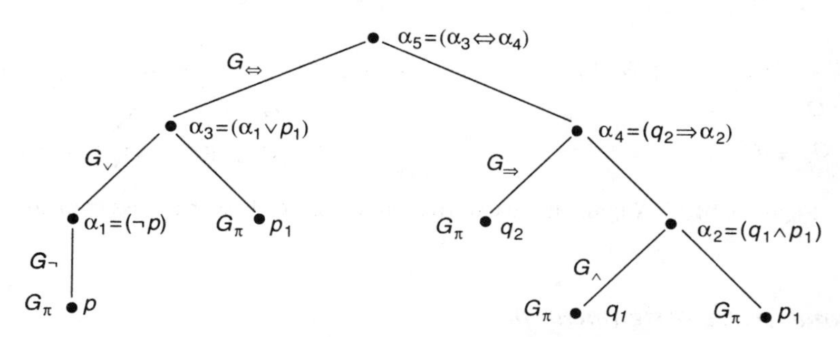

Figure 6.2B.1 Parse tree for wff $\alpha = \alpha_5 : C$.

First truth assignment m

Consider the truth assignment m partially given by the following table.

π	$m(\pi)$
p	F
p_1	T
q_1	F
q_2	T

(1) For each elementary wff π, $\boldsymbol{M}(\pi) = m(\pi)$ by (R1). Therefore,

$$\boldsymbol{M}(p) = \text{F} \qquad \boldsymbol{M}(p_1) = \text{T} \qquad \boldsymbol{M}(q_1) = \text{F} \qquad \boldsymbol{M}(q_2) = \text{T}$$

(2) For compound wffs α_i, $\boldsymbol{M}(\alpha_i)$ is determined by (R2a–e). We compute:

$$\begin{aligned}
\boldsymbol{M}(\alpha_1) &= \boldsymbol{M}(\text{`}(\neg\, p)\text{'}) &&= \text{NOT}(\boldsymbol{M}(p)) &&= \text{NOT(F)} &&= \text{T}\\
\boldsymbol{M}(\alpha_2) &= \boldsymbol{M}(\text{`}(q_1 \wedge p_1)\text{'}) &&= \text{AND}(\boldsymbol{M}(q_1), \boldsymbol{M}(p_1)) &&= \text{AND(F, T)} &&= \text{F}\\
\boldsymbol{M}(\alpha_3) &= \boldsymbol{M}(\text{`}(\alpha_1 \vee p_1)\text{'}) &&= \text{OR}(\boldsymbol{M}(\alpha_1), \boldsymbol{M}(p_1)) &&= \text{OR(T, T)} &&= \text{T}\\
\boldsymbol{M}(\alpha_4) &= \boldsymbol{M}(\text{`}(q_2 \Rightarrow \alpha_2)\text{'}) &&= \text{IF}(\boldsymbol{M}(q_2), \boldsymbol{M}(\alpha_2)) &&= \text{IF(T, F)} &&= \text{F}\\
\boldsymbol{M}(\alpha_5) &= \boldsymbol{M}(\text{`}(\alpha_3 \Leftrightarrow \alpha_4)\text{'}) &&= \text{IFF}(\boldsymbol{M}(\alpha_3), \boldsymbol{M}(\alpha_4)) &&= \text{IFF(T, F)} &&= \text{F}
\end{aligned}$$

These values are added to the parse tree, enclosed in square brackets. The augmented tree is shown in Figure **6**.2B.2.

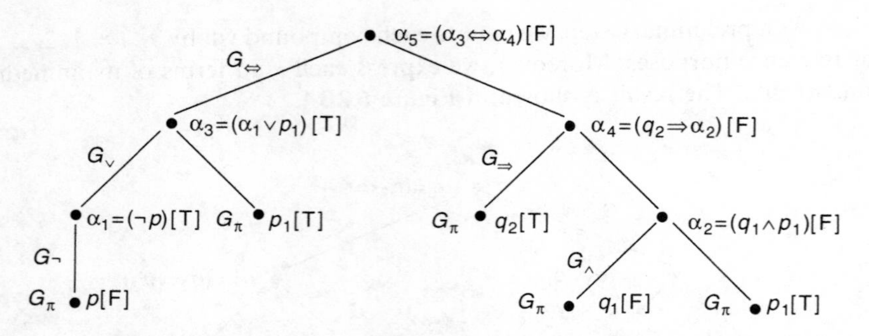

Figure 6.2B.2 Augmented parse tree for wff $\alpha_5 : C$, first truth assignment.

Second truth assignment m

Next, let the truth assignment m be partially given by

$$m(p) = \text{T} \qquad m(p_1) = \text{T} \qquad m(q_1) = \text{T} \qquad m(q_2) = \text{F}$$

(1) For each elementary wff π, $\boldsymbol{M}(\pi) = m(\pi)$ by (R1). Therefore,

$$\boldsymbol{M}(p) = \text{T} \qquad \boldsymbol{M}(p_1) = \text{T} \qquad \boldsymbol{M}(q_1) = \text{T} \qquad \boldsymbol{M}(q_2) = \text{F}$$

(2) For compound wffs α_i, $\boldsymbol{M}(\alpha_i)$ is determined by applying (R2a–e):

$$\begin{array}{lllllllll}
\boldsymbol{M}(\alpha_1) & = & \boldsymbol{M}(\text{`}(\neg\ p)\text{'}) & = & \text{NOT}(\boldsymbol{M}(p)) & = & \text{NOT(T)} & = & \text{F} \\
\boldsymbol{M}(\alpha_2) & = & \boldsymbol{M}(\text{`}(q_1 \wedge p_1)\text{'}) & = & \text{AND}(\boldsymbol{M}(q_1), \boldsymbol{M}(p_1)) & = & \text{AND(T, T)} & = & \text{T} \\
\boldsymbol{M}(\alpha_3) & = & \boldsymbol{M}(\text{`}(\alpha_1 \vee p_1)\text{'}) & = & \text{OR}(\boldsymbol{M}(\alpha_1), \boldsymbol{M}(p_1)) & = & \text{OR(F, T)} & = & \text{T} \\
\boldsymbol{M}(\alpha_4) & = & \boldsymbol{M}(\text{`}(q_2 \Rightarrow \alpha_2)\text{'}) & = & \text{IF}(\boldsymbol{M}(q_2), \boldsymbol{M}(\alpha_2)) & = & \text{IF(F, T)} & = & \text{T} \\
\boldsymbol{M}(\alpha_5) & = & \boldsymbol{M}(\text{`}(\alpha_3 \Leftrightarrow \alpha_4)\text{'}) & = & \text{IFF}(\boldsymbol{M}(\alpha_3), \boldsymbol{M}(\alpha_4)) & = & \text{IFF(T, T)} & = & \text{T}
\end{array}$$

The augmented parse tree for this second truth assignment is given in Figure 6.2B.3.

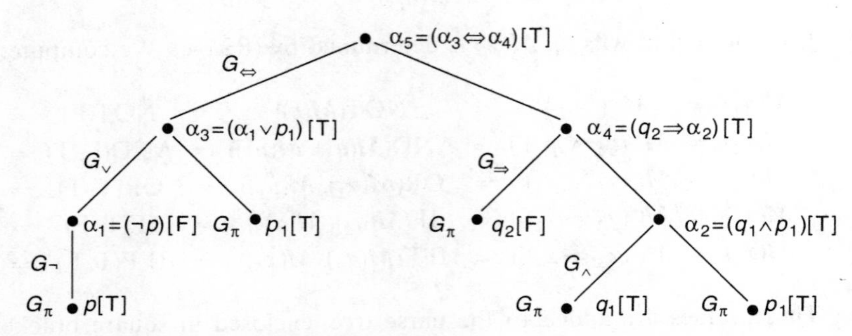

Figure 6.2B.3 Augmented parse tree for wff $\alpha_5 : C$, second truth assignment.

6.2C Well-definedness of *M*

1 It is important to distinguish three types of object:

(1) The propositional connective symbols '$\neg$', '$\wedge$', '$\vee$', '$\Rightarrow$' and '$\Leftrightarrow$'. These are symbols of the formal language we define, that is, members of the alphabet *Al*.

(2) The operations $G_{\neg}$, $G_{\wedge}$, $G_{\vee}$, $G_{\Rightarrow}$ and $G_{\Leftrightarrow}$. These are *not* symbols of the language *C*, but formula-building operations. For instance, '$G_{\neg}$' is the name of the operation which sends any wff $\beta: Wffs$ to the wff '$(\neg\ \beta)$' $\in Wffs$. These functions operate on the set $U = Al^*$ of all strings of symbols from *Al*. They are concerned only with transforming *strings* and do *not* involve semantic considerations.

(3) The operations NOT, AND, OR, IF, IFF. These too are *not* symbols of the language *C*. Each of them denotes a certain *semantic function*, that is, an operation on the set Bool = {true, false}, which is the 'meaning' of the corresponding logical connective in *C*.

The definition of the formal language *C* and its semantics is itself expressed in English and mathematical notation. The mixture of English and special notation used to describe *C* is called *metalanguage*. Thus '$G_{\neg}$', '$G_{\wedge}$',... and 'NOT', 'AND',... are symbols of the metalanguage.

2 There is a one-to-one correspondence between the generators G_π, $G_{\neg}$, $G_{\wedge}$, $G_{\vee}$, $G_{\Rightarrow}$ and $G_{\Leftrightarrow}$ on the one hand, and the functions *m*, NOT, AND, OR, IF and IFF on the other. This correspondence is set out in Table **6**.2C.1.

Table 6.2C.1 Correspondence between generators G_i and semantic functions.

Generators G_i	*Semantic functions*
G_π Unary relation with $\mathrm{Gr}(G_\pi) = Props \subset U$	$m: \mathrm{Gr}(G_\pi) \to \mathrm{Bool}$
$G_{\neg}: U \to U$	$\mathrm{NOT}: \mathrm{Bool} \to \mathrm{Bool}$
$G_{\wedge}: U^2 \to U$	$\mathrm{AND}: \mathrm{Bool}^2 \to \mathrm{Bool}$
$G_{\vee}: U^2 \to U$	$\mathrm{OR}: \mathrm{Bool}^2 \to \mathrm{Bool}$
$G_{\Rightarrow}: U^2 \to U$	$\mathrm{IF}: \mathrm{Bool}^2 \to \mathrm{Bool}$
$G_{\Leftrightarrow}: U^2 \to U$	$\mathrm{IFF}: \mathrm{Bool}^2 \to \mathrm{Bool}$

Observe that (a) with the unary nonfunctional relation G_π is associated the unary function $m: \mathrm{Gr}(G_\pi) \to \mathrm{Bool}$, and (b) with each formula-building operation $G_i: U^n \to U$ is associated a semantic function $H_i: \mathrm{Bool}^n \to \mathrm{Bool}$ of the same arity *n*. Consequently, all the conditions of Theorem **4**.5C.1 (the recursion theorem) are satisfied, and the semantic function $M: C \rightarrow \text{Bool}$ is well-defined and unique.

Remarks

1 Consider the truth assignment function $m: Props \rightarrow \text{Bool}$. For each proposition symbol $\pi: Props$, the value $m(\pi)$ is selected arbitrarily. $m(\pi)$ represents either our *knowledge* about the fact represented by π, or an *assumption* we make about it. For instance, suppose we treat π as a fact. If π stands for 'Paris is the capital of France', then we must set $m(\pi) = \text{true}$, and if π stands for 'Berlin is the capital of France' then we must set $m(\pi) = \text{false}$.

Alternatively, we may treat the truth value of π as an *assumption* in order to examine the consequences of π being either true or false; in this case, $m(\pi)$ is set accordingly, regardless of whether π actually represents a fact or not. To sum up, from the strict point of view of propositional logic, each value $m(\pi)$ is taken as a starting-point, a given which requires no justification.

2 So far, we have assumed that a value $m(\pi)$ must be assigned to *every* proposition symbol π before $M(\alpha)$ is defined for any wff α. Clearly this is not necessary. For any wff α, the value $M(\alpha)$ is determined as soon as $m(\pi)$ is fixed for every proposition symbol π occurring in α. Therefore, we can work with *partial* truth assignments m as long as $m(\pi)$ is defined for every π occurring in any of the wffs we are interested in. ■

EXERCISES

6.2.1 In practice, we never define a truth assignment m completely, but only for *some* proposition symbols. Given a set of wffs in which we are interested, for which proposition symbols π do we need to specify $m(\pi)$ and why? To illustrate, suppose we are interested in the following two formulas simultaneously:

$$\alpha_1 =_d \quad (\neg(p_1 \wedge q)) \Rightarrow (\neg\, q)$$

and

$$\alpha_2 =_d \quad (p_2 \Leftrightarrow p_1) \vee (\neg(q_1 \vee q))$$

What is the answer in this case?

6.2.2 Consider formula α_6 of Exercise **6**.1.2, as well as its components $p, q, \alpha_1, \ldots, \alpha_5$. Let m be the truth assignment partially defined by $m(p) =_d \text{T}$ and $m(q) =_d \text{F}$. Indicate *in detail* how the following values are derived from m: $M(p)$, $M(q)$, $M(\alpha_1)$, $M(\alpha_2)$ and $M(\alpha_4)$.

6.2.3 Consider the parse tree of Figure 6.2B.1. Let m be the partial truth assignment given by

π	$m(\pi)$
p	T
p_1	F
q_1	T
q_2	F

Compute $\boldsymbol{M}(\alpha_i)$ systematically for the various wffs α_i on this parse tree.

6.2.4 Given a set $S \subseteq_d Props$ of proposition symbols, let 'partial truth assignment for S' mean an assignment of truth values to the members of S only.

(a) How many different truth assignments are there for a set S of (i) 1 symbol; (ii) 2 symbols; (iii) 3 symbols; (iv) n symbols, $n \geqslant 1$?
(b) How does this problem relate to counting the powerset of a given set?

6.2.5 Show that a truth assignment m for a set $S \subseteq_d Props$ may be described as the characteristic function of a certain subset of S.

6.2.6 Let $\alpha_3 =_d$ '$(\neg(p \vee (\neg\, q)))$'.

(a) Construct the parse tree of α_3 in which the compound subwffs are represented by α_1 and α_2.

(b) For each partial truth assignment m for $\{p, q\}$, compute $\boldsymbol{M}(\alpha_i)$ systematically for α_3 and each of its components α_i, without giving the computational details. Present the results in a table with columns headed p, q, α_1, α_2 and α_3, with each row corresponding to a different truth assignment m.

6.3 Tautological implication

We now turn to the representation of deductive reasoning in propositional logic. The central concept in this description is *tautological implication.* This concept formalizes what we mean when we say that 'a certain fact logically follows from certain other facts'.

In propositional logic, each fact is represented by a proposition. Consequently by 'tautological implication' we mean a certain rule which exactly determines when a certain set of propositions implies another given proposition.

The phrase 'tautological implication' means implication in a certain technical sense, which is now to be defined.

6.3A Truth tables

In order to determine whether a set of wffs tautologically implies another wff, we must consider every possible assignment m of truth values to proposition symbols occurring in the relevant wffs α, and the resulting values $M(\alpha)$. In applications involving only a few simple wffs, it is convenient to marshal these values into so-called *truth tables*.

A truth table is best introduced by an example. Consider the following wffs:

$$\beta_1 =_d \quad \neg p \qquad \beta_2 =_d \quad \neg q \qquad \beta_3 =_d \quad p \vee q$$

Let Γ be the set of these propositions i.e. $\Gamma =_d \{\beta_1, \beta_2, \beta_3\}$. The proposition symbols occurring in these wffs are p and q. Consequently, for each $\beta : \Gamma$, $M(\beta)$ is entirely determined by an assignment m of truth values to p and q only. There are four different such partial truth assignments. They are given in the truth table set out in Table 6.3A.1

In this table, a row represents a partial truth assignment m and all the values $M(\beta)$ determined by m. More precisely, a cell at the intersection of the row representing m and the column representing a wff β contains the value $M(\beta)$ determined by m.

Table 6.3A.1 Truth table for a set of wffs.

p	q	β_1 $\neg p$	β_2 $\neg q$	β_3 $p \vee q$
T	T	F	F	T
T	F	F	T	T
F	T	T	F	T
F	F	T	T	F

6.3B Satisfiability

In order to define tautological implication, we need a preliminary concept, namely *satisfiability* of a wff or a set of wffs. In outline, a truth assignment m is said to satisfy a set of wffs if the value $M(\alpha)$ determined by m is true for every wff α in the set.

Definition 6.3B.1

Consider the language $C = \mathit{Wffs}$ of propositional logic. Let *Props* denote the set of proposition symbols in C.

(1) Let $\alpha : \mathit{Wffs}$ be a wff and $m : \mathit{Props} \rightarrow \text{Bool}$ any truth assignment. Let $\boldsymbol{M}(\alpha)$ be the truth value of α determined by m. If $\boldsymbol{M}(\alpha) = \text{true}$ then we say that the *truth assignment m satisfies* α.

(2) Let Γ be a set of wffs, finite or infinite. A truth assignment $m : \mathit{Props} \rightarrow \text{Bool}$ *satisfies* Γ iff m satisfies *every wff* $\beta : \Gamma$.

(3) A set Γ of wffs is *satisfiable* iff there exists at least one truth assignment m which satisfies it. ■

Note Recall remark 2 at the end of Section **6**.2C. In the present definition a truth assignment m is required to be total. However, we may allow m to be partial, as long as $m(\pi)$ is defined for every proposition symbol π occurring in at least one wff in Γ. ■

Example 6.3B.1

(1) Consider the set $\Gamma' =_{\mathrm{d}} \{\beta_1, \beta_2\}$, where

$$\beta_1 =_{\mathrm{d}} \quad \neg p \qquad \beta_2 =_{\mathrm{d}} \quad \neg q$$

This set is satisfiable, as is shown in the following truth table: for the truth assignment m on the last line, i.e. given by $m(p) =_{\mathrm{d}} m(q) =_{\mathrm{d}} \mathrm{F}$, $\boldsymbol{M}(\beta_1) = \mathrm{T}$ and $\boldsymbol{M}(\beta_2) = \mathrm{T}$, i.e. $\Gamma' = \{\beta_1, \beta_2\}$ is satisfied by m. In the sequel, a truth assignment m satisfying a specified set Γ of wffs is marked with an asterisk (*) in the column of the last member of Γ.

p	q	β_1 $\neg p$	β_2 $\neg q$
T	T	F	F
T	F	F	T
F	T	T	F
F	F	T	T*

(2) Consider the set $\Gamma =_{\mathrm{d}} \{\beta_1, \beta_2, \beta_3\}$ defined in Section **6**.3A, where β_1 and β_2 are as defined above and

$$\beta_3 =_{\mathrm{d}} \quad p \vee q$$

This set is *not* satisfiable, as Table **6**.3A.1 shows. For *every* truth assignment m, $\boldsymbol{M}(\beta) = \mathrm{F}$ for at least one wff $\beta : \Gamma$. ■

6.3C Definition of tautological implication

We are now in a position to define tautological implication. This is as follows.

Definition 6.3C.1 (tautological implication)
A set Γ of wffs *tautologically implies* a wff α iff every truth assignment m that satisfies Γ also satisfies α. This property is written

$$\Gamma \vDash \alpha$$ ■

In other words, $\Gamma \vDash \alpha$ iff for any truth assignment m such that $\boldsymbol{M}(\beta) = \text{true}$ for all $\beta : \Gamma$, $\boldsymbol{M}(\alpha)$ is also true. Or: if we can find at least one truth assignment m such that (a) $\boldsymbol{M}(\beta) = \text{true}$ for all $\beta : \Gamma$ and (b) $\boldsymbol{M}(\alpha)$ is false, then (and only then) α is *not* tautologically implied by Γ.

Example 6.3C.1
Consider the following propositions, whose parse trees are given in Figure 6.3C.1 without the names of formula-building operations:

$$\beta_1 =_d \quad \neg p \qquad \beta_2 =_d \quad \neg q \qquad \alpha =_d \quad \neg (p \vee q)$$

Let $\Gamma' =_d \{\beta_1, \beta_2\}$, as in Example 6.3B.1(1). We claim that $\Gamma' \vDash \alpha$. In order to verify this claim, we must consider every possible assignment m of truth values to p and q. Then for each m such that $\boldsymbol{M}(\beta_1) = \boldsymbol{M}(\beta_2) = \text{true}$, we must check that $\boldsymbol{M}(\alpha)$ is also true. The truth table is as follows:

p	q	β_1 $\neg p$	β_2 $\neg q$	β_3 $p \vee q$	α $\neg \beta_3$
T	T	F	F	T	F
T	F	F	T	T	F
F	T	T	F	T	F
F	F	T	T*	F	T

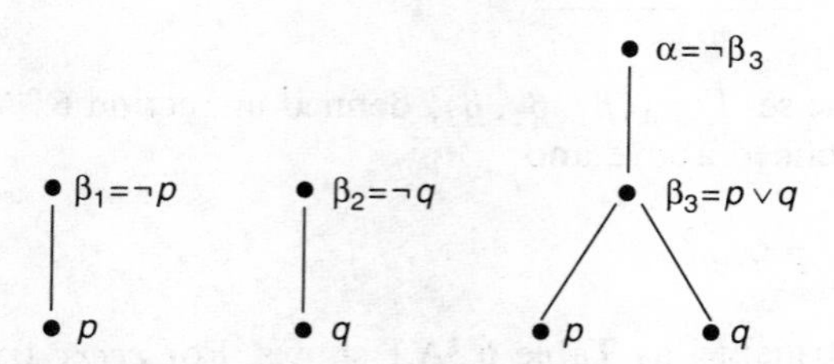

Figure 6.3C.1 Parse trees of three propositions.

From Example 6.3B.1(1), the only truth assignment m which satisfies $\Gamma' = \{\beta_1, \beta_2\}$ is $m(p) =_d m(q) =_d$ F, and for this m, $M(\alpha) =$ T. This completes the proof that $\Gamma' \models \alpha$. ■

Example 6.3C.2

Consider the propositions

$$\beta_1 =_d \quad p \vee q \qquad \beta_2 =_d \quad p \Rightarrow q \qquad \alpha =_d \quad ((\neg p) \wedge q) \vee p$$

The parse trees of these wffs are as shown in Figure 6.3C.2.

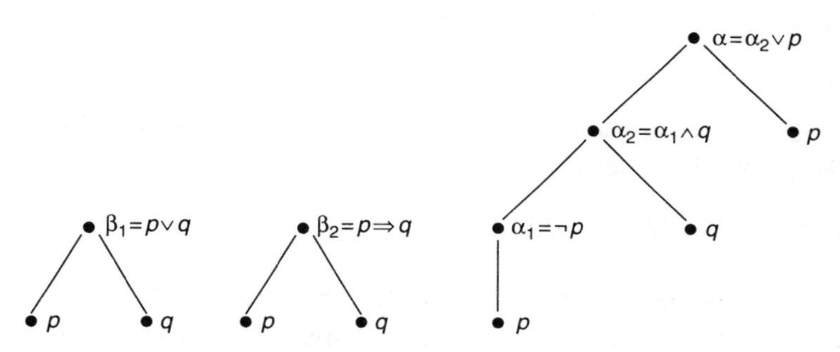

Figure 6.3C.2 Parse trees of three propositions.

Let $\Gamma =_d \{\beta_1, \beta_2\}$. We prove that $\Gamma \models \alpha$. The truth table for Γ, α is as follows:

p	q	β_1 $p \vee q$	β_2 $p \Rightarrow q$	α_1 $\neg p$	α_2 $\alpha_1 \wedge q$	α $\alpha_2 \vee p$
T	T	T	T*	F	F	T
T	F	T	F	F	F	T
F	T	T	T*	T	T	T
F	F	F	T	T	F	F

$\Gamma = \{\beta_1, \beta_2\}$ is satisfied by two truth assignments m, those shown in the first and third rows of the table. For these truth assignments, $M(\alpha) =$ T as is shown in the last column. Therefore, $\Gamma \models \alpha$. ■

There is an alternative way of defining tautological implication. It is a consequence of the following property:

Property 6.3C.1

Consider any set Γ of wffs and any wff α. The two following conditions are equivalent:

(1) $\Gamma \models \alpha$.

(2) The set $\Gamma \cup \{`(\neg\ \alpha)'\}$ is *not satisfiable*. ■

Consequently, instead of Definition 6.3C.1, we could define $\Gamma \models \alpha$ as expressing the condition that $\Gamma \cup \{`(\neg\ \alpha)'\}$ is not satisfiable, that is, that there is *no* truth assignment $m$ which satisfies all the members of $\Gamma$ *as well as* '$(\neg\ \alpha)$'. The merit of this alternative is that it is 'symmetric': every wff $\beta : \Gamma \cup \{`(\neg\ \alpha)'\}$ plays the same role in it. Property 6.3C.1 is easy to verify. The proof is left as an exercise.

Remarks

1 Tautological implication $\models$ is a *relation* between sets of wffs and individual wffs. The graph of this relation satisfies

$$\mathrm{Gr}(\models) \subseteq \mathrm{Pow}(\mathit{Wffs}) \times \mathit{Wffs}$$

2 If Γ is a singleton $\{\beta\}$, then we write '$\{\beta\} \models \alpha$' simply as '$\beta \models \alpha$'.

3 A set Γ of wffs is *unsatisfiable* if no truth assignment satisfies *every* wff $\beta : \Gamma$. In this case Γ is also said to be *inconsistent*. It can be seen from Definition 6.3C.1 that if Γ is unsatisfiable then $\Gamma \models \alpha$ for every wff α! In particular, Γ implies both α and '$(\neg\alpha)$' – that is, it leads to a *contradiction*. ■

6.3D Tautologies

In propositional logic, a tautology is a wff α which is always true, regardless of the truth values assigned to the proposition symbols occurring in it. In other words, for every truth assignment m, the associated value $\boldsymbol{M}(\alpha) = $ true. We now introduce this notion, together with the related concept of tautological equivalence.

Definition 6.3D.1

(1) A *tautology* is a wff α such that $\boldsymbol{M}(\alpha) = $ true for every truth assignment m.

(2) Two wffs α and β are *tautologically equivalent* iff $\beta \models \alpha$ and $\alpha \models \beta$. ■

Example 6.3D.1

Consider the proposition

$$\alpha =_{\mathrm{d}} \quad (p \Rightarrow q) \Leftrightarrow ((\neg\ q) \Rightarrow (\neg\ p))$$

This is a tautology. We verify this by computing $M(\alpha)$ for all truth assignments m, that is, all combinations of values $m(p)$ and $m(q)$. The parse tree for α is set out in Figure **6**.3D.1. The associated truth table is given below. The last column of the table shows that $M(\alpha)$ = true for every possible truth assignment m. Therefore, α is a tautology.

p	q	α_1 $p \Rightarrow q$	α_2 $\neg q$	α_3 $\neg p$	α_4 $\alpha_2 \Rightarrow \alpha_3$	α $\alpha_1 \Leftrightarrow \alpha_4$
T	T	T	F	F	T	T
T	F	F	T	F	F	T
F	T	T	F	T	T	T
F	F	T	T	T	T	T

This tautology is sufficiently important to be given a name; it is called *contraposition.* In English, it can be rendered as follows: 'To say that a fact p implies a fact q is the same as to say that if q is false then p is false.' It has already been used in Section **3**.3C to give two equivalent definitions of an injection. ■

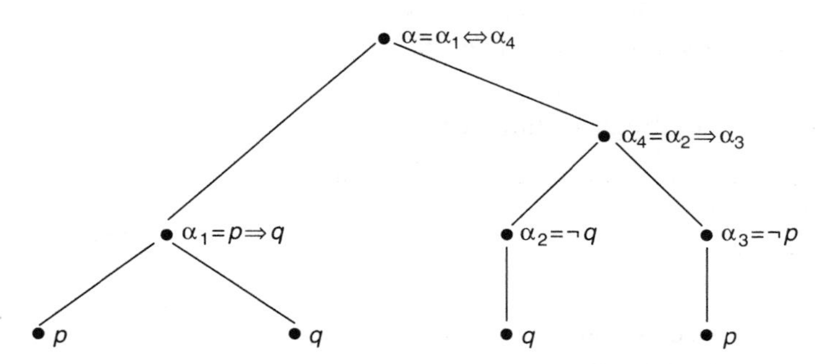

Figure 6.3D.1 Parse tree of a tautology.

Remarks

1 A wff α is a tautology iff it is tautologically implied by nothing, i.e. $\varnothing \models \alpha$. This is easy to see from Definitions **6**.3C.1 and **6**.3D.1. We also simply write '$\models \alpha$' in this case.

2 Given any two wffs α and β, $\alpha \models \beta$ iff '$(\alpha \Rightarrow \beta)$' is a tautology. However '$\alpha \models \beta$' must not be confused with '$(\alpha \Rightarrow \beta)$'. The former is a *metalanguage* statement – that is, it is the English sentence 'α tautologically implies β' – whereas '$(\alpha \Rightarrow \beta)$' is a wff, a member of the language *Wffs* which we are describing.

3 Two wffs α and β are tautologically equivalent iff '$(\alpha \Leftrightarrow \beta)$' is a tautology.

All these facts directly follow from the definitions, as the reader should verify. ■

EXERCISES

6.3.1 Consider the wffs of Exercise **6.1.2**. Construct a two-row truth table for the eight wffs involved (recall that 'p' and 'q' count as wffs!), for the following partially defined truth assignments:

(1) $m(p) =_d \mathrm{T}$ and $m(q) =_d \mathrm{F}$
(2) $m(p) =_d \mathrm{F}$ and $m(q) =_d \mathrm{T}$

6.3.2 Consider the wff

$$\alpha =_d ((p_1 \wedge q_1) \Rightarrow (\neg\, q_1)) \Leftrightarrow ((p_2 \vee q_1) \wedge (p_1 \Rightarrow q_2))$$

of Exercise **6.1.3**. With reference to your parse tree for this wff, construct a one-row truth table for the partially defined truth assignment

$$m(p_1) =_d \mathrm{T} \qquad m(p_2) =_d \mathrm{F} \qquad m(q_1) =_d \mathrm{F} \qquad m(q_2) =_d \mathrm{T}$$

Thus, each entry in the table corresponds to a subwff β of α and contains the value $\boldsymbol{M}(\beta)$ determined by m.

6.3.3 Consider Exercise **5.2.3**. Express statements S1 and S2 as propositions α and β respectively in propositional logic. Then prove $\alpha \models \beta$ by the truth table method.

6.3.4 Consider the following English statements:

β_1: 'If men are equal then there are no privileges.'
β_2: 'There are privileges.'
'Therefore:'
α: 'Men are not equal.'

(a) Express these three statements in propositional logic. Hint: two proposition symbols are required, call them p and q.
(b) Verify that $\{\beta_1, \beta_2\} \models \alpha$.

6.3.5 Consider the following wffs:

$$\beta_1 =_d (p_1 \Rightarrow p_2)$$
$$\beta_2 =_d (p_2 \Rightarrow p_3)$$
$$\alpha =_d (p_1 \Rightarrow p_3)$$

Let $\Gamma =_d \{\beta_1, \beta_2\}$. Prove that $\Gamma \models \alpha$. Hint: Here there are three proposition symbols, hence eight partial truth assignments m: *Props* $\rightarrow$ Bool to consider.

6.3.6 Consider the following wffs:

$$\beta =_d (p \Rightarrow (\neg\, q))$$
$$\alpha =_d ((\neg\, q) \vee (\neg\, p))$$

Verify that (i) $\beta \vDash \alpha$ and (ii) $\alpha \vDash \beta$; that is, α and β are tautologically equivalent. NB: Only one truth table is needed.

6.3.7 Consider the following wffs:

$$\beta_1 =_d (p \Rightarrow (\neg q)) \qquad \beta_2 =_d (q \Rightarrow (p \wedge q))$$
$$\alpha_1 =_d (p \wedge q) \qquad \alpha_2 =_d (p \vee (\neg q))$$

Let $\Gamma =_d \{\beta_1, \beta_2\}$. Determine which of the following are true, if any:

(a) $\Gamma \vDash p$
(b) $\Gamma \vDash q$
(c) $\Gamma \vDash \alpha_1$
(d) $\Gamma \vDash \alpha_2$

NB: A single truth table suffices to answer all parts of the question.

6.3.8 Prove that the wff '$(p \Rightarrow p)$' is a tautology.

6.3.9 Show that Definition **6**.3C.1 of '$\Gamma \vDash \alpha$' is equivalent to stating: 'There is *no* truth assignment m for which (a) $\boldsymbol{M}(\beta) =$ true for all $\beta : \Gamma$ and (b) $\boldsymbol{M}(\alpha) =$ false.'

6.3.10 Prove Property **6**.3C.1. Hint: Build on Exercise **6**.3.9.

6.3.11 Justify briefly but precisely the assertion that if a set Γ of wffs is unsatisfiable then $\Gamma \vDash \alpha$ for any wff α.

6.3.12 Let $\Gamma =_d \{\beta, `(\neg \beta)'\}$, where β is any wff. Show that $\Gamma \vDash \alpha$ for any wff α, using Exercise **6**.3.11.

6.3.13 Show that for any wffs α and β:

(a) $\alpha \vDash \beta$ iff $\vDash$ '$(\alpha \Rightarrow \beta)$'. (Recall that for any wff α, '$\vDash \alpha$' is short for '$\varnothing \vDash \alpha$' and means that α is a tautology.)
(b) $\alpha \vDash \beta$ and $\beta \vDash \alpha$ iff $\vDash$ '$(\alpha \Leftrightarrow \beta)$'.

6.3.14 Show that any wff α is a tautology iff $\vDash \alpha$.

6.4 Fundamental tautologies and applications

6.4A A catalogue of key tautologies

Some elementary tautologies are important means of proof in computing. Some are fairly obvious, others less so. Here is a list of key ones. The reader is advised to study them carefully, in particular to draw their parse trees and verify them using the truth table method. To simplify, negations are written without parentheses: for example '$\neg \alpha$' stands for '$(\neg \alpha)$'. In parsing a wff α, apply '$\neg$' before any other connectives; i.e. apply it to the smallest subwff following it in α.

(1) *Negation*

$$\neg \neg p \Leftrightarrow p$$

(2) *Excluded middle*

$$p \vee \neg p$$

(3) *Contradiction*

$$\neg (p \wedge \neg p)$$

(4) *De Morgan's laws*

$$\neg (p \wedge q) \Leftrightarrow (\neg p \vee \neg q)$$
$$\neg (p \vee q) \Leftrightarrow (\neg p \wedge \neg q)$$

(5) *Conditional and negation of conditional*

$$(p \Rightarrow q) \Leftrightarrow (\neg p \vee q)$$
$$\neg (p \Rightarrow q) \Leftrightarrow (p \wedge \neg q)$$

(6) *Contraposition (two variants)*

$$(p \Rightarrow q) \Leftrightarrow (\neg q \Rightarrow \neg p)$$
$$(\neg p \Rightarrow q) \Leftrightarrow (\neg q \Rightarrow p)$$

(7) *Exportation*

$$((p_1 \wedge p_2) \Rightarrow p_3) \Leftrightarrow (p_1 \Rightarrow (p_2 \Rightarrow p_3))$$

(8) *Biconditional*

$$(p \Leftrightarrow q) \Leftrightarrow ((p \Rightarrow q) \wedge (q \Rightarrow p))$$

(9) *Transitive laws* ($\Rightarrow$ and $\Leftrightarrow$)

$$[(p_1 \Rightarrow p_2) \wedge (p_2 \Rightarrow p_3)] \Rightarrow (p_1 \Rightarrow p_3)$$
$$[(p_1 \Leftrightarrow p_2) \wedge (p_2 \Leftrightarrow p_3)] \Rightarrow (p_1 \Leftrightarrow p_3)$$

(10) *Distributive laws* ($\wedge$ over $\vee$ and vice versa)

$$[p_1 \wedge (p_2 \vee p_3)] \Leftrightarrow [(p_1 \wedge p_2) \vee (p_1 \wedge p_3)]$$
$$[p_1 \vee (p_2 \wedge p_3)] \Leftrightarrow [(p_1 \vee p_2) \wedge (p_1 \vee p_3)]$$

(11) *Commutative laws* ($\wedge$, $\vee$ and $\Leftrightarrow$)

$$(p * q) \Leftrightarrow (q * p)$$

where * is one of the propositional connectives '$\wedge$', '$\vee$' or '$\Leftrightarrow$'.

(12) *Associative laws* ($\wedge$, $\vee$ and $\Leftrightarrow$)

$$((p_1 * p_2) * p_3) \Leftrightarrow (p_1 * (p_2 * p_3))$$

where * is one of the propositional connectives '$\wedge$', '$\vee$' or '$\Leftrightarrow$'.

Remark

From the associative laws for '$\wedge$', '$\vee$' and '$\Leftrightarrow$', it can be shown that we may derive generalized associative laws holding for n proposition symbols and not just three. For instance, in '$p_1 \wedge p_2 \wedge \ldots p_n$' we may restore the necessary parentheses in any way we like: all the resulting wffs are equivalent. Thus we regard '$p_1 \wedge p_2 \wedge \ldots \wedge p_n$' as a shorthand for any one of these equivalent wffs. The same holds for '$\vee$' and '$\Leftrightarrow$'. ■

6.4B Substitution

Next, we describe two general rules for constructing tautologies. These are as follows:

Theorem 6.4B.1

Let α be any tautology and $\pi_1, \pi_2, \ldots, \pi_n$ be the different proposition symbols occurring in α. Note that any π_i may occur in several places in α. Let α' be the wff obtained as follows: for each proposition symbol π_i, replace every occurrence of π_i by some wff β_i (the *same* β_i for each occurrence of π_i). Then α' is a tautology. ■

Proof outline This should be clear. The truth table for α' is an obvious expansion of that of α, with each π_i replaced by the corresponding wff β_i and additional columns introduced for each β_i to compute $\boldsymbol{M}(\beta_i)$. The fact that α is a tautology means $\boldsymbol{M}(\alpha) = $ true for all combinations of the values $\boldsymbol{M}(\pi_i)$. $\boldsymbol{M}(\alpha')$ is computed in the same way from the values $\boldsymbol{M}(\beta_i)$ as $\boldsymbol{M}(\alpha)$ is from the values $\boldsymbol{M}(\pi_i)$. Therefore, whatever the values $\boldsymbol{M}(\beta_i)$, $\boldsymbol{M}(\alpha') = $ true, i.e. α' is a tautology. ■

The practical import of the theorem is this. For each tautology α, the theorem produces a tautology *schema*, or family of tautologies. This may be represented by replacing each proposition symbol π_i by the symbol 'β_i' in α. The result defines the family of all the wffs obtained by substituting an actual wff for each 'β_i'. The theorem states that each such wff is a tautology. For instance, the tautology

$$(\neg(p \wedge q)) \Leftrightarrow ((\neg p) \vee (\neg q))$$

may be rewritten as the schema

$$(\neg(\beta_1 \wedge \beta_2)) \Leftrightarrow ((\neg \beta_1) \vee (\neg \beta_2))$$

This describes the set of wffs obtained by replacing each occurrence of 'β_1' by some wff and each occurrence of 'β_2' by some other wff. Any member of this set is a tautology.

Theorem 6.4B.2

Let α, β and β' be three wffs such that $\models$ '$(\beta \Leftrightarrow \beta')$', i.e. β and β' are tautologically equivalent, and β is a subwff of α. Let α' be obtained by substituting β' for one or more occurrences of β in α. Then

$$\models (\alpha \Leftrightarrow \alpha')$$

That is, α and α' are tautologically equivalent. ■

This property should be clear, considering how $\boldsymbol{M}(\alpha)$ and $\boldsymbol{M}(\alpha')$ are computed. The full proof is left as an exercise. For instance,

$$\models (p \Leftrightarrow \neg \neg p)$$

Therefore, taking $\alpha =_{\mathrm{d}}$ '$(p \Rightarrow \neg q)$', we have

$$\models (p \Rightarrow \neg q) \Leftrightarrow (\neg \neg p \Rightarrow \neg q)$$

Remarks

1 Recall the final remarks of Sections **6**.3D and **6**.4A. To these we may add the following. Consider a finite set of wffs $\Gamma =_{\mathrm{d}} \{\alpha_1, \alpha_2, \ldots, \alpha_n\}$ and a wff β. Then $\Gamma \models \beta$ iff

(1) $\quad (\alpha_1 \wedge \alpha_2 \wedge \ldots \wedge \alpha_n) \Rightarrow \beta$

is a tautology. Likewise, $\Gamma \models \beta$ iff

(2) $\quad \alpha_1 \Rightarrow (\alpha_2 \Rightarrow (\ldots \Rightarrow (\alpha_n \Rightarrow \beta) \ldots))$

is a tautology. Consequently, whether we prove $\Gamma \models \beta$, $\models$(1) or $\models$(2) makes no difference in practice: we just choose the most convenient form.

2 In principle, any tautology α may be proved by the truth table method in a finite number of steps. However, this number grows exponentially with the number of proposition symbols, so the method rapidly becomes unwieldy as the latter increases. We now have an alternative proof method, which is to determine whether α can be obtained from a simpler tautology by application of Theorems **6**.4B.1 or **6**.4B.2. This alternative is quite natural and often used in practice. We shall see in Chapter **8** that it can also be used in first-order logic, where it is referred to as rule T. In this logic, too, it is frequently applied.

■

6.4C Equivalent languages

Let L denote the language of propositional logic as we have defined it. This language contains five logical connective symbols: '$\neg$', '$\wedge$', '$\vee$', '$\Rightarrow$' and '$\Leftrightarrow$'. Each of them has a corresponding phrase in English, which is why it is present in L. An interesting consequence of the tautologies given in Section **6**.4A is that these connectives are redundant. We can eliminate some of them from L without reducing its expressive power.

For instance, let L' be the language defined like L but with only two logical connectives, namely '$\neg$' and '$\vee$'. We can show that for any wff α in L, there is a wff α' in L' which is equivalent. We prove this by defining α' as a function of α constructed by structural recursion.

(1) If α is a proposition symbol then $\alpha' =_d \alpha$.

(2) If $\alpha =$ '$\neg \beta$' then let $\alpha' =_d$ '$\neg \beta'$'. (Thus β' is obtained from β in the same way that α' is obtained from α; this is the recursive aspect of the construction.)

(3) If $\alpha =$ '$(\beta \wedge \gamma)$', then by one of De Morgan's laws, negation and transitive law of $\Leftrightarrow$, α is equivalent to

$$\neg(\neg \beta \vee \neg \gamma)$$

In this case, let $\alpha' =_d$ '$\neg(\neg \beta' \vee \neg \gamma')$'.

(4) If $\alpha =$ '$(\beta \Rightarrow \gamma)$', then by the conditional law α is equivalent to

$$(\neg \beta \vee \gamma)$$

In this case, let $\alpha' =_d$ '$(\neg \beta' \vee \gamma')$'.

(5) If $\alpha =$ '$(\beta \Leftrightarrow \gamma)$', then by the biconditional law α is equivalent to

$$(\beta \Rightarrow \gamma) \wedge (\gamma \Rightarrow \beta)$$

Therefore, let $\alpha'' =_d$ '$(\beta' \Rightarrow \gamma') \wedge (\gamma' \Rightarrow \beta')$' and derive α' from α'' using (3) and (4).

Other reducts of L may be shown to have the same expressive power, for example the language L'' with '$\neg$' and '$\Rightarrow$' as sole logical connectives. The main advantage of working with a smaller language is that this simplifies some theoretical arguments, such as case analyses like the one just carried out. For instance, Andrews (1986) uses mainly L', and Enderton (1972) uses L'' as a basis for first-order logic. One further technique is to adopt a smaller language as 'official' and introduce additional connective symbols as *abbreviations*. For instance, with L' taken as the 'official' language, '$(\beta \wedge \gamma)$' is introduced as an abbreviation for '$\neg(\neg \beta \vee \neg \gamma)$', '$(\beta \Rightarrow \gamma)$' for '$(\neg \beta \vee \gamma)$' and so on. These abbreviations are used for exposition of the theory only.

There is the opposite question to consider: is it possible to *increase* the expressive power of L by extending it with additional logical connectives (of any arity: 1, 2, 3, ...)? In order to answer this question we need to be more precise about the meaning of 'expressive power' of a propositional language. Any wff α of propositional logic (in a given language) may be regarded as defining, or *representing*, an n-ary boolean operation (that is, a function $\text{Bool}^n \rightarrow \text{Bool}$), where n is the number of distinct proposition symbols occurring in α. This is the function which returns the value $\boldsymbol{M}(\alpha)$ for each assignment m of truth values to the n proposition symbols occurring in α. Now in any language we may determine for each n the set of n-ary boolean operations each of which is represented by some wff. The expressive power of the language may be defined as the union of these sets. It can be demonstrated that for each n, *every* n-ary boolean operation is represented by a wff in L. For this reason, L is called *complete*, and its expressive power cannot be increased by adding further logical connectives to it. Of course, the same holds for all the reducts of L of equal expressive power, L' and L'' in particular: these are equally complete. For the details, see Enderton (1972).

6.4D Applications

To end this chapter on propositional logic, here are two concrete applications. They illustrate the types of formal proof which can be expressed in propositional logic, and more specifically the role of basic tautologies.

Example 6.4D.1

Recall that an injection is a function $F: S \nrightarrow T$ such that for each $y: T$, there is at most one $x: S$ such that $F(x) = y$. This concept may be expressed formally as follows:

For any $x, x' : \text{Def}(F)$, if $F(x) = F(x')$ then $x = x'$.

There is an alternative formal definition:

For any $x, x' : \text{Def}(F)$, if $x \neq x'$ then $F(x) \neq F(x')$.

These two definitions are clearly equivalent. Their equivalence is an application of contraposition. We show this formally as follows. The law of contraposition is

(1) $(p \Rightarrow q) \Leftrightarrow (\neg q \Rightarrow \neg p)$

Let p stand for the proposition '$F(x) = F(x')$' and q for '$x = x'$'. Substituting these two formulas in (1) we obtain

(2) $(F(x) = F(x') \Rightarrow x = x') \Leftrightarrow [\neg (x = x') \Rightarrow \neg (F(x) = F(x'))]$

This is the equivalence to be demonstrated. Note that in (2), '$x = x'$' and '$F(x) = F(x')$' are regarded as atomic propositions, that is, statements which are either true or false and which are not to be further analysed, as we are using propositional logic. ■

Example 6.4D.2

In computing, the so-called ASCII set of characters is frequently used. Its members are totally ordered, which means that this 'set' is really a list. Let $<$ denote the order relation on this set. Thus $x < y$ means that character x precedes character y, and $x \leqslant y$ means that x precedes or is equal to y. Within the set, the 26 capital letters form a subrange. Thus a character x is a capital letter iff 'A' $\leqslant x \leqslant$ 'Z'. This, of course, is an abbreviation for the formula

(1) $(\text{'A'} \leqslant x) \wedge (x \leqslant \text{'Z'})$

We wish to study the negation of (1), that is, what it means for x *not* to be a capital letter. Intuitively, the answer is obvious: either ($x <$ 'A') or ('Z' $< x$). The question is: can we demonstrate this formally? This can be done in propositional logic using one of De Morgan's laws.

Here we are considering two elementary propositions:

$p =_{\text{d}} \quad (\text{'A'} \leqslant x)$

and

$q =_{\text{d}} \quad (x \leqslant \text{'Z'})$

We also note that '$\neg p$' is equivalent to ($x <$ 'A') and '$\neg q$' to ('Z' $< x$). Our aim is to find the negation of '$p \wedge q$', in terms of '$\neg p$' and '$\neg q$'. De Morgan's relevant law is

(1) $\neg (p \wedge q) \Leftrightarrow (\neg p \vee \neg q)$

Substituting for p and q in (1), we obtain

(2) $\neg\,((\text{'A'} \leqslant x) \wedge (x \leqslant \text{'Z'})) \Leftrightarrow (\neg\,(\text{'A'} \leqslant x) \vee \neg\,(x \leqslant \text{'Z'}))$

and finally

(3) $\neg\,((\text{'A'} \leqslant x) \wedge (x \leqslant \text{'Z'})) \Leftrightarrow ((x < \text{'A'}) \vee (\text{'Z'} < x))$

This is the equivalence to be demonstrated. ■

These two concrete examples show that useful proofs may be formalized in propositional logic. Further examples will be given in subsequent chapters, as part of applications of first-order logic.

EXERCISES

6.4.1* Verify by simple induction that for any *finite* set $\Gamma = \{\alpha_1, \alpha_2, \ldots, \alpha_n\}$ of wffs and any wff β, the following are equivalent:

(1) $\Gamma \vDash \beta$
(2) $\vDash (\alpha_1 \wedge \alpha_2 \wedge \ldots \wedge \alpha_n) \Rightarrow \beta$
(3) $\vDash \alpha_1 \Rightarrow (\alpha_2 \Rightarrow (\alpha_3 \Rightarrow \ldots \Rightarrow (\alpha_n \Rightarrow \beta) \ldots))$

6.4.2 Consider the tautologies listed in Section **6**.4A.

(a) Rewrite each of them in the 'official' notation by inserting the missing parentheses, and draw their parse trees.
(b) Prove each of them by the truth table method, using $\alpha_1, \alpha_2, \ldots$ systematically to name constituent compound wffs.

6.4.3 Prove Theorem **6**.4B.2 in outline. Hint: The proof is similar to that of Theorem **6**.4B.1.

6.4.4 Let $\alpha =_{\text{d}}$ '$(\neg\, q \Rightarrow \neg\, p) \Leftrightarrow (p \Rightarrow q)$'. Prove $\vDash \alpha$ in two different ways, using the following tautologies of Section **6**.4A:

(a) (6) and (11)
(b) (1), (6) and (9)

6.4.5 Consider the reducts L' and L'' of the language L introduced in Section **6**.4C. Devise wff-conversion rules for L'' similar to those given for L' in order to show that L'' has the same expressive power as L.

6.4.6* A *literal* is a wff which is a proposition symbol, p, q, p_1, etc., or the negation of a proposition symbol, i.e. '$\neg\, p$', '$\neg\, q$', '$\neg\, p_1$', etc. A *conjunction of literals* is a wff of the form

$$\beta =_{\mathrm{d}} \quad \gamma_1 \wedge \gamma_2 \wedge \ldots \wedge \gamma_k$$

where each γ_i is a literal, $i = 1, \ldots, k$. A wff α is said to be a *disjunctive normal formula* or to be in *disjunctive normal form (dnf)*, if

$$\alpha =_{\mathrm{d}} \quad \beta_1 \vee \beta_2 \vee \ldots \vee \beta_r$$

where each β_j is a conjunction of literals, $j =_{\mathrm{d}} 1, \ldots, r$. An example is

$$\alpha =_{\mathrm{d}} \quad (p \wedge q) \vee (\neg\, p \wedge q_1 \wedge p_1) \vee (p_2 \wedge p_2 \wedge \neg\, q_1) \vee p$$

(a) For any n-ary boolean operation $B: \mathrm{Bool}^n \to \mathrm{Bool}$, construct a wff α in the n proposition symbols $p_1, p_2, \ldots, p_n$ which represents B in the sense that for any truth assignment m,

$$\boldsymbol{M}(\alpha) =_{\mathrm{d}} B(m(p_1), m(p_2), \ldots, m(p_n))$$

where $\boldsymbol{M}(\alpha)$ is the truth value of α determined by m. Thus, α is to contain no proposition symbols other than $p_1, p_2, \ldots, p_n$, though it may contain only some of these. Hint: Construct α as a dnf '$\beta_1 \vee \beta_2 \vee \ldots \vee \beta_r$'. Let each β_j be a wff such that $\boldsymbol{M}(\beta_j) = \text{true}$ for *exactly one* truth assignment m for $\{p_1, p_2, \ldots, p_n\}$; define β_j as '$\gamma_1 \wedge \gamma_2 \wedge \ldots \wedge \gamma_n$', where each $\gamma_k = p_k$ or '$(\neg\, p_k)$', depending on the truth value $m(p_k)$ assigned to p_k. The main task now is to define each γ_k precisely.

(b) Construct a dnf α in p_1, p_2 and p_3 to represent the boolean operation $B: \mathrm{Bool}^3 \to \mathrm{Bool}$ given by $B(\mathrm{T}, \mathrm{F}, \mathrm{T}) = \mathrm{T}$, $B(\mathrm{T}, \mathrm{F}, \mathrm{F}) = \mathrm{T}$, $B(\mathrm{F}, \mathrm{T}, \mathrm{F}) = \mathrm{T}$, and $B(x, y, z) = \mathrm{F}$ for all other triples (x, y, z): Bool^3.

6.4.7* Recall that a language of propositional logic is complete if any boolean operation $B: \mathrm{Bool}^n \to \mathrm{Bool}$ may be represented in it. Use Exercise **6**.4.6 to show the following:

(a) The reduct of L with connectives '$\neg$', '$\wedge$' and '$\vee$' is complete.
(b) L is complete.
(c) Any wff α in L is equivalent to some wff α' in dnf.

6.4.8* Using Exercise **6**.4.7 and the appropriate tautologies, show that the reducts of L with sets of connectives given below are complete:

(a) $\{\neg, \vee\}$
(b) $\{\neg, \Rightarrow\}$

6.4.9* Show that the reducts of L with sets of connectives given below are *not* complete.

(a) $\{\neg\}$
(b) $\{\wedge, \vee\}$

6.4.10 Just as we may define alternative languages by removing some of the propositional connectives of L, we may also specify new languages by introducing *new* connectives (of any arity). In each case we may seek to determine whether the language defined is complete or not.

Let '$\downarrow$', alias *nor*, be a binary propositional connective defined by

$$\models (p \downarrow q) \Leftrightarrow (\neg\, (p \vee q))$$

(a) Construct the truth table of a boolean operation NOR defining the semantics of '$p \downarrow q$'.

(b) Show that the language with '$\downarrow$' as sole connective is complete. Hint: 'Derive' $\neg$ from $\downarrow$, then derive $\vee$ and finally use Exercise **6**.4.8.

First-order Predicate Logic

However useful, propositional logic is insufficient as a model of deductive reasoning. First-order predicate logic is a much more powerful model and may be regarded as an extension of the former. This chapter introduces first-order logic and its main properties.

Note that it is no longer acceptable to talk about *one* language. In first-order logic, we explicitly define a *family* of languages, although this is described like any set or class, by specifying the features of any one of its members.

Section 7.1 contrasts the modelling power of propositional logic with that of first-order logic. This is a continuation of the initial comments in Section 5.2C by means of various concrete examples, which are also designed to highlight the practical significance of first-order logic and the ways in which its formulas relate to sentences in natural language.

Section 7.2 describes the syntax of first-order logic, which may be viewed as an extension of propositional logic syntax. Section 7.3 is devoted to semantics, again an extension of propositional semantics. The topic of Section 7.4 is *logical implication*. This corresponds to the propositional notion of tautological implication, and forms the *semantic* basis of first-order logic as a 'complete' model of deductive reasoning.

Throughout, a strong parallel between corresponding features of propositional and first-order logic can be established with a little reflection. The reader is advised to do so systematically. When it is not readily apparent, this correspondence is highlighted.

7.1 Introduction

First-order logic is constructed in the same way as propositional logic: by inductive definition of a formal language, definition of semantics by recursion on the language and definition of logical implication (first-order counterpart of tautological implication). However, the whole edifice is more complex and the reader may well find the difficulty rather daunting at first. It will help to bear in mind that the key ideas are essentially the same as in propositional logic.

7.1A Limitations of propositional logic

Let us first consider some examples of deductions expressed in natural language. For each example we discuss whether the deduction can be expressed in propositional logic and if not, why not.

Example 7.1A.1

α_1: 'If Socrates is a man then Socrates is mortal.'
α_2: 'Socrates is a man.'
α_3: (Therefore:) 'Socrates is mortal.'

This deduction can be expressed in propositional logic. α_2 and α_3 are elementary propositions, α_1 is the compound proposition

$$\alpha_1 =_d \quad (\alpha_2 \Rightarrow \alpha_3)$$

and the above deduction is formally expressed as

$$\{\alpha_1, \alpha_2\} \quad \models \quad \alpha_3$$

which is correct, as can be verified by the truth table method. (Recall that '$\models$' means 'tautologically implies'.) ■

Example 7.1A.2

α_1: 'If all men are equal then there are no privileges.'
α_2: 'There are privileges.'
α_3: (Therefore:) 'Not all men are equal.'

This can be expressed in propositional logic. Introduce

β_1: 'All men are equal.'

Then α_1 and α_3 are formally given by

$$\alpha_1 =_d \quad (\beta_1 \Rightarrow (\neg\, \alpha_2))$$
$$\alpha_3 =_d \quad (\neg\, \beta_1)$$

The deduction is formally expressed as

$$\{\alpha_1, \alpha_2\} \quad \models \quad \alpha_3$$

which is correct, as the reader may again verify by the truth table method. This is an application of *contraposition*. ■

This second example may give the impression that propositional logic can deal with totalities – all objects in a certain class. This is not true in *general* as the next example shows.

Example 7.1A.3

α_1: 'All men are mortal.'
α_2: 'Socrates is a man.'
α_3: (Therefore:) 'Socrates is mortal.'

Intuitively this deduction is correct: if α_1 and α_2 are both true then α_3 must also be true. However, we cannot express this deduction in propositional logic. This is because we cannot decompose any of the three statements (regarded as propositions) into more elementary propositions. So we must take each of them as an *elementary* proposition. But then $\{\alpha_1, \alpha_2\}$ does *not* tautologically imply α_3, as this is contradicted by the truth assignment m in which $m(\alpha_1) =_d m(\alpha_2) =_d$ true and $m(\alpha_3) =_d$ false. ■

Compare this case with that of Example 7.1A.2. In this example we are able to decompose α_1, α_2 and α_3 down to two elementary propositions: β_1 and α_2, and it is this analysis which leads to the formal deduction: $\{\alpha_1, \alpha_2\} \models \alpha_3$; there is no assignment m of truth values to β_1 and α_2 which simultaneously gives $\boldsymbol{M}(\alpha_1) = \boldsymbol{M}(\alpha_2) =$ true and $\boldsymbol{M}(\alpha_3) =$ false.

7.1B Requirements to be met by first-order logic

Why does propositional logic fail to account for the perfectly valid deduction in Example 7.1A.3? Because this logic does not recognize quantifiers, 'for all' in this case. This example, as well as many statements made in Parts **1** and **2**, shows that, to be complete, logic must contain rules reflecting our use of the logical quantifiers, namely the universal quantifier 'for all', alias '$\forall$', and the existential quantifier 'there exists', alias '$\exists$'. Moreover, from the initial review of notation in Section **2**.4, we know that there are other features of natural language which are not properly accounted for in propositional logic. Let us list them again systematically with reference to the example introduced and discussed in Sections **1**.3A and **2**.4A. This is a formula which is intended to describe the set of parents in set theory. We restate it in a simpler and slightly different form, which is more in accordance with the symbolism we are about to define, and which assumes that all entities considered are either persons or sets:

$$\forall x \cdot x \in \text{Parents} \Leftrightarrow \exists y \cdot (x = \text{Mother } y) \vee (x = \text{Father } y)$$

For the precise use of '·', see Section **2**.4E. Recall that as stated in Section **1**.3A, this simple example already illustrates *all* the types of symbol ever needed in our theoretical models. In other words, it illustrates all the fundamental features which should be accounted for in a complete logic. Such a logic should therefore meet the requirements described below, with an outline of the way they are met in first-order logic.

1 There must be symbols representing the entities or objects about which we intend to talk – that is, making up our *universe of discourse*. For instance, in this example we want to talk about persons and sets of persons, so we need symbols to stand for such entities.

The entities we wish to refer to are either variable or constant. In the example, x and y are *variables*: each symbol denotes *any one* entity, person or set. This is quite clear as far as x is concerned, for this symbol is meant to represent all persons, though taken individually, 'one at a time'. Likewise y is also meant to vary, as we do not expect every x to be the parent of the same child! On the other hand, 'Parents' stands for a constant set: as we understand it, there is only one set of parents, and it is this unique set which the symbol 'Parents' stands for.

2 There must be symbols representing entities which are *functions* of other entities. Here we have two examples: the unary functions Mother and Father. In general, we need function symbols of any arity. Likewise, we need so-called *predicate symbols* to represent *relations* of any arity n between entities: that is, properties or predicates which are true of certain n-tuples of objects, and false of all other n-tuples. In the example there are two such symbols: '$\in$' and '$=$', standing for set membership and equality respectively. Both denote binary relations.

3 Next we need the two quantifiers '$\forall$' and '$\exists$'. They render the phrases 'for all' and 'there exists' respectively. Finally, we need the logical connectives already present in propositional logic: '$\neg$' (not), '$\wedge$' (and), '$\vee$' (or), '$\Rightarrow$' (if ... then) and '$\Leftrightarrow$' (iff). These are used in exactly the same way as in propositional logic, except that proposition symbols are now replaced by first-order formulas expressing relations between objects.

4 In addition, the way in which symbols may be combined must satisfy appropriate syntactic and semantic rules consistent with their intended meaning. On the one hand, we want to represent objects of our universe of discourse. These are described in first-order logic by expressions called *terms*. Therefore a term is either a variable, or a constant, or an n-ary function symbol f followed by n more elementary terms, and in each case the intended meaning is the usual one. An example is 'Mother y' in the above formula, which stands for 'mother of y'.

On the other hand, we want to make *statements* about objects, assertions of relations between objects. These are represented by expressions called *well-formed formulas* (*wffs*). These are like propositions: they are either true or false. So we need syntax rules governing the way any wff is built, and semantic rules determining the truth value of any wff. Terms and well-formed formulas are generically called *well-formed expressions* (*wfes*).

To illustrate the rules for wffs, consider the universal quantifier '$\forall$'. This always means 'for all ... ' or, better still, 'for *any* ... '. More precisely, it always introduces a formula meaning 'for any object x, α is true of x', where α is some statement normally containing x and hence asserting a property of x. For instance, in the above example,

$$\alpha =_{\mathrm{d}} \quad x \in \text{Parents} \Leftrightarrow \exists y \cdot (x = \text{Mother } y) \vee (x = \text{Father } y)$$

Therefore, *syntactically*, '$\forall$' must always be followed by a variable, for example x, and then by a formula α normally containing x and stating a certain property of x. Moreover, *semantically*, '$\forall x\, \alpha$' must always have the meaning commonly attached to the phrase 'for any x, α'. Therefore, '$\forall x\, \alpha$' must be true iff, whatever the object represented by x, the statement α is true of that object. In outline, these are the two rules attached to the universal quantifier. They illustrate the way we establish the syntax and semantics of first-order logic in the next two sections: all the other rules are determined by the same process.

5 Finally, rules are needed to model *deductive reasoning* proper: that is, to indicate when a certain fact, represented by some wff, may logically be deduced from other facts, also represented by wffs. These are called rules of *logical implication*, which is the first-order analogue of *tautological implication* of propositional logic. These rules are of a semantic nature. However, in the next chapter we establish corresponding rules which are purely *symbolic operations*, that is, operations on terms and wffs. These form so-called *deductive calculi*, and it is these calculi which constitute our complete formal model of deductive reasoning.

Note that, as mentioned in the introduction, we do not describe just *one* language but a whole class of languages in first-order logic. These may differ in their sets of predicate and function symbols. This is why in the sequel we generally refer to *a* language or to *the class* of first-order languages, rather than to *the* language of first-order logic.

EXERCISES

7.1.1 Prove by the truth table method that if $\alpha_1 =_d$ '$(\alpha_2 \Rightarrow \alpha_3)$', $\{\alpha_1, \alpha_2\} \vDash \alpha_3$ in propositional logic.

7.1.2 Prove the tautological implication of Example 7.1A.2 (a) by the truth table method and (b) using the basic tautologies of Section 6.4.

7.2 Syntax of first-order logic

We now introduce a first-order language which we denote by *L*. In this section we develop the syntax of the language. The main syntactic feature of *L* is a certain subset *Wfes* of strings of symbols from a given alphabet *Al*. We call the members of *Wfes* well-formed expressions (*wfes*), which motivates the name of the set. The syntax of *L* is the collection of rules which define *Al* and *Wfes*. We now describe these in turn.

7.2A Alphabet

The alphabet *Al* consists of two main categories of symbols: *logical symbols* and *parameters*. Parameters are also called *nonlogical symbols*. These two groups are broken down into various subsets; they are as follows:

Logical symbols

(1) *Parentheses*

(		Left parenthesis
)		Right parenthesis

(2) *Propositional connective symbols*

Form 1	*Form 2*	
$\neg$	not	Negation symbol
$\wedge$	and	Conjunction symbol
$\vee$	or	Disjunction symbol
$\Rightarrow$	if ... then	Conditional symbol
$\Leftrightarrow$	iff	Equivalence symbol

(3) *Variables*

$x, x_1, x_2, \ldots; y, y_1, y_2, \ldots; z, z_1, z_2, \ldots$

These form an infinite set denoted by *Vars*.

(4) *Equality predicate symbol (binary)*
Eq
This symbol is *optional*. It stands for equality.

(5) *Quantifiers*

$\forall$	Universal quantifier
$\exists$	Existential quantifier

■

Parameters or nonlogical symbols

(1) *Predicate symbols*
For any natural number $n \geqslant 1$, a set (possibly empty) of *predicate symbols* of *arity n*, also called *n-ary* or *n-place* symbols. We mainly use the following as predicate symbols:

$$P, Q, R, P_1, P_2, \ldots, Q_1, Q_2, \ldots, R_1, R_2, \ldots$$

(2) *Function symbols, including constants*
For any natural number $n \geqslant 0$, a set (possibly empty) of *function symbols* of *arity n*. These are also called *n-ary* or *n-place* function symbols. Nullary function symbols (or arity 0) are also called *constant symbols*. The following are used as function symbols of arity $n \geqslant 1$ (mainly):

$$f, g, h, f_1, f_2, \ldots, g_1, g_2, \ldots$$

The following are used as constant symbols (mainly):

$$c, d, e, c_1, c_2, \ldots, d_1, d_2, \ldots$$

■

We say that L is the first-order language defined on the alphabet Al. The logical symbols are common to all first-order languages, except for 'Eq' (alias '$=$') which may be omitted. The set of parameters may vary from language to language. As in propositional logic, the logical symbols will be given a *constant* meaning, except for the variables. The parameters, or nonlogical symbols, will *not* have a fixed meaning. Their meaning will have to be *assigned* to them according to certain semantic rules, and therefore will be able to vary. The assignment of a meaning to the parameters is the first-order analogue of a truth assignment in propositional logic.

The above symbols are as described informally in the notation review of Section **2**.4. The aim of the present chapter is to establish the syntax and semantics of this notation formally. Semantically, predicate symbols will be used to represent n-ary relations on a given set V (universe), and function symbols n-ary functions $V^n \rightarrow V$.

For any group of symbols, we also need names to stand for *any* symbol in the group. For this purpose, we use the same symbols but in bold face. Thus, each of $\boldsymbol{x}, \boldsymbol{x}_1, \ldots$ stands for any variable of L; each of $\boldsymbol{P}, \boldsymbol{P}_1, \ldots$ for any predicate symbol of any arity; and each of $f, f_1, \ldots$ for any function symbol of any arity. These are *not* symbols of L, as they are not members of the alphabet Al. They are metasymbols standing for symbols of L, and have the same purpose as the Greek letters we use to denote variable strings on Al. They are also called *generic names* or *syntactic variables*. Note that for any function symbol f, n is the *function* arity of f, written $FunArity(f)$.

7.2B Well-formed expressions

Given the alphabet Al, a string of symbols from Al is as defined in Section 4.4D. The *set* of such strings is $U = Al^*$. The set $Wfes$ of wfes is a subset of U, i.e. $Wfes \subseteq U$.

In predicate logic, there are *two* subsets of wfes: the set *Terms* of terms and the set *Wffs* of well-formed formulas (wffs). Each set is determined by syntax rules similar to those of propositional logic. In this section, we introduce these rules informally. In Section 7.2C, we show that these rules may be described formally as a family **G** of relations which generate the set *Wfes* inductively. One of these relations is nonfunctional, the others are partial operations on U.

Terms

The set *Terms* is a subset of the set U of all strings. It is defined intuitively by the following rules:

Informal definition of Terms

(T1) Every variable $\boldsymbol{x}: Vars$ (regarded as a one-symbol *string*) is a term. In other words, $Vars \subseteq Terms$.

(T2) For any function symbol f of arity $n \geqslant 0$, and any n terms $\tau_1, \tau_2, \ldots, \tau_n$, the following is a member of *Terms*:

$$f \tau_1 \tau_2 \ldots \tau_n$$

Note that in this definition spaces are not significant.

(T3) The set *Terms* does not contain any strings not defined by rules (T1) and (T2). ■

It can be shown that the set *Terms* is freely generated by these rules. This is left as an exercise.

Example 7.2B.1

Here are some examples of terms. They are built systematically, each by application of rule (T1), or of rule (T2) to preceding terms. Strings of several symbols are enclosed in quotes whenever appropriate. The arities of c, f, g and f_1 are 0, 1, 2 and 3 respectively.

By (T1): $x, x_1, x_2, x_3, y, y_1, y_2$
By (T2): c, '$f\,x$', '$g\,x_1\,y$', '$f_1\,x_1\,y_2\,x_1$'
By (T2): '$f\,f\,x$', '$f\,g\,x_1\,y$', '$g\,c\,f_1\,x_1\,y_2\,x_1$', '$f_1\,f\,x\,c\,g\,x_1\,y$', '$g\,f\,x\,g\,x_1\,y$'. ■

The parse tree for $\tau =_d$ '$f_1\,f\,x\,c\,g\,x_1\,y$' is given in Figure 7.2B.1, with intermediate terms named τ_1, τ_2, and so on. (Do not confuse the indexing of these terms with that of rule (T2).) A useful exercise is to build more examples of terms and *draw their parse trees.* A good didactic method is to create a construction sequence, a list of terms of increasing complexity, with the more complex ones built from previous terms in the list, as in Example 7.2B.1

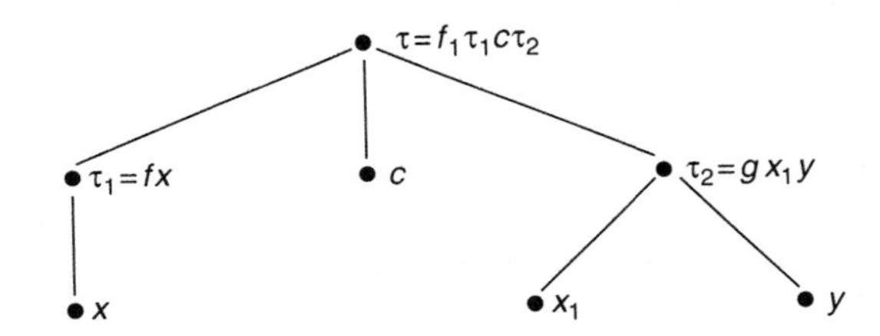

Figure 7.2B.1 Parse tree for the term $\tau =_d$ '$f_1 f\,x\,c\,g\,x_1\,y$'.

Well-formed formulas

The set of wffs is denoted by *Wffs*. Like *Terms*, it is a subset of U. It is defined by the following rules:

Informal definition of Wffs

(F1) For any predicate symbol $\boldsymbol{P}$ of arity $n \geqslant 1$, and any n terms $\tau_1, \tau_2, \ldots, \tau_n$, the following is a wff, that is, a member of *Wffs*. It is called an *atomic wff*:

$$\boldsymbol{P}\,\tau_1\,\tau_2 \ldots \tau_n$$

(F2) For any variable $\boldsymbol{x}$: *Vars* and any α: *Wffs*, the following strings are members of *Wffs*. They are called *quantified wffs*:

(a) $\forall \boldsymbol{x}\,\alpha$
(b) $\exists \boldsymbol{x}\,\alpha$

(F3) For any α: *Wffs*, the following string is a member of *Wffs*:

$$(\neg\ \alpha)$$

(F4) For any two α, β: *Wffs*, the following strings belong to *Wffs*:

(a) $(\alpha \wedge \beta)$
(b) $(\alpha \vee \beta)$
(c) $(\alpha \Rightarrow \beta)$
(d) $(\alpha \Leftrightarrow \beta)$

(F5) The set *Wffs* does not contain any strings not defined by rules (F1) to (F4). In all the definitions, spaces are not significant. ■

The set *Wffs* is freely generated by these rules. The proof is also left as an exercise. Note that rules (F3) and (F4) are 'inherited' from propositional logic, although they operate on a different alphabet *Al* and a different set $U = Al^*$.

Example 7.2B.2

Consider again the function symbols of Example 7.2B.1. Suppose that in addition there are two predicate symbols: *P*, of arity 1, and *Q*, of arity 2. Here are examples of wffs built with the terms of Example 7.2B.1. They are developed in the usual way.

By (F1): '$P\ x$', '$Q\ x_1\ x_2$', '$P\ c$', '$Q\ f\ x\ g\ x_1\ y$',
'$P\ f\ f\ x$', '$Q\ f\ g\ x_1\ y\ c$', '$P\ g\ f\ x\ g\ x_1\ y$'
By (F2): '$\forall x\ P\ x$', '$\exists y\ Q\ x_1\ x_2$', '$\forall x_1\ P\ c$',
'$\exists y\ Q\ f\ x\ g\ x_1\ y$', '$\forall x_2\ P\ f\ f\ x_2$'
By (F3): '$(\neg\ P\ x)$', '$(\neg\ \forall x\ P\ x)$'
By (F4): '$(P\ x \wedge Q\ x_1\ x_2)$', '$(P\ c \vee Q\ f\ x\ g\ x_1\ y)$',
'$(P\ f\ f\ x \Rightarrow Q\ f\ g\ x_1\ y\ c)$', '$(\forall x\ P\ x \Leftrightarrow Q\ x_1\ x_2)$'
By (F2): '$\forall y \forall x\ P\ g\ x_1\ y$', '$\exists y\ (\forall x\ P\ x \Leftrightarrow Q\ x_1\ x_2)$',
'$\forall x_2 \exists y\ Q\ x_1\ x_2$' ■

A parse tree for $\alpha =_d$ '$(\forall x\ P\ x \wedge Q\ x_1\ f\ x)$' is given in Figure 7.2B.2. In this tree, intermediate compound terms and wffs are named $\tau_1, \tau_2, \ldots$ and $\alpha_1, \alpha_2, \ldots$ respectively.

The reader should construct further examples and draw the corresponding parse trees.

Remark

In the semiformal notation used in Part **2**, binary predicate symbols are generally *infix* – that is, written between their operands, as in '$x \in S$', '$m < n$',

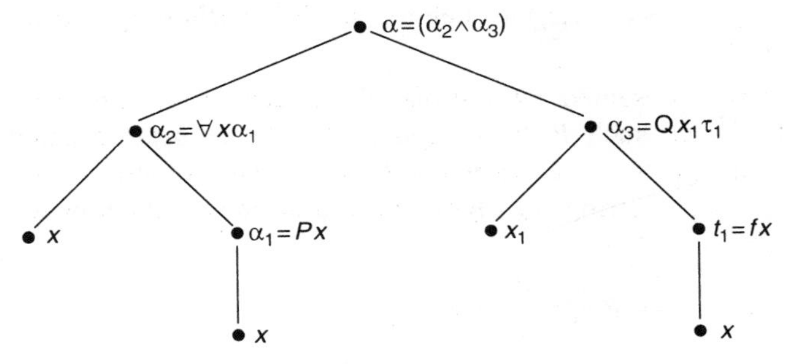

Figure 7.2B.2 Parse tree for the wff $\alpha =_{\mathrm{d}}$ '$(\forall\, x\; P\, x \wedge Q\, x_1\, f\, x)$'.

and so on. The same holds for most binary function symbols, such as '$\cup$', '$+$', and so on. In the 'official' language of first-order logic, *all predicate and function symbols are prefix* – that is, written before their operands. This reduces the need for parentheses in wfes. In practice, we may always convert one form to another if necessary. ■

7.2C Formal definition of well-formed expressions

As with the set *Wffs* of propositional logic, the above generation rules for *Wfes* may be described as a family ***G*** of relations and *Wfes* as the set *inductively generated by* ***G***. We provisionally ignore the distinction between terms and wffs: each relation in ***G*** is regarded just as a generator of wfes.

1 Rule (T1) is modelled by a nonfunctional unary relation G_v with graph $\mathrm{Gr}(G_v) =_{\mathrm{d}} Vars \subset U$. The rule is that $\mathrm{Gr}(G_v) \subseteq Wfes$.

2 Rule (T2) is represented by a subfamily of generators, one per function symbol ***f***. For each such ***f***, let $n =_{\mathrm{d}} FunArity(\boldsymbol{f})$. The associated generator is a term-building *partial* operation $G_f\colon U^n \nrightarrow U$. This function sends any n-tuple $(\tau_1, \tau_2, \ldots, \tau_n)$ of strings satisfying the condition stated below to the string '$\boldsymbol{f}\,\tau_1\,\tau_2 \ldots \tau_n$':

$$(\tau_1, \tau_2, \ldots, \tau_n) \mapsto \text{'}\boldsymbol{f}\,\tau_1\,\tau_2 \ldots \tau_n\text{'}$$

In the special case of $n = 0$, ***f*** is a constant and G_f is the *nullary* operation which returns $\boldsymbol{f} \in U$.

The condition imposed on $(\tau_1, \tau_2, \ldots, \tau_n)$ is defined as follows. For any string $\alpha : U$, let $IsTermStart(\alpha)$ be true iff either $\alpha \in Vars$, that is, α is a variable, or α is of the form $\boldsymbol{g}\,\beta$, where $\boldsymbol{g}$ is any function symbol and β any string. Thus, $IsTermStart(\alpha)$ expresses a *minimal* condition which α must satisfy to be a term. Now $G_f(\tau_1, \tau_2, \ldots, \tau_n)$ is defined iff *IsTermStart*(τ_i) = true for each $i = 1, 2, \ldots, n$.

3 Rule (F1) is represented by a subfamily of generators, one per predicate symbol $\boldsymbol{P}$. For each such $\boldsymbol{P}$, let $n =_d arity(\boldsymbol{P})$. The associated generator is a formula-building partial operation $G_{\boldsymbol{P}}: U^n \nrightarrow U$. This function sends any n-tuple $(\tau_1, \tau_2, \ldots, \tau_n)$ of strings satisfying the condition stated below to the string '$\boldsymbol{P}\, \tau_1\, \tau_2 \ldots \tau_n$':

$$(\tau_1, \tau_2, \ldots, \tau_n) \mapsto \text{'}\boldsymbol{P}\, \tau_1\, \tau_2 \ldots \tau_n\text{'}$$

The condition imposed on $(\tau_1, \tau_2, \ldots, \tau_n)$ for $G_{\boldsymbol{P}}(\tau_1, \tau_2, \ldots, \tau_n)$ to be defined is that *IsTermStart*(τ_i) = true for each $i = 1, 2, \ldots, n$. Thus, the generators associated with the predicate symbols are defined in the same way as those associated with the function symbols.

4 Rule (F2) is represented by two generators, $G_\forall$ and $G_\exists$. The first is the partial function

$$G_\forall : U^2 \nrightarrow U$$

which sends each couple $(\boldsymbol{x}, \alpha)$, where $\boldsymbol{x}$ is any variable and α is any string satisfying the condition below, to the string '$\forall \boldsymbol{x}\, \alpha$':

$$(\boldsymbol{x}, \alpha) \mapsto \text{'}\forall \boldsymbol{x}\, \alpha\text{'}$$

The condition imposed on α is defined as follows. For any string $\beta : U$, let *IsWffStart*(β) be true iff β has one of the following forms:

(1) '$\boldsymbol{P}\, \gamma$', where $\boldsymbol{P}$ is any predicate symbol of any arity and γ is any string, that is, any member of U;

(2) '$\xi\, \gamma$', where ξ is either '$\forall$' or '$\exists$', and γ is any string, that is, any member of U;

(3) '(γ', where γ is any string in U.

Thus, *IsWffStart*(β) expresses a *minimal* condition which β must satisfy to be a wff. Now $G_\forall(\boldsymbol{x}, \alpha)$ is defined iff *IsWffStart*(α) = true.

The second generator is the partial function

$$G_\exists : U^2 \nrightarrow U$$

which sends each couple $(\boldsymbol{x}, \alpha)$, where $\boldsymbol{x}$ is any variable and α is any string such that *IsWffStart*(α) = true, to the string '$\exists \boldsymbol{x}\, \alpha$':

$$(\boldsymbol{x}\ \alpha) \mapsto \text{'}\exists \boldsymbol{x}\, \alpha\text{'}$$

5 Rules (F3) and (F4) are represented by the five generators of propositional logic $G_\neg$, $G_\wedge$, $G_\vee$, $G_\Rightarrow$ and $G_\Leftrightarrow$, suitably qualified. (Recall the definitions of

Section **6**.1C.) $G_{\neg}$ is now defined as the partial unary function $G_{\neg} : U \nrightarrow U$ which sends any string $\alpha : U$ to the string '$(\neg\ \alpha)$' $\in U$, provided *IsWffStart*(α) = true. $G_{\wedge}$, $G_{\vee}$, $G_{\Rightarrow}$ and $G_{\Leftrightarrow}$ are the partial binary functions $U^2 \nrightarrow U$ which send any couple of strings $(\alpha, \beta) : U^2$ to the strings '$(\alpha \wedge \beta)$', '$(\alpha \vee \beta)$', '$(\alpha \Rightarrow \beta)$' and '$(\alpha \Leftrightarrow \beta)$' $\in U$ respectively, provided *IsWffStart*(α) = *IsWffStart*(β) = true.

To sum up, $\boldsymbol{G}$ is the family of all these generators:

$$\begin{aligned}\boldsymbol{G} =_{\mathrm{d}} \{&G_v; G_f, G_{f_1}, \ldots, G_g, G_{g_1}, \ldots, ; G_P, G_{P_1}, \ldots, G_Q, G_{Q_1}, \ldots ;\\ &G_{\forall}, G_{\exists}; G_{\neg}, G_{\wedge}, G_{\vee}, G_{\Rightarrow}, G_{\Leftrightarrow}\}\end{aligned}$$

Given $\boldsymbol{G}$, *Wfes* is defined as the smallest set of strings $\alpha : U$ which includes the set $\mathrm{Gr}(G_v) = Vars$ of variables, and which is closed under all the other operations in $\boldsymbol{G}$. Thus, it is *the set inductively generated by* $\boldsymbol{G}$. This description is the formal counterpart of the informal construction rules (T1)–(F5).

7.2D Unique readability of wfes

Like the set *Wffs* of propositional logic, *Wfes* is *freely generated* by $\boldsymbol{G}$, that is, *each wfe* α: *Wfes has a unique immediate generator, hence a unique parse tree.* Thus $\boldsymbol{G}$ meets the requirements of the recursion theorem, which guarantees that a semantic function (interpretation) may be constructed recursively on *Wfes*. In other words, it is possible to assign a uniquely defined meaning to each wfe, in a manner which agrees with its structure. Without this property, predicate logic would be impossible. Another way of expressing the freeness of *Wfes* is to say that *for any wfe, there is exactly one way of reading it.* To 'read' a wfe is to identify all its constituent parts, that is, to draw its parse tree essentially.

The full proof of this theorem is left to the exercises. A version may be found in Enderton (1972). However, this proof depends on an intermediate property which we give below for two reasons. First, it is simple to express and to understand concretely. It therefore gives a good intuitive explanation of the unique readability of wfes. Second, this result is at the basis of a systematic method of constructing the parse tree of any given wfe, an important practical consideration.

Prefix of a string

We begin with a preliminary definition.

Definition 7.2D.1

Consider any string $\alpha : U$ and the substring $\alpha' : U$ made up of 0 or more leading symbols of α. α' is called a *prefix* of α. More precisely, α' is a *prefix* of α iff there exists another string $\alpha'' : U$ such that

$$\alpha = \alpha'\, \alpha''$$

Moreover, α' is a *proper prefix* of α iff it is different from α. Note that the empty string, often denoted by ε, is a prefix of any string. ■

Example 7.2D.1

Assume $FunArity(f) =_d 1$ and $arity(P) =_d arity(Q) =_d 1$.

(1) Let $\alpha =_d$ '$f\,x\,y\,P\,Q$'$\in U$. (α is *not* a wfe!) The nonempty proper prefixes of α are

'f' '$f\,x$' '$f\,x\,y$' '$f\,x\,y\,P$'

(2) Let $\beta =_d$ '$\forall x\,(\neg\,P\,f\,x)$'$\in U$. ($\beta$ *is* a wfe!) The nonempty proper prefixes of β are

'$\forall$' '$\forall x$' '$\forall x\,($' '$\forall x\,(\neg$' '$\forall x\,(\neg\,P$'
'$\forall x\,(\neg\,P\,f$' '$\forall x\,(\neg\,P\,f\,x$' ■

The intermediate property of *Wfes*, mentioned above, follows.

Property 7.2D.1

For any wfe α: *Wfes*, *no* proper prefix of α is itself a member of *Wfes*. ■

More concretely, the empty string is not a wfe; no term may begin with another term or a wff; and no wff may begin with a term or another wff. This is illustrated by the wff β in Example 7.2D.1(2): we see that every proper prefix of β is incomplete. On the other hand, Example 7.2D.1(1) shows that this property is *not* enjoyed by strings which are *not* wfes: a non-wfe may have a wfe as a proper prefix – just one, of course.

Corollary 7.2D.2

For any string $\alpha: U$, at most one prefix of α is a member of *Wfes*. ■

Parsing an intial wfe

Property 7.2D.1 and its corollary suggest the following method, or *algorithm*, for analysing any wfe α, term or wff. In fact, we address a slightly more general problem. This is to determine for any nonempty string $\alpha: U$ whether one of its prefixes is a member of *Wfes* and if so, what this prefix is. Note that this prefix may be the whole of α.

We call this method, applied to α, *Accept*(α), a name borrowed from language theory. It may be regarded as a function which returns the unique wfe π, which is a prefix of α, together with a parse tree for π as an obvious by-product, if such a wfe exists. *Accept* is also called a *parsing algorithm*.

***Accept*(α)**

Let φ be the first symbol of α, and α' the substring of α made up of the remaining symbols:

$$\alpha = \varphi\ \alpha'$$

For each possible value of φ, the remaining steps are as follows:

Case 1 φ is a variable $\boldsymbol{x}$. Then π exists. It is the term $\boldsymbol{x}$, equal to φ.

Case 2 φ is a function symbol $\boldsymbol{f}$. Then if it exists, π must be a term

$$\boldsymbol{f}\tau_1\ \tau_2 \ldots \tau_n$$

where $n =_{\mathrm{d}} FunArity(\boldsymbol{f})$. If $n = 0$ then wfe $\pi = \boldsymbol{f}$. Otherwise, τ_1 exists and must be the only prefix of α' to be a member of *Wfes*, by Corollary 7.2D.2. Consequently τ_1 is determined by computing *Accept*(α'). This process is repeated to identify $\tau_2, \tau_3, \ldots,$ up to τ_n.

Case 3 φ is a predicate symbol $\boldsymbol{P}$. Then if it exists, π must be an atomic wff

$$\boldsymbol{P}\ \tau_1\ \tau_2 \ldots \tau_n$$

where $n =_{\mathrm{d}} arity(\boldsymbol{P}) \geqslant 1$. The terms $\tau_1, \tau_2, \tau_3, \ldots$ are then determined in the same way as in case 2.

Case 4 φ is a quantifier '$\forall$' or '$\exists$'. Then if it exists, π must be a wff

$$\forall \boldsymbol{x}\ \beta \qquad \text{or} \qquad \exists \boldsymbol{x}\ \beta$$

where $\boldsymbol{x}$ is a variable and β a wff. Identify β by computing *Accept*(α''), where α'' is the substring following '$\forall \boldsymbol{x}$' or '$\exists \boldsymbol{x}$' in α.

Case 5 φ is a left parenthesis followed by '$\neg$' in α. Then if it exists, π must be a wff

$$(\neg\ \beta)$$

where β is a wff. Identify β by computing *Accept*(α''), where $\alpha''$is the substring following '($\neg$' in α, and check that β is followed by ')' in α.

Case 6 φ is a left parenthesis *not* followed by '$\neg$' in α. Then if it exists, π must be a wff

$$(\beta * \gamma)$$

where $*: \{\wedge, \vee, \Rightarrow, \Leftrightarrow\}$ and β and γ are wffs. Identify β by computing *Accept*(α') where α' is as defined above; check that β is followed by $*$ in α. Identify γ by computing *Accept* (α''), where α'' is defined by $\alpha =$ '$(\beta * \alpha''$'; and check that γ is followed by ')' in α.

■

Accept is a *recursive algorithm*: in several places, it calls for the execution of a subtask by applying itself to a residual string. This feature is a direct consequence of the inductive definition of *Wfes*. We must of course be satisfied that, as a function, *Accept* is well-defined. This guarantee is given by the recursion theorem.

Structure of Wfes

The fact that each wfe $\alpha: Wfes$ has a unique generator G_i has a further consequence. In outline, any wfe is either a term, or a wff. *Terms* is the set of all strings $\tau: Wfes$ generated by the first two groups of relations in **G**, namely $(G_v\,;\, G_f, G_{f_1}, \ldots, G_g, G_{g_1}, \ldots)$. *Wffs* is the set of all α: *Wfes* generated by the other three groups of relations, namely

$$(G_p, G_{P_1}, \ldots, G_Q, G_{Q_1}, \ldots;\, G_\forall, G_\exists;\, G_\neg, G_\wedge, G_\vee, G_\Rightarrow, G_\Leftrightarrow)$$

Consequently, *Wfes* is partitioned into the two sets *Terms* and *Wffs*; that is, we may write

$$Wfes = Terms + Wffs$$

The full proof of this property is left as an exercise. Note also that terms are formed exclusively from more elementary terms. Consequently in a parse tree for a wff α, the points representing terms occur in the lower part of the tree, as shown in Figure 7.2B.2.

On notation in practice

As with wffs of propositional logic, in practice we do not adhere strictly to the generating rules of *Wfes*. For instance, we usually drop outer parentheses and occasionally use brackets instead of parentheses to enhance readibility. Likewise, we often use a dot ('·') as described in Section **2**.4E. We allow any departure from the construction rules such that the 'official' wff may be readily reconstructed from its simplified version.

7.2E Free and bound variables

For any wff α containing one or more occurrences of a variable $\boldsymbol{x}$, any *occurrence* of $\boldsymbol{x}$ either immediately follows '$\forall$' or '$\exists$' or is *free* or *bound* (to some quantifier) in α. We now define this distinction precisely. We use the letter ξ generically to represent either of the two quantifiers, '$\forall$' or '$\exists$'.

As a preliminary definition, consider a quantified wff

$$\xi\, \boldsymbol{x}\, \beta$$

where β itself is a wff. We call '$\xi\ \boldsymbol{x}$' the *head* and β the *body* of '$\xi\ \boldsymbol{x}\ \beta$'. We say that $\boldsymbol{x}$ is quantified by ξ in this wff.

Definition 7.2E.1

Consider any wff α, and any *occurrence* of a variable $\boldsymbol{x}$ in α. To be specific, we give the name '$\boldsymbol{x}'$' to this occurrence of $\boldsymbol{x}$. Three cases may arise with regard to $\boldsymbol{x}'$.

Case 1 α contains a subwff of the form '$\xi\ \boldsymbol{x}\ \beta$', and $\boldsymbol{x}'$ immediately follows ξ within '$\xi\ \boldsymbol{x}\ \beta$'. In this case, $\boldsymbol{x}'$ is called a *head* occurrence (of $\boldsymbol{x}$ in α). Note that '$\xi\ \boldsymbol{x}\ \beta$' may be α itself.

Case 2 α contains a subwff of the form '$\xi\ \boldsymbol{x}\ \beta$', and $\boldsymbol{x}'$ occurs within the body β of this subwff but *not* as a head occurrence. In this case, $\boldsymbol{x}'$ is said to be *bound in* α. Again, '$\xi\ \boldsymbol{x}\ \beta$' may be α itself.

Case 3 $\boldsymbol{x}'$ does *not* occur within any subwff '$\xi\ \boldsymbol{x}\ \beta$' of α. In this case, $\boldsymbol{x}'$ is said to be *free* in α. ■

Note that in case 2 of this definition, $\boldsymbol{x}'$ is either free or bound *within β itself*. If $\boldsymbol{x}'$ is *free* in β then $\boldsymbol{x}'$ is *bound to the head* '$\xi\ \boldsymbol{x}$' of '$\xi\ \boldsymbol{x}\ \beta$', or *captured* by '$\xi\ \boldsymbol{x}$'. In other words, '$\xi\ \boldsymbol{x}\ \beta$' is the smallest subwff of α within which $\boldsymbol{x}'$ is bound. Otherwise, that is, if $\boldsymbol{x}'$ is a bound occurrence of $\boldsymbol{x}$ in β, then β in turn contains a subwff '$\xi\ \boldsymbol{x}\ \gamma$' such that $\boldsymbol{x}'$ is free in γ. In this case, $\boldsymbol{x}'$ is bound to the head of '$\xi\ \boldsymbol{x}\ \gamma$', that is, it is captured at this lower level.

Example 7.2E.1

Let

$$\alpha_1 =_{\mathrm{d}} \quad P f x$$

In this wff, there is one occurrence of x. This occurrence is free in α_1, as it is not preceded by '$\xi\ x$'. ■

Example 7.2E.2

Let

$$\alpha_2 =_{\mathrm{d}} \quad \forall x\ P f x$$

In this wff, there are two occurrences of x. Moreover, α_2 may be written as '$\forall x\ \beta$', where $\beta =$ '$P f x$'. The first occurrence of x is a head occurrence. The second occurrence of x is free within β and bound within α_2; more precisely, it is bound to the head '$\forall x$' of α_2. ■

Example 7.2E.3

Let

$$\alpha_3 =_{\mathrm{d}} \quad (\forall x\ P f x \vee Q\, g\, x\, y)$$

In α_3, there are three occurrences of x. The upper part of the parse tree for α_3 is shown in Figure 7.2E.1. The first occurrence of x in α_3 is a head occurrence. The second occurrence is free in β_1 and bound in '$\forall x\ \beta_1$' and α_3. It is bound to the head '$\forall x$' of '$\forall x\ \beta_1$'. The third occurrence of x is free in both β_2 and α_3. This is because the 'effect' of '$\forall x$' is confined to '$\forall x\ \beta_1$', as the parse tree clearly shows. ■

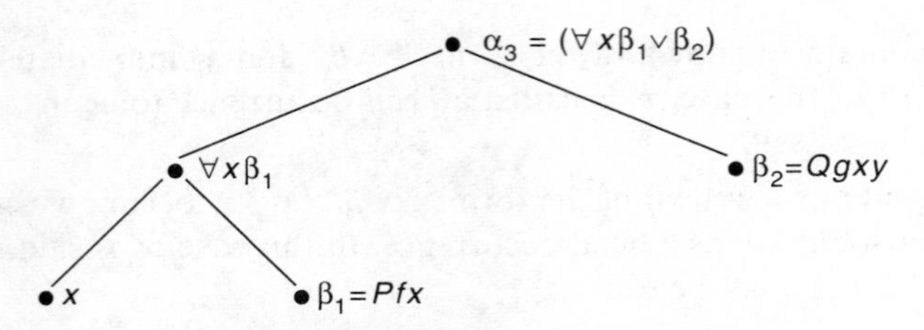

Figure 7.2E.1 Part of the parse tree for α_3.

Example 7.2E.4

Let

$$\alpha_4 =_d \quad \exists x\ (\forall x\ P\,f\,x \vee Q\,g\,x\,y) \quad =_d \quad \exists x\ \alpha_3$$

In α_4, there are four occurrences of x. The upper part of the parse tree for α_4 is as in Figure 7.2E.2. The first two occurrences of x in α_4 are head occurrences. The third occurrence is free in $\beta_1 =_d$ '$P\,f\,x$' and bound in '$\forall x\ \beta_1$', α_3 and α_4. It is captured by the head '$\forall x$' of '$\forall x\ \beta_1$', *not* by the head '$\exists x$' of α_4. The fourth occurrence of x is free in both $\beta_2 =$ '$Q\,g\,x\,y$' and α_3. However, it is now bound in α_4, and as it is free in the body α_3 of α_4, it is bound to the head '$\exists x$' of α_4. ■

To sum up, any *occurrence* $\boldsymbol{x}'$ of a variable $\boldsymbol{x}$ in a wff α may be either head, or bound, or free in α. If $\boldsymbol{x}'$ is bound, then in the parse tree of α it must be free up to a certain point corresponding to a subwff '$\xi\ \boldsymbol{x}\ \beta$', where $\xi : \{\forall, \exists\}$. At this point, $\boldsymbol{x}'$ is captured by the head '$\xi\ \boldsymbol{x}$' of '$\xi\ \boldsymbol{x}\ \beta$', and it is also bound in every subwff of α 'above' '$\xi\ \boldsymbol{x}\ \beta$', if any.

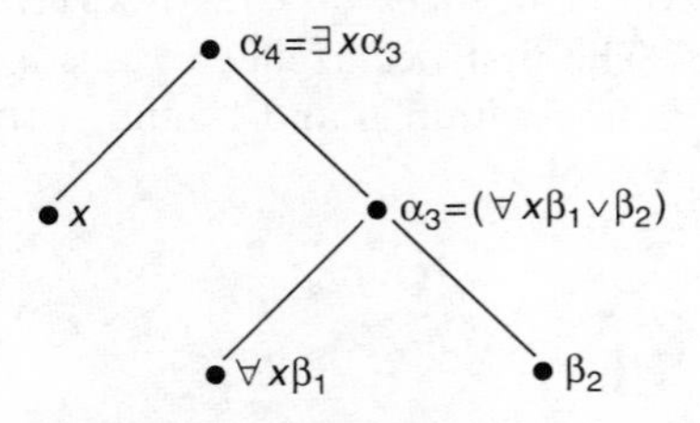

Figure 7.2E.2 Part of the parse tree for α_4.

Remarks

1 The purpose of these rules will become clear when the semantics of wfes is defined. Briefly, the idea is that all free occurrences of a variable x in a wff α denote the same object. Likewise, all occurrences of x bound to a *common* quantifier denote the same object, and this object is independent of the object(s) represented by *any other* occurrences of x. Thus, these rules define the *scope* of any variable x occurring in a wff or a group of wffs: that is, the portion of a formula (or a set of formulas) in which x has a common meaning.

2 The free occurrences of a variable in a wff may also be defined by induction. This alternative definition is given in Section **8**.1 in conjunction with the definition of term substitution in a formula.

3 Let α be a wff which contains *no free* variables. This means that either α contains no variables, or any occurrence of a variable in α is bound to some quantifier. Such a wff is called a *sentence.*

4 The distinction between free and bound variables may be made for all wfes, not just wffs. However, obviously any variable occurring in a term (or an atomic wff) is necessarily free. ■

EXERCISES

7.2.1 Let L_1 be a first-order language with the following function symbols: c, f, g and f_1, with function arity 0, 1, 1 and 2 respectively. Consider the parse tree in this language shown below. Write down each term τ_i in full, from τ_1 to τ_6.

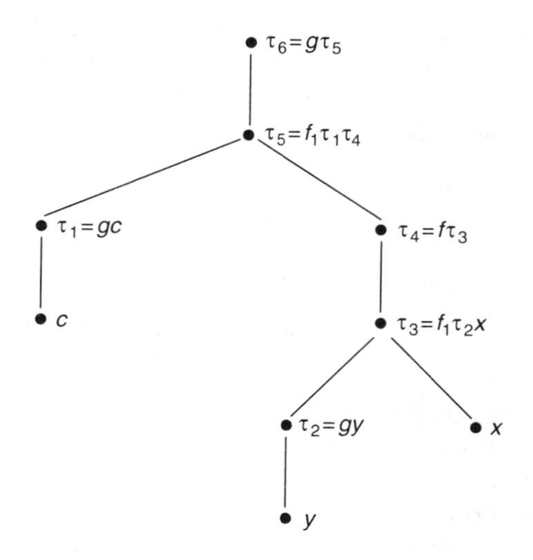

7.2.2 Let L_1 be the language defined in Exercise 7.2.1. Draw the parse tree of the term τ given below (a) without naming intermediate compound terms and (b) using τ_1, $\tau_2, \ldots$ to name intermediate compound terms, as in the tree of Exercise 7.2.1.

$$\tau =_d \quad f_1 f f_1 \, x \, g \, c \, g f c$$

7.2.3 Let L_1 be the language defined in Exercise 7.2.1. Construct *four* groups of *four* terms each as follows: The first group consists of c, x, y and x_1. The members of each following group are obtained by applying each function symbol to terms (not necessarily distinct) of the previous group. Hint: There is one term which occurs in all four groups. Every other term occurs in just one group.

7.2.4 Draw the parse trees of the terms in the last group defined in Exercise 7.2.3 using $\tau_1, \tau_2, \ldots$ to name intermediate compound terms.

7.2.5 Let L_2 be the language with function symbols as in L_1 of Exercise 7.2.1 and two predicate symbols P, of arity 1, and Q, of arity 2. Draw the parse trees of the wffs below, in the style illustrated in Figure 7.2B.2.

$$\alpha =_d \quad (P \, g f x \Rightarrow Q \, f_1 \, g \, x_1 \, c f y)$$
$$\beta =_d \quad \exists y \, (\forall x \, P \, x \Leftrightarrow (Q \, x_1 \, x_2 \wedge (\neg \, \forall y_1 \, P \, g \, y_1)))$$

7.2.6 Consider the following wff in the language L_2 of Exercise 7.2.5:

$$\alpha_0 =_d \quad \exists y \, (\forall x \, (P \, x \vee Q \, y \, x) \Leftrightarrow (Q \, x_1 \, x \wedge \forall y \, (\neg \, P f_1 \, y \, g \, y_1)))$$

(1) Draw the parse tree of α naming its subwffs $\alpha_1, \alpha_2, \ldots$
(2) For each *occurrence* of a variable $\boldsymbol{x}$ in any α_i, indicate its precise status, namely, head, free or bound within α_i.

7.2.7 For this and subsequent exercises, we introduce a language L_3 which may be regarded as an abstract version of the various other languages defined in this section (L, and so on). L_3 is defined on an alphabet *Al* equal to the union of the following disjoint sets of symbols:

(a) The parentheses: '(' and ')'.
(b) A set *Vars* of variables $x, x_1, \ldots$.
(c) A set *Prefixs* of prefix symbols.
(d) A set *Infixs* of infix symbols.

The associated subset $Wfes \subseteq Al^*$ is the set inductively generated by the following rules:

(1) Any $\boldsymbol{x}$: *Vars* belongs to *Wfes*, that is, $Vars \subseteq Wfes$.
(2) For any $\boldsymbol{f}$: *Prefixs* of arity $n \geqslant 0$ and any $\alpha_1, \ldots, \alpha_n$: *Wfes*, '$\boldsymbol{f} \alpha_1 \ldots \alpha_n$' $\in$ *Wfes*.
(3) For any $\boldsymbol{g}$: *Infixs* and any two α, β: *Wfes*, '$(\alpha \, \boldsymbol{g} \, \beta)$' $\in$ *Wfes*.
(4) For any α: *Wfes*, '(α)' $\in$ *Wfes*.

The aim is to prove various properties of L_3 leading to the theorem that its set *Wfes* is freely generated by the above rules. These properties will then automatically hold for L, and so on. These exercises extend Exercises **6**.1.9 ff.

For any $\alpha : Al^*$, let $LP(\alpha)$ and $RP(\alpha)$ be the number of left and right parentheses occurring in α respectively. Prove by structural induction the following properties of any $\alpha : Wfes$, in the given order:

(a) $LP(\alpha) = RP(\alpha)$.
(b) For any prefix α' of α, $LP(\alpha') \geqslant RP(\alpha')$.
(c) If the first symbol of α is '(' then for any nonempty proper prefix α' of α, $LP(\alpha') > RP(\alpha)$.

7.2.8* Prove that the language L_3 defined in Exercise **7**.2.7 has the following properties:

(a) For any $\alpha : Wfes$, no proper prefix of α also belongs to *Wfes*.
(b) Any $\alpha : Al^*$ has at most one prefix in *Wfes*.

The main difficulty is to prove (a) for wfes $\alpha =$ '$f \alpha_1 \ldots \alpha_n$'. This may be done by structural induction, taking as the proposition to be proved that for any $\alpha : Wfes$ (i) no proper prefix of α also belongs to *Wfes*, and (ii) α is not the proper prefix of any member of *Wfes*. Use this as the basis of the induction hypothesis. For wfes starting with '(', the proof follows from Exercise **7**.2.7.

7.2.9* Using Exercise **7**.2.8, prove that L_3 is freely generated. It requires to be shown that for each $\alpha : Wfes$ with a given immediate generator, the latter is unique, that is, its components may be worked out from α. To do that, apply a process similar to *Accept*, defined in Section **7**.2D. For instance, if $\alpha =$ '$f \alpha_1 \ldots \alpha_n$' then the immediate generator of α is $(G_f, \alpha_1, \ldots, \alpha_n)$. G_f and n are determined by f, and then each α_i is determined in turn for $i = 1, \ldots, n$, but indicate exactly why.

7.2.10* (a) Prove Property **7**.2D.1 and Corollary **7**.2D.2 using Exercise **7**.2.8. The main task is to show that the set *Wfes* of the first-order language L is a subset of the set *Wfes* of the language L_3 in which *Prefixs* and *Infixs* are fully specified from L. In particular, let *Prefixs* be the union of the function symbols, the predicate symbols, $\{\forall, \exists\}$ and $\{\neg\}$ of L. The set *Wfes* of L_3 contains many strings not in L, for example '$f(\alpha \wedge \beta)$' and '$f \neg \alpha$', where f is a unary function symbol and α and β are wffs. These extra elements do not matter: we may conclude that every wfe α of L has the property stated in Exercise **7**.2.8.
(b) Identify all the strings which are wfes in L_3 but not in L.
(c) Prove that the set *Wfes* of L is freely generated, following the same reasoning as in (a).

7.2.11* The purpose of this exercise is to demonstrate that the family $\boldsymbol{G}$ of generators introduced in Section **7**.2C inductively generates the same set *Wfes* as the one informally defined in Section **7**.2B.

(a) Recursively define three functions *IsTerm*, *IsWffAtom* and *IsWff*: *Wfes* $\rightarrow$ Bool with the following properties for any $\alpha : Wfes$ in

L: *IsTerm*(α) = true iff α is a term; *IsWffAtom*(α) = true iff α is an atomic wff; and *IsWff*(α) = true iff α is a wff. Here *Wfes* is the set generated by **G**. Note that these three functions are unary predicates, functions returning true or false, but they must not be confused with the predicate symbols of L.

(b) Prove certain obvious relations between these three functions and the predicates *IsTermStart* and *IsWffStart* used to constrain the definition domains of the generators. In particular show that for any α: *Wfes*, (*IsTerm*(α) and *IsWff*(α)) is false.

(c) Prove by induction that for all α: *Wfes*, either *IsTerm*(α) or *IsWff*(α) is true, but not both. Conclude that any wfe α is either a term or a wff but not both; that is, formally: *Wfes* = *Terms* + *Wffs*.

7.3 Semantics of first-order logic

Given a first-order language L, a meaning or semantic value is to be assigned to each well-formed expression (wfe) of L, be it a term or a well-formed formula (wff). This must be done in a manner consistent with our intuitive understanding of terms and wffs. The rules by which a meaning is specified for each wfe form the *semantics* of the language.

In first-order logic, the meaning of *logical symbols* is constant, except for the variables. For instance, the propositional connective symbols inherit their meaning from propositional logic: the function NOT : Bool → Bool is assigned to the symbol '$\neg$' alias 'not', the function AND : $\text{Bool}^2 \rightarrow$ Bool to the symbol '$\wedge$' alias 'and', and so on. The special predicate symbol '*Eq*' (alias '=') is binary. It represents the relation of equality on the set V introduced below.

The meaning of *parameters* or *nonlogical symbols* (predicate symbols other than '*Eq*' and function symbols) is variable. It must be *specified*, in the same way as truth values must be assigned to proposition symbols in propositional logic. The meaning assigned to the parameters of a language is called an *interpretation*, or *structure* by some authors, for example Enderton (1972). So an interpretation in predicate logic plays the same role as a truth assignment in propositional logic.

The main difference between a truth assignment in propositional logic and an interpretation in first-order logic is a matter of complexity. In a truth assignment, each proposition symbol is assigned a *simple value*: true or false. In a first-order interpretation, parameters are assigned more complex objects. Each n-ary predicate symbol is assigned an n-ary relation (represented by its characteristic function), and each n-ary function symbol is assigned an n-ary function. To simplify, it is assumed that all relations and functions are defined on a *single set* called a *universe* and denoted by V. Thus, the graph of any n-ary relation is a subset of V^n, and any n-ary function is a *total* operation $V^n \rightarrow V$. Only one constraint is imposed on V: this set must have *at least one member*.

The idea of assigning a function to a symbol is not new: it is already done in propositional logic when the operation NOT : Bool $\to$ Bool is assigned to the symbol '$\neg$' and so on. However, in propositional logic such assignments are constant: '$\neg$', '$\wedge$', and so on always have the same meaning. In first-order logic the relations and functions assigned to parameters may vary. The universe V itself may vary: it is part of the interpretation of the parameters.

The variables are treated in a somewhat different way. In a given interpretation, a variable $\boldsymbol{x}$ is to represent a member or 'value' of the universe V. However, this value *may vary over* V, with the following consequences. If a variable $\boldsymbol{x}$ occurs *free* in any wfe α, then the interpretation must be *extended* to assign a specific value $v : V$ to $\boldsymbol{x}$. This is necessary if the meaning of the wfe α is to be exactly defined. On the other hand, if $\boldsymbol{x}$ occurs *bound* in a wfe α, then there is no need to assign a value to $\boldsymbol{x}$. The reason is that in this case α is a wff and the meaning of α is determined by *all* the possible values $v : V$ which may be assigned to $\boldsymbol{x}$. In particular, if α is a sentence, that is, if any occurrence of a variable is bound in it, then its semantic value is fixed in an interpretation without any extension to variables.

We call an interpretation together with an assignment of a member of V to each variable $\boldsymbol{x}$ an *extended interpretation*. Given an extended interpretation, a semantic value may be assigned to each wfe α. This value is denoted by $\boldsymbol{M}(\alpha)$. If α is a *term* then $\boldsymbol{M}(\alpha)$ is a member of the universe V. If α is a wff, then $\boldsymbol{M}(\alpha)$ is a truth value. Therefore, $\boldsymbol{M}$ is a function $Wfes \to V \cup$ Bool, where Bool is the set {true, false} of truth values. This function is derived from the extended interpretation by recursion, very much as the meaning $\boldsymbol{M}$ of a wff is derived from a truth assignment m in propositional logic.

7.3A Interpretation

We now formally define the notions of interpretation and extended interpretation of a first-order language.

Definition 7.3A.1

Let L be any first-order language and *Wfes* the set of wfes of L. An *interpretation* of L is a total function M defined by the following rules.

(1) The language L itself is assigned a *nonempty* set M_L called the *universe* of M. Usually, this set is also denoted by V in any context in which L is clear.

(2) Each n-ary predicate symbol $\boldsymbol{P}$ is assigned an n-ary predicate, that is, a function

$$M_{\boldsymbol{P}} : V^n \to \text{Bool}$$

(3) Each n-ary function symbol $\boldsymbol{f}$ is assigned an n-ary operation

$$M_{\boldsymbol{f}} : V^n \to V$$

This includes the case of nullary function symbols, or constants. Thus, each constant symbol $\boldsymbol{c}$ is assigned a value

$$M_{\boldsymbol{c}}: V$$ ∎

Definition 7.3A.2

Let L be a first-order language and *Vars* be the set of variables $\boldsymbol{x}$ in L. An *extended interpretation* of L is an interpretation M together with a function

$$m: Vars \rightarrow V$$

which assigns a value $m(\boldsymbol{x}) \in V$ to every variable $\boldsymbol{x}: Vars$. The extended interpretation is denoted by the couple (M, m). The function m is also called an *assignment*, or an *extension* of M. ∎

Remarks

1 In these definitions, the function M applied to a parameter may be regarded as standing for 'the meaning of the parameter'. For instance, '$M_{\boldsymbol{P}}$' should be read as 'the meaning of (the predicate symbol) $\boldsymbol{P}$'.

2 The two functions M and $\boldsymbol{M}$ must be carefully distinguished. The latter is *derived* from the former. This is the same distinction as in propositional logic between a truth assignment m and the function $\boldsymbol{M}$.

3 For any predicate symbol $\boldsymbol{P}$, the associated function $M_{\boldsymbol{P}}: V^n \rightarrow \text{Bool}$ may be regarded as the *characteristic function* of an n-ary relation on V, which we denote by $M'_{\boldsymbol{P}}$. Thus indirectly $\boldsymbol{P}$ represents this relation in the interpretation M. Recall that $M'_{\boldsymbol{P}}$ is the unique relation whose graph $\text{Gr}(M'_{\boldsymbol{P}}) \subseteq V^n$ is determined by

$$(a_1, a_2, \ldots, a_n) \in \text{Gr}(M'_{\boldsymbol{P}}) \quad \text{iff} \quad M_{\boldsymbol{P}}(a_1, a_2, \ldots, a_n) = \text{true}$$

for all n-tuples $(a_1, a_2, \ldots, a_n): V^n$.

We could, of course, define the interpretation $M_{\boldsymbol{P}}$ of $\boldsymbol{P}$ as the relation named $M'_{\boldsymbol{P}}$ here. This is the solution adopted in Enderton (1972), for instance. The definition of $M_{\boldsymbol{P}}$ as a function $V^n \rightarrow \text{Bool}$ seems preferable for two reasons. First, it brings out more clearly the close connection between function and predicate symbols: all parameters are treated uniformly as functions. Second, it is more consistent with the definition of the derived function $\boldsymbol{M}$, as will be seen below. ∎

7.3B Semantic function of well-formed expressions

An extended interpretation (M, m) of a first-order language L plays essentially the same role in first-order logic as a truth assignment m does in propositional logic. (M, m) is the initial information from which the meaning $\boldsymbol{M}(\alpha)$ may be derived for any wfe of the language. Given (M, m), the function $\boldsymbol{M}$ is entirely determined, by recursion on the set *Wfes* of L. Here again, the fact that $\boldsymbol{M}$ is well defined is a major application of the recursion theorem. As L is fixed, we let $V =_{\mathrm{d}} M_L$.

Definition 7.3B.1

We say that for each wfe α, $\boldsymbol{M}(\alpha)$ is the *meaning* or *semantic value* of α in the *extended interpretation* (M, m). ■

We describe the semantic values of terms and wffs in turn.

Semantic values of terms

Let τ be any term. The meaning $\boldsymbol{M}(\tau)$ is defined inductively by the following rules:

(1) If τ is a variable $\boldsymbol{x}$ then

(R1) $\boldsymbol{M}(\tau) =_{\mathrm{d}} m(\boldsymbol{x}) \in V$

(2) If τ is a term

$$\boldsymbol{f}\tau_1 \tau_2 \ldots \tau_n$$

where $\boldsymbol{f}$ is any n-ary function symbol and each τ_i is a term then

(R2) $\boldsymbol{M}(\tau) =_{\mathrm{d}} M_{\boldsymbol{f}}(\boldsymbol{M}(\tau_1), \boldsymbol{M}(\tau_2), \ldots, \boldsymbol{M}(\tau_n)) \in V$

In particular if τ is a constant $\boldsymbol{c}$ then

$$\boldsymbol{M}(\tau) =_{\mathrm{d}} M_{\boldsymbol{c}} \in V$$

Semantic values of atomic wffs

Let α be any atomic wff. It must be of the form

$$\boldsymbol{P}\tau_1 \tau_2 \ldots \tau_n$$

where $\boldsymbol{P}$ is any n-ary predicate symbol. In this case, $\boldsymbol{M}(\alpha)$ is defined inductively as for function symbols by the rule

(R3) $\boldsymbol{M}(\alpha) =_{\mathrm{d}} M_{\boldsymbol{P}}(\boldsymbol{M}(\tau_1), \boldsymbol{M}(\tau_2), \ldots, \boldsymbol{M}(\tau_n)) \in \mathrm{Bool}$

Note If we had defined the interpretation of $\boldsymbol{P}$ as the relation $M'_{\boldsymbol{P}}$ then the definition of $\boldsymbol{M}(\alpha)$ would be given by

(R3′) $\boldsymbol{M}(\alpha) =_{\mathrm{d}}$ true if $(\boldsymbol{M}(\tau_1), \boldsymbol{M}(\tau_2), \ldots, \boldsymbol{M}(\tau_n)) \in \mathrm{Gr}(M'_{\boldsymbol{P}}) \subseteq V^n$;
false otherwise

(R3) and (R3′) are entirely equivalent. (R3) is preferred as it is simpler than (R3′) and similar in form to (R2). ■

At this point we must define the semantics of the equality binary predicate symbol '*Eq*', alias '='. This semantics is constant. If α is the formula

$$Eq\ \tau_1\ \tau_2$$

then

(R4) $\boldsymbol{M}(\alpha) = \boldsymbol{M}(\text{'}Eq\ \tau_1\ \tau_2\text{'}) =_{\mathrm{d}}$ true iff $\boldsymbol{M}(\tau_1) = \boldsymbol{M}(\tau_2)$

Thus, the predicate symbol '*Eq*' represents the usual equality on the universe V.

Semantic values of other unquantified wffs

Let α and β be any wffs. Then the semantics of '$\neg$', '$\wedge$', '$\vee$', '$\Rightarrow$' and '$\Leftrightarrow$' is defined as in propositional logic, using the semantic functions NOT, AND, and so on, defined in Section **6**.2A. Thus

(R5) (a) $\boldsymbol{M}(\text{'}(\neg\ \alpha)\text{'}) =_{\mathrm{d}}$ NOT $(\boldsymbol{M}(\alpha))$
(b) $\boldsymbol{M}(\text{'}(\alpha \wedge \beta)\text{'}) =_{\mathrm{d}}$ AND $(\boldsymbol{M}(\alpha), \boldsymbol{M}(\beta))$
(c) $\boldsymbol{M}(\text{'}(\alpha \vee \beta)\text{'}) =_{\mathrm{d}}$ OR $(\boldsymbol{M}(\alpha), \boldsymbol{M}(\beta))$
(d) $\boldsymbol{M}(\text{'}(\alpha \Rightarrow \beta)\text{'}) =_{\mathrm{d}}$ IF $(\boldsymbol{M}(\alpha), \boldsymbol{M}(\beta))$
(e) $\boldsymbol{M}(\text{'}(\alpha \Leftrightarrow \beta)\text{'}) =_{\mathrm{d}}$ IFF $(\boldsymbol{M}(\alpha), \boldsymbol{M}(\beta))$

Semantic values of quantified wffs

Next, consider any wff $\alpha =_{\mathrm{d}} \text{'}\forall \boldsymbol{x}\ \beta\text{'}$ where $\boldsymbol{x}$ is any variable and β any wff. Informally, '$\forall \boldsymbol{x}\ \beta$' means '$\beta$ is true for all values represented by $\boldsymbol{x}$ in β'. We must now express this idea formally.

Recall that the truth value $\boldsymbol{M}(\beta)$ depends on both M and the assignment $m: Vars \to V$. More precisely, $\boldsymbol{M}(\beta)$ depends on the value $m(\boldsymbol{y})$ assigned to each variable $\boldsymbol{y}: Vars$ occurring *free* in β. Now let v be any arbitrary value in V. Given $m: Vars \to V$ and $v: V$, we may define a *new* function which we denote, using the overriding notation, by

$$(m \mid \boldsymbol{x} \mapsto v): Vars \to V$$

Recall this function is equal to m for all variables $\boldsymbol{y}: Vars$, except $\boldsymbol{x}$. To $\boldsymbol{x}$, $(m \mid \boldsymbol{x} \mapsto v)$ assigns the value v. Formally:

Definition 7.3B.2

Given $m: Vars \to V$, any variable $\boldsymbol{x}: Vars$ and any value $v: V$, the function $(m|\boldsymbol{x} \mapsto v): Vars \to V$ is defined as in Section 3.6C by

$$(m|\boldsymbol{x} \mapsto v)\ (\boldsymbol{x}) =_{\mathrm{d}} v$$
$$(m|\boldsymbol{x} \mapsto v)\ (\boldsymbol{y}) =_{\mathrm{d}} m(\boldsymbol{y}) \text{ for any } \boldsymbol{y}: Vars \text{ with } \boldsymbol{y} \neq \boldsymbol{x}$$

■

Clearly each value $v: V$ defines a different assignment $(m|\boldsymbol{x} \mapsto v)$, and each of these assignments determines a different truth value $\boldsymbol{M}(\beta)$. Then if $\boldsymbol{M}(\beta) =$ true *in all cases*, $\boldsymbol{M}(\alpha) = \boldsymbol{M}(\text{'}\forall \boldsymbol{x}\ \beta\text{'}) =$ true; otherwise $\boldsymbol{M}(\alpha) =$ false. To sum up, $\boldsymbol{M}(\alpha)$ is determined by the rule

(R6) $\boldsymbol{M}(\alpha) = \boldsymbol{M}(\text{'}\forall \boldsymbol{x}\ \beta\text{'}) =_{\mathrm{d}}$ true if *for all* $v: V$, $\boldsymbol{M}(\beta) =$ true when evaluated with $(m|\boldsymbol{x} \mapsto v): Vars \to V$ instead of $m: Vars \to V$;
false otherwise

Finally, let $\alpha =_{\mathrm{d}} \text{'}\exists \boldsymbol{x}\ \beta\text{'}$ where $\boldsymbol{x}$ is any variable and β any wff. Informally, '$\exists \boldsymbol{x}\ \beta$' means 'there exists *at least one* value of $\boldsymbol{x}$ for which β is true'. Now this is equivalent to saying: 'It is *not* true that β is false for all values represented by $\boldsymbol{x}$ in β'. Consequently, we may define '$\exists \boldsymbol{x}\ \beta$' as equivalent to

$$\neg\ \forall \boldsymbol{x}\ (\neg\ \beta)$$

and derive the semantics of '$\exists$' from that of '$\forall$' by the rule

(R7)
$$\begin{aligned}\boldsymbol{M}(\alpha) &= \boldsymbol{M}(\text{'}\exists \boldsymbol{x}\ \beta\text{'}) \\ &=_{\mathrm{d}} \boldsymbol{M}(\text{'}\neg\ \forall \boldsymbol{x}(\neg\ \beta)\text{'}) \\ &= \text{NOT}\ (\boldsymbol{M}(\text{'}\forall \boldsymbol{x}\ (\neg\ \beta)\text{'})\end{aligned}$$

This completes our definition of the semantic function $\boldsymbol{M}$ of a first-order language L. Once more, this has been done inductively. The fact that $\boldsymbol{M}$ is well-defined follows from the recursion theorem and the fact that the wfes are *freely* generated.

Remarks

1 In any extended interpretation (M, m), for any wff α, the truth value $\boldsymbol{M}(\alpha)$ depends only on the values $m(\boldsymbol{x})$ of the variables $\boldsymbol{x}$ occurring *free* in α. We can see precisely why this is so from (R6) and (R7): for any bound variable $\boldsymbol{x}$, $m(\boldsymbol{x})$ ceases to play a role when $m: Vars \to V$ is replaced by $(m|\boldsymbol{x} \mapsto v): Vars \to V$ in the definition of $\boldsymbol{M}$. In particular, a simple interpretation M is sufficient to determine the semantic value $\boldsymbol{M}(\alpha)$ of any *sentence* α. There is no need for an *extended* interpretation in that case.

2 Any semantic function $\boldsymbol{M}$ is determined by a certain extended interpretation (M, m). In a context in which the latter is uniquely defined, the symbol '$\boldsymbol{M}$' is unambiguous. However, if we wish to refer simultaneously to different interpretations and the corresponding functions $\boldsymbol{M}$, it may be necessary to extend the symbol '$\boldsymbol{M}$' with an indication of the interpretation (M, m) on which it depends. We shall do so in this case by writing $\boldsymbol{M}_{(M,m)}(\alpha)$ or simply $\boldsymbol{M}_M(\alpha)$ instead of $\boldsymbol{M}(\alpha)$. ■

7.3C Example

Let L be the first-order language with equality 'Eq' and the following parameters:

P	Unary predicate symbol
Q	Binary predicate symbol
c	Constant symbol
g	Unary function symbol
f	Binary function symbol

Some terms of L are:

$$c, \quad `g\ c', \quad `g\ x_1', \quad `f\ c\ x_2', \quad `g\ f\ c\ g\ x_1', \quad `f\ g\ c\ c'$$

Some atomic wffs are:

$$`P\ c', \quad `P\ g\ c', \quad `Q\ c\ f\ c\ x_2', \quad `Q\ g\ c\ g\ c', \quad `Q\ g\ c\ f\ g\ c\ x_4', \quad `Eq\ c\ x_2'$$

Now we construct an *extended* interpretation (M, m) for L. We begin with the function $\boldsymbol{M}$.

(1) Let the universe $V =_{\mathrm{d}} M_L =_{\mathrm{d}} \{1, 2, 3\}$.

(2) Let $M_P: V \to \mathrm{Bool}$ be defined by the table

$v: V$	$M_P(v)$
1	T
2	T
3	F

Equivalently, we may specify M_P by giving the graph of the relation M'_P itself, which is unary:

$$\mathrm{Gr}(M'_P) = \{1, 2\} \subseteq V$$

(3) Let $M_Q: V^2 \to \mathrm{Bool}$ be defined by the following table, in which any entry in a row v and column w is $M_Q(v, w)$:

		$w : V$		
		1	2	3
$v : V$	1	F	T	T
	2	F	F	T
	3	F	F	F

Equivalently, we may specify M_Q by giving the graph $\mathrm{Gr}(M'_Q) \subseteq V^2$:

$$\mathrm{Gr}(M'_Q) = \{(1, 2), (1, 3)\ (2, 3)\}$$

(4) Let $M_c = 3 \in V$.
(5) Let the function $M_g : V \to V$ be determined by the table

$v : V$	$M_g(v) \in V$
1	3
2	2
3	1

(6) Let the function $M_f : V^2 \to V$ be determined by the following table, in which each entry is $M_f(v, w) \in V$ for any v, $w : V$

		$w : V$		
		1	2	3
$v : V$	1	1	2	3
	2	2	3	1
	3	3	1	2

(7) As for the extension $m : Vars \to V$ of the interpretation M, let this be given by

$m(x_1) =_d 2 \qquad m(x_2) =_d 1 \qquad m(x_3) =_d 2 \qquad m(x_4) =_d 3$
$m(\boldsymbol{x}) =_d 1$ for all other variables $\boldsymbol{x}$

From this extended interpretation (M, m), we may derive the corresponding value $\boldsymbol{M}(\alpha)$ of any wfe $\alpha \in Wfes$. Here are some examples.

α *(term)*	$\boldsymbol{M}(\alpha)$	α *(atomic wff)*	$\boldsymbol{M}(\alpha)$
c	3	$P\ c$	F
$g\ c$	1	$P\ g\ c$	T
$g\ x_1$	2	$P\ g\ x_1$	T
$f\ c\ x_2$	3	$Q\ c\ f\ c\ x_2$	F
$f\ c\ g\ x_1$	1	$Q\ g\ c\ g\ c$	F
$g\ f\ c\ g\ x_1$	3	$Q\ g\ c\ f\ g\ c\ c$	T
$f\ g\ c\ c$	3	$Q\ x_3\ g\ x_1$	F

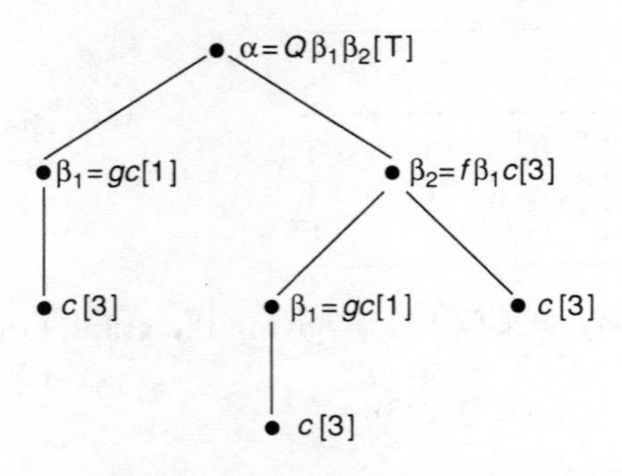

Figure 7.3C.1 Parse tree for the term α.

For instance, the computation of $\boldsymbol{M}$('$Q\ g\ c\ f\ g\ c\ c$') is illustrated by the augmented parse tree for $\alpha =$ '$Q\ g\ c\ f\ g\ c\ c$' in Figure **7**.3C.1. As in Chapter **6**, for each wfe β occurring in the tree, the value $\boldsymbol{M}(\beta)$ is entered in square brackets on the right of β.

Here are further examples, involving nonatomic wffs. The reader should construct more examples and work out the computation details with the help of parse trees, as illustrated above.

α *(other wff)*	$\boldsymbol{M}(\alpha)$
$\neg P\ c$	T
$(\neg P\ g\ c) \vee P\ g\ x_1$	T
$P\ c \wedge Q\ c\ f\ c\ x_2$	F
$\forall x_1\ P\ g\ x_1$	F (See text)
$\exists x_1\ P\ g\ x_1$	T (See text)

In order to evaluate $\boldsymbol{M}$('$\forall x_1\ P\ g\ x_1$'), we must compute $\boldsymbol{M}$('$P\ g\ x_1$') in *every modified* extended interpretation $(M, (m|x_1 \mapsto v))$, where v is a member of V. The computation of $\boldsymbol{M}$('$\forall x_1\ P\ g\ x_1$') is set out in the following table. In this table, each row corresponds to the extended interpretation $(M, (m|x_1 \mapsto v))$ determined by the value of v in column 1.

v	$\boldsymbol{M}$('$g\ x_1$')	$\boldsymbol{M}$('$P\ g\ x_1$')
1	3	F
2	2	T
3	1	T

In the extended interpretation $(M, (m|x_1 \mapsto 1)$ (first row), $\boldsymbol{M}$('$P\ g\ x_1$') = false. Therefore, $\boldsymbol{M}$('$\forall x_1\ P\ g\ x_1$') = false. We may use the same table to find that $\boldsymbol{M}$('$\exists x_1\ P\ g\ x_1$') = true. We need at least one value $v : V$ such that $\boldsymbol{M}$('$P\ g\ x_1$') =

true in the extended interpretation $(M, (m|x_1 \mapsto v))$. This is the case for $v =_d 2$ and $v =_d 3$.

The two wfes $\alpha =_d$ '$\forall x_1\ P\ g\ x_1$' and $\alpha' =_d$ '$\exists x_1\ P\ g\ x_1$' are sentences: they contain no free variables. We can see that their semantic values $\boldsymbol{M}(\alpha)$ and $\boldsymbol{M}(\alpha')$ are independent of the given extension $m: Vars \to V$ of M.

7.3D A theorem

To end this section, here is a fundamental property of first-order wffs. It plays a central role in the demonstration of the semantic properties of the quantifiers. Here it is necessary to use the more complex notation introduced at the end of Section 7.3B: for any wff α and interpretation (M, m), $\boldsymbol{M}_{(M,m)}(\alpha)$ denotes the value of $\boldsymbol{M}(\alpha)$ in the interpretation (M, m). The theorem is given with an almost complete demonstration. This illustrates proof by structural induction. The completion of the demonstration is left as an exercise.

Theorem 7.3D.1

Let L be any first-order language, and α any wfe in L. Let (M, m) and (M, m') be any two interpretations of L such that $m(\boldsymbol{x}) = m'(\boldsymbol{x})$ for every variable $\boldsymbol{x}$ occurring *free* in α. Then $\boldsymbol{M}_{(M,m)}(\alpha) = \boldsymbol{M}_{(M,m')}(\alpha)$ ■

Proof The proof is by structural induction. If α is a variable $\boldsymbol{x}$ then $\boldsymbol{M}_{(M,m)}(\alpha) = m(\boldsymbol{x}) = m'(\boldsymbol{x}) = \boldsymbol{M}_{(M,m')}(\alpha)$. For other wfes, we introduce the function $FreeVars(\alpha)$, which is the set of variables with at least one free occurrence in α. (If α is quantifier-free, then this set coincides with the set of variables simply occurring in α.) If α is a term '$\boldsymbol{f}\tau_1\ \tau_2 \ldots \tau_n$', then clearly $FreeVars(\alpha) = \cup\{FreeVars(\tau_i) | 1 \leqslant i \leqslant n\}$. Therefore, if $m(\boldsymbol{x}) = m'(\boldsymbol{x})$ for all $\boldsymbol{x}: FreeVars(\alpha)$ then $m(\boldsymbol{x}) = m'(\boldsymbol{x})$ for all $\boldsymbol{x}: FreeVars(\tau_i)$ and for all i with $1 \leqslant i \leqslant n$, and so for each τ_i, $\boldsymbol{M}_{(M,m)}(\tau_i) = \boldsymbol{M}_{(M,m')}(\tau_i)$ by the induction hypothesis. This implies

$$\begin{aligned}\boldsymbol{M}_{(M,m)}(\alpha) &= \boldsymbol{M}_{\boldsymbol{f}}(\boldsymbol{M}_{(M,m)}(\tau_1), \ldots, \boldsymbol{M}_{(M,m)}(\tau_n))\\ &= \boldsymbol{M}_{\boldsymbol{f}}(\boldsymbol{M}_{(M,m')}(\tau_1), \ldots, \boldsymbol{M}_{(M,m')}(\tau_n))\\ &= \boldsymbol{M}_{(M,m')}(\alpha)\end{aligned}$$

If α is an atomic wff then the proof is identical. If $\alpha =_d$ '$(\neg\ \beta)$' or $\alpha =_d$ '$(\beta * \gamma)$' for any binary propositional connective * then the proof is similar, and is left as an exercise.

There remains the case $\alpha =_d$ '$\xi\boldsymbol{x}\ \beta$', where $\xi: \{\forall, \exists\}$. If $\alpha =_d$ '$\forall\boldsymbol{x}\ \beta$' then

$$FreeVars(\alpha) = FreeVars(\beta) \backslash \{\boldsymbol{x}\}$$

We must show that for any m and $m': Vars \to V$ such that $m(\boldsymbol{y}) = m'(\boldsymbol{y})$ for all $\boldsymbol{y}: FreeVars(\alpha)$, $\boldsymbol{M}_{(M,m)}(\alpha) = \boldsymbol{M}_{(M,m')}(\alpha)$. Now for all $v: V$,

$$(m|\boldsymbol{x} \mapsto v)\ (\boldsymbol{y}) = (m'|\boldsymbol{x} \mapsto v)\ (\boldsymbol{y})$$

for all $y: FreeVars(\beta)$. Therefore, by the induction hypothesis,

$$\boldsymbol{M}_{(M,(m|x \mapsto v))}(\beta) = \boldsymbol{M}_{(M,(m'|x \mapsto v))}(\beta)$$

for all $v: V$, which implies $\boldsymbol{M}_{(M,m)}(\alpha) = \boldsymbol{M}_{(M,m')}(\alpha)$.

As for $\alpha =_{\text{d}}$ '$\exists x\ \beta$', the proof of this case is now easily derived from the definition of $\boldsymbol{M}$('$\exists x\ \beta$'). This is left as an exercise. ■

Corollary 7.3D.2

For any wfe α in which no variables occur free, $\boldsymbol{M}_{(M,m)}(\alpha)$ depends on M only. That is, if M is fixed, $\boldsymbol{M}_{(M,m)}(\alpha)$ is constant: it is not affected by variations in the extension m. ■

This is an immediate consequence of Theorem 7.3D.1. Note that in this corollary, if α is a term then it must contain no variables, as any occurrence of a variable in a term is necessarily free. If α is a wff then any variable occurring in it must be quantified.

EXERCISES

7.3.1 In this and subsequent exercises, let L and (M, m) be the language and the extended interpretation defined in Section 7.3C, unless otherwise stated.

(a) Let $\tau_0 =_{\text{d}}$ '$f\,c\,f\,g\,x_1\,x_2$'. Draw the parse tree of τ_0, naming intermediate terms $\tau_1, \tau_2, \ldots$.

(b) Taking the terms τ_i in order of complexity, compute each value $\boldsymbol{M}(\tau_i)$ in (M, m). Fully justify the computation of each $\boldsymbol{M}(\tau_i)$.

7.3.2 Extend Exercise 7.3.1 to the wff $\alpha_0 =_{\text{d}}$ '$(Q\ c\ g\ x_1 \vee (\neg\ P\,f\,g\,x_1\,x_2))$', using $\alpha_1, \alpha_2, \ldots$ to name intermediate wffs.

7.3.3 Let $\alpha =_{\text{d}}$ '$Eq\ g\ x_1\,f\,g\ x_1\ x_3$'. Evaluate $\boldsymbol{M}(\alpha)$ in (M, m).

7.3.4 (a) Let $\beta =_{\text{d}}$ '$P\,f\,x_1\,x_3$'. For each value $v: V$, compute $\boldsymbol{M}(\beta)$ in the modified interpretation $(M, (m|x_1 \mapsto v))$. Tabulate the results.

(b) Let $\alpha_1 =_{\text{d}}$ '$\forall x_1\ \beta$' and $\alpha_2 =_{\text{d}}$ '$\exists x_1\ \beta$'. Compute $\boldsymbol{M}(\alpha_1)$ and $\boldsymbol{M}(\alpha_2)$ in (M, m) using (a).

7.3.5 Let β be defined as in Exercise 7.3.4 and $\alpha =_{\text{d}}$ '$\forall x_1\ \forall x_3\ \beta$'. Compute $\boldsymbol{M}(\alpha)$ in the interpretation M. Note that this requires evaluating $\boldsymbol{M}$('$\forall x_3\ \beta$') in every interpretation $(M, (m|x_1 \mapsto v))$ with $v: V$. In turn, in order to determine each such value, we must (in principle) compute $\boldsymbol{M}(\beta)$ in every interpretation $(M, ((m|x_1 \mapsto v)|x_3 \mapsto w))$ with $w: V$. As $V = \{1, 2, 3\}$, there are $3 \times 3 = 9$ values $\boldsymbol{M}(\beta)$ to calculate all told.

7.3.6 Give the general definition of $\boldsymbol{M}(\text{`}\forall \boldsymbol{x}\ \beta\text{'})$, derived from $\boldsymbol{M}(\beta)$, using the notation $\boldsymbol{M}_{(M,m)}(\alpha)$ instead of the simpler $\boldsymbol{M}(\alpha)$.

7.3.7 (a) In any language L, for any wffs β and $\alpha =_{\text{d}} \text{`}\forall \boldsymbol{x}\ \beta\text{'}$ and any interpretation (M, m), it is often not necessary to compute $\boldsymbol{M}(\beta)$ for all modified interpretations $(M, (m|x \mapsto v))$ in order to determine $\boldsymbol{M}(\alpha)$. When can we stop evaluating $\boldsymbol{M}(\beta)$?
(b) Same question for $\alpha =_{\text{d}} \text{`}\exists \boldsymbol{x}\ \beta\text{'}$.

7.3.8 Consider any first-order language L. Show that for any $\boldsymbol{x}, \boldsymbol{y}$: *Vars* and any β: *Wffs*,

$$\boldsymbol{M}(\text{`}\forall \boldsymbol{x}\ \forall \boldsymbol{y}\ \beta\text{'}) = \boldsymbol{M}(\text{`}\forall \boldsymbol{y}\ \forall \boldsymbol{x}\ \beta\text{'})$$

in any extended interpretation. We may conclude that universal quantifiers may be applied in any order.

7.3.9 Assuming the result stated in Exercise 7.3.8 and the definition of the semantics of '$\exists$', show that

$$\boldsymbol{M}(\text{`}\exists \boldsymbol{x}\ \exists \boldsymbol{y}\ \beta\text{'}) = \boldsymbol{M}(\text{`}\exists \boldsymbol{y}\ \exists \boldsymbol{x}\ \beta\text{'})$$

in any extended interpretation. Thus, existential quantifiers may be applied in any order.

7.3.10 In general it is not possible to interchange a universal quantifier with an existential one. Demonstrate this fact by providing a counterexample, such as a wff β in the language of Section 7.3C containing just two free variables, x_1 and x_2, and an interpretation M in which

$$\boldsymbol{M}(\text{`}\forall x_1\ \exists x_2\ \beta\text{'}) \neq \boldsymbol{M}(\text{`}\exists x_2\ \forall x_1\ \beta\text{'})$$

7.3.11 Complete the proof of Theorem 7.3D.1 for the cases $\alpha =_{\text{d}} \text{`}(\neg\ \beta)\text{'}$, $\alpha =_{\text{d}} \text{`}(\beta * \gamma)\text{'}$, $*: \{\wedge, \vee, \Rightarrow, \Leftrightarrow\}$ and $\alpha =_{\text{d}} \text{`}\exists \boldsymbol{x}\ \beta\text{'}$.

7.3.12 *Substitution lemma for quantifier-free wfes* Let α be any quantifier-free wfe (term or wff), τ any term and $\boldsymbol{x}$ any variable, in any first-order language. Let α' be the wfe obtained by substituting τ for every occurrence of $\boldsymbol{x}$ in α. Informally verify that for any interpretation (M, m),

$$\boldsymbol{M}_{(M,m)}(\alpha') = \boldsymbol{M}_{(M,m')}(\alpha)$$

where $m' = (m|\boldsymbol{x} \mapsto \boldsymbol{M}_{(M,m)}(\tau))$. To guide your reasoning, select an arbitrary quantifier-free wfe α with, say, two occurrences of $\boldsymbol{x}$, select a simple arbitrary term τ, draw the parse trees of α and α' and observe how $\boldsymbol{M}$ is determined on these two trees (for the relevant extended interpretation). A general substitution theorem for any wff is treated in Chapter **8**.

7.3.13* Prove by structural induction the result stated in Exercise 7.3.12.

7.4 Logical implication

In propositional logic, deductive reasoning is represented by the concept of *tautological implication.* The first-order analogue of tautological implication is *logical implication.* This formalizes the idea of a set Γ of wffs implying a certain wff α in a first-order language L.

We first define the related notions of *models* and of *satisfiability* in first-order logic. Then we define logical implication.

7.4A Models and satisfiability

Recall that in propositional logic, a truth assignment m is said to satisfy a wff α iff the semantic value $\boldsymbol{M}(\alpha)$ determined by m is true. Satisfiability is defined in an analogous way in first-order logic. In outline, given a language L and an extended interpretation (M, m) for L, a wff α is satisfied by (M, m) iff the value $\boldsymbol{M}(\alpha)$ determined by (M, m) is true. We also say that in this case, (M, m) is a model of α.

Definition 7.4A.1

Let L be a first-order language and (M, m) an extended interpretation for L. Let *Wfes* be the set of well-formed expressions of L.

(1) For any wff α: *Wfes*, (M, m) *satisfies* α iff $\boldsymbol{M}(\alpha) =$ true in (M, m). In this case, we also say that (M, m) is a *model* of α or, more precisely, an *extended model* of α.

(2) For any set Γ of wffs of L, (M, m) is a *model* of Γ iff it is a model of every wff $\alpha : \Gamma$. ■

Remark

Recall that for a *sentence* α, which contains no free variables, the value $\boldsymbol{M}(\alpha)$ is entirely determined by an interpretation M without extension m. In other words, any extension m of M does not affect $\boldsymbol{M}(\alpha)$. Consequently for *sentences*, models may consist of *unextended* interpretations M. The term 'model' is often used in this restricted sense for sentences only; for example, in Enderton (1972). ■

7.4B Definition of logical implication

The definition of logical implication follows.

Definition 7.4B.1 (logical implication)

Let Γ be a set of wffs and α be any wff in L. The set Γ *logically implies* α iff every extended model (M, m) of Γ is also a model of α. This property is written

$$\Gamma \vDash \alpha$$

If Γ is a singleton $\{\beta\}$ we simply write $\beta \vDash \alpha$. ■

The reader should compare the definition of *logical* implication with that of *tautological* implication given in Section **6**.3C. Recall that in propositional logic, a set Γ of wffs tautologically implies another wff α iff every truth assignment m that satisfies Γ also satisfies α. The similarity between these two types of implication is apparent: The wffs of propositional logic correspond to the first-order wffs of the language L; truth assignments correspond to extended interpretations; and truth assignments satisfying sets of wffs correspond to extended models of sets of wffs.

A simple property of logical implication is *monotonicity*, defined as follows:

Property 7.4B.1

Let L be a first-order language and Γ and Γ' be two subsets of wffs in L such that $\Gamma \subseteq \Gamma'$. Any wff α logically implied by Γ is also logically implied by Γ'.

■

This is immediate: every model of Γ' is a model of Γ; therefore if every model of Γ satisfies α, so does every model of Γ'.

Various concepts and properties related to tautological implication have counterparts in first-order logic. For instance, the first-order analogue of Property **6**.3C.1 is as follows:

Property 7.4B.2

Consider any set Γ of wffs and any wff α in a first-order language L. The following conditions are equivalent:

(1) $\Gamma \models \alpha$.

(2) The set $\Gamma \cup \{`(\neg\ \alpha)'\}$ is *not satisfiable*, i.e. admits no extended model (M, m).

■

This property gives an alternative way of defining logical implication. Instead of Definition **7**.4B.1, we may define '$\Gamma \models \alpha$' as stating the condition that $\Gamma \cup \{`(\neg\ \alpha)'\}$ has no model, that is, there is *no* extended intrepretation (M, m) that satisfies all the members of Γ *as well as* '$(\neg\ \alpha)$'.

Proof of Property 7.4B.2 We must show that in this property, (1) implies (2) and (2) implies (1).

(1) Suppose $\Gamma \models \alpha$ – that is, every model (M, m) of Γ is a model of α. Then in every such model, $\boldsymbol{M}(`(\neg\ \alpha)') = \text{false}$. Therefore, there is *no* extended interpretation in which $\boldsymbol{M}(\alpha) = \text{true}$ for every $\beta : \Gamma \cup \{`(\neg\ \alpha)'\}$, that is, $\Gamma \cup \{`(\neg\ \alpha)'\}$ is not satisfiable.

(2) Suppose it is not true that $\Gamma \models \alpha$. Consequently, there exists a model (M, m) of Γ which is *not* a model of α. Then in this model $\boldsymbol{M}(`(\neg\ \alpha)') = \text{true}$,

and so (M, m) is a model of $\Gamma \cup \{`(\neg\ \alpha)'\}$. Therefore, $\Gamma \cup \{`(\neg\ \alpha)'\}$ *is* satisfiable. ■

The first-order analogue of a tautology is a *valid formula*:

Definition 7.4B.2

(1) A *valid* wff is a wff α such that $M(\alpha) =$ true in every extended interpretation (M, m). In other terms a wff α is valid iff it is logically implied by 'nothing', that is, $\varnothing \vDash \alpha$. In this case, we simply write $\vDash \alpha$.

(2) Two wffs α and β are *logically equivalent* iff $\beta \vDash \alpha$ and $\alpha \vDash \beta$. ■

Valid formulas have the following property, which immediately follows from Property 7.4B.1:

Corollary 7.4B.3

Any valid formula is logically implied by any set Γ of wffs (including $\Gamma = \varnothing$). ■

A last result with its counterpart in propositional logic is as follows:

Property 7.4B.4

For any wffs α and β,

(a) $\alpha \vDash \beta$ iff '$(\alpha \Rightarrow \beta)$' is valid.

(b) α and β are logically equivalent iff '$(\alpha \Leftrightarrow \beta)$' is valid. ■

The proof is left as an exercise.

The analogy between tautological and logical implications stops here. In particular, there is no first-order analogue of the truth table method to determine whether $\Gamma \vDash \alpha$ for any finite set $\Gamma \cup \{\alpha\}$ of wffs. This is because in general there is an infinite number of extended interpretations (M, m) of Γ. Obviously these cannot be enumerated exhaustively, as the strict counterpart of the truth table method would require. Fortunately, there is an alternative approach to the problem of verifying $\Gamma \vDash \alpha$ in first-order logic. This is studied in the next chapter.

7.4C Examples of valid formulas

Example 7.4C.1

Consider a first-order language L with a unary predicate symbol P, a constant symbol c and a unary function symbol f. The following is a valid formula:

$$\forall x\, P\, x \Rightarrow P\, f\, c$$

This formula states that if the property P is true for any value of x, then it must be true for the value of $f c$ in particular. This fact is intuitively obvious. The point is that we should be able to derive this result *from our formal definition of the function* $\boldsymbol{M}$. Let us do that.

For any interpretation (M, m), by definition of $\boldsymbol{M}$, the semantic value $\boldsymbol{M}(\text{`}\forall x\ P\ x \Rightarrow P\ f\ c\text{'}) = \text{true}$ if $\boldsymbol{M}(\text{`}\forall x\ P\ x\text{'}) = \text{false}$ or $\boldsymbol{M}(\text{`}P\ f\ c\text{'}) = \text{true}$. This follows from the definition of the function $\text{IF}: \text{Bool}^2 \rightarrow \text{Bool}$. So we must show that for any interpretation $(M, m)$ in which $\boldsymbol{M}(\text{`}\forall x\ P\ x\text{'}) = \text{true}$, we must also have $\boldsymbol{M}(\text{`}P\ f\ c\text{'}) = \text{true}$. Let $V = M_L$. $\boldsymbol{M}(\text{`}\forall x\ P\ x\text{'}) = \text{true}$ means that for any value $v : V$, $\boldsymbol{M}(\text{`}P\ x\text{'}) = M_P(\boldsymbol{M}(x)) = M_P(v) = \text{true}$ in the modified interpretation $(M, (m|x \mapsto v))$. Therefore, $\boldsymbol{M}(\text{`}\forall x\ P\ x\text{'}) = \text{true}$ iff $M_P(v) = \text{true}$ for all values $v : V$, and in particular for $v =_{\text{d}} \boldsymbol{M}(\text{`}f\ c\text{'}) \in V$. Consequently,

$$\boldsymbol{M}(\text{`}P\ f\ c\text{'}) = M_P(\boldsymbol{M}(\text{`}f\ c\text{'})) = \text{true}$$

which completes the proof. ■

Tautologies in first-order logic

Consider any tautology α in propositional logic: for example, the contraposition

$$(p \Rightarrow q) \Leftrightarrow ((\neg\ q) \Rightarrow (\neg\ p))$$

where p and q are *proposition symbols*. Let L be a first-order language, and construct a new wff α' by replacing each proposition symbol occurring in α by a wff β of L. Note that for each proposition symbol π, *every* occurrence of π in α is replaced by *the same* wff β. Clearly the result α' is a wff in the language L. Moreover, α' may still rightly be called a tautology, for whatever truth value is assigned to any wff β in any interpretation (M, m), $\boldsymbol{M}(\alpha')$ must be true, as α is a tautology. Consequently, α' is a valid wff of L.

Definition 7.4C.1

A *tautology of first-order logic* is a wff α' in a first-order language L derived from a tautology α of propositional logic by the following operation: for each proposition symbol π occurring in α, select a wff β in L and replace every occurrence of π by β. As pointed out, α' is a valid wff. ■

Note that a first-order tautology is a *special kind* of valid formula, namely one obtained by the substitution procedure just described. There are other types of valid formula.

Example 7.4C.2

Consider the above contraposition

$$\alpha =_{\text{d}} \quad (p \Rightarrow q) \Leftrightarrow ((\neg\ q) \Rightarrow (\neg\ p))$$

Let L be the first-order language defined in Example 7.4C.1 and consider two wffs

$$\beta_1 =_{\mathrm{d}} \quad \forall x\,(P\,x \vee P\,f\,x)$$
$$\beta_2 =_{\mathrm{d}} \quad (P\,y \Rightarrow P\,f\,f\,y)$$

Substitute β_1 and β_2 for p and q respectively in α. The result is

$$\begin{aligned}\alpha' &= (\beta_1 \Rightarrow \beta_2) \Leftrightarrow ((\neg\, \beta_2) \Rightarrow (\neg\, \beta_1))\\ &= [\forall x(P\,x \vee P\,f\,x) \Rightarrow (P\,y \Rightarrow P\,f\,f\,y)]\\ &\qquad \Leftrightarrow [(\neg\,(P\,y \Rightarrow P\,f\,f\,y)) \Rightarrow (\neg\,\forall x(P\,x \vee P\,f\,x))]\end{aligned}$$

The wff α' is a tautology, hence a valid formula in the language L: in any interpretation (M, m), $\boldsymbol{M}(\alpha')$ is true. ■

EXERCISES

7.4.1 Consider the language L and the (extended) interpretation (M, m) of L specified in Section 7.3C. Let

$$\alpha =_{\mathrm{d}} \quad Eq\,x_1\,x_2 \qquad \text{and} \qquad \beta =_{\mathrm{d}} \quad Q\,x_1\,x_1 \Rightarrow Q\,x_1\,x_2$$

It can be shown that $\alpha \vDash \beta$, i.e. α logically implies β. Show that this is confirmed by the values of $\boldsymbol{M}(\alpha)$ and $\boldsymbol{M}(\beta)$ in this interpretation.

7.4.2 Repeat Exercise 7.4.1 with the following variations:

(a) Use $(M, (m|x_2 \mapsto 2))$ as interpretation.
(b) Use (M', m) as interpretation, where M' differs from M by the fact that $M_Q\,(2, 2) =_{\mathrm{d}}$ true.
(c) Use $(M', (m|x_2 \mapsto 2))$ as interpretation.

7.4.3 Repeat Exercises 7.4.1 and 7.4.2 with

$$\alpha =_{\mathrm{d}} \quad \neg\, Q\,x_2\,x_3 \qquad \text{and} \qquad \beta =_{\mathrm{d}} \quad Q\,x_2\,x_3 \Rightarrow P\,x_1$$

7.4.4 Let L be a first-order language with binary predicate Q. Let $\alpha =_{\mathrm{d}}$ '$Q\,x\,x$' in L. Construct an (extended) interpretation (M, m) of L with universe $V =_{\mathrm{d}} M_L =_{\mathrm{d}} \{1, 2\}$ and M_Q such that $\boldsymbol{M}(\alpha)$ = false. Conclude that in general '$Q\,x\,x$' is not valid. Stated in English: a binary relation is not necessarily reflexive.

7.4.5 Repeat Exercise 7.4.4 with the wff $\alpha =_d$ '$Q\ x\ y \Rightarrow Q\ y\ x$'. This shows that a binary relation is not necessarily symmetric.

7.4.6 Let α and β be defined as in Exercise 7.4.1. Prove that $\alpha \models \beta$. (Recall that this requires showing that in any interpretation (M, m) in which $\boldsymbol{M}(\alpha) =$ true, $\boldsymbol{M}(\beta) =$ true, given the way in which $\boldsymbol{M}$ is derived from (M, m).)

7.4.7 Repeat Exercise 7.4.6 with α and β as defined in Exercise 7.4.3.

7.4.8 In any language with binary predicate symbol Q, prove that $\alpha =_d$ '$(\forall x_1\ Q\ x_1\ y \Rightarrow Q\ x_2\ y)$' is a valid wff. (Recall that this requires showing that in any interpretation (M, m), $\boldsymbol{M}(\alpha) =$ true.)

7.4.9 Consider the wffs α and α' of Example 7.4C.2. Draw the parse tree T of α' and draw a line around the part of T corresponding to the parse tree of α. Then with the help of this diagram show that α' is a valid wff, that is, that in any interpretation (M, m), $\boldsymbol{M}(\alpha') =$ true.

7.4.10 Prove Property 7.4B.4.

7.4.11 Let $\alpha =_d$ '$\forall x\ (P\ x \Rightarrow Q\ x)$', $\beta =_d$ '$P\ c$' and $\gamma =_d$ '$Q\ c$' in any language in which both P and Q are unary predicate symbols and c is a constant. Prove that $\{\alpha, \beta\} \models \gamma$.

7.4.12 Recall the deduction given in Section 7.1A:

α_1: 'All men are mortal.'
α_2: 'Socrates is a man.'
α_3: (Therefore:) 'Socrates is mortal.'

(a) Re-express each α_i in first-order logic.
(b) Prove that $\{\alpha_1, \alpha_2\} \models \alpha_3$, with the help of Exercise 7.4.11.

7.4.13 Prove that for any wffs α and β, and any variable $\boldsymbol{x}$,

$$\forall \boldsymbol{x}\ (\alpha \Rightarrow \beta) \quad \models \quad (\forall \boldsymbol{x}\ \alpha \Rightarrow \forall \boldsymbol{x}\ \beta)$$

7.4.14 Construct a simple counterexample to demonstrate that in general '$(\forall \boldsymbol{x}\ \alpha \Rightarrow \forall \boldsymbol{x}\ \beta)$' does *not* logically imply '$\forall \boldsymbol{x}\ (\alpha \Rightarrow \beta)$'. This requires specifying a simple language L, two wffs α and β in L and a suitable interpretation M of L.

7.4.15 Let L be any language with equality (predicate symbol 'Eq') and constant symbol c.

(a) Show that for any model M of the sentence '$\forall x\ Eq\ x\ c$', the universe $V =_d M_L$ must be a singleton.
(b) Show that any model M of '$\forall x\ \forall y\ Eq\ x\ y$' has the same property.

7.4.16 Let L be defined as in Exercise 7.4.15.

(a) Show that for any model M of the sentence

$$\forall x_1 \, \forall x_2 \, \forall x_3 \cdot [(\neg \, Eq \; x_1 \; x_2) \wedge (\neg \, Eq \; x_1 \; x_3)] \Rightarrow Eq \; x_2 \; x_3$$

the universe $V =_{\mathrm{d}} M_L$ may have only one or two values.

(b) Show that for any model M of the sentence

'$\forall x \, \exists y \, (\neg \, Eq \; x \; y)$'

the universe $V =_{\mathrm{d}} M_L$ has at least two values. Caution: this property depends on a certain general assumption made about any universe V, which you should state.

(c) Show that for any model M of the sentence

$$\exists x \, \exists y \, (\neg \, Eq \; x \; y)$$

the universe $V =_{\mathrm{d}} M_L$ has at least two values. Note that this does not depend on the assumption mentioned in (b).

Formal Deduction in First-order Logic

8.1 Formal deductions

It has been stated that logic is a model of deductive reasoning. Before proceeding, let us reconsider this statement in the light of previous developments.

Informally, deductive reasoning consists of (a) taking a certain set Γ of 'initial facts' for granted and (b) deriving new facts from Γ according to certain rules. The facts making up Γ are called *axioms*. They represent an initial description of a certain situation. The new facts derived from Γ according to the rules are the *consequences* of the initial facts. They are all the properties *logically implied* by Γ.

What have we achieved so far in first-order logic? First, we have established rules which indicate how to establish a formal language L. These rules define the set *Wfes* of well-formed expressions (wfes) of L. Of these wfes, the terms are to represent certain objects and the well-formed formulas (wffs) certain properties or relations between these objects. Second, we have established rules which indicate exactly how a *meaning* or semantic value is assigned to each wfe. This involves establishing an extended interpretation (M, m) of L. Then, given (M, m), the rules assign a semantic value $M(\alpha)$ to each wfe α. This value is uniquely determined for each α by recursion on *Wfes*. Finally, we have given a precise definition of *logical implication*. We have stated a precise condition which must be satisfied for any set Γ of wffs to imply another wff α: *Γ logically implies α iff every extended model of Γ is also a model of α.* When this condition is satisfied we write $\Gamma \models \alpha$.

As it is, our model of deductive reasoning is still incomplete. The definition of logical implication tells us *what* we must prove in order to be able to assert $\Gamma \models \alpha$. However, it does not say *how* to go about that task. Also, it does not give us a precise – or 'mechanical' – method of verifying that our steps are correct and that indeed $\Gamma \models \alpha$. A third limitation of this definition is that it explicitly invokes all possible *interpretations* of a set of wffs. Although it is possible to reason in terms of interpretations – that is, semantics – we should not have to. *We should be able to carry out every proof by manipulating symbols only, without ever referring to interpretations.* This is because a deduction process may be said to be totally rigorous, and may even be automated, only if it is entirely formal – that is, its rules operate solely on the symbols of L and make no references to interpretations.

Is it possible to construct a purely *formal deduction system*, a set of operations on wfes which enable us to determine whether $\Gamma \models \alpha$ for any set $\Gamma \cup \{\alpha\}$? The answer is *yes*, and this is demonstrated below by building precisely such a system. The construction of this system and the analysis of its properties is one of the great achievements of this century's mathematics. It is also of major significance in computing, as it provides the means necessary *to prove* programs rigorously. A formal deduction system is called a *deductive calculus*. However, we shall continue to use the term 'formal deduction system' as this seems to indicate the purpose of the system more clearly.

8.1A Outline of a formal deduction system

What characteristics should we expect of a formal deduction system (fds)? Suppose we have a first-order language L, a set Γ of wffs taken as axioms and a further wff α in L. First, the fds should enable us to determine whether or not $\Gamma \models \alpha$. Second, *if* $\Gamma \models \alpha$ then the fds should tell us precisely why. In other words, it should determine a finite sequence of elementary steps leading from Γ to α and thereby demonstrating that $\Gamma \models \alpha$. Third, every step required by the fds to prove $\Gamma \models \alpha$ should consist of *an operation on wfes of L only*. There should be no reference whatsoever to possible interpretations. Steps of this type are called *formal*. A sequence of formal steps leading from Γ to α and so proving $\Gamma \models \alpha$ is called a *formal deduction* or simply a deduction. It is the set of formal deductions and their generating rules which constitutes our complete formal model of deductive reasoning.

We now define a formal deduction system meeting these requirements, which we call FDS. Given the set Γ of axioms, FDS generates a set Th_Γ of wffs inductively. The wffs generated are called *formal theorems* (*derived from* or *produced by* Γ). The set Th_Γ has three fundamental properties, which are presented now in order to explain at once in what sense FDS meets the requirements specified above.

(1) *Soundness* Every wff $\alpha: Th_\Gamma$ is logically implied by Γ. Thus, FDS does not generate any wff which is not a consequence of the axioms.

(2) *Completeness* For every wff α such that $\Gamma \vDash \alpha$, $\alpha \in Th_\Gamma$. This means that if a wff is logically implied by Γ then this wff is generated by FDS.

(3) *Existence of formal deductions* For each wff $\alpha: Th_\Gamma$, there exists a *finite* sequence $Ded =_d (\alpha_1, \alpha_2, \ldots, \alpha_n)$ with each $\alpha_k: Wffs$ and with the following property:

(a) $\alpha = \alpha_n$

(b) $\alpha_k \in Th_\Gamma$ for all $k =_d 1, 2, \ldots, n$

Moreover, for each α_k the fact that $\alpha_k \in TH_\Gamma$ can be proved in one elementary formal step, in a sense we shall define. Each such step may use wffs α_j preceding α_k in *Ded*.

The sequence $Ded = (\alpha_1, \alpha_2, \ldots, \alpha_n)$ contains all the information defining a formal deduction of α. We also call *Ded* itself a *formal deduction*. The details of FDS are presented in the next two sections. For any set Γ of wffs and any wff α, we denote $\Gamma \cup \{\alpha\}$ simply by 'Γ, α'.

8.1B Generation of formal theorems

Consider any first-order language L and the set *Wffs* of well-formed formulas in L. In order to define FDS, we must establish rules which determine how the set Th_Γ of formal theorems is derived from any given set $\Gamma \subseteq Wffs$. There are many different ways of doing this. The rules adopted here are from Enderton (1972). They have been chosen for their simplicity.

In outline, FDS involves essentially three rules for generating Th_Γ. The first states that Th_Γ must include a certain set Λ of *valid* wffs, together with Γ itself, of course. The second rule is that for any two wffs α and β, if α and $\gamma =_d$ '$(\alpha \Rightarrow \beta)$' are members of Th_Γ, then so is β. This second rule is called *modus ponens* (MP). The third rule is the usual induction principle that Th_Γ must not contain any wff not accounted for by the first two rules.

The set Λ is defined precisely later. Its members are called *logical axioms*. Recall that a *valid wff* is a wff α such that $\mathbf{M}(\alpha) =$ true in every extended interpretation (M, m). Λ is a subset of all the valid wffs, and has two important properties. First, this set is not defined by reference to interpretations: each logical axiom may be constructed in a finite number of steps by purely symbolic operations. Second, for any valid wff α, there is a deduction $Ded =_d (\alpha_1, \ldots, \alpha_n = \alpha)$ in which every wff α_k is valid and is either a member of Λ or is obtained by MP from two predecessors in *Ded*, as described in Definition **8**.1B.2 below.

Definition 8.1B.1

Let L be a first-order language, *Wffs* the set of wffs of L and Γ any subset of *Wffs*. Let Λ be the set of *logical axioms* just mentioned and formally established in Definition **8**.1C.1 below. Th_Γ is the set of wffs $\alpha : Wffs$ determined by the following rules.

(1) Every logical axiom $\lambda : \Lambda$ is a member of Th_Γ, and so is every axiom $\alpha : \Gamma$. Formally

$$\Lambda \cup \Gamma \subseteq Th_\Gamma$$

(2) *Modus Ponens* (*MP*) For any formulas α, β and $\gamma : Wffs$ such that $\gamma =_{\mathrm{d}}$ '$(\alpha \Rightarrow \beta)$',

$$\begin{array}{ll} \text{if} & \alpha \in Th_\Gamma \quad \text{and} \quad \gamma \in Th_\Gamma \\ \text{then} & \beta \in Th_\Gamma \end{array}$$

(3) Th_Γ does not contain any wff not accounted for by rules (1) and (2).

For any wff α, we write

$$\Gamma \vdash \alpha$$

to assert that $\alpha \in Th_\Gamma$, that is α is a formal theorem derived from Γ. ■

Thus, Th_Γ is the set inductively generated by rules (1) and (2). This point is elaborated on at the end of Section **8**.1E. We say that rule (2) of Definition **8**.1B.1, MP, is a *rule of inference*, because it states that from any two wffs, namely α and $\gamma =_{\mathrm{d}}$ '$(\alpha \Rightarrow \beta)$', we may *infer* a third wff, namely β.

Deductions

To complete this overall description of FDS, we may now formally define a deduction $Ded =_{\mathrm{d}} (\alpha_1, \ldots, \alpha_n)$.

Definition 8.1B.2

For any wff α, a *deduction for* α (or: *of* α) is a finite sequence $Ded =_{\mathrm{d}} (\alpha_1, \ldots, \alpha_n)$ of wffs such that $\alpha = \alpha_n$ and for each $\alpha_k : Ded$, one of the following two conditions is satisfied:

(1) either $\alpha_k \in \Lambda \cup \Gamma$

(2) or there exist two wffs α_i, $\alpha_j : Ded$ such that $i < k$, $j < k$ and

$$\alpha_j = \text{'}(\alpha_i \Rightarrow \alpha_k)\text{'}$$

■

In other words, in a deduction *Ded*, each wff $\alpha_k : Ded$ is either an axiom in $\Lambda \cup \Gamma$, or it may be derived by MP from two of its predecessors α_i and $\alpha_j =_{\mathrm{d}}$ '$(\alpha_i \Rightarrow \alpha_k)$' in *Ded*.

The set Th_Γ, as specified in Definition **8**.1B.1, has the following property.

Theorem 8.1B.1

For any set Γ, α of wffs, $\Gamma \vdash \alpha$ iff there exists a deduction $Ded =_{\text{d}} (\alpha_1, \ldots, \alpha_n = \alpha)$ for α. ■

Theorem **8**.1B.1 is a special case of Theorem **4**.4E.1. It means that Th_Γ may also be *defined* 'from the bottom up' as the set of wffs α for which a deduction $Ded =_{\text{d}} (\alpha_1, \alpha_2, \ldots, \alpha_n = \alpha)$ exists. Note that by Definition **8**.1B.2, for any $k < n$, the *prefix* $(\alpha_1, \ldots, \alpha_k)$ of *Ded* is also a deduction. Consequently not only α but every wff $\alpha_k : Ded$ is itself a formal theorem in Th_Γ.

The difference between the two metasymbols '$\models$' and '$\vdash$' is fundamental. '$\models$' represents *logical implication*, which is defined in terms of *semantic* notions, that is, interpretations. '$\vdash$' makes no reference to semantics. For any set Γ, α of wffs, '$\Gamma \vdash \alpha$' only means that α can be derived from Γ by performing a finite number of purely symbolic operations (identifying logical axioms and applying MP).

There remains one main task to carry out: to define the set Λ of *logical axioms*. This is done in the next section.

8.1C Logical axioms

We now turn to the definition of the set Λ of *logical axioms* for a given language L. These axioms are from Enderton (1972). As stated in Section **8**.1B, Λ consists of a certain set of *valid* wffs. The validity of these axioms is fairly obvious. The proofs are left as exercises. They may also be found in the reference.

Definition 8.1C.1

Let L be a first-order language. The set Λ of logical axioms in L is determined by the following rules:

(1) Every *first-order tautology* is a member of Λ. (See remark below.)

(2) For any wfe α, any variable $\boldsymbol{x}$ and any term τ, let '$\alpha^{\boldsymbol{x}}{}_{\tau}$' denote the result of substituting τ for every *free* occurrence of $\boldsymbol{x}$ in α. In addition, say that τ is *substitutable for* $\boldsymbol{x}$ *in* α if a certain condition specified in Definition **8**.1C.2 below is satisfied. If α is a wff and τ is substitutable for $\boldsymbol{x}$ in α, the following wff is a member of Λ:

$$\forall \boldsymbol{x}\, \alpha \Rightarrow \alpha^{\boldsymbol{x}}{}_{\tau}$$

(3) For any wffs α and β and any variable $\boldsymbol{x}$, the following wffs are members of Λ:

(a) $\forall \boldsymbol{x}\, (\alpha \Rightarrow \beta) \Rightarrow (\forall \boldsymbol{x}\, \alpha \Rightarrow \forall \boldsymbol{x}\, \beta)$

(b) $\alpha \Rightarrow \forall \boldsymbol{x}\, \alpha$ provided $\boldsymbol{x}$ is not free in α

(4) If the predicate symbol 'Eq' (equality) is in the language L then for any *atomic* wff α and any variables $\boldsymbol{x}$ and $\boldsymbol{y}$ in L, the following wffs are members of Λ:

(a) $Eq\, \boldsymbol{x}\, \boldsymbol{x}$

(b) $Eq\, \boldsymbol{x}\, \boldsymbol{y} \Rightarrow (\alpha \Rightarrow \alpha')$

where α' is obtained by replacing zero or more occurrences of $\boldsymbol{x}$ by $\boldsymbol{y}$ in α.

(5) For any wff $\alpha : \Lambda$ and any variable $\boldsymbol{x}$, the formula

$$\forall \boldsymbol{x}\, \alpha$$

is also a member of Λ. '$\forall \boldsymbol{x}\, \alpha$' is called a *generalization* of α. We say that Λ is closed under generalization.

(6) Λ does not contain any wff not accounted for by the preceding rules. ■

Remarks on Definition 8.1C.1

1 Recall that by Definition **7**.4C.1, a tautology in first-order logic is a wff derived from a propositional tautology α by the following operation: for every proposition symbol π occurring in α, substitute some *unique* (first-order) wff for every occurrence of π in α.

2 The universal quantifier '$\forall$' is one of the distinctive features of first-order logic. The main purpose of the logical axioms defined by rules (2) and (3) is to manipulate this quantifier. The effect of rule (2) is to *eliminate* '$\forall$' from a formula. Given '$\forall \boldsymbol{x}\, \alpha \Rightarrow \alpha^{\boldsymbol{x}}{}_{\tau}$', from the *one* wff '$\forall \boldsymbol{x}\, \alpha$', we may by MP infer a whole *set* of wffs. These are all the wffs $\alpha^{\boldsymbol{x}}{}_{\tau}$ which may be obtained by substituting any term τ for $\boldsymbol{x}$ in α, provided τ is substitutable for $\boldsymbol{x}$ in α. In other words, they are all the particular wffs that can be obtained by *instantiating* $\boldsymbol{x}$ in α. Note that $\boldsymbol{x}$ need not occur free in α, but if it does not then obviously $\alpha^{\boldsymbol{x}}{}_{\tau} = \alpha$ – the substitution of τ for $\boldsymbol{x}$ has 'no effect'.

3 Rule (3) has the opposite purpose, namely to enable the generalization of a wff whenever possible. Formally, to generalize a wff α is to prefix it with '$\forall \boldsymbol{x}$', where $\boldsymbol{x}$ may be *any* variable. (In particular, $\boldsymbol{x}$ need not even occur in α.) Thus, rule (3) enables the *introduction* of '$\forall$' into a wff.

Now the question is: 'When can a wff legitimately be generalized?' More specifically, given a set Γ of nonlogical axioms and a wff α such that $\Gamma \models \alpha$, on which condition does this imply that $\Gamma \models$ '$\forall \boldsymbol{x}\, \alpha$'? The answer is: from $\Gamma \models \alpha$, we may infer that $\Gamma \models$ '$\forall \boldsymbol{x}\, \alpha$' *if $\boldsymbol{x}$ does not occur free in any member of Γ.*

Consequently, our logical axioms should be sufficiently strong to ensure that for any Γ and α, if $\Gamma \vdash \alpha$ and $\boldsymbol{x}$ does not occur free in any member of Γ, then $\Gamma \vdash$ '$\forall \boldsymbol{x}\, \alpha$'. This property results from the axioms defined by rule (3) and is known as the *generalization theorem.* Rule (3) has no other purpose than to justify this theorem, which is proved in Section **8**.2C.

4 Rule (4) holds only if the language L under consideration contains the predicate symbol 'Eq', which represents equality. The purpose of this rule is to ensure that Eq has the basic properties of equality. These are *reflexivity, symmetry, transitivity* and *substitutability of equal terms* as arguments of a function. These properties are indeed implied by the axioms of rule (4). They are proved in Section **8**.3E.

Substitution

It remains to develop the twin notions of substitution and substitutability. We begin with the former.

As stated in Definition **8**.1C.1, given any wfe α, variable $\boldsymbol{x}$ and term τ, '$\alpha^{\boldsymbol{x}}{}_{\tau}$' denotes the wfe obtained by substituting τ for every *free* occurrence of $\boldsymbol{x}$ in α. Note that τ may be any term: a constant, another variable $\boldsymbol{y}$, $\boldsymbol{x}$ itself, or a compound term '$\boldsymbol{f}\tau_1\,\tau_2 \ldots \tau_n$' where $\boldsymbol{f}$ is any n-ary function symbol.

The notion of substitution should be clear from this informal definition, together with the example below. A formal inductive definition is given in Section **8**.1E. The reader may try to work it out beforehand as an exercise.

Example 8.1C.1

Let $\alpha =_{\mathrm{d}}$ '$\forall y\,(Q\,x\,y \wedge P\,x)$' and $\tau =_{\mathrm{d}}$ '$f\,c\,d$', where Q is binary, P is unary, f is a binary function symbol and c and d are constants. Note x and y are different variables. In α, the second occurrence of y is bound and every occurrence of x is free. Thus,

$$\alpha^{x}{}_{\tau} = \forall y\,(Q\,f\,c\,d\,y \wedge P\,f\,c\,d)$$

However,

$$\alpha^{y}{}_{\tau} = \alpha = \forall y\,(Q\,x\,y \wedge P\,x)$$

that is, substituting τ for y in α has no effect (it is *vacuous*) because there is no free occurrence of y in α. ■

Substitutability

In general, given a wff α and a variable $\boldsymbol{x}$, not every term τ may be substituted for $\boldsymbol{x}$ in α. This is because τ itself may contain a variable $\boldsymbol{y}$ which occurs bound in α. In this case the occurrence(s) of $\boldsymbol{y}$ in τ might get 'captured' by a quantifier '$\forall\boldsymbol{y}$' or '$\exists\boldsymbol{y}$' in α, and this would be incorrect.

Example 8.1C.2

Suppose $\boldsymbol{x} = x$ and $\boldsymbol{y} = y$. Let $\alpha =_{\mathrm{d}}$ '$(P\,x \wedge \forall y\,Q\,x\,y)$' and $\tau =_{\mathrm{d}}$ '$f\,c\,y$', where P and Q are predicate symbols of arities 1 and 2 respectively, f is a binary function symbol and c a constant. Then

$$\alpha^x_\tau = (P\,f\,c\,y \wedge \forall y\,Q\,f\,c\,\underline{y}\,y)$$

The underlined occurrence of y in $\alpha^x{}_\tau$ has been captured by '$\forall y$', which is incorrect: in *every* instance of '$f\,c\,y$', the occurrence of y should be the same free variable, ready to denote the same object. ■

For this reason, a term may be substituted for a variable in a wfe only if the following condition is satisfied:

Definition 8.1C.2 (substitutability)

For any wfe α and any variable $\boldsymbol{x}$, a term τ is *substitutable* for $\boldsymbol{x}$ in α iff the substitution of τ for $\boldsymbol{x}$ does *not* cause the capture in $\alpha^{\boldsymbol{x}}{}_\tau$ of a variable $\boldsymbol{y}$ occurring in τ. In other words: every occurrence of a variable in τ must remain free in $\alpha^{\boldsymbol{x}}{}_\tau$.

■

Note that if α is a term or a quantifier-free wff in Definition **8**.1C.2 then the substitutability condition is automatically satisfied. There is a formal inductive definition of substitutability, given in Section **8**.1E. The reader should first try to work this out as an exercise.

8.1D Fundamental properties of FDS

We are now in a position to introduce another basic property of first-order wfes called the *substitution theorem*, and to restate formally the two fundamental properties of FDS, namely *soundness* and *completeness*. The substitution theorem follows from Theorem 7.3D.1. One of its main implications is that for any wff α, variable $\boldsymbol{x}$, and term τ substitutable for $\boldsymbol{x}$ in α, '$\forall \boldsymbol{x}\,\alpha$' logically implies $\alpha^{\boldsymbol{x}}{}_\tau$. In other words, it is this theorem which guarantees that the logical axioms '$\forall \boldsymbol{x}\,\alpha \Rightarrow \alpha^{\boldsymbol{x}}{}_\tau$' are valid.

Theorem 8.1D.1 (substitution theorem)

Let L be any first-order language. For any wfe α, variable $\boldsymbol{x}$ and term τ substitutable for $\boldsymbol{x}$ in α,

$$\boldsymbol{M}_{(M,m)}(\alpha^{\boldsymbol{x}}{}_\tau) = \boldsymbol{M}_{(M,m')}(\alpha)$$

where (M, m) is any interpretation of L and $m' = (m|\boldsymbol{x} \mapsto \boldsymbol{M}_{(M,m)}(\tau))$. ■

The proof is left as an exercise. It may also be found in Enderton (1972). The implication that wffs '$\forall \boldsymbol{x}\,\alpha \Rightarrow \alpha^{\boldsymbol{x}}{}_\tau$' are valid is almost immediate. The demonstration is also left as an exercise.

Next we turn to the soundness and completeness of FDS.

Theorem 8.1D.2 (soundness)

Let L be a first-order language and Γ, α any set of wffs in L. If $\Gamma \vdash \alpha$ then $\Gamma \vDash \alpha$. In other words, any wff α is a formal theorem derived from Γ only if it is logically implied by Γ. ■

The completeness property is the opposite implication:

Theorem 8.1D.3 (completeness)

For any set Γ, α of wffs, if $\Gamma \vDash \alpha$ then $\Gamma \vdash \alpha$. In other words, if α is logically implied by Γ, then α is a formal theorem derived from Γ, and consequently there is a deduction $Ded =_d (\alpha_1, \alpha_2, \ldots, \alpha_n = \alpha)$ of α from Γ. ■

From Theorem **8**.1D.3, it follows that in order to determine whether $\Gamma \vDash \alpha$ for any Γ, α, we must find a deduction *Ded* for α. If this can be found then we have a *formal proof* (the deduction *Ded*) that $\Gamma \vDash \alpha$. If we can show that there is no such deduction *Ded* for α, then we may conclude that α is *not* logically implied by Γ.

The soundness and completeness properties of Th_Γ are important theorems. Soundness is straightforward, albeit somewhat tedious to prove. The bulk of the proof is a demonstration that every logical axiom is valid, and that MP preserves logical implication – that is, if α_k is derived by MP from α_i and α_j then $\{\alpha_i, \alpha_j\} \vDash \alpha_k$.

Completeness is a deeper result, and its proof is fairly advanced. It was presented by Kurt Gödel in his doctoral dissertation (1930) and must not be confused with Gödel's famous Incompleteness Theorem of 1931. These results, with detailed proofs, are given in Enderton (1972). One consequence of the completeness theorem must be mentioned:

Corollary 8.1D.4

For any valid wff α, $\varnothing \vdash \alpha$: that is, there is a deduction $Ded =_d (\alpha_1, \alpha_2, \ldots, \alpha_n = \alpha)$ in which each α_k is either a logical axiom or generated by MP from predecessors in *Ded*. ■

Henceforth, we shall simply write '$\vdash \alpha$' to state that α is a formal theorem derived from $\varnothing$.

8.1E Inductive constructions AT

We again assume given a first-order language L. For most of the first-order concepts introduced semiformally so far, a rigorous definition must be based on the inductive definition of L. Some of these 'official' definitions are given now.

Free variable occurrences and substitution

As stated above, for any wfe α, term τ and variable $\boldsymbol{x}$ in L, the substitution of τ for $\boldsymbol{x}$ in α is obtained by replacing every *free* occurrence of $\boldsymbol{x}$ in α by τ. The result is denoted by $\alpha^{\boldsymbol{x}}{}_{\tau}$. Consequently the two concepts of free occurrence and substitution are closely related. They are defined inductively in very similar ways, so much so that the two definitions are now given simultaneously. They closely follow the inductive construction of the set *Wfes*, which the reader should refer to. (See Section 7.2B.)

Our aim is to define, for any wfe α, term τ and variable $\boldsymbol{x}$: (a) for any *occurrence* of $\boldsymbol{x}$ in α, whether it is free or not; and (b) the wfe $\alpha^{\boldsymbol{x}}{}_{\tau}$. We do this for each possible way in which α may be generated by a term- or formula-building operation.

Definition 8.1E.1 (free variable occurrences and substitution)

Consider any wfe α, term τ and variable $\boldsymbol{x}$ in a language L.

Case 1 α is a variable $\boldsymbol{y}$: Here two subcases must be envisaged.

(a) $\boldsymbol{y} = \boldsymbol{x}$. Then there is one occurrence of $\boldsymbol{x}$ in α, and this occurrence is free. Consequently, $\alpha^{\boldsymbol{x}}{}_{\tau} = \tau$.

(b) $\boldsymbol{y} \neq \boldsymbol{x}$. Consequently there is no free occurrence of $\boldsymbol{x}$ in α, and so $\alpha^{\boldsymbol{x}}{}_{\tau} = \alpha$. Note that the operation of substitution is defined, but with no change in α. It operates like the identity function, sending α to α.

Case 2 α is a term '$\boldsymbol{f}\tau_1 \tau_2 \ldots \tau_n$', where n is the arity of $\boldsymbol{f}$. Then any occurrence of $\boldsymbol{x}$ in α is in some subterm τ_i, where it is necessarily free. Consequently,

$$\alpha^{\boldsymbol{x}}{}_{\tau} = \boldsymbol{f}\, \tau_1{}^{\boldsymbol{x}}{}_{\tau}\, \tau_2{}^{\boldsymbol{x}}{}_{\tau} \cdots \tau_n{}^{\boldsymbol{x}}{}_{\tau}$$

In particular if $n = 0$ then $\alpha^{\boldsymbol{x}}{}_{\tau} = \alpha = \boldsymbol{f}$.

Case 3 α is an atomic wff '$\boldsymbol{P}\,\tau_1 \tau_2 \ldots \tau_n$', where $n \geqslant 1$ is the arity of $\boldsymbol{P}$. Then any occurrence of $\boldsymbol{x}$ in α is in some subterm τ_i, where it is necessarily free. Consequently,

$$\alpha^{\boldsymbol{x}}{}_{\tau} = \boldsymbol{P}\; \tau_1{}^{\boldsymbol{x}}{}_{\tau}\, \tau_2{}^{\boldsymbol{x}}{}_{\tau} \ldots \tau_n{}^{\boldsymbol{x}}{}_{\tau}$$

Case 4 $\alpha =_{\mathrm{d}}$ '$\xi\, \boldsymbol{y}\, \beta$', where $\xi : \{\forall, \exists\}$, $\boldsymbol{y}$ is any variable and β any wff. Here again two subcases must be considered.

(a) $\boldsymbol{y} = \boldsymbol{x}$, that is, $\alpha =$ '$\xi\, \boldsymbol{x}\, \beta$'. Then every occurrence of $\boldsymbol{x}$ in α is either *head* or *bound*. Consequently, $\alpha^{\boldsymbol{x}}{}_{\tau} = \alpha$, that is, there is no change in α.

(b) $\boldsymbol{y} \neq \boldsymbol{x}$. Then every occurrence of $\boldsymbol{x}$ is free in $\alpha =$ '$\xi\, \boldsymbol{y}\, \beta$' iff it is free in β. Consequently, $\alpha^{\boldsymbol{x}}{}_{\tau} =$ '$\xi\, \boldsymbol{y}\, \beta^{\boldsymbol{x}}_{\tau}$'.

Case 5 $\alpha =_{\mathrm{d}}$ '$(\neg\, \beta)$' where β is any wff. Then every occurrence of $\boldsymbol{x}$ is free in α iff it is free in β. Consequently, $\alpha^{\boldsymbol{x}}{}_{\tau} =$ '$(\neg\, \beta^{\boldsymbol{x}}_{\tau})$'.

Case 6 $\alpha =_d$ '$(\beta * \gamma)$', where β and γ are any wffs and $*$ any binary propositional connective – that is, $*:\{\wedge, \vee, \Rightarrow, \Leftrightarrow\}$. Then any occurrence of $\boldsymbol{x}$ in α is either in β or in γ. It is free in α iff it is free in the subwff in which it occurs. Consequently, $\alpha^{\boldsymbol{x}}{}_{\tau} =$ '$(\beta^{\boldsymbol{x}}{}_{\tau} * \gamma^{\boldsymbol{x}}{}_{\tau})$'. ■

Substitutability

Our next aim is to specify by induction whether τ is *substitutable for* $\boldsymbol{x}$ *in* α, for any wfe α, term τ and variable $\boldsymbol{x}$. The definition of substitutability is similar to that of substitution, but with some important differences.

Definition 8.1E.2 (substitutability)

Consider any wfe α, term τ and variable $\boldsymbol{x}$ in a language L.

Case 1 α is a term or an atomic wff. Then τ is substitutable for $\boldsymbol{x}$ in α.

Case 2 $\alpha =_d$ '$\xi\, \boldsymbol{y}\, \beta$', where $\xi:\{\forall, \exists\}$, $\boldsymbol{y}$ is any variable and β any wff. We consider and refine the two subcases of the definition of substitution.

(a) $\boldsymbol{y} = \boldsymbol{x}$, that is, $\alpha =$ '$\xi\, \boldsymbol{x}\, \beta$'. Then τ is substitutable for $\boldsymbol{x}$ in α. (Note that $\alpha^{\boldsymbol{x}}{}_{\tau} = \alpha$, therefore no variable occurring in τ is captured in $\alpha^{\boldsymbol{x}}{}_{\tau}$.)

(b) $\boldsymbol{y} \neq \boldsymbol{x}$. Then τ is substitutable for $\boldsymbol{x}$ in $\alpha =$ '$\xi\, \boldsymbol{y}\, \beta$' iff one of the following two conditions is satisfied:

  (i) either: $\boldsymbol{y}$ occurs in τ but $\boldsymbol{x}$ does not occur free in β;
  (ii) or: $\boldsymbol{y}$ does not occur in τ *and* τ is substitutable for $\boldsymbol{x}$ in β, that is, no other variable in τ is captured in $\beta^{\boldsymbol{x}}{}_{\tau}$.

Case 3 $\alpha =_d$ '$(\neg\, \beta)$', where β is any wff. Then τ is substitutable for $\boldsymbol{x}$ in α iff τ is substitutable for $\boldsymbol{x}$ in β.

Case 4 $\alpha =_d$ '$(\beta * \gamma)$', where β and γ are any wffs and $*:\{\wedge, \vee, \Rightarrow, \Leftrightarrow\}$. Then τ is substitutable for $\boldsymbol{x}$ in α iff τ is substitutable for $\boldsymbol{x}$ in *both* β and γ. ■

It may also be useful to spell out when τ is *not* substitutable for $\boldsymbol{x}$ in α in case 2(b). The reader should do this before reading on.

In case 2(b), τ is *not* substitutable for $\boldsymbol{x}$ when

(i′) either: $\boldsymbol{y}$ occurs in τ and $\boldsymbol{x}$ occurs free in β;
(ii′) or: $\boldsymbol{y}$ does not occur in τ, but τ is not substitutable for $\boldsymbol{x}$ in β.

Carefully check that the four conditions (i), (ii), (i′) and (ii′) are *mutually exclusive* and *totally exhaustive* (account for every possible α) in this case. In (i′), the occurrence of $\boldsymbol{y}$ in τ is bound to '$\xi\, \boldsymbol{y}$' in $\alpha^{\boldsymbol{x}}{}_{\tau} =$ '$\xi\, \boldsymbol{y}\, \beta^{\boldsymbol{x}}{}_{\tau}$'. In (ii′), $\boldsymbol{x}$ must occur free in β and at least one variable *other than* $\boldsymbol{y}$ in τ is captured by some quantifier in $\beta^{\boldsymbol{x}}{}_{\tau}$.

Note When the substitution of τ for $\boldsymbol{x}$ in α is vacuous, because $\boldsymbol{x}$ does not occur free in α, τ is nevertheless defined as *substitutable* for $\boldsymbol{x}$ in α. This may seem odd but it is entirely rational. All we are doing is defining a certain predicate *substitutable* (a relation between any wfe α, term τ and variable $\boldsymbol{x}$). We may define this predicate in any way that suits our purpose. Now this purpose is to ensure that τ is defined as *substitutable* for $\boldsymbol{x}$ in α *in all the cases* in which no variable in τ is captured in $\alpha^{\boldsymbol{x}}{}_{\tau}$. These include the cases where no actual substitution is taking place, hence $\alpha^{\boldsymbol{x}}{}_{\tau} = \alpha$. ■

Inductive generation of formal theorems

Finally, consider the set Th_{Γ} of formal theorems derived from a set Γ of wffs. We now show exactly how Th_{Γ} may be described as the set inductively generated by a family $\boldsymbol{G}$ of relations, as defined in the theory of Section **4**.4 (structural induction). The family $\boldsymbol{G}$ contains two relations on the set *Wffs*: *Ax* (for 'axioms') and *MP* (for 'modus ponens').

(1) The relation *Ax* represents rule (1) of Definition **8**.1B.1. It is the nonfunctional unary relation with graph $\mathrm{Gr}(Ax) =_{\mathrm{d}} \Lambda \cup \Gamma \subseteq Wffs$.

(2) *MP* is a *partial* binary operation $MP: Wffs^2 \nrightarrow Wffs$. For any couple $(\alpha, \gamma): Wffs^2$, $MP(\alpha, \gamma)$ is defined iff $\gamma =$ '$(\alpha \Rightarrow \beta)$' for some wff $\beta: Wffs$. If it is defined,

$$MP(\alpha, \gamma) = MP(\alpha, `(\alpha \Rightarrow \beta)') =_{\mathrm{d}} \beta$$

Rule (1) of Definition **8**.1B.1 states that $\mathrm{Gr}(Ax) = \Lambda \cup \Gamma \subseteq Th_{\Gamma}$, rule (2) that Th_{Γ} is closed under MP, and rule (3) that Th_{Γ} is the smallest set satisfying rules (1) and (2). This is exactly the same as stating that Th_{Γ} is the set inductively generated by $\boldsymbol{G} =_{\mathrm{d}} (Ax, MP)$. Note that in general, for any set Γ, Th_{Γ} is *not* freely generated by $\boldsymbol{G} = (Ax, MP)$.

Final remarks

1 The first three inductive definitions of free occurrence of a variable, substitution and substitutability are *recursive functions*. They are based on the inductive construction of *Wfes* by the family $\boldsymbol{G}$ of wfe-building operations established in Section **7**.2C. That these three functions are well-defined depends on the recursion theorem and the fact that *Wfes* is *freely generated* by $\boldsymbol{G}$.

2 In contrast, the inductive construction of Th_{Γ} is based on the set *Wfes*, but *not* on the inductive construction of *Wfes*. It is a new inductive construction, determined by a different family $\boldsymbol{G}$ of generators, namely $\boldsymbol{G} = (Ax, MP)$. It is *not* free, and does *not* depend on the recursion theorem. ■

EXERCISES

8.1.1 (a) Prove that the inference rule MP is sound in the sense that for any wffs α and β (in any language L), $\{\alpha, `(\alpha \Rightarrow \beta)'\} \models \beta$. Note that this is a straightforward application of the definition of $\boldsymbol{M}$ in any interpretation (M, m), and of the relation $\models$.

(b) Prove that for any set Γ of wffs and any $\alpha : \Gamma$, $\Gamma \models \alpha$.
(c) Using (a) and (b), prove by simple induction that for any deduction $Ded = (\alpha_1, \alpha_2, \ldots, \alpha_n)$ from a set Γ of wffs, $\Lambda \cup \Gamma \models \alpha_k$ for all $k : \{1, 2, \ldots, n\}$.

8.1.2 Prove in outline that any first-order tautology is valid. See Exercise 7.4.9 for a special case; use the method suggested there.

8.1.3 Prove that for any variable $\boldsymbol{x}$ and wffs α and β, the following wff is valid, using Exercise 7.4.13 and Property 7.4B.4.

$$\forall \boldsymbol{x}\,(\alpha \Rightarrow \beta) \Rightarrow (\forall \boldsymbol{x}\,\alpha \Rightarrow \forall \boldsymbol{x}\,\beta)$$

8.1.4 (a) Prove that for any variable $\boldsymbol{x}$ and wff α, '$\alpha \Rightarrow \forall \boldsymbol{x}\,\alpha$' is valid provided $\boldsymbol{x}$ does not occur free in α. Hint: Use Theorem 7.3D.1.
(b) Let L and (M, m) be the language and interpretation given as the example in Section 7.3C and let $\alpha =_{\text{d}}$ '$P\,x_1$'. Compute the values of $\boldsymbol{M}(\alpha)$ and $\boldsymbol{M}$('$\forall x_1\,\alpha$') in (M, m). Then, with these values, show that α is a counterexample demonstrating that in general, given any wff α and any variable $\boldsymbol{x}$, '$\alpha \Rightarrow \forall \boldsymbol{x}\,\alpha$' is not valid if $\boldsymbol{x}$ is free in α.

8.1.5 (a) Prove that the following wff is valid for all wffs α and β and any variable $\boldsymbol{x}$: '$(\forall \boldsymbol{x}\,\alpha \wedge \forall \boldsymbol{x}\,\beta) \Rightarrow \forall \boldsymbol{x}\,(\alpha \wedge \beta)$'.
(b) Prove that if in addition $\boldsymbol{x}$ does not occur free in α, the following are valid, using (a) and Exercise 8.1.4(a):

(i) $(\alpha \wedge \forall \boldsymbol{x}\,\beta) \Rightarrow (\forall \boldsymbol{x}\,\alpha \wedge \forall \boldsymbol{x}\,\beta)$
(ii) $(\alpha \wedge \forall \boldsymbol{x}\,\beta) \Rightarrow \forall \boldsymbol{x}\,(\alpha \wedge \beta)$

This illustrates a practical application of '$\alpha \Rightarrow \forall \boldsymbol{x}\,\alpha$' when $\boldsymbol{x}$ is not free in α: the quantifier '$\forall \boldsymbol{x}$' may be 'factored out' in '$(\alpha \wedge \forall \boldsymbol{x}\,\beta)$'.

8.1.6 Prove that for any variables $\boldsymbol{x}$ and $\boldsymbol{y}$, and any *atomic* wff α, the following are valid: (a) '$Eq\,\boldsymbol{x}\,\boldsymbol{x}$'; (b) '$Eq\,\boldsymbol{x}\,\boldsymbol{y} \Rightarrow (\alpha \Rightarrow \alpha')$', where α' is obtained by replacing zero or more occurrences of $\boldsymbol{x}$ by $\boldsymbol{y}$ in α.

8.1.7 Prove by a simple counterexample that in general, for any set (Γ, α) of wffs, if a variable $\boldsymbol{x}$ occurs free in some wffs of Γ then it may be that Γ logically implies α but not '$\forall \boldsymbol{x}\,\alpha$'. Hint: Use Exercise 8.1.4(b).

8.1.8* Prove that for any set (Γ, α) of wffs and any variable $\boldsymbol{x}$, if $\boldsymbol{x}$ does not occur free in any member of Γ and $\Gamma \models \alpha$ then $\Gamma \models$ '$\forall \boldsymbol{x}\,\alpha$'. This is the generalization theorem, at the semantic level.

8.1.9 Let L and $\boldsymbol{M}$ be defined as in Section 7.3C, except that $M_Q(1, 3) =_{\text{d}} \text{F}$ and $M_Q(3, 2) =_{\text{d}} \text{T}$. Let $\alpha =_{\text{d}}$ '$\exists y\,Q\,x\,y$' and $\tau =_{\text{d}}$ '$g\,y$'. Verify that in (M, m), $\boldsymbol{M}$('$\forall \boldsymbol{x}\,\alpha \Rightarrow \alpha^{\boldsymbol{x}}{}_{\tau}$') = false because the occurrence of y in τ is captured by

'$\exists y$' in α^{x}_{τ} = '$\exists y\ Q\ g\ y\ y$'. This provides a counterexample to show that in general, for any wff α, variable $\boldsymbol{x}$ and term τ, '$\forall \boldsymbol{x}\ \alpha \Rightarrow \alpha^{x}_{\tau}$' is not valid if τ is not substitutable for $\boldsymbol{x}$ in α.

8.1.10* Prove Theorem **8**.1D.1 by structural induction, building on Exercise 7.3.13. This is fairly easy for all wfes except wffs $\alpha =_{d}$ '$\forall \boldsymbol{x}\ \beta$'. For these, Theorem 7.3D.1 is needed. Take care to determine at precisely which point the substitutability condition is invoked, and to formulate the induction hypothesis properly.

8.1.11 Using Theorem **8**.1D.1, prove that for any wff α, variable $\boldsymbol{x}$ and term τ substitutable for $\boldsymbol{x}$ in α, '$\forall \boldsymbol{x}\ \alpha \Rightarrow \alpha^{x}_{\tau}$' is valid.

8.2 Fundamental metatheorems

The description of the formal deduction system FDS is only the first step in the development of a practical establishment method. *In theory*, FDS meets all our requirements. We may describe any type of situation by selecting an appropriate first-order language L and a suitable set Γ of axioms. Once this has been done, any property of the situation described is represented as a theorem $\alpha : Th_{\Gamma}$ and may be obtained by working out a deduction for it. Any such deduction is an entirely formal proof that α is a property of the situation described, that is, logically implied by Γ. Consequently, the proof of the deduction itself may be carried out by entirely mechanical means, and so may be completely automated, as all it involves is a finite number of symbol manipulation steps.

Although possible in theory, this method is still far from being a practical proposition, for two main reasons. First, for any wff α presumed to be implied by the axioms, there is still the task of finding a deduction for α in the first place. Second, any formal deduction may be relatively lengthy. Consequently, its verification may prove to be unacceptably time-consuming, and error-prone if it is performed manually.

Fortunately, there is no absolute need to work out an explicit formal deduction whenever we seek to demonstrate that a wff α is implied by a set Γ of axioms. All we need to do is prove that *there exists* such a deduction for α. If this can be done, then the fact that α is a consequence of Γ is as good as demonstrated.

Consequently, our next step is to establish means of providing such demonstrations. These means exist. They are general theorems about FDS. They are also called *metatheorems* to distinguish them from the *formal* theorems of L. The former assert properties *of FDS* and are expressed in the metalanguage used to describe it, whereas the latter are wffs of the formal language L. (The other general properties of first-order logic given in previous sections are likewise metatheorems.)

The benefits that may be gained from these metatheorems are twofold. First, they are of great assistance in the actual search for a deduction, when such a deduction is presumed to exist. Second, if these theorems may be applied, then the proof that a deduction for a wff exists may be considerably shorter than the deduction itself.

The aim of this section is to introduce and prove a first group of fundamental metatheorems about FDS. Their use in practice is discussed in Section **8**.3. Each property states that, for any set Γ of wffs in L, if certain conditions are satisfied then a certain wff α is a formal theorem derived from Γ. Note that in most cases the proof yields more than a demonstration that $\Gamma \vdash \alpha$. It produces an actual deduction for α, which sheds considerable light on the working of FDS.

In each case, we assume given a first-order language L and all related sets of wfes, including the set Λ of logical axioms. In some cases, we consider several sets Γ of nonlogical axioms simultaneously. We then use the term 'deduction *from* Γ' to avoid ambiguity. Unless otherwise stated, a reference to a rule (*i*) means 'rule (*i*) of Definition **8**.1C.1', which specifies the set Λ of logical axioms.

8.2A Subset and transitivity properties of ⊢

We begin with a number of basic properties of '⊢' which do not refer to any specific symbols of L. First, we introduce some notation.

Definition 8.2A.1

(1) Let Γ and Θ be any two sets of wffs in L. We write '$\Gamma \vdash \Theta$' to assert that $\Gamma \vdash \theta$ for *each* wff $\theta : \Theta$.

(2) For any sequence $Seq =_{\mathrm{d}} (\alpha_1, \alpha_2, \ldots, \alpha_n)$ of wffs, we also denote by Seq the *set* of wffs α_i. (Technically, in this second sense Seq is an abbreviation for Ran(Seq).) This justifies writing '$\alpha_i \in Seq$' and so on.

(3) *Concatenation* Let $Seq_1 =_{\mathrm{d}} (\alpha_1, \ldots, \alpha_m)$ and $Seq_2 =_{\mathrm{d}} (\beta_1, \ldots, \beta_n)$ be any two sequences of wffs. The *concatenation* of Seq_1 and Seq_2 is the sequence denoted by $Seq_1 \mathbin{+\!\!\!+} Seq_2$ and defined by

$$\begin{aligned} Seq_1 \mathbin{+\!\!\!+} Seq_2 &=_{\mathrm{d}} (\alpha_1, \ldots, \alpha_m) \mathbin{+\!\!\!+} (\beta_1, \ldots, \beta_n) \\ &=_{\mathrm{d}} (\alpha_1, \ldots, \alpha_m, \beta_1, \ldots, \beta_n) \end{aligned}$$

The concatenation of more than two sequences is defined by analogy.

■

Property 8.2A.1 (expandability of assumptions)

Consider any sets of wffs Γ and Δ such that $\Gamma \subseteq \Delta$, and any wff α. If $\Gamma \vdash \alpha$ then $\Delta \vdash \alpha$. ■

This is immediate: if $\Gamma \vdash \alpha$ then there exists a deduction *Ded* of α from Γ, and *Ded* is a deduction of α from Δ.

Property 8.2A.2

Consider any set Γ, α of wffs. If $\Gamma \vdash \alpha$ then there exists a *finite* subset $\Gamma' \subseteq \Gamma$ such that $\Gamma' \vdash \alpha$. ■

Proof If $\Gamma \vdash \alpha$ then there exists a deduction *Ded* of α from Γ. Let $\Gamma' =_{\mathrm{d}} \Gamma \cap$ *Ded*. Γ' is finite, as is *Ded*, and $\Gamma' \vdash \alpha$. ■

Property 8.2A.3 (transitivity of ⊢, Trans)

Let Γ, Θ and Δ be three sets of wffs such that $\Gamma \vdash \Theta$ and $\Theta \vdash \Delta$. Then $\Gamma \vdash \Delta$. ■

Proof Assume $\Gamma \vdash \Theta$ and $\Theta \vdash \Delta$. We must prove that for any $\delta : \Delta$, there exists a deduction *Ded* of δ from Γ.

As $\Theta \vdash \delta$, there exists a deduction

$$Ded' =_{\mathrm{d}} (\delta_1, \ldots, \delta_p =_{\mathrm{d}} \delta)$$

of δ from Θ. Let $\Theta' =_{\mathrm{d}} \Theta \cap Ded'$. Θ' is finite and so may be written $\{\theta_1, \ldots, \theta_q\}$. Moreover, for each $\theta_k : \Theta'$ there is a deduction Ded_k of θ_k from Γ. We shall prove that the concatenation

$$Ded =_{\mathrm{d}} Ded_1 \mathbin{+\!\!+} \ldots \mathbin{+\!\!+} Ded_q \mathbin{+\!\!+} Ded'$$

is a deduction of δ from Γ.

For instance, suppose $\Theta' =_{\mathrm{d}} \{\theta_1, \theta_2\}$. Let $Ded_1 =_{\mathrm{d}} (\alpha_1, \ldots, \alpha_m =_{\mathrm{d}} \theta_1)$ and $Ded_2 =_{\mathrm{d}} (\beta_1, \ldots, \beta_n =_{\mathrm{d}} \theta_2)$ be deductions of θ_1 and θ_2 from Γ respectively. Then

$$Ded = Ded_1 \mathbin{+\!\!+} Ded_2 \mathbin{+\!\!+} Ded' = (\alpha_1, \ldots, \alpha_m, \beta_1, \ldots, \beta_n, \delta_1, \ldots, \delta_p = \delta)$$

Consider now the general case. Let γ be any wff in *Ded*. We must prove:

Condition C: $\gamma \in \Delta \cup \Gamma$ or there exist two wffs η and '$(\eta \Rightarrow \gamma)$' preceding γ in *Ded*.

Case 1 γ is in one of the deductions Ded_k (it is some wff α_i or β_j in the example). Then $\gamma \in \Delta \cup \Gamma$ or there exist two wffs η and '$(\eta \Rightarrow \gamma)$' preceding γ in Ded_k, and so condition C is satisfied, as Ded_k is a segment of *Ded*.

Case 2 γ is a member δ_i of Ded'. Then $\gamma \in \Delta$ or $\gamma \in \Theta'$ or there exist two wffs η and '$(\eta \Rightarrow \gamma)$' preceding γ in Ded'. Therefore, condition C is satisfied in all three subcases as Ded' is the last segment of *Ded*. In particular if $\gamma \in \Theta'$ then γ is also in one of the deductions Ded_k which precedes Ded', so condition C is satisfied by case 1. ■

Observe that there is some redundancy in *Ded*, as each θ_k occurs at least twice in it, once in Ded_k and once in Ded'. Redundant wffs could be eliminated, though they do no harm.

An important special case of Property **8**.2A.3 is the following:

Corollary 8.2A.4 (rule T)

Let Γ and Θ be two sets of wffs such that $\Gamma \vdash \Theta$, Θ is finite and Θ tautologically implies some wff δ. In other words, Θ is of the form $\{\theta_1, \ldots, \theta_q\}$, and

$$\gamma =_{\mathrm{d}} (\theta_1 \Rightarrow (\theta_2 \Rightarrow (\theta_3 \Rightarrow \cdots \Rightarrow (\theta_q \Rightarrow \delta) \ldots)))$$

is a (first-order) tautology. Then $\Gamma \vdash \delta$. ■

Proof First, we show that $\Theta =_{\mathrm{d}} \{\theta_1, \ldots, \theta_q\} \vdash \delta$. For $i =_{\mathrm{d}} 1, 2, \ldots, q$, let

$$\gamma_i =_{\mathrm{d}} (\theta_i \Rightarrow (\theta_{i+1} \Rightarrow \cdots \Rightarrow (\theta_q \Rightarrow \delta) \ldots))$$

Thus $\gamma_1 = \gamma$ and $\gamma_q = (\theta_q \Rightarrow \delta)$. The following is a deduction of δ from Θ:

$$(\theta_1, \ldots, \theta_q, \gamma_1, \gamma_2, \ldots, \gamma_q, \delta)$$

$\gamma = \gamma_1 \in \Lambda$; γ_2 is justified by applying MP to θ_1 and γ_1; γ_3 by applying MP to θ_2 and γ_2; and so on.

Second, as $\Gamma \vdash \Theta$ and $\Theta \vdash \delta$, $\Gamma \vdash \delta$ by Property **8**.2A.3. ■

Note The tautology γ in Corollary **8**.2A.4 could be rewritten as

$$\gamma' =_{\mathrm{d}} \quad [(\theta_1 \wedge \theta_2 \wedge \theta_3 \wedge \cdots \wedge \theta_q) \Rightarrow \delta]$$

Recall from Section **6**.4B that γ and γ' are tautologically equivalent. The formal proof of this fact is set as an exercise. ■

8.2B Deduction theorem and corollaries

Next, we introduce the so-called deduction theorem and several of its corollaries. Its import is that a deduction of any wff α from a set Γ, γ of assumptions can be turned into a deduction of '$(\gamma \Rightarrow \alpha)$' from Γ.

Theorem 8.2B.1 (deduction theorem, Ded)

Let Γ, γ, α be any set of wffs.

If $\quad \Gamma, \gamma \vdash \alpha$

then $\quad \Gamma \vdash (\gamma \Rightarrow \alpha)$ ■

Proof Assume $\Gamma, \gamma \vdash \alpha$. There exists a deduction

$$Seq =_{\mathrm{d}} \quad (\alpha_1, \alpha_2, \ldots, \alpha_n =_{\mathrm{d}} \alpha)$$

for α from Γ, γ. The proof of Theorem **8**.2B.1 is by induction on the length n of *Seq*. In n steps, we transform this deduction into a new deduction *Seq'* for '$(\gamma \Rightarrow \alpha)$' from Γ.

For $k =_{\mathrm{d}} 1, 2, \ldots, n$, let Seq_{k-1} be the sequence obtained after $k - 1$ steps. It is of the form

$$Seq_{k-1} =_{\mathrm{d}} \quad (\beta_1, \beta_2, \ldots, \beta_m, \alpha_k, \alpha_{k+1}, \ldots, \alpha_n = \alpha)$$

with $Seq_0 =_{\mathrm{d}} Seq$. The induction hypothesis is in two parts:

(1) If $m \geqslant 1$ then $(\beta_1, \beta_2, \ldots, \beta_m)$ is a deduction of β_m from Γ.
(2) For any $j < k$, the wff '$(\gamma \Rightarrow \alpha_j)$' $\in (\beta_1, \beta_2, \ldots, \beta_m)$.

This condition is vacuously satisfied by Seq_0. Note that for any $k \geqslant 1$, Seq_k is *generally not* a deduction of α from Γ.

The kth step consists of replacing α_k by *one or three* new wffs in Seq_{k-1}, depending on the justification of α_k in *Seq*. Consequently, in general the number m of wffs β_i may be up to three times $(k - 1)$. One of three *nonexclusive* cases may arise:

Case 1 $\alpha_k = \gamma$. In this case, replace α_k by $\beta_{m+1} =_{\mathrm{d}}$ '$(\gamma \Rightarrow \gamma)$' $=$ '$(\gamma \Rightarrow \alpha_k)$'. The new wff is a tautology, hence a member of Λ by rule (1). Moreover $(\beta_1, \beta_2, \ldots, \beta_m, \beta_{m+1})$ is a deduction from Γ, so the induction hypothesis holds for Seq_k.

Case 2 $\alpha_k \in \Lambda \cup \Gamma$. In this case, replace α_k by the three wffs

$$\beta_{m+1} =_{\mathrm{d}} \quad \alpha_k$$
$$\beta_{m+2} =_{\mathrm{d}} \quad (\alpha_k \Rightarrow (\gamma \Rightarrow \alpha_k))$$
$$\beta_{m+3} =_{\mathrm{d}} \quad (\gamma \Rightarrow \alpha_k)$$

Now $(\beta_{m+1}, \beta_{m+2}, \beta_{m+3})$ is a deduction from Γ, as $\beta_{m+1} = \alpha_k \in \Lambda \cup \Gamma$, β_{m+2} is a tautology and hence a member of Λ, and β_{m+3} is obtained by MP from its predecessors. Therefore $(\beta_1, \beta_2, \ldots, \beta_{m+3})$ is a deduction from Γ, and the induction hypothesis holds for Seq_k.

Case 3 α_k is obtained by MP from two predecessors α_i and $\alpha_j =_{\mathrm{d}}$ '$(\alpha_i \Rightarrow \alpha_k)$' in *Seq*. Consequently at step k of the transformation process, by condition (2) of the induction hypothesis, α_k is preceded by two wffs

$$\beta_p =_d \quad (\gamma \Rightarrow \alpha_i)$$
$$\beta_q =_d \quad (\gamma \Rightarrow \alpha_j) \quad = \quad (\gamma \Rightarrow (\alpha_i \Rightarrow \alpha_k))$$

within the prefix $(\beta_1, \beta_2, \ldots, \beta_m)$ of Seq_{k-1}. Then replace α_k by the three wffs

$$\beta_{m+1} =_d \quad (\beta_p \Rightarrow (\beta_q \Rightarrow (\gamma \Rightarrow \alpha_k)))$$
$$\beta_{m+2} =_d \quad (\beta_q \Rightarrow (\gamma \Rightarrow \alpha_k))$$
$$\beta_{m+3} =_d \quad (\gamma \Rightarrow \alpha_k)$$

We can see that

$$\{\beta_p = \text{`}(\gamma \Rightarrow \alpha_i)\text{'}, \ \beta_q = \text{`}(\gamma \Rightarrow (\alpha_i \Rightarrow \alpha_k))\text{'}\}$$

tautologically implies '$(\gamma \Rightarrow \alpha_k)$'. Therefore β_{m+1} is a tautology, hence a member of Λ by rule (1). β_{m+2} is obtained by MP applied to β_p and β_{m+1}, and β_{m+3} by MP applied to β_q and β_{m+2}. Consequently, the induction hypothesis holds for Seq_k. The last sequence obtained, Seq_n, is the desired deduction Seq'. ■

Remarks

1 In the proof of Ded, the length of the final deduction Seq' is about three times that of the initial one. This gives a measure of the benefit resulting from applying Ded, that is, from *not* computing the deduction Seq' explicitly.

2 In the proof of the theorem, the three cases are not exclusive. For instance, we might have $\gamma = \alpha_k \in \Lambda \cup \Gamma$. If there is a tie, we may arbitrarily choose any allowed step. We say that the construction of Seq' we have described is a *nondeterministic* algorithm. ■

The *inverse implication* of Ded is also true, but much easier to prove.

Property 8.2B.2

Let Γ, α, γ be any set of wffs.

$$\text{If} \quad \Gamma \vdash \text{`}(\gamma \Rightarrow \alpha)\text{'} \quad \text{then} \quad \Gamma, \gamma \vdash \alpha$$ ■

Proof If $\Gamma \vdash$ '$(\gamma \Rightarrow \alpha)$' then $\Gamma, \gamma \vdash \{\gamma, \text{`}(\gamma \Rightarrow \alpha)\text{'}\}$. Therefore, we obtain $\Gamma, \gamma \vdash \alpha$ by MP. ■

This property is so close to MP that we shall often refer to it not directly but as 'MP'.

From Ded and Trans or rule T, we can derive various corollaries often used in proofs. Here are some important examples:

Corollary 8.2B.3 (rule of cases)
Let Γ, α, β, γ be any set of wffs satisfying the following conditions:

(1) $\Gamma \vdash \alpha \vee \beta$
(2) $\Gamma, \alpha \vdash \gamma$
(3) $\Gamma, \beta \vdash \gamma$

Then

$$\Gamma \vdash \gamma$$ ■

Proof By Ded, conditions (1)–(3) imply

$$\Gamma \vdash \Theta =_{\text{d}} \{\text{`}(\alpha \vee \beta)\text{'}, \text{`}(\alpha \Rightarrow \gamma)\text{'}, \text{`}(\beta \Rightarrow \gamma)\text{'}\}$$

Moreover, Θ tautologically implies γ. The result follows by rule T. ■

Note that the cases in Corollary 8.2B.3 are *nonexclusive*, as '$\vee$' is *inclusive*.

The next property involves the notion of contradiction. A *contradiction* is a wff α whose negation '$(\neg \alpha)$' is a tautology; thus, $\boldsymbol{M}(\alpha)$ = false in all interpretations. We use the symbol F to represent any contradiction, for example '$(\beta \wedge (\neg \beta))$' for any wff β. F is *a partly determined wff*; it is not the same as the *semantic value* false, although the two are related.

Corollary 8.2B.4 (contradiction, RAA)
Let Γ, α be any set of wffs such that

$$\Gamma, \text{`}(\neg \alpha)\text{'} \vdash F$$

Then

$$\Gamma \vdash \alpha$$ ■

Proof By Ded, $\Gamma \vdash$ '$((\neg \alpha) \Rightarrow F)$'. Moreover, '$((\neg \alpha) \Rightarrow F)$' tautologically implies α. Therefore, $\Gamma \vdash \alpha$ by rule T. ■

This property is also called *indirect proof* or *reductio ad absurdum* (*RAA*). It is frequently used in proofs.

Corollary 8.2B.5 (contraposition′)

Let Γ, α be any set of wffs.

Variant 1 (a) $\Gamma, \alpha \vdash \beta$ iff (b) $\Gamma, (\neg\ \beta) \vdash (\neg\ \alpha)$

Variant 2 (a) $\Gamma, (\neg\ \alpha) \vdash \beta$ iff (b) $\Gamma, (\neg\ \beta) \vdash \alpha$ ■

Proof of variant 1 We derive (a) from (b) and vice versa by a chain of double implications. The justification of each step is shown to its right.

$\Gamma, \alpha \vdash \beta$

iff [Ded, Property **8**.2B.2]

$\Gamma \vdash \alpha \Rightarrow \beta$

iff [T: contraposition (variant 1)]

$\Gamma \vdash (\neg\ \beta) \Rightarrow (\neg\ \alpha)$

iff [Property **8**.2B.2, Ded]

$\Gamma, (\neg\ \beta) \vdash (\neg\ \alpha)$

The proof of variant 2 is similar. ■

Note This metatheorem must be distinguished from the *tautology* of the same name – see Section **6**.4A; the latter is a wff used in the proof of the former.

■

8.2C Generalization theorem

Recall that for any wff α, a generalization of α is obtained by prefixing it with the quantifier '$\forall \boldsymbol{x}$', where $\boldsymbol{x}$ is any variable. Note that this operation may be repeated any number of times. Thus, successive generalizations of α are '$\forall \boldsymbol{x}_1\ \alpha$', '$\forall \boldsymbol{x}_2\ \forall \boldsymbol{x}_1\ \alpha$', '$\forall \boldsymbol{x}_3\ \forall \boldsymbol{x}_2\ \forall \boldsymbol{x}_1\ \alpha$', ..., where each $\boldsymbol{x}_i$ is *any* variable, not necessarily distinct from other variables $\boldsymbol{x}_j$.

As we have seen, any generalization of any $\alpha : \Lambda$ is also contained in Λ by rule (5). For other wffs α, we now restate the basic result:

Theorem 8.2C.1 (generalization theorem, Gen)

For any set Γ, α of wffs and any variable $\boldsymbol{x}$, if $\Gamma \vdash \alpha$ and $\boldsymbol{x}$ does not occur free in any member of Γ, then

$$\Gamma \vdash \quad \forall \boldsymbol{x}\ \alpha$$ ■

Proof Assume $\Gamma \vdash \alpha$. There exists a deduction

$$Seq =_{\mathrm{d}} (\alpha_1, \alpha_2, \ldots, \alpha_n =_{\mathrm{d}} \alpha)$$

The proof is by induction on the length n of *Seq*, and has a structure similar to that of Ded. In n steps, we transform *Seq* into a new deduction *Seq′* of '$\forall \boldsymbol{x}\ \alpha$' from Γ.

For $k =_d 1, 2, \ldots, n$, let Seq_{k-1} be the sequence obtained after $k-1$ steps. It is of the form

$$Seq_{k-1} =_d (\beta_1, \beta_2, \ldots, \beta_m, \alpha_k, \alpha_{k+1}, \ldots, \alpha_n = \alpha)$$

with $Seq_0 = Seq$. The induction hypothesis is in two parts:

(1) If $m \geqslant 1$, then $(\beta_1, \beta_2, \ldots, \beta_m)$ is a deduction of β_m from Γ.

(2) For any $j < k$, the wff '$\forall \boldsymbol{x}\, \alpha_j$' $\in (\beta_1, \beta_2, \ldots, \beta_m)$.

This condition is vacuously satisfied by Seq_0. For any $k \geqslant 1$, Seq_k is *generally not* a deduction of α from Γ.

The kth step consists of replacing α_k by *one or three* new wffs in Seq_{k-1}, depending on the justification of α_k in *Seq*. One of three nonexclusive cases may arise:

Case 1 $\alpha_k \in \Lambda$. In this case, replace α_k by $\beta_{m+1} =_d$ '$\forall \boldsymbol{x}\, \alpha_k$'. The new wff is a member of Λ by rule (5) of Definition **8**.1C.1.

Case 2 $\alpha_k \in \Gamma$. In this case, replace α_k by the three wffs

$$\begin{aligned} \beta_{m+1} &=_d \alpha_k \\ \beta_{m+2} &=_d (\alpha_k \Rightarrow \forall \boldsymbol{x}\, \alpha_k) \\ \beta_{m+3} &=_d \forall \boldsymbol{x}\, \alpha_k \end{aligned}$$

The first wff is justified as in the original deduction. The second is a member of Λ by rule (3b), as $\boldsymbol{x}$ does not occur free in any member of Γ. The third is obtained by MP from its predecessors.

Case 3 $\alpha_k \notin \Lambda \cup \Gamma$. In this case, α_k is obtained by MP from two predecessors α_i and $\alpha_j =_d$ '$(\alpha_i \Rightarrow \alpha_k)$' in *Seq*. At step k, by the induction hypothesis, α_k is preceded in Seq_{k-1} by '$\forall \boldsymbol{x}\, \alpha_i$' and '$\forall \boldsymbol{x}\, \alpha_j$' $=$ '$\forall \boldsymbol{x}\, (\alpha_i \Rightarrow \alpha_k)$'. Then, replace α_k by the three wffs

$$\begin{aligned} \beta_{m+1} &=_d [\forall \boldsymbol{x}\, (\alpha_i \Rightarrow \alpha_k) \Rightarrow (\forall \boldsymbol{x}\, \alpha_i \Rightarrow \forall \boldsymbol{x}\, \alpha_k)] \\ \beta_{m+2} &=_d (\forall \boldsymbol{x}\, \alpha_i \Rightarrow \forall \boldsymbol{x}\, \alpha_k) \\ \beta_{m+3} &=_d \forall \boldsymbol{x}\, \alpha_k \end{aligned}$$

β_{m+1} is a member of Λ by rule (3a). β_{m+2} is obtained by MP applied to '$\forall \boldsymbol{x}\, (\alpha_i \Rightarrow \alpha_k)$' and β_{m+1}, while β_{m+3} results from applying MP to '$\forall \boldsymbol{x}\, \alpha_i$' and β_{m+2}.

Clearly, the induction hypothesis holds for the new sequence Seq_k in all three cases. The last sequence obtained, Seq_n, is the desired deduction Seq' of '$\forall \boldsymbol{x}\, \alpha_n$' from Γ. ■

Remark

In this proof, cases 1 and 2 are nonexclusive. As in the case of Ded, this does not matter. If both cases obtain, we may choose either of the corresponding steps arbitrarily. ■

Corollary 8.2C.2

For any variable $\boldsymbol{x}$ and any valid wff α,

$$\vdash \alpha \quad \text{implies} \quad \vdash \forall \boldsymbol{x}\, \alpha.$$ ■

Proof Put $\Gamma =_{\rm d} \varnothing$ in Theorem 8.2C.1. It is vacuously true that $\boldsymbol{x}$ does not occur free in any member of Γ. ■

This corollary is only of theoretical interest as, if α is valid, then so is '$\forall \boldsymbol{x}\, \alpha$', and by the completeness theorem every valid wff is a theorem derived from $\varnothing$. However, Corollary 8.2C.2 mirrors the fact that generalization preserves validity, at the symbolic level.

EXERCISES

8.2.1 The notation we use to describe a first-order language L and its properties is a *metalanguage* with respect to L. By way of metalanguage, we may use any notation we like as long as it is clearly distinct from L; in particular, we may use logic and set theory themselves. (We have already done so in small ways: for example, when writing '$\alpha =$ '$\forall \boldsymbol{x}\, \beta$'' or '$\alpha \in \Lambda$'.)

(a) Let T_1 be the set of all tautologies of the form $\gamma =_{\rm d}$ '$(\alpha \Leftrightarrow \beta) \Rightarrow (\alpha \Rightarrow \beta)$'. Express T_1 as an abstraction in the notation of set theory. (Recall that for any language L the set of wffs is denoted by *Wffs*.)
(b) Let T_2 be the set of all tautologies of the form $\gamma =_{\rm d}$ '$(\alpha \Leftrightarrow \beta) \Rightarrow (\beta \Rightarrow \alpha)$'. Express T_2 in set-theoretical notation.
(c) Express $T_3 =_{\rm d} T_1 \cup T_2$ as an abstraction without referring to T_1 and T_2.

8.2.2 Let $\alpha =_{\rm d}$ '$(\gamma \Rightarrow (\beta \Rightarrow \delta))$' where β, γ and δ are any wffs, and let $\Gamma =_{\rm d} \{\alpha, \beta\}$. The following list is a deduction D of δ from Γ, γ.

.1	$\Gamma \quad \vdash (\gamma \Rightarrow (\beta \Rightarrow \delta))$
.2	$\Gamma, \gamma \vdash \gamma$
.3	$\Gamma, \gamma \vdash (\beta \Rightarrow \delta)$
.4	$\Gamma \quad \vdash \beta$
.5	$\Gamma, \gamma \vdash \delta$

Copy D and annotate each member φ with a brief but precise justification: for example, '[$\varphi \in \Gamma$]', or '[MP: $.i$, $.j$]' to indicate that φ results from applying MP to members in position $.i$ and $.j$ in D. These conventions are elaborated into a systematic proof format in the next section. Note that in a justification of the form '[MP: $.i$, $.j$]' of any wff β' from a set $\{\alpha', `(\alpha' \Rightarrow \beta')'\}$, $.i$ should be the position of α' and $.j$ that of '$(\alpha' \Rightarrow \beta')$' in D.

8.2.3 In FDS, every tautology α is included in the set Λ of logical axioms, that is, taken as a 'starting-point' in any deduction, and so, for any set Γ of wffs, $\Gamma \vdash \alpha$ is immediate. In order to study FDS, it is also instructive to take as starting-points only members of some subset T of tautologies and see how other tautologies may be derived from T by repeated application of MP.

(a) Let T_1 be as defined in Exercise **8**.2.1. Write down six instances of T_1 in a language L with two predicate symbols P (unary) and Q (binary) and one unary function symbol f.

(b) Let $\delta =_{\text{d}}$ '$(P\,x \Leftrightarrow \neg\neg\, P\,x)$' and $T_4 =_{\text{d}} T_1 \cup \{\delta\}$. Construct a three-member deduction D for $\delta' =_{\text{d}}$ '$(P\,x \Rightarrow \neg\neg P\,x)$' from T_4. Here, by *deduction from a set* T is meant a sequence of wffs $D =_{\text{d}} (\alpha_1, \ldots, \alpha_n)$ such that each α_k is either in T or is obtained by MP from two predecessors in D.

(c) Repeat (b) with $\delta =_{\text{d}}$ '$((\neg\, Qxy \vee Pfz) \Leftrightarrow (Qxy \Rightarrow Pfz))$'.

(d) Repeat (b) with $\delta =_{\text{d}}$ '$((\neg\, \alpha' \vee \beta') \Leftrightarrow (\alpha' \Rightarrow \beta'))$'. Here we leave the wff variables α' and β' uninstantiated. The result may be regarded as a *deduction schema*, of which (c) is an instance.

8.2.4 Let α be any wff. The following is a deduction of '$\alpha \vee \neg\, \alpha$' from four other tautologies, those indicated by the label '[LA1]' (for 'logical axioms in group 1').

.1	$\vdash (\alpha \vee \alpha) \Rightarrow \alpha$	[LA1]
.2	$\vdash [(\alpha \vee \alpha) \Rightarrow \alpha] \Rightarrow [(\neg\, \alpha \vee (\alpha \vee \alpha)) \Rightarrow (\alpha \vee \neg\, \alpha)]$	[LA1]
.3	$\vdash (\neg\, \alpha \vee (\alpha \vee \alpha)) \Rightarrow (\alpha \vee \neg\, \alpha)$	[...]
.4	$\vdash (\alpha \Rightarrow (\alpha \vee \alpha)) \Rightarrow (\neg\, \alpha \vee (\alpha \vee \alpha))$	[LA1]
.5	$\vdash \alpha \Rightarrow (\alpha \vee \alpha)$	[LA1]
.6	$\vdash \neg\, \alpha \vee (\alpha \vee \alpha)$	[...]
.7	$\vdash \alpha \vee \neg\, \alpha$	[...]

(a) Copy this deduction and add the missing justifications of the form '[MP: $.i$, $.j$]', as in Exercise **8**.2.2.

(b) Verify that .2, .5 and .7 are indeed tautologies, using the truth table method.

8.2.5 Let Γ, α, β be any set of wffs. Prove that if $\Gamma \vdash \alpha$ and $\Gamma \vdash \beta$ then $\Gamma \vdash$ '$(\alpha \wedge \beta)$', (a) without using Trans or rule T and (b) using rule T.

8.2.6 Let Γ, α, β be as in Exercise **8**.2.5. Prove that if $\Gamma \vdash$ '$(\alpha \Leftrightarrow \beta)$' then $\Gamma \vdash$ '$(\alpha \Rightarrow \beta)$' and $\Gamma \vdash$ '$(\beta \Rightarrow \alpha)$', (a) without using Trans or rule T and (b) using rule T.

8.2.7 Prove the converse of Exercise **8**.2.6: If $\Gamma \vdash$ '$(\alpha \Rightarrow \beta)$' and $\Gamma \vdash$ '$(\beta \Rightarrow \alpha)$' then $\Gamma \vdash$ '$(\alpha \Leftrightarrow \beta)$', (a) without using Trans or rule T and (b) using rule T.

8.2.8* Let D be the deduction of δ from Γ, γ given in Exercise **8**.2.2. By Ded, we may conclude that $\Gamma \vdash$ '$\gamma \Rightarrow \delta$'. Transform D into a deduction D' of '$\gamma \Rightarrow \delta$' from Γ, as an instantiation of the proof of Ded. Note that the final sequence, D', has 13 members. To avoid repetitions, write each intermediate sequence Seq_k from its new elements onward.

8.2.9 Let P be a unary predicate symbol and f a unary function symbol.

(a) Prove

$$\forall x\ P\ x \vdash P\ f\ y$$

by constructing a three-step deduction for '$P\ f\ y$' from $\Gamma =_{\mathrm{d}} \{$'$\forall x\ P\ x$'$\}$. This requires a logical axiom generated by rule (2) of Definition **8**.1C.1, to substitute '$f\ y$' for x in '$P\ x$'.

(b) Prove

$$\forall x\ P\ x \vdash P\ x$$

as in (a). This is to illustrate that x may be substituted for itself in $P\ x$.

(c) Prove

$$\forall x\ P\ x \vdash \forall y\ P\ f\ y$$

This requires extending (a) by one step using Gen.

(d) Prove

$$\vdash \forall x\ P\ x \Rightarrow \forall y\ P\ f\ y$$

This requires extending (c) by one step using Ded.

8.2.10 (a) Prove that for any wff α and any variable $\boldsymbol{x}$,

$$\forall \boldsymbol{x}\ \alpha \vdash \alpha$$

as in Exercise **8**.2.9(b). This construction may be regarded as a deduction schema of which the deduction of Exercise **8**.2.9(b) is an instance. The main purpose of such a deduction is to eliminate the quantifier '$\forall \boldsymbol{x}$' in '$\forall \boldsymbol{x}\ \alpha$' in order to enable the application of other rules, for example rule T, to α or part of it.

(b) Indicate precisely which substitution is performed and which substitutability condition must be satisfied in (a), and show that this condition is indeed satisfied.

8.2.11 (a) Prove that for any unary function symbol $\boldsymbol{f}$,

$$\forall x\,(\neg\ Eq\ xy \Rightarrow \neg\ Eq\,\boldsymbol{f}\,x\,\boldsymbol{f}\,y) \vdash \forall x\,(Eq\,\boldsymbol{f}\,x\,\boldsymbol{f}\,y \Rightarrow Eq\ xy)$$

using Exercise 8.2.9(b) as a guide. This requires the application of rule T at the appropriate stage, followed by the reintroduction of '$\forall x$' using Gen. To simplify the formal deduction use $\alpha =_d$ '$Eq\,xy$' and $\beta =_d$ '$Eq\,f\,x\,f\,y$' as abbreviations.

(b) Extend (a) to a proof of

$$\vdash \quad \forall x\,(\neg\, Eq\,xy \Rightarrow \neg\, Eq\,f\,x\,f\,y) \Rightarrow \forall x\,(Eq\,f\,x\,f\,y \Rightarrow Eq\,xy)$$

using Ded.

(c) Note that the special logical axioms of *Eq* (defined by rule (4) of Definition 8.1C.1) are *not* involved here. Therefore, verify that the above deductions hold for any binary predicate symbol ***P*** used instead of '*Eq*'.

8.2.12 Repeat Exercise 8.2.11(a) and (b) for

$$\vdash \quad \forall y\,\forall x\,(\neg\, Eq\,xy \Rightarrow \neg\, Eq\,fx\,fy) \Rightarrow \forall y\,\forall x\,(Eq\,fx\,fy \Rightarrow Eq\,xy)$$

8.2.13 Repeat Exercise 8.2.11(a) and (b) for

$$\vdash \quad \forall y\,\forall x\,(\neg\, Eq\,xy \Rightarrow \neg\, Eq\,f\,x\,f\,y) \Leftrightarrow \forall y\,\forall x\,(Eq\,f\,x\,f\,y \Rightarrow Eq\,xy)$$

This final result formalizes the equivalence between the two definitions of an injective function given in Section 3.3C.

8.2.14* Transform the deduction of Exercise 8.2.9(a) into a deduction of '$\forall y\, P\,f\,y$' from $\Gamma =_d \{$'$\forall x\, P\,x$'$\}$ without using Gen as a derived inference rule. This transformation is an instantiation of the proof of Gen.

8.3 Natural deduction and further metatheorems

We now return to a fundamental question of this book: what is the nature of proof, or, to emphasize the interplay between specification and analysis, establishment?

We now have a precise definition of a proof: a formal deduction of a wff α from a set Γ of axioms, obtained by the purely symbolic operations described in Section 8.1. However, does this give us a *practical* reasoning method which can be used on the scale of the problems that arise in practice? The answer is still *no*, at least *not directly*.

Recall that in mathematics there are not one but two distinct definitions of a proof. In one sense, a proof is a formal deduction of the type described in Section 8.1; that is, it is completely formal. In the other, more traditional sense, a proof is just an argument formulated in such way as to convince a competent reader of the truth of some statement, and to do so *compellingly*. In general, such proofs are only *semiformal.*

The advantages of totally formal proofs are their absolute accuracy and the simplicity and transparency of each of their steps. However, for all but trivial theorems, formal deductions tend to be very, if not extremely lengthy, and consequently impractical. The advantage of semiformal proofs is that by leaving out a myriad of details they are natural, meaningful and practical. Their disadvantage, of course, is that they offer no absolute guarantee of validity; they can only command a high degree of confidence. Even so, they 'work': most of mathematics is expressed in this form, with the tremendous efficiency which has characterized this discipline for millennia.

Is it possible to reconcile these two types of proof, or at least to bring them closer together? The answer is *yes*: we can develop proof methods which combine the rigour of formal deductions with the naturalness, practicality and scalability of semiformal proofs. The key to this enterprise is given by the metatheorems about formal deductions.

What is the common feature of metatheorems? Essentially, a metatheorem asserts *the existence* of a certain formal deduction of some wff α from some set Γ of axioms. Consequently, a metatheorem may be used as a (derived) inference rule to demonstrate $\Gamma \vdash \alpha$. There is no real need to exhibit the formal deduction of α explicitly: provided the conditions and conclusion of the metatheorem are formally expressed, the inference is just as rigorous as the formal deduction that is asserted to exist. (For instance, the various metatheorems given so far, such as rule T, Ded, Gen, and so on clearly meet this requirement: they are entirely formal.)

This observation may be linked to the concept of semiformal proof. The criterion used so far in the definition of a semiformal proof is purely psychological, but we may now characterize such a proof more objectively. Why should a competent mathematician regard a semiformal proof as compelling? The safest reason must be that he or she can clearly see *how the proof can be turned into a completely formal deduction.* Thus, we may define a semiformal proof of an assertion $\Gamma \vdash \alpha$ as *a demonstration that there exists a formal deduction of* α *from* Γ. Now such a demonstration is precisely the type of information provided by metatheorems.

The aim of this section is to present and illustrate a proof method based on these observations. In essence, it consists of demonstrating statements of the form $\Gamma \vdash \alpha$ using the metatheorems established so far, as well as any additional ones to be derived. Thus, the method may be described as both formal and natural: in most respects it is as formal as the deductions defined in Section **8**.1, but its systematic reliance on metatheorems brings it close to the semiformal arguments of mathematical tradition. Note that the method is not fundamentally different from the proofs given so far. Its distinctive feature is a more *systematic format*.

First, we describe the format of the method in Section **8**.3A. Then in the remaining sections, we introduce a number of further metatheorems and prove them with the method. These results are important in their own right, though perhaps not as fundamental as rule T, Ded and Gen. However, the main reason for introducing and proving these additional theorems is to illustrate the proof method. A careful study of the proofs developed is very instructive. It gives insights into the nature of completely formal proofs as well as the power of metatheorems in reducing the gap between natural proofs and formal deductions.

8.3A Proof format

Recall that in general a proof consists of showing that given some set Γ of wffs taken as axioms or assumptions, and some wff α, $\Gamma \vdash \alpha$; that is, there exists a (formal) deduction of α from Γ. This may be done either by producing a deduction explicitly or by demonstrating by other means that such a deduction exists.

Proof lines

Our method constructs a proof as a collection of *proof lines*. Each proof line is approximately a line of text. It contains (a) a unique name or reference number, (b) an assertion of the form $\Gamma \vdash \alpha$ and (c) a justification of this assertion. It is written in the following format:

Reference $\Gamma \vdash \alpha$ [*Justification*]

Very occasionally the assertion is more general: for example, it may be of the form $\Gamma \vdash \Theta$. Recall that $\Gamma \vdash \Theta$ means $\Gamma \vdash \alpha$ for each $\alpha : \Theta$.

The justification is crucial. It indicates exactly how to arrive at the assertion $\Gamma \vdash \alpha$ in one or a few elementary steps, either from logical axioms, or from members of Γ, or from similar assertions in other proof lines. By 'elementary step' is meant either a hint showing that $\alpha \in \Lambda \cup \Gamma$ or the application of a single inference rule. The latter is either MP or a previously proven metatheorem used as a derived inference rule.

The simplest justification of $\Gamma \vdash \alpha$ is that α is either a logical axiom or a member of Γ. Definition **8**.1C.1 specifies four main groups of logical axioms, each corresponding to one of the rules (1) to (4). These groups are referred to as LA1, LA2, LA3 and LA4 respectively. (Note that they are not necessarily disjoint.) Subgroups are named by adding the suffix (a) or (b) as in the corresponding rule. Thus if α is a logical axiom, the justification is given by the name of the group to which it belongs; for example, [LA1] to state that α is a tautology. If an axiom in LA2 is used, a note may be added in the justification to demonstrate that the substitutability condition is satisfied. If α is a member of Γ, the justification is a hint to that effect, for example, 'assumption', or a more detailed explanation if necessary.

For each application of a certain inference rule, the justification has a form determined by this rule. For MP, T, Ded and Gen, this is as follows. The application of MP as the last step in a proof of an assertion $\Gamma \vdash \beta$ requires two other similar statements: $\Gamma \vdash \alpha$ and $\Gamma \vdash$ '$(\alpha \Rightarrow \beta)$'. Thus in this case the justification for $\Gamma \vdash \beta$ has the form

[MP: Ref_1, Ref_2]

where Ref_1 and Ref_2 are references to $\Gamma \vdash \alpha$ and $\Gamma \vdash$ '$(\alpha \Rightarrow \beta)$' respectively, always in this order. Usually the reference Ref_1 to $\Gamma \vdash \alpha$ is the name or number of a proof line containing this statement. In some cases, Ref_1 is a name for α itself if this has been shown to be a member of $\Lambda \cup \Gamma$. Alternatively, if α is a logical axiom, Ref_1 may indicate the group of logical axioms to which α belongs. Similar rules hold for Ref_2.

In some cases, Ref_1 may refer to a proof line asserting $\Gamma' \vdash \alpha$, where Γ' is a subset of Γ. This is correct, by expandability of assumptions (Property **8**.2A.1). The same holds for Ref_2.

In order to apply rule T to prove $\Gamma \vdash \alpha$ we need references to q statements $\Gamma \vdash \theta_i$, $i =_d 1, \ldots, q$, where $q \geqslant 1$ and $\{\theta_i | i =_d 1, \ldots, q\}$ tautologically implies α. (See Corollary **8**.2A.4.) Thus in this case, the justification is of the form

[T: Ref_1, Ref_2, $\ldots$, Ref_q]

where each Ref_i is described as for MP. It is then for the reader to prove that $\{\theta_i | i =_d 1, \ldots, q\}$ tautologically implies α, using the truth table method, or the basic tautologies and other results of Section **6**.4, for instance.

In order to justify an assertion $\Gamma \vdash$ '$(\alpha \Rightarrow \beta)$' by Ded, only one reference is needed, namely to $\Gamma, \alpha \vdash \beta$. Therefore the justification in this case is of the form

[Ded: Ref]

Similarly, an assertion $\Gamma \vdash$ '$\forall \boldsymbol{x}\, \alpha$' justified by Gen requires only one reference, to $\Gamma \vdash \alpha$. However, in this case we must also establish that $\boldsymbol{x}$ does not occur free in any wff in Γ. A brief demonstration of this fact may be included in the justification if necessary. Thus, the form of the justification in this case is

[Gen: Ref (optionally, why $\boldsymbol{x}$ is not free in Γ)]

Justifications based on other metatheorems will be formed in a similar way.

In some cases, we apply several elementary proof steps simultaneously. The successive justifications are separated by semicolons. For instance,

[Ded: Ref; Gen]

justifies the derivation of $\Gamma \vdash$ '$\forall \boldsymbol{x}\,(\alpha \Rightarrow \beta)$' directly from $\Gamma, \alpha \vdash \beta$ referred to by *Ref*. If the same inference rule R is applied n times in succession, we may indicate this by writing R^n. For instance, if *Ref* refers to $\Gamma \vdash \alpha$,

[Gen^2: *Ref* (optionally, why $\boldsymbol{x}$ and $\boldsymbol{y}$ are not free in Γ)]

may be used to derive $\Gamma \vdash \forall \boldsymbol{x}\, \forall \boldsymbol{y}\, \alpha$ in one step from $\Gamma \vdash \alpha$.

Proof units

A *proof unit* is a set of proof lines demonstrating a statement $\Gamma \vdash \alpha$, where α is an important theorem or intermediate result (lemma). In general, proofs are organized as hierarchies of proof units. An *elementary* proof unit usually has the form of a list of proof lines referenced sequentially by .1, .2, and so on.

Here is an example illustrating two related elementary proof units. They demonstrate two basic properties of the equality predicate *Eq* resulting from the logical axioms in group LA4. (The full treatment of *Eq* is given in Section **8**.3E.) Recall that if $\Gamma =_{\mathrm{d}} \varnothing$, in order to assert that $\Gamma \vdash \alpha$ we simply write $\vdash \alpha$.

Property X

For any variables $\boldsymbol{x}$ and $\boldsymbol{y}$,

$$\vdash \forall \boldsymbol{x}\, \forall \boldsymbol{y} \cdot Eq\ \boldsymbol{x}\ \boldsymbol{y} \Rightarrow Eq\ \boldsymbol{y}\ \boldsymbol{x}$$ ■

Proof

.1	$\vdash Eq\ \boldsymbol{x}\ \boldsymbol{x}$	[LA4(a)]
.2	$\vdash Eq\ \boldsymbol{x}\ \boldsymbol{y} \Rightarrow (Eq\ \boldsymbol{x}\ \boldsymbol{x} \Rightarrow Eq\ \boldsymbol{y}\ \boldsymbol{x})$	[LA4(b)]
.3	$\vdash Eq\ \boldsymbol{x}\ \boldsymbol{y} \Rightarrow Eq\ \boldsymbol{y}\ \boldsymbol{x}$	[T: .1, .2]
.4	$\vdash \forall \boldsymbol{x}\, \forall \boldsymbol{y} \cdot Eq\ \boldsymbol{x}\ \boldsymbol{y} \Rightarrow Eq\ \boldsymbol{y}\ \boldsymbol{x}$	[Gen^2: .3]

Property Y

For any variables $\boldsymbol{x}$, $\boldsymbol{y}$ and $\boldsymbol{z}$,

$$\vdash \forall \boldsymbol{x}\, \forall \boldsymbol{y}\, \forall \boldsymbol{z} \cdot Eq\ \boldsymbol{x}\ \boldsymbol{y} \Rightarrow (Eq\ \boldsymbol{y}\ \boldsymbol{z} \Rightarrow Eq\ \boldsymbol{x}\ \boldsymbol{z})$$ ■

Proof

.1	$\vdash Eq\ \boldsymbol{x}\ \boldsymbol{y} \Rightarrow Eq\ \boldsymbol{y}\ \boldsymbol{x}$	[Prop. X.3]
.2	$\vdash Eq\ \boldsymbol{y}\ \boldsymbol{x} \Rightarrow (Eq\ \boldsymbol{y}\ \boldsymbol{z} \Rightarrow Eq\ \boldsymbol{x}\ \boldsymbol{z})$	[LA4(b)]
.3	$\vdash Eq\ \boldsymbol{x}\ \boldsymbol{y} \Rightarrow (Eq\ \boldsymbol{y}\ \boldsymbol{z} \Rightarrow Eq\ \boldsymbol{x}\ \boldsymbol{z})$	[T: .1, .2]
.4	$\vdash \forall \boldsymbol{x}\, \forall \boldsymbol{y}\, \forall \boldsymbol{z} \cdot Eq\ \boldsymbol{x}\ \boldsymbol{y} \Rightarrow (Eq\ \boldsymbol{y}\ \boldsymbol{z} \Rightarrow Eq\ \boldsymbol{x}\ \boldsymbol{z})$	[Gen^3: .3]

Note that in any justification, a reference *.i* obviously refers to the proof line *.i* of the *current* elementary proof unit (the one in which the justification occurs). In order to refer to a property given outside the current elementary proof unit, we use the full name of the property. To refer to a proof line .i occurring in the elementary proof unit of such an external property, we use the name of the property suffixed with '.i'. An example is the justification of line .1 in the proof of Property Y, namely [Prop. X.3].

Syntactic variables and their scope

In many cases, a proof is in fact a *proof schema* (or family of proofs), because it involves names denoting *variable symbolic expressions.* Examples are α, β, and so on for wffs, and τ and so on for terms. In any context, α may represent either a specified wff in the language L, or any one of a specified set of wffs. Likewise, τ may be either a specified term, or it may stand for any one of a given set of terms. Such names are sometimes called *syntactic variables.* Thus, the assertion

$$\vdash \alpha \Rightarrow \alpha$$

in a context in which α does not denote a fixed wff means that there is a deduction of '$\alpha \Rightarrow \alpha$' from the logical axioms for *every* wff obtained by instantiating α. Likewise, when we explicitly state that $\boldsymbol{x}$ (for instance) is *any* variable of L, we mean that in the current context the symbol $\boldsymbol{x}$ stands for *any* variable in L: $x, x_1, x_2, \ldots, y, y_1, \ldots, z, z_1, \ldots$.

So far, our use of syntactic variables has been entirely natural and straightforward. However, when developing proofs on a large scale, special care must be taken to avoid errors. What we must do is ensure that, for any occurrence of a syntactic variable, its *scope* is well defined. *The scope of a name is the area of text in which all the occurrences of the name have the same meaning.* In general this is the context (section or categorized text unit such as definition, example, theorem, and so on) in which the name is introduced. It is usually clearly indicated and simple to determine as text units are normally not nested at this level. Consequently, we shall give only one precise rule of scope for syntactic variables: If a proof unit of a metatheorem is *elementary* then the scope of any name occurring in this proof always includes at least the metatheorem and the whole of the proof unit.

For example, in Properties X and Y above, every occurrence of the symbol $\boldsymbol{x}$ within the proof of X denotes the same variable of L. Likewise, every occurrence of $\boldsymbol{x}$ within the proof of Y denotes the same variable of L. However, the variable represented by $\boldsymbol{x}$ in the proof of X need not be the same as the variable represented by $\boldsymbol{x}$ in the proof of Y. That is, the instantiations of $\boldsymbol{x}$ in the first proof are independent of the instantiations of $\boldsymbol{x}$ in the second.

Difficulties may arise when a reference in a proof unit is made to another proof unit, or to a line in such an external unit. In this case, care must be taken in interpreting the external proof line referred to. An example is the reference within the proof unit of Property Y (line Y.1) to line X.3 of Property X above. Line X.3 contains two occurrences of the symbol $\boldsymbol{x}$. The scope of these occurrences is always the proof of Property X, *not* that of Property Y; the fact that line X.3 is referred to within the proof of Y does *not* alter this fact!

Thus in general we must check that any reference to an external proof line is correct given the definition of scope. In this particular case, the argument is as follows. From the statement of Property X, line X.3 asserts that *for any* variables $\boldsymbol{x}$ and $\boldsymbol{y}$, $\vdash$ '$Eq\ \boldsymbol{x}\ \boldsymbol{y} \Rightarrow Eq\ \boldsymbol{y}\ \boldsymbol{x}$'. Therefore, this assertion may be used in *any* context, that is, whatever specific variables of L are represented by $\boldsymbol{x}$ and $\boldsymbol{y}$ where it is invoked. This is so in particular within line Y.1, so the justification of this line is correct. The situation would have been different if (for any reason) we had stated, for example 'for any *distinct* variables $\boldsymbol{x}$ and $\boldsymbol{y}$' in Property X but *not* in Property Y. Had we done so, the reference to line X.3 as justification of line Y.1 would have been incorrect.

Note that the scoping of syntactic variables must be carefully distinguished from that of the variables of L itself within a wff. The latter is governed by the rules determining free and bound occurrences of variables in wffs. It is more complex as wffs, hence scopes, may be nested within one another. The reader should compare these two different problems.

Finding proofs

The rules established above define only a proof *format*. They do not indicate what concrete steps to take in order to demonstrate an assertion $\Gamma \vdash \alpha$ in practice, when this is believed to be true. This question is discussed in Enderton (1972) as the matter of devising a *proof strategy*; see also Andrews (1986). The problem is perhaps better described as that of devising general *heuristic rules* to guide the search for a proof.

Enderton outlines essentially two ways of finding a proof of an assertion $\Gamma \vdash \alpha$. The first is to develop a semiformal proof in natural language, based on intuitive grounds, and then to express this proof formally. The second is to derive a proof by applying a number of heuristic symbolic manipulation rules to the formulas involved. Both methods are to be carried out with the aid of metatheorems, of course.

Here it must be pointed out that, given Γ on the one hand and α on the other, there are two general approaches to proving $\Gamma \vdash \alpha$, formally or informally. One is to develop a deduction 'from left to right', starting with wffs in Γ. Each extension of the deduction leads to a new theorem which, it is hoped, is closer to the final target α, and the construction terminates when α is reached. This is the *forward* method of proof construction.

The alternative approach is to take α as a starting point, and to develop a deduction of α 'from right to left'. At any stage the output of the process is a deduction of α from some set Θ of intermediate wffs. The members of Θ which are not in $\Lambda \cup \Gamma$ may be regarded as provisional assumptions, to be deduced in turn from Γ. The process terminates when all the 'starting' wffs of the current deduction are members of $\Lambda \cup \Gamma$.

This second method is called *backward* proof construction. It is often used in practice, partly because intermediate proof goals may be worked out from the structure of the final target α by systematic symbol manipulation rules. The heuristic deduction rules given in Enderton (1972) are of this type. Andrews

(1986) gives similar rules. They are not repeated here as they closely follow the fundamental metatheorems on which they are based, and as we do not use them explicitly in subsequent developments.

Final remarks

1 The process of constructing a proof must be distinguished from the final presentation of the proof as a static textual object. The *development* of a proof often involves a combination of more elementary proofs, some worked out forward and some backward. An elementary proof unit is usually sequenced in the forward direction, which is the natural order of deduction, whether it has been developed in this direction or not.

As for the order in which proof units are presented, this varies. Sometimes it may be convenient to proceed 'from the bottom up', that is, to prove a number of elementary results first, before major results, if the former are to be used in different applications. In contrast, consider the proof of a single major theorem which is such that the demonstration may be naturally broken down into a hierarchy of more elementary results together with their own proofs. If the intermediate results have no other applications, then it is usually appropriate to follow a 'top-down' order of presentation, in which the proof units of the more complex results precede those of the more elementary ones.

2 Minimality principle Property **8**.2A.1 (expandability of assumptions) states that for any wff α and sets Γ and Δ of wffs, if $\Gamma \subseteq \Delta$ and $\Gamma \vdash \alpha$ then $\Delta \vdash \alpha$. This suggests that in any proof line asserting $\Gamma \vdash \alpha$, Γ should be *minimal.* Adhering to this rule has several advantages. First, a smaller set Γ of wffs is obviously more manageable than a larger one. Second, the line conveys more information than any other line $\Delta \vdash \alpha$ where $\Gamma \subset \Delta$, as the latter is implied by the former. Third, if Γ is minimal, then the line indicates exactly on which assumptions α depends, and this may make the overall proof more meaningful and easier to understand intuitively. Note that in principle a set Γ is minimal relative to a specific deduction. This minimality principle is generally followed in subsequent developments. A similar principle is discussed in Section **10**.3B.

3 Most of the formal proofs given in subsequent sections are written in the format described above. However, occasionally we shall find it convenient to vary this format slightly or to resort to a different presentation altogether.

4 To simplify the proofs, we shall generally regard any wff '$\exists \boldsymbol{x}\, \alpha$' as an abbreviation for '$\neg \forall \boldsymbol{x} \neg \alpha$'. Consequently, we shall not consider wffs of the form '$\exists \boldsymbol{x}\, \alpha$' in case analyses.

8.3B Substitutivity of equivalence

Various so-called *substitution metatheorems* may be deduced from the logical axioms; see Andrews (1986), for instance. We now present just one such metatheorem, chosen for its usefulness in practice. The proof of this result is quite instructive. It gives another example of a structural inductive construction, and illustrates the preponderant role of MP, Rule T, Ded and Gen as primary or derived inference rules in formal proofs.

Property 8.3B.1 (SubEq)

Let α and α' be two wffs such that

$$\vdash \alpha \Leftrightarrow \alpha'$$

Let β and β' be two wffs such that $\beta = \beta'$ or β contains α and β' is obtained by substituting α' for exactly one occurrence of α in β. Then

$$\vdash \beta \Leftrightarrow \beta'$$ ■

Proof If $\beta = \beta'$ then '$(\beta \Leftrightarrow \beta')$' is a tautology. For the other case, the proof is by structural induction on β. Note that each of the four cases below gives rise to a *different* elementary proof unit, hence a different scope for the syntactic variables introduced therein.

Case 1 $\beta =_{\mathrm{d}} \alpha$. Then $\beta' = \alpha'$ and $\vdash$'$(\beta \Leftrightarrow \beta')$' as $\vdash$'$(\alpha \Leftrightarrow \alpha')$'.

Case 2 $\beta =_{\mathrm{d}}$ '$(\neg\, \gamma)$'. hence $\beta' =$ '$(\neg\, \gamma')$'. Therefore:

.1	$\vdash \gamma \Leftrightarrow \gamma'$	[Induction hypothesis]
.2	$\vdash (\neg\, \gamma) \Leftrightarrow (\neg\, \gamma')$	[T: .1]

Case 3 $\beta =_{\mathrm{d}}$ '$(\gamma * \delta)$', with $*$:$\{\wedge, \vee, \Rightarrow, \Leftrightarrow\}$. So $\beta' =$ '$(\gamma' * \delta')$' and

.1	$\vdash \gamma \Leftrightarrow \gamma'$	[Induc. hypo.]
.2	$\vdash \delta \Leftrightarrow \delta'$	[Induc. hypo.]
.3	$\vdash (\gamma * \delta) \Leftrightarrow (\gamma' * \delta')$	[T: .1, .2]

Case 4 $\beta =_{\mathrm{d}}$ '$\forall \boldsymbol{x}\, \gamma$', so $\beta' =$ '$\forall \boldsymbol{x}\, \gamma'$', where $\boldsymbol{x}$ is any variable. Thence:

.1	$\vdash \gamma \Leftrightarrow \gamma'$	[Induc. hypo.]
.2	$\vdash \forall \boldsymbol{x}\, \gamma \Rightarrow \gamma$	[LA2]
.3	$\forall \boldsymbol{x}\, \gamma \vdash \gamma$	[MP: assumption, .2]
.4	$\forall \boldsymbol{x}\, \gamma \vdash \gamma'$	[T: .3, .1]
.5	$\forall \boldsymbol{x}\, \gamma \vdash \forall \boldsymbol{x}\, \gamma'$	[Gen: .4]
.6	$\vdash \forall \boldsymbol{x}\, \gamma \Rightarrow \forall \boldsymbol{x}\, \gamma'$	[Ded: .5]
.7	$\vdash \forall \boldsymbol{x}\, \gamma' \Rightarrow \gamma'$	[LA2]
.8	$\forall \boldsymbol{x}\, \gamma' \vdash \gamma'$	[MP: assum., .7]
.9	$\forall \boldsymbol{x}\, \gamma' \vdash \gamma$	[T: 8, .1]
.10	$\forall \boldsymbol{x}\, \gamma' \vdash \forall \boldsymbol{x}\, \gamma$	[Gen: 9]
.11	$\vdash \forall \boldsymbol{x}\, \gamma' \Rightarrow \forall \boldsymbol{x}\, \gamma$	[Ded: .10]
.12	$\vdash \forall \boldsymbol{x}\, \gamma \Leftrightarrow \forall \boldsymbol{x}\, \gamma'$	[T: .6, .11]

■

8.3C Alphabetic variants

In proving theorems, we often need to substitute a *variable* for another variable in a wff. Such substitutions must be carried out carefully as they offer plenty of scope for errors. We now present a number of metatheorems on such transformations. Their proofs should further clarify the nature of substitution. Recall that for any two variables $\boldsymbol{x}$ and $\boldsymbol{y}$, '$\boldsymbol{x} = \boldsymbol{y}$' means that $\boldsymbol{x}$ and $\boldsymbol{y}$ are the same variable, that is, the same *symbol* of L.

Property 8.3C.1

For any wff α and any variable $\boldsymbol{x}$, $\boldsymbol{x}$ is substitutable for $\boldsymbol{x}$ in α and

$$\alpha^{\boldsymbol{x}}{}_{\boldsymbol{x}} = \alpha \qquad \blacksquare$$

Proof This should be obvious. In $\alpha^{\boldsymbol{x}}{}_{\boldsymbol{x}}$, the symbols of α replaced by $\boldsymbol{x}$ are precisely all the free occurrences of $\boldsymbol{x}$ in α, so the new occurrences of $\boldsymbol{x}$ remain free. Consequently, $\boldsymbol{x}$ is substitutable for itself in α. As for $\alpha^{\boldsymbol{x}}{}_{\boldsymbol{x}} = \alpha$, this is immediate. $\blacksquare$

Property 8.3C.2

For any wff α and any *distinct* variables $\boldsymbol{x}$ and $\boldsymbol{y}$,

$$(\alpha^{\boldsymbol{x}}{}_{\boldsymbol{y}})^{\boldsymbol{y}}{}_{\boldsymbol{x}} = \alpha$$

iff

(a) $\boldsymbol{y}$ is substitutable for $\boldsymbol{x}$ in α and
(b) there are no free occurrences of $\boldsymbol{y}$ in α.

Moreover, if this condition is satisfied, $\boldsymbol{x}$ is substitutable for $\boldsymbol{y}$ in $\alpha^{\boldsymbol{x}}{}_{\boldsymbol{y}}$. In any case, there are no free occurrences of $\boldsymbol{x}$ in $\alpha^{\boldsymbol{x}}{}_{\boldsymbol{y}}$. $\blacksquare$

Proof Consider any wff α. It will help to regard α as a *list* of n symbols

$$\alpha = (\alpha_1, \alpha_2, \ldots, \alpha_n)$$

Let $I =_{\mathrm{d}} \{1, \ldots, n\}$. For each $i : I$, α_i is the symbol occurring in position i in α. (Note that, to be completely accurate, we should define the *occurrence* of α_i in position i as the *couple* (i, α_i).) Furthermore, let $\beta =_{\mathrm{d}} \alpha^{\boldsymbol{x}}{}_{\boldsymbol{y}}$ and $\gamma =_{\mathrm{d}} (\alpha^{\boldsymbol{x}}{}_{\boldsymbol{y}})^{\boldsymbol{y}}{}_{\boldsymbol{x}}$. We may write $\beta = (\beta_1, \beta_2, \ldots, \beta_n)$ and $\gamma = (\gamma_1, \gamma_2, \ldots, \gamma_n)$ as in each substitution, each symbol is replaced by exactly one symbol. For each $i : I$, the first substitution replaces α_i by β_i, and the second β_i by γ_i.

Given α, we may partition $I = \{1, \ldots, n\}$ into five sets defined as follows:

Xf Any $i : Xf$ iff the *occurrence* of α_i in position i is a free occurrence of $\boldsymbol{x}$ and does *not* occur within a subwff '$\forall \boldsymbol{y}\ \delta$' of α.

Xb $i : Xb$ iff the occurrence of α_i in position i is a free occurrence of $\boldsymbol{x}$ and *does* occur within a subwff '$\forall \boldsymbol{y}\ \delta$' of α.

Yf $i : Yf$ iff the occurrence of α_i in position i is a free occurrence of $\boldsymbol{y}$ and does *not* occur within a subwff '$\forall \boldsymbol{x}\ \delta$' of α.

Yb $i : Yb$ iff the occurrence of α_i in position i is a free occurrence of $\boldsymbol{y}$ and *does* occur within a subwff '$\forall \boldsymbol{x}\ \delta$' of α.

R $i : R$ iff i does not belong to any of the previous sets.

With this partition of I, we may now precisely describe for each $i : I$ the effect of the two successive substitutions on the symbol occurring in position i. It is given in Table **8**.3C.1, whose justification is immediate.

Table 8.3C.1

	In α	*In* β	*In* γ
$i{:}Xf$	$\alpha_i = \boldsymbol{x}$ (free)	$\beta_i = \boldsymbol{y}$ (free)	$\gamma_i = \boldsymbol{x}$ (free)
$i{:}Xb$	$\alpha_i = \boldsymbol{x}$ (free)	$\beta_i = \boldsymbol{y}$ (bound)	$\gamma_i = \boldsymbol{y}$ (bound)
$i{:}Yf$	$\alpha_i = \boldsymbol{y}$ (free)	$\beta_i = \boldsymbol{y}$ (free)	$\gamma_i = \boldsymbol{x}$ (free)
$i{:}Yb$	$\alpha_i = \boldsymbol{y}$ (free)	$\beta_i = \boldsymbol{y}$ (free)	$\gamma_i = \boldsymbol{x}$ (bound)
$i{:}R$		$\beta_i = \alpha_i$	$\gamma_i = \alpha_i$

From this table we may make the following observations:

(1) $\boldsymbol{y}$ is substitutable for $\boldsymbol{x}$ in α iff $Xb = \varnothing$.

(2) $\boldsymbol{x}$ is substitutable for $\boldsymbol{y}$ in $\beta = \alpha^{\boldsymbol{x}}{}_{\boldsymbol{y}}$ iff $Yb = \varnothing$. (Note that the set of positions of free occurrences of $\boldsymbol{y}$ in β is $Xf + Yf + Yb$.)

(3) $(\alpha^{\boldsymbol{x}}{}_{\boldsymbol{y}})^{\boldsymbol{y}}{}_{\boldsymbol{x}} = \alpha$ iff $Xb = Yf = Yb = \varnothing$, which is equivalent to the condition stated in Property **8**.3C.2. In turn, $Xb = Yf = Yb = \varnothing$ implies the substitutability of $\boldsymbol{y}$ for $\boldsymbol{x}$ in α and $\boldsymbol{x}$ for $\boldsymbol{y}$ in $\beta = \alpha^{\boldsymbol{x}}{}_{\boldsymbol{y}}$, by the previous observations. Finally, that $\alpha^{\boldsymbol{x}}{}_{\boldsymbol{y}}$ has no free occurrences of $\boldsymbol{x}$ is immediate.

With this final remark, the proof is complete. ∎

Property 8.3C.3

For any wff α and any variables $\boldsymbol{x}$ and $\boldsymbol{y}$ such that

(a) $\boldsymbol{y}$ is substitutable for $\boldsymbol{x}$ in α and
(b) there are no free occurrences of $\boldsymbol{y}$ in '$\forall \boldsymbol{x}\ \alpha$',

$$\vdash \forall \boldsymbol{x}\ \alpha \Leftrightarrow \forall \boldsymbol{y}\ \alpha^{\boldsymbol{x}}{}_{\boldsymbol{y}}$$

Note that y may be x itself, in which case conditions (a) and (b) are necessarily satisfied, by Property **8**.3C.1. ■

Proof

.1	$\vdash \forall x\, \alpha \Rightarrow \alpha^x{}_y$	[LA2, as y is substitutable for x in α]
.2	$\forall x\, \alpha \vdash \alpha^x{}_y$	[MP: assum., .1]
.3	$\forall x\, \alpha \vdash \forall y\, \alpha^x{}_y$	[Gen: .2, as y is not free in '$\forall x\, \alpha$']
.4	$\vdash \forall x\, \alpha \Rightarrow \forall y\, \alpha^x{}_y$	[Ded: .3]

Next, replace α by $\alpha^x{}_y$ in this proof, and interchange x and y. $(\alpha^x{}_y)^y{}_x = \alpha$ and so x is substitutable for y in $\alpha^x{}_y$, by Property **8**.3C.1 or **8**.3C.2. Therefore, we obtain:

.5	$\vdash \forall y\, \alpha^x{}_y \Rightarrow (\alpha^x{}_y)^y{}_x$	[LA2, as x is substitutable for y in $\alpha^x{}_y$]
.6	$\vdash \forall y\, \alpha^x{}_y \Rightarrow \alpha$	[Same as .5, as $(\alpha^x{}_y)^y{}_x = \alpha$]
.7	$\forall y\, \alpha^x{}_y \vdash \alpha$	[MP: assum., .6]
.8	$\forall y\, \alpha^x{}_y \vdash \forall x\, \alpha$	[Gen: .7, as x is not free in '$\forall y\, \alpha^x{}_y$']
.9	$\vdash \forall y\, \alpha^x{}_y \Rightarrow \forall x\, \alpha$	[Ded: .8]

Finally:

.10	$\vdash \forall x\, \alpha \Leftrightarrow \forall y\, \alpha^x{}_y$	[T: .4, .9]

■

The next property generalizes Property **8**.3C.3.

Property 8.3C.4 (AlVa, alphabetic variant)

Let α and β be two wffs, and x and y be two variables such that

(a) y is substitutable for x in α; and

(b) there are no free occurrences of y in '$\forall x\, \alpha$'.

Note that y may be x itself, as in Property **8**.3C.3. Assume β contains '$\forall x\, \alpha$' as subwff, and let β' be the wff obtained by substituting '$\forall y\, \alpha^x{}_y$' for one occurrence of '$\forall x\, \alpha$' in β. Then

$$\vdash \beta \Leftrightarrow \beta'$$

■

Proof By Property **8**.3C.3, $\vdash$ '$\forall x\, \alpha \Leftrightarrow \forall y\, \alpha^x{}_y$'. The result follows by SubEq (Property **8**.3B.1). ■

Property **8**.3C.3 and its generalization, Property **8**.3C.4, formalize the following idea. In any wff β, a bound variable x is not essential: it may always be replaced by another variable y, provided y is such that the distinctions existing between the variables in β are maintained (which is the purpose of conditions (a) and (b)). The two wffs β and β' in AlVa are called *alphabetic variants*, and AlVa asserts that alphabetic variants are formally, hence logically, equivalent.

The equivalence of alphabetic variants has several applications. An important one is this. Recall that given a wff α, a variable $\boldsymbol{x}$ and a term τ, τ is not necessarily substitutable for $\boldsymbol{x}$ in α. The substitutability condition is broken if τ contains a variable $\boldsymbol{y}$ which is captured in $\alpha^{\boldsymbol{x}}{}_{\tau}$ (because a free occurrence of $\boldsymbol{x}$ in α occurs within a subwff '$\forall \boldsymbol{y}\ \beta$' of α – see rule (2) in Definition **8**.1C.1). We may wonder whether this substitutability constraint is likely to complicate formal deductions unpredictably. The answer is no, as we shall now see. If τ is not substitutable for $\boldsymbol{x}$ in α for the reason mentioned, we may replace the bound variable $\boldsymbol{y}$ in α by a new variable $\boldsymbol{z}$ occurring neither in α nor in τ, using Property **8**.3C.4. The resulting wff α' is equivalent to α and τ is substitutable for $\boldsymbol{x}$ in α'. Consequently, we may use α' instead of α in deductions.

We must, of course, allow for the fact that the occurrence(s) of $\boldsymbol{y}$ in τ may be captured by several different quantifiers '$\forall \boldsymbol{y}$' in $\alpha^{\boldsymbol{x}}{}_{\tau}$. Each of these would have to be replaced. Furthermore, τ may contain several distinct variables which, like $\boldsymbol{y}$, are captured in $\alpha^{\boldsymbol{x}}{}_{\tau}$. Each of these must be treated like $\boldsymbol{y}$. The next property states that this can always be done, and the proof shows how.

Property 8.3C.5

For any wff α, variable $\boldsymbol{x}$ and term τ, there is another wff α' with the following properties:

(1) α' is obtained by replacing zero or more bound variables in α by new variables.

(2) τ is substitutable for $\boldsymbol{x}$ in α'.

(3) α and α' are equivalent in the sense that $\vdash$ '$(\alpha \Leftrightarrow \alpha')$'. ■

Proof The proof is by structural induction on α and indicates how to construct the wff α' with the desired properties. The structure of the proof is similar to that of SubEq (Property **8**.3B.1). For any wff ϕ introduced below, let ϕ' be the wff derived from ϕ exactly in the manner recursively defined for α. Again, each of the cases below corresponds to a different elementary proof unit, hence a different scope for the syntactic variables introduced therein.

Case 1 τ is substitutable for $\boldsymbol{x}$ in α. Then let $\alpha' =_{\mathrm{d}} \alpha$. '$(\alpha \Leftrightarrow \alpha')$' is a tautology and τ is substitutable for $\boldsymbol{x}$ in α'.

Case 2 τ is *not* substitutable for $\boldsymbol{x}$ in α and $\alpha =_{\mathrm{d}}$ '$(\neg\ \gamma)$'. Let $\alpha' =_{\mathrm{d}}$ '$(\neg\ \gamma')$'. Thence:

.1	$\vdash \gamma \Leftrightarrow \gamma'$	[Induc. hypo.]
.2	$\vdash \alpha \Leftrightarrow \alpha'$	[SubEq: .1]

Moreover, τ is substitutable for $\boldsymbol{x}$ in γ' by the induction hypothesis, hence τ is substitutable for $\boldsymbol{x}$ in α'.

Case 3 τ is *not* substitutable for $\boldsymbol{x}$ in α and $\alpha =_d$ '$(\gamma * \delta)$', where $*: \{\wedge, \vee, \Rightarrow, \Leftrightarrow\}$. Let $\alpha' =_d$ '$(\gamma' * \delta')$'. Thence:

.1	$\vdash \gamma \Leftrightarrow \gamma'$	[Induc. hypo.]
.2	$\vdash \delta \Leftrightarrow \delta'$	[Induc. hypo.]
.3	$\vdash \alpha \Leftrightarrow (\gamma' * \delta)$	[SubEq: .1]
.4	$\vdash (\gamma' * \delta) \Leftrightarrow \alpha'$	[SubEq: .2]
.5	$\vdash \alpha \Leftrightarrow \alpha'$	[T: .3, .4]

Moreover, τ is substitutable for $\boldsymbol{x}$ in γ' and δ' by the induction hypothesis, hence τ is substitutable for $\boldsymbol{x}$ in α'.

Case 4 τ is *not* substitutable for $\boldsymbol{x}$ in α and $\alpha =_d$ '$\forall \boldsymbol{y}\, \gamma$', where $\boldsymbol{y}$ is distinct from $\boldsymbol{x}$. (The case $\boldsymbol{x} = \boldsymbol{y}$ is vacuously covered by case 1.) Let $\boldsymbol{z}$ be any variable which does not occur in τ or γ', and let $\alpha' =_d$ '$\forall \boldsymbol{z}\, (\gamma')^{\boldsymbol{y}}_{\boldsymbol{z}}$'.

Proof of $\vdash$ '$\alpha \Leftrightarrow \alpha'$'

.1	$\vdash \gamma \Leftrightarrow \gamma'$	[Induc. hypo.]
.2	$\vdash \forall \boldsymbol{y}\, \gamma \Leftrightarrow \forall \boldsymbol{y}\, \gamma'$	[SubEq: .1]
.3	$\vdash \forall \boldsymbol{y}\, \gamma' \Leftrightarrow \forall \boldsymbol{z}\, (\gamma')^{\boldsymbol{y}}_{\boldsymbol{z}}$	[Property **8**.3C.3, as $\boldsymbol{z}$ is substitutable for $\boldsymbol{y}$ in γ' and $\boldsymbol{z}$ is not free in '$\forall \boldsymbol{y}\, \gamma'$', given that $\boldsymbol{z}$ does not occur in γ']
.4	$\vdash \forall \boldsymbol{y}\, \gamma \Leftrightarrow \forall \boldsymbol{z}\, (\gamma')^{\boldsymbol{y}}_{\boldsymbol{z}}$	[T: .2, .3]

Proof that τ is substitutable for $\boldsymbol{x}$ *in* α'. By the induction hypothesis, τ is substitutable for $\boldsymbol{x}$ *in* γ'.

Subcase (a) $\boldsymbol{x} = \boldsymbol{z}$ Then τ is substitutable for $\boldsymbol{x}$ in α', vacuously.

Subcase (b) $\boldsymbol{x} \neq \boldsymbol{z}$ Then, if a variable in τ was captured in $(\alpha')^{\boldsymbol{x}}_{\tau}$, it would have to be by '$\forall \boldsymbol{z}$', as τ is substitutable for $\boldsymbol{x}$ in γ'. This is impossible as $\boldsymbol{z}$ does not occur in τ.

■

Example 8.3C.1

In $\alpha =_d$ '$(P\, x \wedge \forall y\, Q\, x\, y)$', replace y by z. This gives $\alpha' =_d$ '$(P\, x \wedge \forall z\, Q\, x\, z)$'. It is obvious that α and α' are equivalent. Thence for $\tau =_d$ '$f\, c\, y$', $(\alpha')^{\boldsymbol{x}}_{\tau} =$ '$(P\, f\, c\, y \wedge \forall z\, Q\, f\, c\, y\, z)$'. This is a valid substitution as the occurrence of y in τ is not captured in $(\alpha')^{\boldsymbol{x}}_{\tau}$. Unlike $\alpha^{\boldsymbol{x}}_{\tau}$, $(\alpha')^{\boldsymbol{x}}_{\tau}$ clearly produces the intended result: every occurrence of '$f\, c\, y$' in it denotes the same object in any interpretation.

■

Remark

Some authors define substitution differently: they incorporate the necessary changes of bound variables in the substitution operation itself. With this alternative definition of substitution, every term τ is substitutable for $\boldsymbol{x}$ in any wff α and the substitutability condition is no longer necessary. ■

8.3D Universal instantiation and existential theorems

We now study some theorems involving the quantifiers, '∀' and '∃'. These properties are not as fundamental as Ded and Gen, in the sense that they follow directly from the latter or the logical axioms. They are given for their usefulness in the development of proofs.

The first property is called universal instantiation (∀I). It follows from rule (2) of Definition **8**.1C.1.

Property 8.3D.1 (universal instantiation, ∀I)

Let Γ, α be any set of wffs, $\boldsymbol{x}$ any variable and τ any term substitutable for $\boldsymbol{x}$ in α.

(a) If

$$\Gamma \vdash \forall \boldsymbol{x}\, \alpha$$

then

$$\Gamma \vdash \alpha^{\boldsymbol{x}}{}_{\tau}$$

(b) Reciprocally, if

$$\Gamma \vdash \neg \alpha^{\boldsymbol{x}}{}_{\tau}$$

then

$$\Gamma \vdash \neg \forall \boldsymbol{x}\, \alpha$$

■

Proof By rule (2) of Definition **8**.1C.1,

$$\forall \boldsymbol{x}\, \alpha \Rightarrow \alpha^{\boldsymbol{x}}{}_{\tau}$$

is a logical axiom. Part (a) follows by MP. Furthermore, by rule T (more precisely, contraposition) applied to this logical axiom,

$$\vdash \neg \alpha^{\boldsymbol{x}}{}_{\tau} \Rightarrow \neg \forall \boldsymbol{x}\, \alpha$$

and part (b) follows by MP. ■

The next property is called existential generalization ($\exists$G). It is the dual of the previous result. Note that one must not be misled by the term 'generalization' in the title: it does *not* imply that the property depends on Gen.

Property 8.3D.2 (existential generalization, $\exists$G)

Let Γ, α be any set of wffs, $\boldsymbol{x}$ any variable and τ any term substitutable for $\boldsymbol{x}$ in α. If

$$\Gamma \vdash \alpha^{\boldsymbol{x}}{}_{\tau}$$

then

$$\Gamma \vdash \exists \boldsymbol{x}\, \alpha \qquad \blacksquare$$

Proof Recall that '$\exists \boldsymbol{x}\, \alpha$' is an abbreviation for '$\neg \forall \boldsymbol{x} \neg \alpha$'. By rule T, if

$$\Gamma \vdash \alpha^{\boldsymbol{x}}{}_{\tau}$$

then

$$\Gamma \vdash \neg (\neg \alpha^{\boldsymbol{x}}{}_{\tau})$$

Thence, by Property **8**.3D.1(b) in which '$(\neg \alpha)$' is substituted for α, and by the fact that '$(\neg \alpha^{\boldsymbol{x}}{}_{\tau})$' = '$(\neg \alpha)^{\boldsymbol{x}}{}_{\tau}$',

$$\Gamma \vdash \neg \forall \boldsymbol{x}\, (\neg \alpha) \qquad \blacksquare$$

Sometimes it is convenient to use the following informal argument. 'Our set Γ of assumptions implies that there exists an object with a certain property. Let $\boldsymbol{y}$ be any object satisfying this property. Γ, together with this additional assumption, implies a new property which does not depend on $\boldsymbol{y}$. Then this new property must already be implied by Γ alone.' In other words, we introduce an object $\boldsymbol{y}$ as a temporary aid in our reasoning and then get rid of (the assumption introducing) $\boldsymbol{y}$ in drawing any conclusion which does not depend on $\boldsymbol{y}$. This argument is formalized as rule C (for 'choice') given below. First, we need a preliminary result.

Property 8.3D.3 (existential rule)

Let Γ, β, α be any set of wffs and $\boldsymbol{x}$ any variable which does not occur free in Γ or α. If

$$\Gamma, \beta \vdash \alpha$$

then

$$\Gamma, \exists \boldsymbol{x}\, \beta \vdash \alpha \qquad \blacksquare$$

Proof

.1 $\Gamma, \beta \vdash \alpha$ [Given]
.2 $\Gamma \vdash (\neg\, \alpha) \Rightarrow (\neg\, \beta)$ [Ded: .1; T (contraposition)]
.3 $\Gamma, (\neg\, \alpha) \vdash \forall \boldsymbol{x}\, (\neg\, \beta)$ [MP: assumption, .2; Gen, as $\boldsymbol{x}$ is not free in Γ or α]
.4 $\Gamma, (\neg\, \forall \boldsymbol{x}\, (\neg\, \beta)) \vdash \alpha$ [contraposition′: .3]

Property 8.3D.4 (rule C, choice)

Let Γ, β, α be any set of wffs. Let $\boldsymbol{x}$ and $\boldsymbol{y}$ be any variables such that (a) $\boldsymbol{y}$ is substitutable for $\boldsymbol{x}$ in β and (b) $\boldsymbol{y}$ is not free in Γ, '$\exists \boldsymbol{x}\, \beta$' or α. Note that $\boldsymbol{y}$ may be $\boldsymbol{x}$ itself. If

$$\Gamma \vdash \exists \boldsymbol{x}\, \beta$$

and

$$\Gamma, \beta^{\boldsymbol{x}}{}_{\boldsymbol{y}} \vdash \alpha$$

then

$$\Gamma \vdash \alpha$$

■

Proof

.1 $\Gamma \vdash \exists \boldsymbol{x}\, \beta$ [Given]
.2 $\Gamma, \beta^{\boldsymbol{x}}{}_{\boldsymbol{y}} \vdash \alpha$ [Given]
.3 $\Gamma \vdash \exists \boldsymbol{y}\, \beta^{\boldsymbol{x}}{}_{\boldsymbol{y}}$ [AlVa (Prop. **8**.3C.4): .1, as $\boldsymbol{y}$ is substitutable for $\boldsymbol{x}$ in β and $\boldsymbol{y}$ is not free in '$\exists \boldsymbol{x}\, \beta$']
.4 $\Gamma, \exists \boldsymbol{y}\, \beta^{\boldsymbol{x}}{}_{\boldsymbol{y}} \vdash \alpha$ [Prop. **8**.3D.3: .2, as $\boldsymbol{y}$ is not free in Γ or α]
.5 $\Gamma \vdash \alpha$ [Trans (Prop. **8**.2A.3): .3, .4 (taking $\Theta =_{\mathrm{d}} \Gamma$, '$\exists \boldsymbol{y}\, \beta^{\boldsymbol{x}}{}_{\boldsymbol{y}}$')]

■

Note how all the assumptions stated in Property **8**.3D.4, in particular the conditions imposed on $\boldsymbol{y}$, are used in the proof. This is an application of the minimality principle mentioned in the final remarks of Section **8**.3A.

8.3E Equality

Our last metatheorems are concerned with equality, and so hold only in languages containing the equality predicate symbol '*Eq*'. A first group states that at the symbolic level *Eq*, as defined by rule (4) of Definition **8**.1C.1, determines a formal equivalence, that is, a reflexive, symmetric and transitive relation. A second group asserts that this equivalence is in fact a congruence in the sense that any function f formally maps equivalent arguments to equivalent objects, and the analogous property holds for predicates.

Property 8.3E.1 (reflexivity)

For any variable $\boldsymbol{x}$,

$$\vdash \forall \boldsymbol{x}\ Eq\ \boldsymbol{x}\ \boldsymbol{x}$$ ■

Proof '$\forall \boldsymbol{x}\ Eq\ \boldsymbol{x}\ \boldsymbol{x}$' is a logical axiom by rules (4a) and (5) of Definition **8**.1C.1. ■

Property 8.3E.2 (symmetry)

For any variables $\boldsymbol{x}$ and $\boldsymbol{y}$,

$$\vdash \forall \boldsymbol{x}\ \forall \boldsymbol{y}\ (Eq\ \boldsymbol{x}\ \boldsymbol{y} \Leftrightarrow Eq\ \boldsymbol{y}\ \boldsymbol{x})$$ ■

Proof

.1	$\vdash Eq\ \boldsymbol{x}\ \boldsymbol{x}$	[LA4(a)]
.2	$\vdash Eq\ \boldsymbol{x}\ \boldsymbol{y} \Rightarrow (Eq\ \boldsymbol{x}\ \boldsymbol{x} \Rightarrow Eq\ \boldsymbol{y}\ \boldsymbol{x})$	[LA4(b)]
.3	$\vdash Eq\ \boldsymbol{x}\ \boldsymbol{y} \Rightarrow Eq\ \boldsymbol{y}\ \boldsymbol{x}$	[T: .1, 2]
.4	$\vdash Eq\ \boldsymbol{y}\ \boldsymbol{x} \Rightarrow Eq\ \boldsymbol{x}\ \boldsymbol{y}$	[Interchange $\boldsymbol{x}$ and $\boldsymbol{y}$ in proof of .3]
.5	$\vdash Eq\ \boldsymbol{x}\ \boldsymbol{y} \Leftrightarrow Eq\ \boldsymbol{y}\ \boldsymbol{x}$	[T: .3, .4]
.6	$\vdash \forall \boldsymbol{x}\ \forall \boldsymbol{y}\ (Eq\ \boldsymbol{x}\ \boldsymbol{y} \Leftrightarrow Eq\ \boldsymbol{y}\ \boldsymbol{x})$	[Gen^2: .5]

■

Property 8.3E.3 (transitivity)

For any variables $\boldsymbol{x}$, $\boldsymbol{y}$ and $\boldsymbol{z}$,

$$\vdash \forall \boldsymbol{x}\ \forall \boldsymbol{y}\ \forall \boldsymbol{z} \cdot Eq\ \boldsymbol{x}\ \boldsymbol{y} \Rightarrow (Eq\ \boldsymbol{y}\ \boldsymbol{z} \Rightarrow Eq\ \boldsymbol{x}\ \boldsymbol{z})$$ ■

Proof

.1	$\vdash Eq\ \boldsymbol{x}\ \boldsymbol{y} \Rightarrow Eq\ \boldsymbol{y}\ \boldsymbol{x}$	[Prop. **8**.3E.2.3]
.2	$\vdash Eq\ \boldsymbol{y}\ \boldsymbol{x} \Rightarrow (Eq\ \boldsymbol{y}\ \boldsymbol{z} \Rightarrow Eq\ \boldsymbol{x}\ \boldsymbol{z})$	[LA4(b)]
.3	$\vdash Eq\ \boldsymbol{x}\ \boldsymbol{y} \Rightarrow (Eq\ \boldsymbol{y}\ \boldsymbol{z} \Rightarrow Eq\ \boldsymbol{x}\ \boldsymbol{z})$	[T: 1, .2]
.4	$\vdash \forall \boldsymbol{x}\ \forall \boldsymbol{y}\ \forall \boldsymbol{z} \cdot Eq\ \boldsymbol{x}\ \boldsymbol{y} \Rightarrow (Eq\ \boldsymbol{y}\ \boldsymbol{z} \Rightarrow Eq\ \boldsymbol{x}\ \boldsymbol{z})$	[Gen^3: 3]

■

Property 8.3E.4 ('function' congruence)

Let $\boldsymbol{f}$ be any n-ary function symbol and $\boldsymbol{x}_1, \boldsymbol{x}_2, \ldots, \boldsymbol{x}_n, \boldsymbol{y}_1, \boldsymbol{y}_2, \ldots, \boldsymbol{y}_n$ be any variables.

$$\begin{aligned}&\vdash \forall \boldsymbol{x}_1\ \forall \boldsymbol{x}_2 \ldots \forall \boldsymbol{x}_n\ \forall \boldsymbol{y}_1\ \forall \boldsymbol{y}_2 \ldots \forall \boldsymbol{y}_n \cdot\\ &\quad Eq\ \boldsymbol{x}_1\ \boldsymbol{y}_1 \Rightarrow (Eq\ \boldsymbol{x}_2\ \boldsymbol{y}_2 \Rightarrow (\ldots \Rightarrow (Eq\ \boldsymbol{x}_n\ \boldsymbol{y}_n \Rightarrow\\ &\quad Eq\ \boldsymbol{f}\boldsymbol{x}_1 \ldots \boldsymbol{x}_n\ \boldsymbol{f}\boldsymbol{y}_1 \ldots \boldsymbol{y}_n) \ldots\ ))\end{aligned}$$ ■

Proof

.1	$\vdash \forall x\ Eq\ x\ x$	[LA4(a); Gen]
.2	$\vdash Eq\ fx_1 \ldots x_n fx_1 \ldots x_n$	[∀I (Prop **8**.3D.1): .1]
.3	$Eq\ x_1 y_1 \vdash Eq\ fx_1 \ldots x_n fx_1 \ldots x_n \Rightarrow Eq\ fx_1 \ldots x_n fy_1 x_2 \ldots x_n$	[MP: assum., LA4(b)]
.4	$Eq\ x_1 y_1 \vdash Eq\ fx_1 \ldots x_n fy_1 x_2 \ldots x_n$	[MP: .2, .3]
.5	$Eq\ x_2 y_2 \vdash Eq\ fx_1 \ldots x_n fy_1 x_2 \ldots x_n \Rightarrow Eq\ fx_1 \ldots x_n fy_1 y_2 x_3 \ldots x_n$	[MP: assum., LA4(b)]
.6	$Eq\ x_1 y_1, Eq\ x_2 y_2 \vdash Eq\ fx_1 \ldots x_n fy_1 y_2 x_3 \ldots x_n$	[MP: .4, .5]

etc. Finally:

.m	$Eq\ x_1 y_1, \ldots, Eq\ x_n y_n \vdash Eq\ fx_1 \ldots x_n fy_1 \ldots y_n$	[as above]

Then apply MP n times and Gen $2 \times n$ times. ■

Property 8.3E.5 ('predicate' congruence)

Let P be any n-ary predicate symbol and $x_1, x_2, \ldots, x_n, y_1, y_2, \ldots, y_n$ be any variables.

$$\vdash \forall x_1 \forall x_2 \ldots \forall x_n \forall y_1 \forall y_2 \ldots \forall y_n \cdot Eq\ x_1 y_1 \Rightarrow (Eq\ x_2 y_2 \Rightarrow (\ldots \Rightarrow (Eq\ x_n y_n \Rightarrow Px_1 \ldots x_n \Leftrightarrow Py_1 \ldots y_n) \ldots))$$ ■

Proof The proof is essentially the same as for Property **8**.3E.4: substitute '$Px_1 \ldots x_n \Leftrightarrow Py_1 \ldots y_n$' for '$Eq\ fx_1 \ldots x_n fy_1 \ldots y_n$' and so on in this proof. ■

Remarks

1 In each of the above properties, the variables introduced are not necessarily distinct.

2 A fully rigorous proof of Properties **8**.3E.4 and **8**.3E.5 is by induction. This is left as an exercise. The above proof is only partial, but it highlights the successive elementary steps of the formal deduction involved. ■

EXERCISES

8.3.1 Let P be a unary predicate symbol. Let

$$\alpha =_{\rm d} P\ x$$

$$\alpha' =_{\rm d} (P\ x \wedge P\ x)$$

$$\beta =_{\rm d} \forall x \cdot P\ y \wedge \forall z\ P\ x$$

$$\beta' =_{\rm d} \forall x \cdot P\ y \wedge \forall z\ (P\ x \wedge P\ x)$$

(a) Prove $\vdash$ '$\alpha \Leftrightarrow \alpha'$'.
(b) Prove $\vdash$ '$\beta \Leftrightarrow \beta'$' (i) with SubEq (Property **8**.3B.1) and (ii) without using SubEq, but in a way that reflects (or 'instantiates') the proof of SubEq.

8.3.2 Repeat Exercise **8**.3.1 with

$$\alpha =_{\rm d} \forall x\ P\ x$$

$$\alpha' =_{\rm d} \neg\ \exists x \neg\ P\ x$$

$$\beta =_{\rm d} \forall\ x \cdot P\ y \wedge \forall\ x\ P\ x$$

$$\beta' =_{\rm d} \forall\ x \cdot P\ y \wedge (\neg\ \exists x \neg\ P\ x)$$

8.3.3 Verify the 'semantic equivalent' of SubEq: that is, given wffs α, α', β, and β' as defined in this property, if $\models$ '$\alpha \Leftrightarrow \alpha'$' then $\models$ '$\beta \Leftrightarrow \beta'$'. Recall that this requires reasoning with the semantic function $\boldsymbol{M}$ determined by any interpretation (M, m).

8.3.4 Let α be any wff in a first-order language L, n the number of symbols occurring in it and $I =_{\rm d} \{1, 2, \ldots, n\}$ as in Property **8**.3C.2. Thus, regard α as a list $(\alpha_1, \ldots, \alpha_n)$ where α_i is a symbol of L for each $i : I$. An effective method of representing the partition of I into the five sets Xf, Xb, Yf, Yb and R is to label each symbol occurrence α_i in α according to the following scheme:

1 if $i \in Xf$
2 if $i \in Xb$
3 if $i \in Yf$
4 if $i \in Yb$
0 if $i \in R$

For instance, $\alpha =_{\rm d}$ '$P\ \boldsymbol{x} \vee \forall \boldsymbol{y}\ (P\ \boldsymbol{y} \Rightarrow P\ \boldsymbol{x}) \vee P\ \boldsymbol{y} \vee \exists \boldsymbol{x}\ P\ \boldsymbol{y}$' is labelled

	P	$\boldsymbol{x}$	$\vee$	$\forall$	$\boldsymbol{y}$	(	P	$\boldsymbol{y}$	$\Rightarrow$	P	$\boldsymbol{x}$	)	$\vee$	P	$\boldsymbol{y}$	$\vee$	$\exists$	$\boldsymbol{x}$	P	$\boldsymbol{y}$
	0	1	0	0	0	0	0	0	0	0	2	0	0	0	3	0	0	0	0	4
$I = ($	1	2	3	4	...													...	19	20)

in this scheme. (This labelling is a function $\lambda: I \to \{0, 1, 2, 3, 4\}$; it is a generalization of the concept of a characteristic function on I.)

Assume L has predicate symbols P (1-ary) and Q (2-ary) and let $\boldsymbol{x} =_{\mathrm{d}} x$ and $\boldsymbol{y} =_{\mathrm{d}} y$. (Thus, $\boldsymbol{x}$ and $\boldsymbol{y}$ are distinct.) For each wff α of L listed below, represent the partition (Xf, Xb, Yf, Yb, R) by the labelling method just described (omitting zeros); compute $\alpha^x{}_y$ and $(\alpha^x{}_y)^y{}_x$; determine whether $(\alpha^x{}_y)^y{}_x = \alpha$ or not; and justify your conclusion using (Xf, Xb, Yf, Yb, R).

(i) $\alpha =_{\mathrm{d}} Q\ x\ z \Rightarrow \forall y\ (P\ x \vee Q\ y\ y)$
(ii) $\alpha =_{\mathrm{d}} \forall z\ Q\ y\ z \vee (P\ y \Rightarrow P\ x)$
(iii) $\alpha =_{\mathrm{d}} \forall x\ Q\ y\ x \wedge \forall y\ Q\ z\ y$
(iv) $\alpha =_{\mathrm{d}} (P\ y \wedge \forall x\ Q\ x\ y) \Rightarrow \forall y\ Q\ y\ x$
(v) $\alpha =_{\mathrm{d}} P\ z \vee \forall x\ Q\ z\ x$
(vi) $\alpha =_{\mathrm{d}} (\forall y\ Q\ z\ y \vee P\ x) \Rightarrow \forall x\ Q\ z\ x$

8.3.5 Let $\alpha =_{\mathrm{d}}$ '$P\ x \vee \forall y \cdot Q\ xy \wedge \forall z\ (Q\ zx \vee Q\ yz)$', where P and Q are defined as in Exercise **8.3.4**, and $\tau =$ '$f\ xyz$', where f is a 3-ary function symbol. Compute $\alpha^x{}_\tau$ and establish whether τ is substitutable for x in α or not.

8.3.6 Let P, Q and α be defined as in Exercise **8.3.5** and

$$\alpha' =_{\mathrm{d}} P\ x \vee \forall y_1 \cdot Q\ xy_1 \wedge \forall z_1\ (Q\ z_1 x \vee Q\ y_1 z_1)$$

(a) Verify $\vdash$'$\alpha \Leftrightarrow \alpha'$' using Properties **8**.3C.4 (AlVa) and **8**.3C.5; in particular show that α' is derived from α by the construction given in the proof of the latter property. Draw the parse tree T of α and then transform T progressively (from the bottom up) into the parse tree of α'.
(b) Compute $(\alpha')^x{}_\tau$ and draw appropriate conclusions.
(c) Prove '$\forall x\ \alpha$' $\vdash (\alpha')^x{}_\tau$, using (a).

8.3.7 Let Γ, α, $\boldsymbol{x}$ and τ be defined as in $\forall$I (Property **8**.3D.1). Let $D1$ be a deduction of '$\forall \boldsymbol{x}\ \alpha$' from Γ, if any, and $D2$ a deduction of '$\neg\ \alpha^{\boldsymbol{x}}{}_\tau$' from Γ, if any.
(a) Show how $D1$, if it exists, may be extended to a deduction of $\alpha^{\boldsymbol{x}}{}_\tau$ from Γ.
(b) Likewise, extend $D2$ (assuming it exists) to a deduction of '$\neg\ \forall \boldsymbol{x}\ \alpha$' from Γ.
(c) Under which circumstances could we simultaneously have deductions $D1$ and $D2$?

8.3.8 Prove the following metatheorem:

Property Let Γ, α be any set of wffs and $\boldsymbol{x}$ any variable.

(1) $\Gamma \vdash (\neg\ \exists \boldsymbol{x}\ \alpha)$

iff

$\Gamma \vdash \forall \boldsymbol{x}\ (\neg\ \alpha)$

Conversely,

(2) $\Gamma \vdash (\neg \forall \boldsymbol{x}\, \alpha)$

iff

$\Gamma \vdash \exists \boldsymbol{x}\, (\neg \alpha)$ ■

Recall that '$\exists \boldsymbol{x}\, \alpha$' is an abbreviation for '$(\neg \forall \boldsymbol{x}\, (\neg \alpha))$'.

8.3.9 Prove the following so-called *substitution theorem*, using Gen in particular:

Property Let Γ, α be any set of wffs, $\boldsymbol{x}$ any variable which does not occur free in Γ, and τ any term substitutable for $\boldsymbol{x}$ in α. If

$\Gamma \vdash \alpha$

then

$\Gamma \vdash \alpha^{\boldsymbol{x}}_{\tau}$ ■

8.3.10 (a) Prove Property **8**.3E.4 by induction.
(b) Transform (a) into a proof of Property **8**.3E.5

Formal Proofs in Set Theory

So far in this book we have developed two main subjects: set theory and logic. In Part **2**, set theory was described in an intuitive, semiformal manner only. In contrast, the aims of Part **3** are twofold: to present the elements of propositional and first-order logic, of course, but also to emphasize their nature as formal languages and as the basis for the formalization of any theory. In this final chapter of Part **3**, we pull these two strands together by formalizing set theory completely within first-order logic. This involves (a) establishing set theory as a first-order language, (b) specifying a set of axioms as wffs in this language and finally (c) deriving theorems by formal deductions from the axioms. Thus, the main aim of this chapter is to describe set theory as an application of first-order logic, and to illustrate how deductions in set theory are completely formalized. We refer to this formalization of set theory as *axiomatic set theory*, or *AST* for short.

Section **9**.1 first defines the 'core language' of AST. Then it specifies a number of axioms of this theory. Finally, the problem of adding predicate and function symbols to the core language is discussed. AST is based on a set of ten axioms or axiom schemas which are now regarded as standard by mathematicians, the so-called *Zermelo–Fraenkel* (ZF) postulates already mentioned in Chapter **2**. As it is not the purpose of this book to provide an exhaustive treatment of set theory, only the first seven of them are given, those on which the rest of the book depends. Note that these axioms have already been presented semiformally in Part **2**. All that remains to do now is to restate them completely formally.

Section **9**.2, which makes up the remainder of this chapter, presents formal proofs for a number of basic set-theoretical results stated in various sections of Part **2**. Here again, we are selective. The aim is not to prove all the properties given there, but to present a number of typical proofs carefully worked out. We use the proof method described in Section **8**.3A. Each proof line has a full justification of the assertion it contains, with all the necessary references, as in the proofs of Section **8**.3. Therefore the details provided are such that each step should again appear to the reader as a game of symbol manipulation according to a few simple and transparent rules, with all the information required immediately available.

9.1 Axiomatic set theory (AST)

9.1A The language of AST

The first-order language of axiomatic set theory (AST) may be defined in different ways. We may first define a *minimum* language, containing the smallest set of symbols necessary to express all the required axioms and resulting theorems. However, sooner or later, this language may prove to be unwieldy. So we may then extend it by adding new function and predicate symbols, to be defined by further axioms. This is a natural pattern of development, one which we have in fact followed semiformally in Part **2**. We may call the initial language the *core language*, and any extension of it an *extended language*. In this chapter, we mainly work with the core language of AST, which we now define.

The core language of AST is very simple. It contains no function symbols and exactly two binary predicate symbols: the equality '*Eq*' and the membership symbol '∈'. Recall that '*Eq*' is classified as an optional (but nonetheless logical) symbol, with the fixed standard interpretation defined in Section 7.3B. Membership, on the other hand, is a nonlogical symbol.

The reader may well be surprised at the bareness of this definition; many more symbols were introduced in the description of Part **2**, and it would be natural to regard them as essential elements of the language. However, they need not be! The only truly primitive symbols introduced in Part **2** were '=' and '∈'; all other symbols were *defined* in terms of these two primitives and can be ignored *without essentially altering the theory*. In Section **9**.1C below, most of our axioms are expressed without difficulty with these two symbols only.

In the strict definition of a first-order language given in Section 7.2, n-ary predicate symbols are *prefix* symbols, that is they are written before the string of n terms to which they apply. This holds in particular for the two binary symbols

'*Eq*' and '$\in$'. However, we shall henceforth use the standard '$=$' instead of '*Eq*', and write '$=$' and '$\in$' as infix operators – that is, placed between their operands – according to the usual mathematical convention. It must be understood that this is just a convenient symbolic translation of the 'official' language: for any two terms τ_1 and τ_2, we regard '$\tau_1 = \tau_2$' and '$\tau_1 \in \tau_2$' as new forms standing for the official '$Eq\ \tau_1\ \tau_2$' and '$\in \tau_1\ \tau_2$', respectively. Likewise, in addition to the symbols x, y, ... we also use capital letters A, B, ... to denote variables. We continue using boldface letters as syntactic variables to represent variables of AST, and Greek letters to represent any strings of AST, such as wfes. As '$=$' is now a symbol of AST itself, we introduce the metasymbol '$=_{\text{sym}}$' to denote symbolic equality. For instance, '$\mathbf{x} =_{\text{sym}} \mathbf{y}$' means that $\mathbf{x}$ and $\mathbf{y}$ are the same variable of AST.

Any extension of the core language is obtained by introducing additional symbols, such as the binary predicate symbols '$\subseteq$', '$\subset$', the nullary function (that is, constant) symbol '$\varnothing$', the binary function symbols '$\cup$', '$\cap$', '$\setminus$', and so on. We shall continue writing binary symbols in infix position as in Part **2**, under the convention stated for '$=$' and '$\in$'.

9.1B Interpretation of AST

In this chapter we are only concerned with purely *symbolic* aspects of set theory: language syntax, axioms and deductive calculus. In principle, the precise interpretation (semantics) of AST is beyond our concern here: all we want to do is show how the laws of set theory are expressed as formal axioms and theorems, and how the latter may be derived from the former by formal deductions. Even so, it may be useful briefly to discuss possible interpretations of AST, if only to satisfy the reader that the axioms of the theory 'make sense' – that is, may be given an intuitively valid meaning.

In practice, the sets we talk about may contain other sets, or other types of objects , for example, physical or conceptual things. Such other objects are called *atoms* in textbooks on set theory, as they are viewed as primitive elements. We may allow for such objects in the theory, but it is also possible to take the opposite course and rule them out. This means that in the interpretation of AST, every object, that is, every member of the universe of discourse, is just a set. This is the standard interpretation of AST; we may call it *pure set theory*.

The reason why mathematicians prefer the pure interpretation of AST is a matter of convenience. The universe of discourse is homogeneous: its members are just sets. (Note that the universe itself is not a set, lest it belong to itself. It must be regarded as a proper class.) Thus there is no need to distinguish between different types of object, such as atoms on the one hand and sets on the other. In turn, predicates and functions are easier to define. In particular, functions are naturally *total* on the universe. For instance, the union operation is naturally defined for every couple of members of the universe, as these necessarily are sets. If atoms were allowed, then the union of objects other than sets would have to be defined in some way, typically as a special element called Undefined. All these are unnecessary complications which are avoided in pure set theory. Note that there is nothing artificial about this theory. It is just the theory of sets and no other objects. Moreover, it is not restrictive. It is generally accepted that all concepts arising in mathematics may actually be represented in it. For instance, we have seen how the natural numbers may be represented by pure sets in Section **4**.1D.

Accordingly, although we do not impose any interpretation of AST in this chapter, it may be useful to regard the axioms defined below as formalizing the standard interpretation, in which the only objects to be considered are sets. It is under this interpretation that the axioms given in Section **9**.1C make complete sense, intuitively.

Note that in the models of Parts **4** and **5** we shall often assume certain sets given as primitive. In general, these sets will be introduced as additional constants. Intuitively, they will represent collections of certain physical or conceptual objects. However, the intuitive meaning of such sets will not be captured in the models, beyond the properties which will be represented explicitly by additional axioms. Thus the models of Parts **4** and **5** will in essence be very simple extensions of pure set theory.

9.1C Seven axioms of AST

We now present seven of the ten axioms or axiom schemas of ZF set theory, each with a short name for reference in future proofs. These are:

(1)	*Ext*	Extensionality principle
(2)	*Null*	Existence of an empty (or 'null') set
(3)	*Pair*	Existence of pairs
(4)	*Union*	Existence of (generalized) unions
(5)	*Pow*	Existence of powersets
(6)	*Subset*	Existence of subsets of objects satisfying a formula (axiom schema)
(7)	*Inf*	Existence of an infinite set

These axioms have all been introduced in Part **2**. It is interesting to know that they are all we require to formalize AST, at least the part of the theory which we need. The three remaining axioms of ZF theory, called axioms of choice, regularity and replacement, are given in Enderton (1977). They are only required in advanced set theory.

We now restate each axiom in detail and express it as a wff. Note that each axiom is a *closed wff* – it contains no free variables. Note also that the only nonlogical symbol used in each wff is the membership predicate symbol '$\in$': we are using the core language of AST here.

Extensionality principle (Ext)

This axiom states that for any two sets A and B, if these have the same members, then they are equal. Equality of membership is rendered by writing: for any x, x belongs to A iff x belongs to B. The resulting wff is as follows:

Ext $\forall A\, \forall B \cdot (\forall x \cdot x \in A \Leftrightarrow x \in B) \Rightarrow A = B$

This is a 'genuine' axiom in the sense that it is not a consequence of the *logical* axioms. In contrast, the reverse implication, stating that two equal sets have the same members, is a logical theorem. The proof is given in Section **9**.2. ■

Existence of an empty set (Null)

This states that there exists a set N which has no members:

Null $\exists N\, \forall x\; x \notin N$

Here '$x \notin N$' is an abbreviation for '$\neg\, (x \in N)$'. Note that all this axiom does is assert the existence of an empty set, using the variable N existentially quantified. It does *not* assert that this set is unique, and does not *name* it. That the empty set is unique is a consequence of Ext and must be proved. We will be able to name it ($\varnothing$) only once this has been done, in Section **9**.2. ■

Existence of pairs (Pair)

This asserts that given any two sets x and y, there is a set A whose members are x and y exactly; that is, for any z, z is a member of A iff z is equal to x or to y:

Pair $\forall x\, \forall y\, \exists A\, \forall z \cdot z \in A \Leftrightarrow (z = x \vee z = y)$

Again, this axiom only asserts the existence of a certain set, denoted by $\{x, y\}$ in Part **2**. It does not state that this set is unique, nor does it name it. Similar comments apply to the next two axioms. ■

Existence of generalized unions (Union)

This axiom states that for any set A (whose members necessarily are sets in pure set theory), there is another set B which is the union of all the members of A. We express this by saying that for any x, x belongs to B iff there exists a set C to which x belongs, and C is a member of A:

Union $\forall A\, \exists B\, \forall x \cdot x \in B \Leftrightarrow \exists C\; (x \in C \wedge C \in A)$

Recall that this asserts the existence of the generalized union $\cup A$ defined in Section **2**.2B. The existence of the union of two sets X and Y is a special case:

simply let A in the axiom be the pair consisting of X and Y. (This pair exists, by the previous axiom.) The proof is developed in Section **9**.2C. ■

Existence of powersets (Pow)

This asserts that for any set A, there is another set B whose members are all the subsets S of A. This is the powerset Pow(A) defined in Section **2**.2F. The notion of subset itself must be expressed in terms of '$\in$'. Thus, we must state that for any S, S is a member of B iff for any x, if x belongs to S then x is a member of A:

Pow $\forall A\ \exists B\ \forall S \cdot S \in B \Leftrightarrow \forall x\ (x \in S \Rightarrow x \in A)$ ■

Existence of subsets (Subset)

The next wff defines an *axiom schema*, as it contains various syntactic variables. This schema determines a whole family of axioms, namely all the wffs obtained by instantiating the various syntactic variables appropriately. Its precise definition is as follows.

Let $\boldsymbol{x}, \boldsymbol{y}_1, \boldsymbol{y}_2, \ldots \boldsymbol{y}_n$, $\boldsymbol{A}$ and $\boldsymbol{S}$ be *any distinct* variables. Let φ be a wff whose free variables are among $\boldsymbol{x}, \boldsymbol{y}_1, \boldsymbol{y}_2, \ldots \boldsymbol{y}_n$ and $\boldsymbol{A}$. (Thus $\boldsymbol{S}$ does not occur free in φ.) The axiom states that for any $\boldsymbol{y}_1, \boldsymbol{y}_2, \ldots \boldsymbol{y}_n$ and $\boldsymbol{A}$, there exists a set $\boldsymbol{S}$ such that any $\boldsymbol{x}$ is a member of $\boldsymbol{S}$ iff $\boldsymbol{x}$ belongs to $\boldsymbol{A}$ and φ is true:

Subset $\forall \boldsymbol{y}_1\ \forall \boldsymbol{y}_2 \ldots \forall \boldsymbol{y}_n\ \forall \boldsymbol{A}\ \exists \boldsymbol{S}\ \forall \boldsymbol{x} \cdot \boldsymbol{x} \in \boldsymbol{S} \Leftrightarrow (\boldsymbol{x} \in \boldsymbol{A} \wedge \varphi)$

Any axiom in the family thus defined is obtained as follows. (a) Replace φ by any actual wff. (b) Replace $\boldsymbol{x}, \boldsymbol{y}_1, \boldsymbol{y}_2, \ldots \boldsymbol{y}_n$, $\boldsymbol{A}$ and $\boldsymbol{S}$ by distinct actual variables of AST such that all the free variables of the chosen φ are amongst $\boldsymbol{x}, \boldsymbol{y}_1, \boldsymbol{y}_2, \ldots \boldsymbol{y}_n$ and $\boldsymbol{A}$. In practice the wff φ is often given first. The variables are then chosen so as to satisfy the stated constraints. ■

Existence of an infinite set (Inf)

The last of our axioms states that there is a set A with the following properties: (a) A contains the empty set and (b) for any set $x \in A$, $y = x \cup \{x\}$ is also a member of A. This axiom is the basis for the natural numbers as defined in pure set theory (Section **4**.1D), with the empty set as first element and for each x, $y = x \cup \{x\}$ its successor. It can be shown that any set A satisfying the stated conditions must necessarily be infinite, which is what motivates the name of the axiom. Again, we seek to establish this axiom without reference to any operations. So we must express the two defining conditions as follows:

(a) There exists an empty set N which is a member of A.

(b) For any x, if x is a member of A then there exists y with the following property:
  (i) For any z, $z \in y$ iff $z \in x$ or $z = x$. (This defines y as $x \cup \{x\}$.)
  (ii) $y \in A$.

Formally:

Inf $\quad \exists A \cdot \exists N\,(\forall x\; x \notin N \wedge N \in A)$
$\quad\quad \wedge\; \forall x \cdot x \in A \Rightarrow \exists y \cdot \forall z (z \in y \Leftrightarrow (z \in x \vee z = x)) \wedge y \in A$ ■

This completes our list of axioms. In Section **9**.2 we formally derive theorems from these axioms.

9.1D Defining predicates and functions

In first-order logic, a *theory* is the set of all closed wffs logically implied by some set Γ of (closed) axioms. In any application, given a theory T in an initial core language L, a common step is to extend L by adding predicate and function symbols and axioms defining them. These new symbols and their axiomatic definitions are introducted only to express the consequences (theorems) of T in a more concise and meaningful fashion. Therefore, they should not 'substantially' extend T: any wff *in the core language* L and deducible from the extended set of axioms should already be a theorem of T. We say that the additional axioms should be *noncreative*. (Note that the only possible effect of new axioms on a theory is either to leave it unchanged or to extend it: they *cannot remove* some consequences of the original set of axioms!)

Set theory is a good illustration of this principle. In Part **2**, we have introduced many predicate and function symbols in addition to the membership symbol, and further such symbols are routinely introduced in applications for the stated purpose. In each case we are faced with two problems. First, we must make sure that the additional axioms are noncreative. Second, we must know how to eliminate the new symbols from wfes in order to prove the theorems formulated in the extended language from the axioms of the initial theory. These problems are treated in detail in Enderton (1972). We shall only briefly discuss and illustrate them here.

Noncreative definitions

In order to introduce a new n-ary predicate symbol $\boldsymbol{P}$, we define a wff of the form

(1) $\quad \alpha =_{\text{sym}} \boldsymbol{P}\, \boldsymbol{x}_1\, \boldsymbol{x}_2 \ldots \boldsymbol{x}_n \Leftrightarrow \varphi$

where φ is any wff in the core language L and $\boldsymbol{x}_1, \boldsymbol{x}_2, \ldots, \boldsymbol{x}_n$ any variables normally occurring free in φ. Then we close α by universally quantifying all its free variables, and the result α' is the new axiom by which $\boldsymbol{P}$ is defined as equivalent to φ. It is intuitively clear that α' is noncreative, that is, does not add any information expressible in L and which cannot already be derived from the axioms of the original theory T.

Example 9.1D.1

The subset symbol '$\subseteq$' denotes a binary predicate. It is defined in AST by

$$\forall S\, \forall T \cdot S \subseteq T \Leftrightarrow \forall x \cdot x \in S \Rightarrow x \in T$$ ■

The introduction of a new n-ary function symbol $\boldsymbol{f}$ may be done in a similar way but is more delicate. Recall that a function symbol is intended to represent a *total function,* which is a special type of $(n+1)$-ary relation. This means that the defining wff φ must describe a relation of this type in any model of the original theory T. In a language L with equality, like AST, the natural way of defining $\boldsymbol{f}$ is to introduce a wff

(2) $$\beta =_{\text{sym}} \forall \boldsymbol{x}_1 \ldots \forall \boldsymbol{x}_n\, \forall \boldsymbol{x}_{n+1} \cdot \boldsymbol{f}\, \boldsymbol{x}_1\, \boldsymbol{x}_2 \ldots \boldsymbol{x}_n = \boldsymbol{x}_{n+1} \Leftrightarrow \varphi$$

where φ is a wff in the core language L, such that the variables occurring free in it are among $\boldsymbol{x}_1 \ldots, \boldsymbol{x}_n$ and $\boldsymbol{x}_{n+1}$. It can be shown that for an initial theory T, β is noncreative iff the wff

(3) $$\gamma =_{\text{sym}} \forall \boldsymbol{x}_1 \ldots \forall \boldsymbol{x}_n\, \exists 1\, \boldsymbol{x}_{n+1} \cdot \varphi$$

is in T, that is, is logically implied by the axioms of T. This should be intuitively clear. The proof is given in Enderton (1972).

Example 9.1D.2

The empty set symbol '$\varnothing$' is a constant, or nullary function symbol. It is defined in AST by

$$\forall N \cdot \varnothing = N \Leftrightarrow \forall x \cdot x \notin N$$

which is an instance of (2) with $n = 0$ and is clearly equivalent to the simpler

$$\forall x \cdot x \notin \varnothing$$

The existence of $\varnothing$ follows from Null, and its uniqueness from Ext. The formal proof of the latter property is developed in Section **9**.2B. ■

Example 9.1D.3

The binary union symbol '$\cup$' is defined in AST by

$$\forall A\, \forall B\, \forall C \cdot A \cup B = C \Leftrightarrow \forall x \cdot x \in C \Leftrightarrow (x \in A \lor x \in B)$$

This is an instance of (2) with $n = 2$; it is equivalent to the simpler

$$\forall A\ \forall B\ \forall x \cdot x \in A \cup B \Leftrightarrow (x \in A \lor x \in B)$$

The existence of $A \cup B$ follows from Pair and Union, and its uniqueness from Ext. The formal proof of the former property is constructed in Section **9**.2C.

■

Eliminating symbols

A frequent problem is to prove properties of new predicates or functions in the initial theory T. Two typical examples in AST are (a) the transitivity of the subset predicate $\subseteq$ and (b) the commutativity of the binary union $\cup$. The first property is that for any three sets A, B, and C, is $A \subseteq B$ and $B \subseteq C$ then $A \subseteq C$. We wish to prove that this follows from the axioms of AST and the definition of $\subseteq$. We may do this by eliminating $\subseteq$ in the proof precisely by using the definition of $\subseteq$. Likewise, the second property is that for any two sets A and B, $A \cup B = B \cup A$ and we wish to demonstrate that this is logically implied by the axioms of AST and the definition of $\cup$. Again, we may do this by eliminating $\cup$ in the proof by using the definition of this operator.

There is a systematic method of eliminating a defined symbol from wfes using its definition. As the way to do this is generally clear in each case, we do not present this method here. The interested reader may find it in Enderton (1972). We only give two examples.

Example 9.1D.4 Transitivity of $\subseteq$

The property to prove in the extended language is

$$\forall A\ \forall B\ \forall C \cdot (A \subseteq B \land B \subseteq C) \Rightarrow A \subseteq C$$

Using the definition

$$\forall S\ \forall T \cdot S \subseteq T \Leftrightarrow \forall x \cdot x \in S \Rightarrow x \in T$$

given in Example **9**.1D.1 we obtain (by instantiations and generalizations)

$$\forall A\ \forall B\ \forall C \cdot (\forall x\ (x \in A \Rightarrow x \in B) \land \forall x\ (x \in B \Rightarrow x \in C)) \Rightarrow \forall x \cdot x \in A \Rightarrow x \in C$$

as the wff to prove in the core AST. ■

Example 9.1D.5 Commutativity of $\cup$

The property to prove in the extended language is

(C1) $\forall A\ \forall B \cdot A \cup B = B \cup A$

Using the definition

(C2) $\forall A\ \forall B\ \forall C \cdot A \cup B = C \Leftrightarrow \forall x \cdot x \in C \Leftrightarrow (x \in A \vee x \in B)$

given in Example 9.1D.3 we obtain

$$\begin{aligned}(\text{C3})\quad \forall A\ \forall B\ \forall C\ \forall D \cdot [&\forall x(x \in C \Leftrightarrow (x \in A \vee x \in B)) \\ &\wedge \forall x(x \in D \Leftrightarrow (x \in B \vee x \in A))] \\ &\Rightarrow C = D\end{aligned}$$

as the wff to prove in the core AST. ■

In Example 9.1D.5, observe how the two terms containing $\cup$ in (C1) are represented by the new variables C and D in (C3). This is typical of the way in which any function symbol $\boldsymbol{f}$ is eliminated in general, given its introduction by (2). In order to eliminate $\boldsymbol{f}$, we replace any term $\boldsymbol{f}\ldots$ by a new variable defined so as to represent the same value as $\boldsymbol{f}\ldots$ in the wff to be proved.

EXERCISES

9.1.1 (a) Prove $\vdash$ '$\forall A\ \forall B \cdot A = B \Rightarrow \forall x \cdot x \in A \Leftrightarrow x \in B$'. This depends on the logical axioms for equality.
(b) Prove $\vdash$ '$S = T \Rightarrow \forall y \cdot y \in T \Leftrightarrow y \in S$' by extending (a).

9.1.2 (a) Prove Ext $\vdash$ '$(\forall y \cdot y \in T \Leftrightarrow y \in S) \Rightarrow S = T$' using AlVa (Property **8**.3C.4).
(b) Let $\alpha =_{\text{sym}}$ '$\forall y \cdot y \in S \Rightarrow y \in T$' and $\beta =_{\text{sym}}$ '$\forall z \cdot z \in T \Rightarrow z \in S$'. Prove Ext, $\alpha \vdash$ '$\beta \Rightarrow S = T$' by extending *part of* (a).

9.1.3 Let α be any wff and $\boldsymbol{x}$ any variable.
(a) Prove $\vdash$ '$\forall \boldsymbol{x}\ \alpha \Leftrightarrow \forall \boldsymbol{x} \neg \neg \alpha$' (i) using SubEq (Property **8**.3B.1) and (ii) without using this property.
(b) Prove '$\neg \forall \boldsymbol{x}\ \alpha$' $\vdash$ '$\exists \boldsymbol{x} \neg \alpha$' by extending (a).

9.1.4 (a) Prove Ext, '$S \neq T$' $\vdash$ '$\exists y \neg (y \in S \Leftrightarrow y \in T)$' using part of Exercise **9**.1.2(a) and Exercise **9**.1.3(b).
(b) Prove Ext, '$S \neq T$' $\vdash$ '$\exists y \cdot (y \in S \wedge y \notin T) \vee (y \notin S \wedge y \in T)$' by extending (a) and using SubEq.

9.1.5 (a) Write a wff α (in 'core AST' – that is, without using the pair notation $\{\}$) to express the notion that for any y there exists a set S such that $S = \{y\}$.
(b) Prove Pair $\vdash \alpha$ (in core AST).

9.1.6 (a) Write a wff α (in core AST) to express the idea that for any x, y and z, there exists a set S such that $S = \{x, y, z\}$.
(b) Prove Pair, Union $\vdash \alpha$ (in core AST). Hint: $\{x, y, z\} = \cup\{\{x, y\}, \{z\}\}$.

9.1.7 (a) Write a wff α (in core AST) to express the fact that for any set A there is a set E such that $E \subseteq A$.
(b) Prove Null $\vdash \alpha$ (in core AST).

9.1.8 (a) Write a wff α (in core AST) to express the fact that for any set A there is a set N and a set P such that $N \in P$ and $A \in P$.
(b) Prove Pow $\vdash \alpha$ (in core AST).

9.1.9 'Adding new axioms to a theory cannot remove some of the consequences of the original theory.' Give a precise justification of this assertion by reference to the appropriate property of formal deductions.

9.1.10 Explain exactly how the syntactic variables $\boldsymbol{x}_1, \boldsymbol{x}_2, \ldots \boldsymbol{x}_n$ in α given by **9**.1D(1) are instantiated in Example **9**.1D.1.

9.1.11 Explain exactly how the syntactic variables $\boldsymbol{x}_1, \boldsymbol{x}_2, \ldots \boldsymbol{x}_{n+1}$ in β given by **9**.1D(2) are instantiated in Example **9**.1D.2.

9.1.12* Convert γ given by **9**.1D(3) to an equivalent wff in which $\exists$ is used instead of $\exists 1$ (a) for the special case $n = 1$ and (b) for the general case.

9.2 Some formal proofs in AST

In this section we formally prove a number of basic results of AST. Each result is first outlined informally and then expressed in the form $\Gamma \vdash \alpha$, where α is the formal theorem to be proved and Γ the set of (nonlogical) axioms on which α depends. In each case the set Γ is kept to a minimum, in accordance with the minimality principle stated in Section **8**.3A. The more complex proofs are decomposed hierarchically and explained intuitively. The proof format is as defined in Section **8**.3A. Note that in the informal outline of a property, we write 'in AST' to emphasize that the asserted result depends on some or all of the axioms given in Section **9**.1C.

In addition to MP, rule T, Ded and Gen, we also use some of the other metatheorems established in Chapter **8**, in particular $\forall$I, or universal instantiation (Property **8**.3D.1). Recall $\forall$I states that if $\Gamma \vdash$ '$\forall \boldsymbol{x}\ \alpha$' then $\Gamma \vdash \alpha^{\boldsymbol{x}}{}_{\tau}$ provided τ is substitutable for $\boldsymbol{x}$ in α. Note that the term τ may be $\boldsymbol{x}$ itself, or it may be another variable. These special cases are frequent. If τ is different from $\boldsymbol{x}$ then we may write '($\boldsymbol{x}$ RBy τ)' in the justification to indicate that $\boldsymbol{x}$ *is replaced by* τ.

9.2A Three simple proofs

We begin with three short proofs. The first theorem we demonstrate is the opposite of Ext. As mentioned, it is a consequence of the logical axioms, that is, it is a valid wff as defined in Section **7**.4B.

Property 9.2A.1

In AST, if two sets A and B are equal then they have the same members:

$$\vdash \forall A\, \forall B \cdot A = B \Rightarrow \forall x \cdot x \in A \Leftrightarrow x \in B$$ ■

Proof First, we apply the general properties of equality established in Section **8**.3E.

.1	$\vdash \forall A\, \forall B \cdot A = B \Leftrightarrow B = A$	[Prop. **8**.3E.2]
.2	$\vdash A = B \Rightarrow B = A$	[$\forall$I^2: .1; T]

Second, we prove two intermediate results:

.3	$\vdash A = B \Rightarrow (x \in A \Rightarrow x \in B)$	[LA4(b)]
.4	$\vdash B = A \Rightarrow (x \in B \Rightarrow x \in A)$	[LA4(b)]
.5	$\vdash A = B \Rightarrow (x \in B \Rightarrow x \in A)$	[T: .2, .4]

Finally, we combine and generalize:

.6	$\vdash A = B \Rightarrow (x \in A \Leftrightarrow x \in B)$	[T: .3, .5]
.7	$A = B \vdash \forall x \cdot x \in A \Leftrightarrow x \in B$	[MP: assum., .6; Gen]
.8	$\vdash \forall A\, \forall B \cdot A = B \Rightarrow \forall x \cdot x \in A \Leftrightarrow x \in B$	[Ded: .7; Gen^2]

■

Next, we formally prove that the union of two sets A and B is commutative, without formally introducing the operator $\cup$. This property results from Ext and the commutativity of the logical connective $\vee$, which is shown to be a tautology by the truth table method. We represent $A \cup B$ and $B \cup A$ by two variables C and D respectively. Here it is useful to abbreviate some intermediate wffs.

Property 9.2A.2

In AST, the union of two sets is commutative:

Let

$$\alpha_1 =_{\text{sym}} \forall x \cdot x \in C \Leftrightarrow (x \in A \vee x \in B)$$
$$\alpha_2 =_{\text{sym}} \forall x \cdot x \in D \Leftrightarrow (x \in B \vee x \in A)$$

Then

$$\text{Ext} \vdash \forall A\ \forall B\ \forall C\ \forall D \cdot (\alpha_1 \wedge \alpha_2) \Rightarrow C = D$$ ■

Proof First, we prove that assuming α_1 and α_2, C and D have the same members.

.1	$\vdash (x \in A \vee x \in B) \Leftrightarrow (x \in B \vee x \in A)$	[LA1]
.2	$\alpha_1 \vdash x \in C \Leftrightarrow (x \in A \vee x \in B)$	[$\forall$I: assum.]
.3	$\alpha_2 \vdash x \in D \Leftrightarrow (x \in B \vee x \in A)$	[$\forall$I: assum.]
.4	$\alpha_1, \alpha_2 \vdash x \in C \Leftrightarrow x \in D$	[T: .2, .1, .3]
.5	$\alpha_1, \alpha_2 \vdash \forall x \cdot x \in C \Leftrightarrow x \in D$	[Gen: .4]

Second, we apply Ext and complete the proof.

.6	$\text{Ext} \vdash (\forall x \cdot x \in C \Leftrightarrow x \in D) \Rightarrow C = D$	[$\forall$I^2: assum. (A RBy C; B RBy D)]
.7	$\text{Ext}, \alpha_1, \alpha_2 \vdash C = D$	[MP: .5, .6]
.8	$\text{Ext} \vdash (\alpha_1 \wedge \alpha_2) \Rightarrow C = D$	[Ded^2: .7; T]
.9	$\text{Ext} \vdash \forall A\ \forall B\ \forall C\ \forall D \cdot (\alpha_1 \wedge \alpha_2) \Rightarrow C = D$	[Gen^4: .8]

■

As a third example of a formal proof, we demonstrate the transitivity of the set relation $\subseteq$.

Property 9.2A.3

For all sets A, B and C, if $A \subseteq B$ and $B \subseteq C$ then $A \subseteq C$. ■

Proof First, we express this property formally and without using the derived predicate $\subseteq$:

$$\vdash \forall A\ \forall B\ \forall C \cdot (\forall x(x \in A \Rightarrow x \in B) \wedge \forall x(x \in B \Rightarrow x \in C)) \\ \Rightarrow \forall x(x \in A \Rightarrow x \in C)$$

Note that the theorem to be proved does not depend on any axioms of AST: it is a valid wff. It results from the transivity of implication in propositional logic, which may be proved to be a tautology by the truth table method. Thus, we take this fact as a starting point.

Let

$$\alpha_{AB} =_{\text{sym}} \quad x \in A \Rightarrow x \in B$$
$$\alpha_{BC} =_{\text{sym}} \quad x \in B \Rightarrow x \in C$$
$$\alpha_{AC} =_{\text{sym}} \quad x \in A \Rightarrow x \in C$$

The formal deduction follows:

.1	$\vdash \alpha_{AB} \Rightarrow (\alpha_{BC} \Rightarrow \alpha_{AC})$	[LA1]
.2	$\vdash \forall x \cdot \alpha_{AB} \Rightarrow (\alpha_{BC} \Rightarrow \alpha_{AC})$	[Gen: .1]
.3	$\vdash \forall x\, \alpha_{AB} \Rightarrow \forall x \cdot \alpha_{BC} \Rightarrow \alpha_{AC}$	[MP: .2, LA3(a)]
.4	$\forall x\, \alpha_{AB} \vdash \forall x \cdot \alpha_{BC} \Rightarrow \alpha_{AC}$	[MP: .assum, .3]
.5	$\forall x\, \alpha_{AB} \vdash \forall x\, \alpha_{BC} \Rightarrow \forall x\, \alpha_{AC}$	[MP: .4, LA3(a)]
.6	$\vdash \forall x\, \alpha_{AB} \Rightarrow (\forall x\, \alpha_{BC} \Rightarrow \forall x\, \alpha_{AC})$	[Ded: .5]
.7	$\vdash (\forall x\, \alpha_{AB} \wedge \forall x\, \alpha_{BC}) \Rightarrow \forall x\, \alpha_{AC}$	[T: .6]
.8	$\vdash \forall A\, \forall B\, \forall C \cdot (\forall x\, \alpha_{AB} \wedge \forall x\, \alpha_{BC}) \Rightarrow \forall x\, \alpha_{AC}$	[Gen^3: .7]

■

These three examples are straightforward. They illustrate how formal proofs shadow their intuitive counterparts. The former are lengthier as they are more detailed. However, each step may be verified very easily and quickly as it involves the application of a simple symbol transformation rule and all the symbolic elements required are provided. Once the formal proof has been worked out, any flaw in the semiformal proof will have been tracked down and eliminated.

9.2B Uniqueness of the empty set

As a fourth example, we turn to a more elaborate case: the proof that in AST, the empty set is unique. In general, whenever we define a function by means of a formula, we must verify that the function is well defined; that is, that each element in its domain of definition is mapped to exactly one element by the function. In particular, this check should be carried out for every set-theoretical operation we have defined in Part **2**. The empty set $\varnothing$ may be regarded as such an operation, namely the nullary function returning $\varnothing$. The *existence* of $\varnothing$ is postulated in AST without naming this set: it is the Null axiom. It remains to verify the *uniqueness* of $\varnothing$, which we have so far regarded as intuitively obvious. It is a consequence of Ext.

In this section, we give the formal proof that there is a unique empty set, without actually naming it $\varnothing$. This proof may be regarded as typical: the uniqueness of other operations may be demonstrated by following a similar pattern. We leave such proofs to the reader.

We must first consider the following question: in general, how should we express the idea that an object x with a certain property is unique? The standard answer is: by asserting that for any object y, if y has the given property then $x = y$. (Thus, uniqueness may be expressed only in a language with equality.) We first express this idea formally.

Definition 9.2B.1

For any wff α and any variable $\boldsymbol{x}$, the wff

$$\exists 1\ \boldsymbol{x}\ \alpha$$

informally stands for 'there exists exactly one $\boldsymbol{x}$ such that α is true'. Formally, it is an abbreviation for

$$\exists \boldsymbol{x} \cdot \alpha \wedge \forall \boldsymbol{y}\ (\alpha^{\boldsymbol{x}}{}_{\boldsymbol{y}} \Rightarrow \boldsymbol{x} = \boldsymbol{y})$$

where $\boldsymbol{y}$ is any variable which is distinct from $\boldsymbol{x}$ and does not occur in α. (Note that in this definition $\boldsymbol{y}$ is not fully determined. This does not matter as the different wffs obtained by varying the symbol $\boldsymbol{y}$ are alphabetic variants, that is, equivalent.) ■

We may now assert the uniqueness of the empty set, both informally and formally.

Property 9.2B.1

In AST, there exists exactly one empty set. More precisely: there exists an empty set N, and for any set T, if T is empty then $N = T$. Formally:

(1) $\quad \text{Ext, Null} \vdash \exists 1\ N \cdot \forall x\ x \notin N$

Equivalently:

(2) $\quad \text{Ext, Null} \vdash \exists N \cdot (\forall x\ x \notin N) \wedge (\forall T \cdot (\forall x\ x \notin T) \Rightarrow N = T)$ ■

Proof First, (1) and (2) are equivalent by Definition 9.2B.1 with $\boldsymbol{x}$ instantiated to N, $\boldsymbol{y}$ to T and $\alpha =_{\text{sym}} (\forall x\ x \notin N)$. It remains to prove (2).

Second, we introduce a few abbreviations for wffs. Let

$$\begin{aligned}
\alpha_1 &=_{\text{sym}} \forall x\ x \notin N \\
\alpha_2 &=_{\text{sym}} \forall x\ x \notin T \\
\alpha_3 &=_{\text{sym}} \forall T \cdot \alpha_2 \Rightarrow N = T \ =_{\text{sym}} \forall T \cdot \forall x\ x \notin T \Rightarrow N = T \\
\alpha_4 &=_{\text{sym}} \forall x \cdot x \in N \Leftrightarrow x \in T
\end{aligned}$$

Now our main goal is to demonstrate that Ext, Null $\vdash$ '$\exists N \cdot \alpha_1 \wedge \alpha_3$'. We begin by working out a main proof, first intuitively and then formally. In so doing we identify intermediate results to be proved, or proof subgoals, and these are demonstrated separately. The overall proof is a hierarchy of elementary proof units.

For the main proof, we note that the wff to prove has two main components, α_1 and α_3. This suggests a way of organizing the proof, though we must allow for the fact that α_1 and α_3 occur within the scope of '$\exists N$'. We observe that '$\exists N\ \alpha_1$' is the Null axiom, so we immediately have Null $\vdash$ '$\exists N\ \alpha_1$'. It is also clear (in fact a tautology) that if α_1 implies α_3, α_1 implies '$(\alpha_1 \wedge \alpha_3)$' and consequently '$\exists N\ \alpha_1$' implies '$\exists N\ (\alpha_1 \wedge \alpha_3)$', which is our main proof goal. Consequently, the overall proof is:

(1) Record Null $\vdash$ '$\exists N\ \alpha_1$'

(2) Prove '$\forall N\ (\alpha_1 \Rightarrow \alpha_3)$'. This depends on Ext, so we must show that Ext $\vdash$ '$\forall N\ (\alpha_1 \Rightarrow \alpha_3)$'. This is our first proof subgoal, Property **9**.2B.2.

(3) Show that '$\forall N\ (\alpha_1 \Rightarrow \alpha_3)$' implies '$(\exists N\ \alpha_1 \Rightarrow \exists N \cdot \alpha_1 \wedge \alpha_3)$'. This is our second proof subgoal, Property **9**.2B.3. It does not depend on any assumptions.

(4) From '$\exists N\ \alpha_1$', Property **9**.2B.2 and Property **9**.2B.3, conclude that Ext, Null $\vdash$ '$\exists N \cdot \alpha_1 \wedge \alpha_3$'.

We formalize this reasoning as follows. The justifications of line .2 and .3 are forward references to Properties **9**.2B.2 and **9**.2B.3, respectively.

.1	Null $\vdash \exists N\ \alpha_1$	[assum.]
.2	Ext $\vdash \forall N\ (\alpha_1 \Rightarrow \alpha_3)$	[Prop. **9**.2B.2]
.3	$\vdash \forall N\ (\alpha_1 \Rightarrow \alpha_3) \Rightarrow (\exists N\ \alpha_1 \Rightarrow \exists N \cdot \alpha_1 \wedge \alpha_3)$	[Prop. **9**.2B.3]
.4	Ext $\vdash \exists N\ \alpha_1 \Rightarrow \exists N \cdot \alpha_1 \wedge \alpha_3$	[MP: .2, .3]
.5	Ext, Null $\vdash \exists N \cdot \alpha_1 \wedge \alpha_3$	[MP: .1, .4]

The last line is our main proof goal. It could also be derived in one step from lines .1, .2 and .3 by rule T as follows:

.4′	Ext, Null $\vdash \exists N \cdot \alpha_1 \wedge \alpha_3$	[T: .1, .2, .3]

Here, rule T accounts for the two successive applications of MP in the first derivation. The reader should compare these two alternatives. The second derivation is more compact but also less explicit. ■

It remains to prove the intermediate results on which Property **9**.2B.1 relies.

Property 9.2B.2

Let wffs α_1, α_2, α_3 and α_4 be defined as in the proof of Property **9**.2B.1. Then

$$\text{Ext} \vdash \forall N \cdot \alpha_1 \Rightarrow \alpha_3$$ ■

Proof The proof requires a preliminary result, namely that assuming α_1, α_2 implies α_4. We demonstrate this independently (Property 9.2B.2a).

.1	$\alpha_1 \vdash \alpha_2 \Rightarrow \alpha_4$	[Prop. 9.2.B.2a]
.2	$\text{Ext} \vdash \alpha_4 \Rightarrow N = T$	[$\forall I^3$: assum. (A RBy N; B RBy T)]
.3	$\text{Ext}, \alpha_1 \vdash \alpha_2 \Rightarrow N = T$	[T: .1, .2]
.4	$\text{Ext}, \alpha_1 \vdash \forall T \cdot \alpha_2 \Rightarrow N = T$	[Gen: .3]
.5	$\text{Ext}, \alpha_1 \vdash \alpha_3$	[$=_{\text{sym}}$ .4]
.6	$\text{Ext} \vdash \alpha_1 \Rightarrow \alpha_3$	[Ded: .5]
.7	$\text{Ext} \vdash \forall N \cdot \alpha_1 \Rightarrow \alpha_3$	[Gen: .6]

Property 9.2B.2a

Let wffs α_1, α_2 and α_4 be defined as in the proof of Property 9.2B.1. Then $\alpha_1 \vdash$ '$\alpha_2 \Rightarrow \alpha_4$'. ■

Proof

.1	$\alpha_1, \alpha_2 \vdash x \notin N \wedge x \notin T$	[$\forall I^2$: assumptions; T]
.2	$\vdash (x \notin N \wedge x \notin T) \Rightarrow (x \in N \Leftrightarrow x \in T)$	[LA1]
.3	$\alpha_1, \alpha_2 \vdash x \in N \Leftrightarrow x \in T$	[MP: .1, .2]
.4	$\alpha_1, \alpha_2 \vdash \alpha_4$	[Gen: .3]
.5	$\alpha_1 \vdash \alpha_2 \Rightarrow \alpha_4$	[Ded: .4]

■

Property 9.2B.3

Let wffs α_1 and α_3 be defined as in the proof of Property 9.2B.1. Then

$$\vdash \forall N (\alpha_1 \Rightarrow \alpha_3) \Rightarrow (\exists N\, \alpha_1 \Rightarrow \exists N \cdot \alpha_1 \wedge \alpha_3)$$ ■

Proof

.1	$\vdash (\alpha_1 \Rightarrow \alpha_3) \Rightarrow (\alpha_1 \Rightarrow (\alpha_1 \wedge \alpha_3))$	[LA1]
.2	$\forall N (\alpha_1 \Rightarrow \alpha_3) \vdash \alpha_1 \Rightarrow \alpha_3$	[$\forall$I: assum.]
.3	$\forall N (\alpha_1 \Rightarrow \alpha_3) \vdash \neg (\alpha_1 \wedge \alpha_3) \Rightarrow \neg \alpha_1$	[MP: .2, .1; T (contrap.)]
.4	$\forall N (\alpha_1 \Rightarrow \alpha_3) \vdash \forall N \cdot \neg (\alpha_1 \wedge \alpha_3) \Rightarrow \neg \alpha_1$	[Gen: .3]
.5	$\forall N (\alpha_1 \Rightarrow \alpha_3) \vdash \forall N \neg (\alpha_1 \wedge \alpha_3) \Rightarrow \forall N \neg \alpha_1$	[MP: .4, LA3(a)]
.6	$\vdash \forall N (\alpha_1 \Rightarrow \alpha_3) \Rightarrow (\neg \forall N \neg \alpha_1 \Rightarrow \neg \forall N \neg (\alpha_1 \wedge \alpha_3))$	[T(contrap.): .5; Ded]

Property 9.2B.3 is the symbolic equivalent of .6 by the definition of $\exists$.

■

$\alpha_1 =_{\text{sym}} \forall x\, x \notin N$

$\alpha_2 =_{\text{sym}} \forall x\, x \notin T$

$\alpha_3 =_{\text{sym}} \forall T \cdot \alpha_2 \Rightarrow N = T =_{\text{sym}} \forall T \cdot \forall x\, x \notin T \Rightarrow N = T$

$\alpha_4 =_{\text{sym}} \forall x \cdot x \in N \Leftrightarrow x \in T$

This completes the overall proof of Property 9.2B.1. Its hierarchic, modular organization is noteworthy. See Figure 9.2B.1. Each property is an articulation point of the overall proof, an important goal or subgoal. It is first identified and proved intuitively, and then demonstrated formally by the corresponding elementary proof unit.

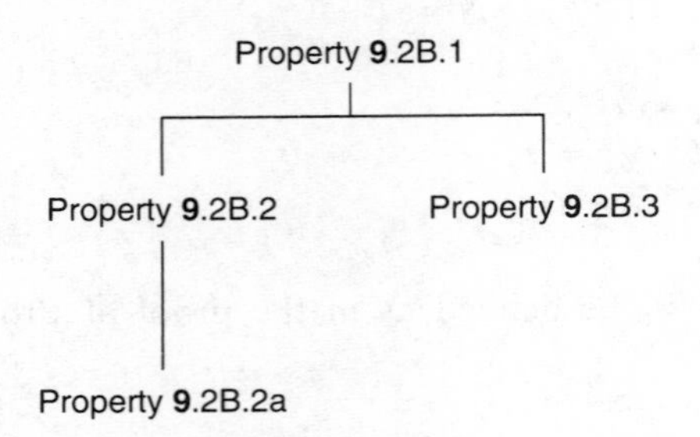

Figure 9.2B.1 Hierarchic structure of the proof of Property 9.2B.1.

9.2C Union of two sets

As a final example, we formally derive the existence of the union of two sets A and B from the existence of a set whose members are A and B (Pair axiom), and the existence of the generalized union of any set of sets (Union). This formal proof is also developed modularly, and illustrates the application of further metatheorems: rule of cases (Corollary 8.2B.3), contraposition′ (Corollary 8.2B.5), AlVa or alphabetic variant (Property 8.3C.4), $\exists$G or existential generalization (Property 8.3D.2), and rule C or choice (Property 8.3D.4). The proof is not given in its entirety. The missing elements are left as exercises.

The problem is formally to prove that in AST, for any sets A and B, we have $A \cup B = \cup \{A, B\}$, but without using the pair and union operations; that is, to demonstrate:

Property 9.2C.1

$$\text{Pair, Union} \quad \vdash \forall A\, \forall B\, \exists C\, \forall x \cdot x \in C \Leftrightarrow (x \in A \vee x \in B) \qquad \blacksquare$$

We use the following variables, with the corresponding stated meaning:

A, B	Given sets
C	Union $A \cup B$ (whose existence is to be proved)
P	Pair $\{A, B\}$
D	Any member of P
x	Any member of C

We also introduce the following abbreviations, which represent obvious intermediate properties given the intended meaning of the variables:

$$\alpha =_{\text{sym}} \quad \forall D \cdot D \in P \Leftrightarrow (D = A \lor D = B)$$
$$\beta =_{\text{sym}} \quad \forall x \cdot x \in C \Leftrightarrow \exists D\,(x \in D \land D \in P)$$
$$\gamma =_{\text{sym}} \quad \forall x \cdot x \in C \Leftrightarrow (x \in A \lor x \in B)$$

Thus, Property 9.2C.1 may be restated as Pair, Union $\vdash$ '$\forall A\, \forall B\, \exists C\, \gamma$'.

The overall proof consists of demonstrating five main properties as follows:

- Property 9.2C.1: Pair, Union $\vdash \forall A\, \forall B\, \exists C\, \gamma$ by Prop. 9.2C.2
- Property 9.2C.2: Union, $\alpha \vdash \exists C\, \gamma$ by Prop. 9.2C.3
- Property 9.2C.3: $\alpha, \beta \vdash \gamma$ by Prop. 9.2C.3 a,b
- Property 9.2C.3a: $\alpha \vdash \exists D\,(x \in D \land D \in P) \Rightarrow (x \in A \lor x \in B)$
- Property 9.2C.3b: $\alpha \vdash (x \in A \lor x \in B) \Rightarrow \exists D\,(x \in D \land D \in P)$

We can see intuitively that this proof outline is valid. We formalize it by constructing an elementary proof unit for each of the five properties.

Proof of Property 9.2C.1 First, we convert Pair to a suitable alphabetic variant instantiation, using AlVa and $\forall$I. This introduces the provisional variable P, which stands for $\{A, B\}$. Second, we introduce Property 9.2C.2 and eliminate P and the provisional assumption α, using rule C (choice), which leads to the main result.

.1 Pair $\vdash \forall x\, \forall y\, \exists P\, \forall D \cdot D \in P \Leftrightarrow (D = x \lor D = y)$
[AlVa²: assum. (A RBy P; z RBy D)]

.2 Pair $\vdash \exists P\, \forall D \cdot D \in P \Leftrightarrow (D = A \lor D = B)$
[$\forall$I²: .1 (x RBy A; y RBy B). Note the reintroduction of A]

.2′ Pair $\vdash \exists P\, \alpha$ [$=_{\text{sym}}$ .2]

.3 Union, $\alpha \vdash \exists C\, \gamma$ [Prop. 9.2C.2]

.4 Pair, Union $\vdash \exists C\, \gamma$ [C: .2, .3 (elimination of P and α)]

.5 Pair, Union $\vdash \forall A\, \forall B\, \exists C\, \gamma$ [Gen²: .4]

■

Property 9.2C.2

Union, $\alpha \vdash \exists C\, \gamma$ ■

Proof This is similar to the proof of Property 9.2C.1. First, we convert Union to a suitable alphabetic variant instantiation, using AlVa and $\forall$I. Second, we introduce Property 9.2C.3, quantify C existentially using $\exists$G and eliminate the provisional assumption β of Property 9.2C.3 using rule C. The application of

AlVa initially must be done with caution: we must first replace C by D, and then B by C. As C is thus reintroduced in a new role, these two steps must be carried out separately and in the right order.

.1	$\text{Union} \vdash \forall A\ \exists B\ \forall x \cdot x \in B \Leftrightarrow \exists D\ (x \in D \wedge D \in A)$	[AlVa: assumption (C RBy D)]
.2	$\text{Union} \vdash \forall A\ \exists C\ \forall x \cdot x \in C \Leftrightarrow \exists D\ (x \in D \wedge D \in A)$	[AlVa: .1 (B RBy C)]
.3	$\text{Union} \vdash \exists C\ \forall x \cdot x \in C \Leftrightarrow \exists D\ (x \in D \wedge D \in P)$	[∀I: .2 (A RBy P)]
.3′	$\text{Union} \vdash \exists C\ \beta$	[$=_{\text{sym}}$ .3]
.4	$\alpha, \beta \vdash \gamma$	[Prop. **9**.2C.3]
.5	$\alpha, \beta \vdash \exists C\ \gamma$	[∃G: .4]
.6	$\text{Union}, \alpha \vdash \exists C\ \gamma$	[C: .3, .5 (elimination of β)]

■

Property 9.2C.3

$$\alpha, \beta \vdash \gamma$$

■

The proof is a straightforward derivation from Properties **9**.2C.3a and **9**.2C.3b and the definition of β, using rule T and ∀I. It is left as an exercise.

Property 9.2C.3a

$$\alpha \vdash \exists D\ (x \in D \wedge D \in P) \Rightarrow (x \in A \vee x \in B)$$

Proof outline The proof is in four stages:

(1) We apply the axioms of equality via Property **8**.3E.5 to derive

$$\vdash D = A \Rightarrow (x \in D \Leftrightarrow x \in A)$$

and

$$\vdash D = B \Rightarrow (x \in D \Leftrightarrow x \in B)$$

(2) We apply the rule of cases to derive

$$x \in D \vdash (D = A \vee D = B) \Rightarrow (x \in A \vee x \in B)$$

$\alpha =_{\text{sym}}\ \ \forall D \cdot D \in P \Leftrightarrow (D = A \vee D = B)$
$\beta =_{\text{sym}}\ \ \forall x \cdot x \in C \Leftrightarrow \exists D\ (x \in D \wedge D \in P)$
$\gamma =_{\text{sym}}\ \ \forall x \cdot x \in C \Leftrightarrow (x \in A \vee x \in B)$

(3) We introduce α as an assumption and derive

$$\alpha, (x \in D \wedge D \in P) \vdash (x \in A \vee x \in B)$$

(4) Finally, we obtain the result by applying contraposition′ twice, Gen and Ded. ■

Formal proof of Property 9.2C.3a

.1	$\vdash x = x \Rightarrow (D = A \Rightarrow (x \in D \Leftrightarrow x \in A))$	
		[$\forall I^4$: Prop. **8**.3E.5 ($\boldsymbol{x}_1$ RBy x, $\boldsymbol{x}_2$ RBy D, $\boldsymbol{y}_1$ RBy x, $\boldsymbol{y}_2$ RBy A)]
.2	$\vdash D = A \Rightarrow (x \in D \Leftrightarrow x \in A)$	[MP: LA4(a), .1]
.3	$\vdash D = B \Rightarrow (x \in D \Leftrightarrow x \in B)$	[A RBy B in .1, .2]
.4	$x \in D, D = A \vdash x \in A \vee x \in B$	[T: assumptions, .2]
.5	$x \in D, D = B \vdash x \in A \vee x \in B$	[T: assumptions, .3]
.6	$x \in D, (D = A \vee D = B) \vdash x \in A \vee x \in B$	[cases: ass., .4, .5]
.7	$x \in D \vdash (D = A \vee D = B) \Rightarrow (x \in A \vee x \in B)$	[Ded: .6]
.8	$\alpha \vdash D \in P \Leftrightarrow (D = A \vee D = B)$	[$\forall$I: assum.]
.9	$\alpha, D \in P \vdash D = A \vee D = B$	[T: assum., .8]
.10	$\alpha, x \in D, D \in P \vdash x \in A \vee x \in B$	[MP: .9, .7]
.11	$\alpha \vdash (x \in D \wedge D \in P) \Rightarrow (x \in A \vee x \in B)$	[Ded^2: .10; T]
.12	$\alpha, (x \in D \vee D \in P) \vdash (x \in A \vee x \in B)$	[MP: assum., .11]
.13	$\alpha, \neg (x \in A \vee x \in B) \vdash \forall D \neg (x \in D \wedge D \in P)$	
		[contraposition′ (variant 1): .12; Gen]
.14	$\alpha, \exists D\, (x \in D \wedge D \in P) \vdash x \in A \vee x \in B$	
		[contraposition′ (variant 2): .13; def. of $\exists$]
.15	$\alpha \vdash \exists D (x \in D \wedge D \in P) \Rightarrow (x \in A \vee x \in B)$	[Ded: .14]

■

Property 9.2C.3b

$$\alpha \vdash (x \in A \vee x \in B) \Rightarrow \exists D\, (x \in D \wedge D \in P)$$

Proof outline The proof is in five stages:

(1) Prove $\alpha \vdash$ '$A \in P$'

(2) Derive α, '$x \in A$' $\vdash$ '$\exists D\, (x \in D \wedge D \in P)$' using $\exists$G.

(3) Prove $\alpha \vdash$ '$B \in P$' as in (1).

(4) Derive: α, '$x \in B$' $\vdash$ '$\exists D\, (x \in D \wedge D \in P)$' as in (2).

(5) Finally, derive Property **9**.2C.3b using the rule of cases. ■

Formal proof of Property 9.2C.3b

.1	$\alpha \vdash A \in P \Leftrightarrow (A = A \vee A = B)$	[$\forall$I: assum. (D RBy A)]
.2	$\alpha \vdash (A = A \vee A = B) \Rightarrow A \in P$	[T: .1]
.3	$\vdash A = A \vee A = B$	[LA4(a); T]
.4	$\alpha \vdash A \in P$	[MP: .3, .2]
.5	$\alpha, x \in A \vdash (x \in A \wedge A \in P)$	[T: assum., .4]
.6	$\alpha, x \in A \vdash \exists D\,(x \in D \wedge D \in P)$	[$\exists$G: .5 (A RBy D)]
.7		
...		
.10	$\alpha \vdash B \in P$	[Exercise: by analogy with .1–.4]
.11		
.12	$\alpha, x \in B \vdash \exists D\,(x \in D \wedge D \in P)$	[Exercise: by analogy with .5, .6]

Let $\delta =_{\text{sym}} (x \in A \vee x \in B)$

.13	$\alpha, \delta \vdash x \in A \vee x \in B$	[assum.]
.14	$\alpha, \delta, x \in A \vdash \exists D\,(x \in D \wedge D \in P)$	[.6]
.15	$\alpha, \delta, x \in B \vdash \exists D\,(x \in D \wedge D \in P)$	[.12]
.16	$\alpha, \delta \vdash \exists D\,(x \in D \wedge D \in P)$	[cases: .13, .14, .15]
.17	$\alpha \vdash \delta \Rightarrow \exists D\,(x \in D \wedge D \in P)$	[Ded: .16]

■

$\alpha =_{\text{sym}} \forall D \cdot D \in P \Leftrightarrow (D = A \vee D = B)$
$\beta =_{\text{sym}} \forall x \cdot x \in C \Leftrightarrow \exists D\,(x \in D \wedge D \in P)$
$\gamma =_{\text{sym}} \forall x \cdot x \in C \Leftrightarrow (x \in A \vee x \in B)$

EXERCISES

9.2.1 Consider line .5 of the proof of Property **9**.2A.1. Fully justify the application of rule T in this line.

9.2.2 Spell out the condition which must be satisfied for Gen to be correctly applied in line .5, Property **9**.2A.2, and verify that this condition is met.

9.2.3 Give the full justification of line .8, Property **9**.2A.2.

9.2.4 Outline two methods of verifying that line .1 of Property **9**.2A.3 is indeed a tautology, and carry out the proof with the simpler method.

9.2.5 Repeat Exercise 9.2.2 for lines .4 and .7 of Property 9.2B.2, and line .4 of Property 9.2B.2a.

9.2.6 (a) Verify that line .2 of Property 9.2B.2a is indeed a tautology.
(b) Verify that line .1 of Property 9.2B.3 is a tautology.

9.2.7 Consider the reference to a logical axiom LA3(a) in line .5 of Property 9.2B.3. Write down this axiom.

9.2.8 (a) State the specific conditions which must be satisfied for the applications of AlVa to be correct in line .1 of Property 9.2C.1, and verify that these conditions are met.
(b) Repeat (a) for the applications of ∀I in line .2.

9.2.9 Verify the application of ∃G in line .5 of Property 9.2C.2.

9.2.10 Verify the application of rule C (choice) (a) in line .4 of Property 9.2C.1 and (b) in line .6 of Property 9.2C.2. In both cases, indicate how $\boldsymbol{x}$ and $\boldsymbol{y}$ are instantiated, spell out the specific conditions which the instance of $\boldsymbol{y}$ must satisfy and check that these conditions are met.

9.2.11 Prove Property 9.2C.3. The proof unit is five lines long.

9.2.12 Consider line .2 of the proof of Property 9.2C.3a. How is $\boldsymbol{x}$ instantiated in the logical axiom LA4(a) referred to in the justification?

9.2.13 Fully justify the application of rule T in line .4 of Property 9.2C.3a.

9.2.14 Consider lines .4–.6, Property 9.2C.3a. Establish the exact correspondence between the rule of cases (Corollary 8.2B.3) and this subdeduction by writing down how Γ, α, β and γ are instantiated.

9.2.15 Consider line .3 of the proof of Property 9.2C.3b.
(a) Indicate how $\boldsymbol{x}$ is instantiated in the logical axiom LA4(a) referred to in the justification.
(b) Justify the application of rule T in this line.

9.2.16 Write lines .7–.10 of the proof of Property 9.2C.3b by *suitably* updating lines .1–.4.

9.2.17 Derive lines .11 and .12 of the proof of Property 9.2C.3b from lines .5 and .6.

9.2.18 Fully justify the application of the rule of cases in line .16 of Property 9.2C.3b.

9.2.19* Formally prove that for any sets A, B, the pair $\{A, B\}$ exists and is *unique* (as a consequence of Ext and Pair). Conclude that $\{A, B\}$ is a well-defined function of A and B.

9.2.20* Formally prove that for any set A, $\varnothing \in \text{Pow}(A)$.

9.2.21* Formally prove some of the properties of set operations listed in Section **2**.3.

Part 4

Feature Notation, Lists and Trees

10 Complex Models and Feature Notation

10.1 Complex models, lists and trees

In the remaining chapters of this book, we develop theoretical models of 'realistic' and concrete objects or situations, what we have called 'distant systems' in Chapter **1**. These models typically involve multiple sets, and multiple relations or functions on these sets. Thus, we may regard the main concepts introduced in Chapters **2** and **3**, namely sets, relations and functions, as basic models, building blocks which we now combine to form new objects. Accordingly, we call the latter *complex models.*

In this section, we first consider a simple but typical and concrete example of a complex model. This is the description of a human organization, such as a business company or a leisure club. Second, we introduce various classes of *lists*, *trees* and related concepts informally. Lists and trees will be developed in Chapters **11** and **12** respectively. Finally, we outline a general class of complex models and a broad *taxonomy* giving the main dimensions of variation of objects in this class. We show that lists and trees, as described here, form subfamilies of this general class. Our taxonomy highlights the main relations between these subclasses. The advantages of this unified approach to lists and trees are briefly discussed.

Recall that in general, when we establish a theoretical model or concept, we do not seek to describe a single object, but a whole *class* of similar objects. For instance, the aim of our model of an organization is to describe not a particular entity, but a certain class of possible organizations, past, present or future, actual or potential. This is not new. Our purpose in defining the concepts of set, relation and function in Part **2** for instance was to describe the class of all sets, the class of all relations and the class of all functions. As a rule, a model nearly always represents not an individual object but a certain *class* of entities.

Furthermore, a model often involves not only a certain class of objects, but also certain *operations* on its members. An idea of fundamental importance in both computing and mathematics is to regard the description of a class and its associated operations (and perhaps other relations between members) as *one*, that is, as forming a *single model*. The reason for this view is that in general the *description* of a class of objects is bound up with the operations defined on them. In a sense, we may even define a description as an operation on the objects it describes.

Accordingly, all the models we develop in this and subsequent chapters are in two parts: first, a description of a class of objects, and second, a definition of operations on these objects. Again there is nothing really new here. In Chapter **2** we proceeded in this way with sets; we introduced first the concepts of elements and sets and second various relations and operations on these objects, such as membership, inclusion, union, intersection, and so on. In Chapter **3**, we first described relations and functions, and then operations on these, the so-called *higher-order* operations of Section **3**.6 essentially.

10.1A Concrete example of a complex model

A simple model of an organization, such as a business firm or a school, is as follows. It is an object, call it O, consisting of a set A of people and a set B of various resources: desks, books, telephones, tools, and so on. In addition, the organization features two relations. The first, say R, is on the set of people: for any $p, q : A$, $p \; R \; q$ means that *p reports to q*. The second relation, U, is between people and resources. For any $p : A$ and any $r : B$, $p \; U \; r$ means that *p uses r* – that is, r is currently allocated to p. Recall that ':' means '*by definition* a member of'.

It makes sense to consider these four features jointly, because we perceive the organization O as a single entity. It is an object with a single purpose, and the four features decribed are just 'aspects' of it.

As usual, this description is a model, that is, an enormously simplified representation of any organization. More precisely, it is a *theoretical* or *conceptual* model. Furthermore, it is by no means the only possible description of an organization. We could establish many different models, more or less similar to this one. Each would either describe the features mentioned in less or greater detail, or emphasize other features, for example relationships with other organizations, technological or financial considerations, and so on.

This model illustrates the general manner in which we describe classes of objects in the remaining chapters. In each case, an object is described as *an entity with a number of features*. Some of these features are variable, others are fixed. Moreover, each feature is an object in its own right, typically a component of the main object. Thus, to describe a class of objects always is a matter of *listing a minimum number of variable and fixed features of each of its members*, enough to define them completely.

For instance, we may summarize our model of an organization as follows. It is an object O with four variable features: the two sets A and B, and the two relations R and U described above. These are called *variable* because they generally vary from organization to organization. In addition O has certain fixed features. From our initial description, clearly both the domain and the codomain of R must be equal to A: $\mathrm{Dom}(R) =_{\mathrm{d}} \mathrm{Cod}(R) =_{\mathrm{d}} A$. Likewise, the initial description implies that $\mathrm{Dom}(U) =_{\mathrm{d}} A$ and $\mathrm{Cod}(U) =_{\mathrm{d}} B$. To these properties, we may add the condition that the two sets A (people) and B (resources) are disjoint. These properties are called fixed features because they are *constant*, that is, *true in any organization O*, by our very definition of an organization.

Our description of an organization is a *complex model* in the sense defined above, as it involves two sets, A and B, and two relations, R and U. Moreover, these four features are themselves interrelated in various ways: $\mathrm{Dom}(R) = A$, $\mathrm{Cod}(R) = B$, and so on.

As stated above, the definition of a class of objects is (almost) always accompanied by a collection of operations on these objects. We briefly outline basic operations on organizations by way of initial illustration. This aspect is only touched upon here, as operations are well illustrated in each of the models developed in subsequent chapters.

The first question to ask is: what is the purpose of operations on the class of objects under consideration? One answer in the present example is that we wish to describe not just the possible state of any organization at any point in time, but *the laws which determine the evolution of an organization.* This of course implies that we now regard an organization *not* as a static object, but as an *evolving one.*

Nine operations are needed for our purpose. Each operation is a function which may take one or two arguments, possibly including a given organization, and returns a new organization. The first operation is a nullary function which returns the 'empty' organization, in which the two sets are empty. Second, there are two operations on the human members of an organization O. One function adds a specified new member to O, and the other removes an existing member. Third, there are two similar operations on the resources of the organization, one to insert a new unit into the set of resources and one to remove a unit. Fourth, two operations are needed to make a person p report to another person q, and to annul such a relationship. Finally, another two operations are needed to allocate a resource unit to a member and to deallocate a resource. In each case, the initial and final organizations are regarded as *two distinct and static entities* linked by the operation.

These operations are typical. Naturally, in each case it is necessary to ensure that the operation is *consistently defined*. For instance, an authority relationship may be created only between two actual members of the given organization. Similarly, we may want to enforce the rules (actually additional conditions imposed on organizations) that nobody reports to more than one superior or that (at any time) a resource may not be used by more than one person. To ensure the consistency of operations is the analysis part of establishment.

In Section **10**.2, we introduce the Feature Notation we shall use in the sequel to express our theoretical models. Our first illustration is a formulation of the above model of an organization. The various ideas outlined here on the establishment of a model will be elaborated on in this section.

10.1B An approach to lists and related objects

Many concrete objects may be described as finite sets which are *totally* or *linearly* ordered. The most common example is a piece of text. It consists of a finite sequence, or *string*, of characters: letters, digits, other printed symbols and spaces. Another important example is a queue of people or facilities waiting to be served. Many more examples could be given. In each case, the object is the same. It consists of a set of elements, and these are totally ordered in the sense that each member has a successor, except for the last one of course (if it exists).

A list need not be finite. We have already come across an important instance of an infinite list: the natural numbers, totally ordered by their successor function. Here the elements on the list are not physical: they are numbers, conceptual objects. However, for the moment we shall consider only finite lists.

These examples show that a general, theoretical description of lists is of wide applicability. This is why we shall establish such a model and illustrate its applications here and in Chapter **11**. Our aims in this section are twofold. The first is to highlight a critical aspect of lists. The second is to outline the approach to lists used in this book. As pointed out in Section **1**.3D, this is the set-theoretical view, *not* the standard recursive description of functional programming.

What is a list?

The above informal description of a list is a common view, but it is *only partly correct*. The key question is: what do we mean by the *elements* of a list? We have already discussed a similar question in other contexts – see Sections **2**.1E and **3**.4C.

Consider, for instance, a list of characters such as

(L) a n a t h e m a

A *careless* description of this list would be something like this: "It consists of 'a', followed by 'n', followed by 'a', followed by 't', ... " This description is misleading, because it suggests that the elements of the list are the letters 'a', 'n', 'a', 't', ..., and that 'a', for instance, is followed by 'n' *and also by* 't'. This cannot be right, because in a total order each element can have only *one* successor.

Therefore the 'real elements' of (L) are *not* 'a', 'n', ...; they are *occurrences* of 'a', 'n', ..., which is totally different. A proper theoretical model of a list must capture this nuance, and must do it explicitly and clearly. So we are led to another question: 'How do we distinguish the various *occurrences* of letters in (L)?' The common sense reply is to distinguish them by their *position* in the list, that is, to say: "(L) has a first element 'a', a second element 'n', ..." This time, common sense does not let us down. It leads us to conclude that each element of (L) is *a position*, that is 1, 2, 3, ..., *together with* a letter in this position. Consequently ('a' in position 1) is not the same as ('a' in position 3).

Standard lists

There remains only a very small step to take from this description to the standard set-theoretical definition of a list, a matter of elementary formalization. A position together with a letter is a couple. Thus, the elements of (L) explicitly described form the set

$$\{(1, a), (2, n), (3, a), (4, t), (5, h), (6, e), (7, m), (8, a)\}$$

This is nothing other than the graph of a total function from the set $\{1, 2, \ldots, 8\}$ to a set of characters. Therefore we are naturally led to define a list as a total function from the set $I =_d \{1, 2, \ldots, n\}$, where n is any natural number, to some nonempty set. This is the standard set-theoretical definition or model of a list. Once more we see how a set-theoretical concept may in fact be very close to its natural counterpart, provided the latter is sound.

Next, we extend the notation slightly. First, for any natural number n:Nat, we denote the set $\{1, 2, \ldots, n\}$ by Pos_n. This may be described as the set of all positive natural numbers no greater than n; formally:

$$\text{Pos}_n =_d \{k\text{:Nat} \mid 1 \leqslant k \leqslant n\}$$

Second, the elements of a list need not be 'positioned characters'. They may be any 'positioned objects'. Therefore in general we assume that associated with any list L there is a set of elements called *values*, and the list itself is a total function from Pos_n to this set of values, where n is any natural number. We denote the value set by *Vals*. In the case of the list (L) given above, Vals is an appropriate alphabet. In general, *Vals* may be any set. We only impose the requirement that *Vals* be *nonempty*, for otherwise no list L could be defined for any positive n. The list L is introduced as usual by

$$L\colon \text{Pos}_n \to \mathit{Vals}$$

Note that as n may be any number, L is defined even if $n = 0$. In this case, $\text{Pos}_n = \varnothing$ and L is the *empty list*.

This is the standard set-theoretical definition of the concept of a list, or class of all possible lists (Mac Lane and Birkhoff, 1979). It is an object with the following variable features: (a) the number n, which determines its length; (b) the set Pos_n, although this is entirely determined by n (in future, we will call this set a *secondary* variable feature of L); (c) the value set *Vals*; (d) the function from Pos_n to *Vals*, also denoted by L; and (e) the *successor function* which defines the total order of Pos_n and therefore of the list L as a whole.

This last feature must be emphasized. It is the successor function S of Nat restricted to Pos_n, that is $\text{Pos}_n \diamond S$, with graph $\{(1, 2), (2, 3), \ldots, (n - 1, n)\}$. Thus a standard list involves not one but *two* functions, which is why we may call it a complex model, as defined in the introduction.

Henceforth we shall call Pos_n the *base set* of L, and the function $L\colon \text{Pos}_n \to \mathit{Vals}$ on its own the *value map* of L. Thus, the symbol 'L' has a narrow meaning (the value map), and a broader meaning (the list with all its features). Later, we shall remove this slight ambiguity. The total description of a list L is illustrated in Figure **10**.1B.1.

In addition to these variable features, a list L has various *fixed* features, properties true of *any* list. Examples are the conditions which the successor function must satisfy; as we shall see they are a subset of Peano's postulates for the natural numbers.

Generalized lists

The standard concept of a list is a useful starting point, but it is too restrictive. Therefore we generalize it in various ways. First, the total order of the base set

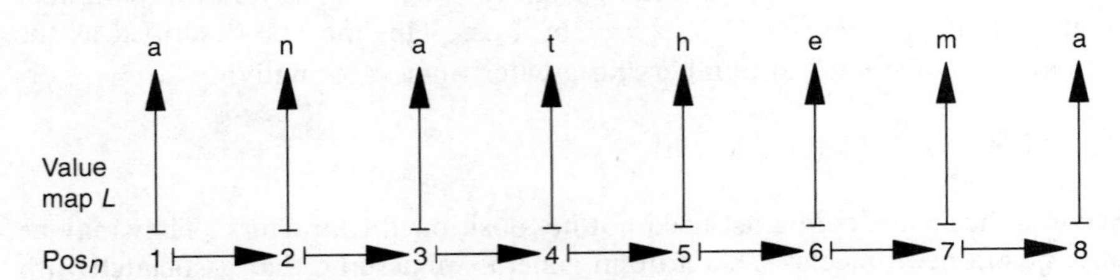

Figure 10.1B.1 A standard list L as a 'complex' model.

is often not an essential feature of the object modelled. In this case, a *family*, essentially an 'unordered list', is the appropriate model. Families were introduced in Section **3**.4C and are redefined in Chapter **11**. Second, there is generally no reason why the base set should be of the form Pos_n. We may allow the base set to be *any* countable set (see Exercise **4**.3.3), and if the total order matters, we order it by an arbitrary successor function. In general this is adequate because the individual nature of the members of the base set is immaterial: they are essentially *indexes*. This strategy, which we adopt, has important advantages. The members of the base set are called *base points*, and the set itself is denoted by *Pts*. Third, it is useful sometimes to consider a list just as an ordered set, *without values* associated with its base points. Such a list is called *unvalued*. Any set Pos_n together with its successor function is an example. Fourth, in addition to finite lists, we also allow lists with an infinite base set. Although such lists are not used explicitly in our applications, they are important in theory.

To sum up, we may define various classes of objects, all sharing some features of standard lists. Our approach is to establish the taxonomy of these classes, and then develop them systematically on this basis. Note that in Chapter **11**, lists and related concepts are expressed in the Feature Notation introduced in Sections **10**.2 and **10**.3, which is an 'extension' of the one used here.

Pointed lists

A useful extension of a list is the addition of a *pointer* to an element in the list. Consider for instance a piece of text as represented on a computer screen by a word processor. This can be described as a list of characters together with a *cursor*, a pointer to one of the characters. The purpose of the cursor is to indicate the position of the next input character, or of the character which would be removed by inputting the delete command ('backspace'). By moving the cursor forward or backward on the text, the user may delete characters selectively, or insert new text segments anywhere in the original text. A (valued) list together with a pointer to one of its elements will be called a *pointed list*. Formally it is a list L with a base set *Pts*, together with a selected base point C:*Pts*. This

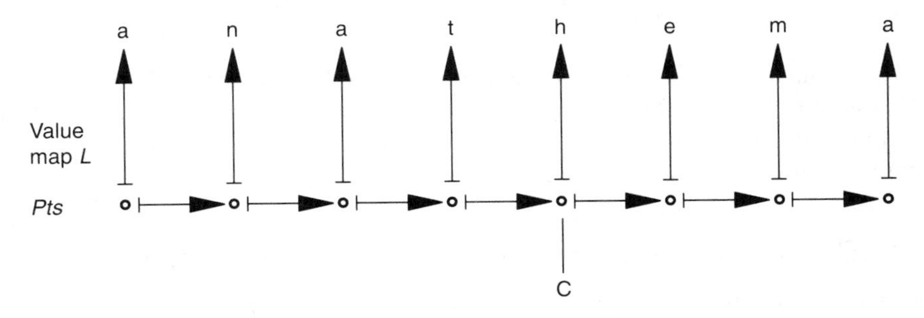

Figure 10.1B.2 A pointed list.

may also be regarded as a nullary function to the base set. An example, in which the base points are 'anonymous', is illustrated in Figure **10**.1B.2. The main taxonomy of generalized lists to be described is given in Table **10**.1B.1.

Table 10.1B.1 Main classes of generalized lists.

Family alias Fam
Class of all families, i.e. '*unordered valued* lists'
List
Class of '*unvalued*' lists, i.e. sequenced sets
ListV (etc.)
Class of *valued* lists, including *standard* lists
ListPTd0 (etc.)
Class of *pointed* lists (valued)

Operations on generalized lists

Various operations are defined for each class of generalized lists in Chapter **11**. In outline, these are as follows.

1 Operations on List The class of *unvalued lists* is named List. Operations on List consist of (a) two initialization operations which return an empty list and a list of just one unvalued point; (b) two inverse functions to concatenate two lists, and to split a list into two lists; (c) two inverse functions to insert a list between two points in another list, and to remove a sublist from another list.
2 Operations on ListV The class of *valued lists* is named ListV. This includes the standard lists. Operations on ListV are essentially the same as on List, extended with obvious definitions of value maps.
3 Operations on pointed lists Functions on pointed lists fall into two main groups: (a) *navigation operations*, which modify the pointer(s) without changing the underlying list; and (b) *list transformation operations*, which modify the underlying list or its values. The latter are essentially those defined on ListV.

The various classes of objects described above are constructed *modularly*, by successive extensions, in Chapter **11**. Corresponding operations are defined in a similar manner. Thus the taxonomy of operations mirrors that of list classes, from which it is actually derived.

10.1C An approach to trees and related objects

A tree is a theoretical model of hierarchies, or sets over which a 'parenthood' relation is defined. Instances of hierarchies abound. A familiar example is a book, whose components typically are parts, chapters, sections, subsections, and so on. These have the following fundamental property.

(1) The book may have one or several parts, but *each part belongs to exactly one book.*

(2) Each part may have one or more chapters, but *each chapter belongs to exactly one part.*

(3) Each chapter may have one or more sections, but *each section belongs to exactly one chapter.*

This rule extends to the lower units of the book. Equivalently we may say that each component proper of the book has exactly one '*parent*': each part, the book itself; each chapter, a certain part; each section, a certain chapter; and so on. The book itself has no parent. It is this general property which makes books instances of hierarchies.

Many more examples of hierarchies could be given: classification systems; structure of human organizations; modular structure of systems; and so on. These show that hierarchies may be found in all walks of life. Consequently, their abstract, theoretical model, namely the concept of a tree, is of universal applicability. This and related notions are established in Chapter **12** and further developed in Chapter **16**.

As with lists, there are two main approaches to trees: the recursive approach of functional programming, and the set-theoretical approach. The latter, which we have adopted, conveys the notion of a tree in a simple and natural way, as it closely reflects the above informal description of a book as a hierarchy. Our approach to trees is also very close to our construction of lists. This is not surprising, given that lists may be described as special cases of trees, as we shall see.

Basic definition of trees

The key characteristics of trees are as follows:

1 Like a list, a tree has a *base set* of '*points*', which we denote by Pts. This set is structured in a manner similar to the total order of lists.

2 A tree is either *unvalued* or *valued*, exactly as lists are: a valued tree is a tree with a *value map* $V: Pts \to Vals$ from the base set to some nonempty value set $Vals$.

3 It is often useful to augment a tree with one or more *pointers*, that is, selected base points, for the same reasons as with lists.

The main difference between a list and a tree is the structure imposed on the base set. In this respect, we must distinguish two types of tree: unordered and ordered. We first define *unordered, unvalued* trees.

Definition 10.1C.1

An (unvalued, unordered) tree is an object T with two primary variable features: a set *Pts*, the base set, and a relation *ParentOf* on *Pts*, that is, with domain and codomain equal to *Pts*. It is subject to the following conditions (fixed features):

(1) One of the points is singled out and called the *root* of the tree. It is named r. Thus, $r \in Pts$

(2) The relation *ParentOf* has the following interpretation: For any two points $i, j: Pts$,

$$i\ ParentOf\ j$$

means that i is the 'parent' of j.

(3) The root r has no parent: there is no $i: Pts$ such that $i\ ParentOf\ r$.

(4) For every other point $j: Pts$, j has exactly one parent, that is, there is exactly one $i: Pts$ such that $i\ ParentOf\ j$.

(5) For each point $j: Pts$, there must be a 'path' from the root r to j, that is a sequence $(r = i_0, i_1, \ldots, i_n = j)$ such that

$$i_0\ ParentOf\ i_1,\ i_1\ ParentOf\ i_2, \ldots, i_{n-1}\ ParentOf\ i_n$$ ■

The two features *Pts* and *ParentOf* of T are *variable* because in general they vary as we vary T over the class of trees. The conditions are called fixed features of T because they must be satisfied by every tree T, by the very definition of a tree. The fifth condition will be formulated precisely as an induction principle for trees in Chapter **12**. The root is a *secondary* variable feature of T because it is entirely determined by *Pts* and *ParentOf*.

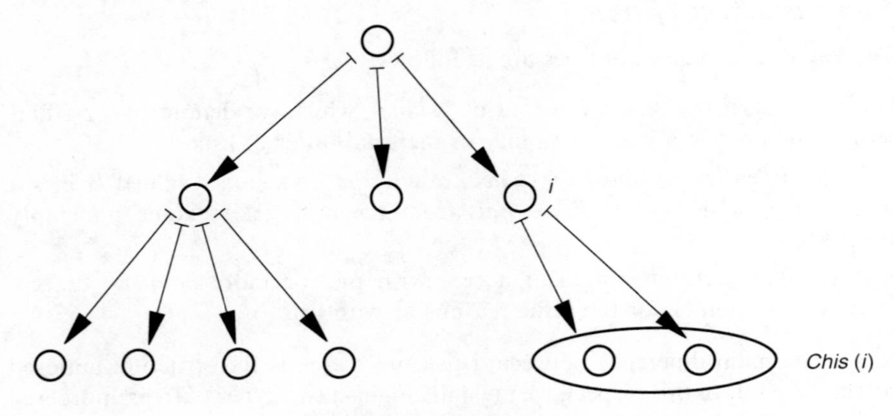

Figure 10.1C.1 A pure tree T.

For any point $i : Pts$, the set of 'children' of i is

$$Chis(i) =_d \{j : Pts \mid i \ ParentOf \ j\}$$

A list is a special case of an *unordered* tree: it is a tree in which for each point $i : Pts$, $Chis(i)$ contains *at most* one element. Thus in this case the relation *ParentOf* is functional. It is nothing other than the successor function of the list.

Ordered trees

In a pure tree, each set $Chis(i)$ is unstructured. An *ordered* tree is more structured. It is a tree in which each set $Chis(i)$ is itself totally ordered. More precisely, each set $Chis(i)$ is structured as a list.

A typical example of ordered valued tree is the parse tree T of an expression in a textual language. The value $V(i)$ of each $i : Pts$ is a component or subcomponent of the expression. $V(r)$ is the expression itself. For any $i, j : Pts$, $i \ ParentOf \ j$ represents the fact that $V(j)$ is a direct subexpression of $V(i)$. The tree is ordered, as the components of the expression are themselves totally ordered. For instance, the parse tree of the expression 'sqr(b) − 4 ∗ a ∗ c' is given in Figure **10**.1C.2. It reflects a certain decomposition of the expression; alternatives are possible.

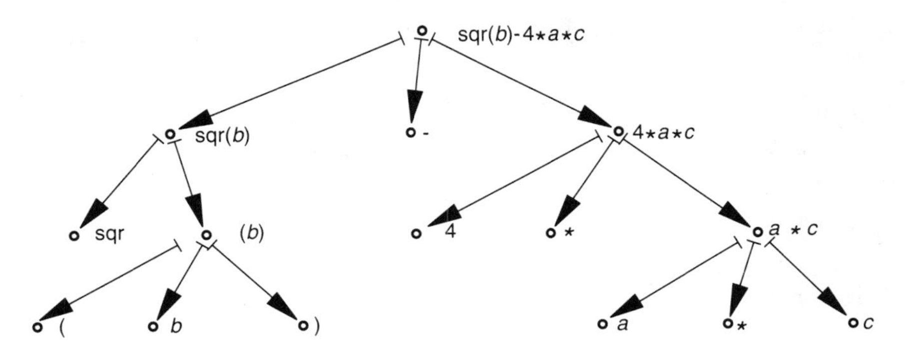

Figure 10.1C.2 Parse tree of a numeric expression.

Forests

A forest is another concept closely related to trees. A forest is usually defined as a set of trees. For reasons given in Chapter **12**, we shall *not* use this definition, however. We shall define a forest as a *generalization* of a tree: a forest is like a tree, except that it may have *any number of roots*, not just one. Conversely, a tree may be defined as a forest with exactly one root. Thus in this approach, the former is a special case of the latter. The special case of a forest with *no* roots is allowed. It is easy to see that in such a forest, the base set *Pts* must be empty.

Forests may be classified in the same way as trees. Thus we may distinguish between unordered and ordered forests, and between valued and unvalued forests. An ordered forest is ordered like a tree. In addition, its set of roots is also in sequence. In principle we may also add pointers to a forest, although the forests we shall use are all unpointed.

Taxonomy of forests and trees

The various distinctions defined above form a *taxonomy* of forests and trees. This is summarized in Table **10**.1C.1.

These various classes are developed *modularly*, by successive extensions, in Chapter **12**. Additional classes are established in Chapter **16**. As the table suggests, each extension adds a further feature to a previous class. Note the class ForOV1 is derived by so-called *specialization* of ForOV. This is a kind of extension; it is explained at the end of Section **10**.3D.

Table 10.1C.1 Taxonomy of forests and trees.

Forest Classes	*Tree Classes*
Forest alias For Basic class of forests, unordered and unvalued	Tree Basic class of trees, i.e. forests with one root
ForOrd Class of *ordered* forests (Extension of Forest)	TreeOrd Class of *ordered* trees
ForV Class of *valued* forests (Extension of Forest)	TreeV Class of *valued* trees
ForOV Class of *ordered valued* forests (Extension of ForOrd)	TreeOV Class of *ordered valued* trees
ForOV1 Class of *finite*, *ordered valued* forests (Specialization of ForOV)	TreeOV1 Class of *finite*, *ordered valued* trees
	TreePtd0 Class of *pointed*, *finite*, *ordered valued* trees (Extension of TreeOV1)

Operations on forests and trees

Various operations are defined in Chapter **12** on these classes of objects. These functions are similar to those outlined in Section **10**.1B on classes of generalized lists. They are also defined by successive extensions derived from the taxonomy of their underlying classes.

10.1D A general class of complex models

Our descriptions of lists and trees in Sections **10**.1B and **10**.1C are very similar. In each case, we are led to define a family of classes of objects, all sharing some features, and varying in complexity. Moreover, these two families are closely related. The difference between the various types of list and the various types of forest and tree is purely a matter of *structure imposed on the base set*. In the first case this structure is linear, and in the second it is the more general *ParentOf* relation, possibly augmented with an order on sets of children. Otherwise, the two families and their associated operations are developed in the same way.

This suggests that it may be useful to regard these two families of classes as part of a common and more general class of complex models. We first give a broad-brush description of such a class and its main taxonomy. Then we briefly discuss the advantages that this unified approach may yield. It is interesting to note the method we are using here: the common class is defined by *generalization* from the two families of subclasses we have defined. This method is a form of *abstraction*, as we obtain the general class by ignoring the distinctive features of the subclasses. It is also called *common induction* to distinguish it from *mathematical induction*, as defined in Chapter **4**.

The general class and its taxonomy

As usual, we introduce the general class by characterizing any object in it. A member X of this class is an object with *three main groups of features*:

(1) A *base set Pts* of '*points*', normally structured in some way

(2) Normally, a *value set Vals*, and a *value map* $V: Pts \rightarrow Vals$

(3) Optionally, one or more *pointers* to base points

The adverb 'normally' is used to indicate a feature which is optional but whose absence is somewhat exceptional. For instance, we allow objects whose base set is totally unstructured; these include simple sets and families. However, these are regarded here as special cases and used mainly as components of more complex objects.

We briefly consider these three groups of features in turn.

1 Structured base set The base set *Pts* is common to all objects X in the class. Moreover, it is *the linchpin connecting all other features* of X. It is structured by imposing one or more relations on it. In the case of a pure set or a family (in the mathematical sense), *Pts* is not structured at all. In the case of a proper list, there is one relation, namely a successor function $Pts \leftrightarrow Pts$. In the case of a forest or a tree there is also one relation, which we have named *ParentOf*. Its graph is a subset of $Pts \times Pts$, and it must satisfy the conditions given in Definition **10**.1C.1. Other ways of structuring *Pts* may be defined, possibly involving several relations. For instance, a *graph*, according to a certain concept belonging to the mathematical theory of graphs, may be described as a set *Pts* structured by *any* relation on it. Hence, lists, forests and trees are special cases of graphs defined in this way.

2 Value map $V: Pts \rightarrow Vals$ If it is defined, the value map is always described in the same way. First, there must be a nonempty set *Vals*, and second, there is the map itself, which we generally denote by *V*. In the applications treated in this book, this feature is totally independent from the structure imposed on the base set: the only link between these two features is the base set *Pts* itself. The value map may be generalized in various ways. For instance, we may define not one but several maps, perhaps a main one and a number of auxiliary ones for various purposes.

In some important computing data structures, the value map *is* related to the structure of the base set. For instance, in a (binary) search tree – essentially an ordered valued tree in our taxonomy – the set *Vals* is totally ordered, say by the relation $\leqslant$; the tree structure of the base set determines a total order on *Pts*, say *Bef*; and the order of the values $V(i)$ on *Pts* must be consistent with $\leqslant$, in the sense that for all $i, j: Pts$, if $i \; Bef \; j$ then $V(i) \leqslant V(i)$. This is a condition relating the value map and the structure of the base set.

3 Pointers In its simplest form, a pointer is a selected element of the base set *Pts*. Equivalently, it is a nullary function to *Pts*. This concept may be generalized in various ways. Thus, we may define a *set P* of pointers, which is essentially equivalent to a total function $P \rightarrow Pts$. For instance, in the applications of Chapter **16**, we define lists and trees with *two ordered* pointers. These are used to delimit two specific subobjects, a sublist and a subforest. More pointers could be added, to model the various types of marker found in word processors, for instance. We may go even further and impose a structure on the pointers themselves, though we shall not pursue this idea.

In all cases, pointers have one main role: they are *auxiliaries* in the definition of certain operations on the subclass of objects under consideration. They normally only depend on the base set *Pts* and, possibly, its structure; in general there is no direct connection between pointer(s) on the one hand and value map(s) on the other.

Induced taxonomy of operations

The above taxonomy of complex objects induces a corresponding taxonomy of associated operations. This has already been outlined for lists. The general principle is as follows. Any operation must determine some features of certain objects. Therefore the three main groups of features just defined suggest corresponding groups of operations: first, operations (re)defining the base set *Pts* of an object and/or its structure; second, operations (re)defining the value map of an object; third, operations (re)defining pointers, the so-called navigation functions. To these, we may add so-called *retrieve operations.* These are essentially informational functions: they return direct or implied features (functions) of a complex object, without transforming it in any way.

As a general strategy, we seek first to define '*minimal*' and '*orthogonal*' operations, each affecting as small a number of features as possible. Then, we seek to combine these basic operations to form more complex ones as appropriate. This is the essence of modular design, and it is illustrated in all the models developed in the remaining chapters.

Advantages of the unified approach

The general class of complex objects outlined above provides a unified approach to these objects, with the following benefits.

1 The description of the *main* common features of objects we have identified clarifies the multiple subclasses we have already mentioned. More precisely, it explains the relationships which exist between these various classes, in particular how they may be developed from one another by successive extensions. Thus it serves as a basis for the systematic development of these subclasses, and provides us with a map charting what is, after all, fairly complex territory. This is the main purpose of taxonomy.

This description also clarifies the multiple *operations* on the various subclasses involved, and their relationships. The systematic development of classes by successive extensions is naturally extended to the operations on these classes. This is very significant as, for each class, we generally define many different operations. In a nutshell, the unified approach lends conceptual clarity and coherence to our models, descriptions of objects *and* operations.

2 More specifically, this description is part and parcel of model *establishment.* One of its main aims is to determine the *dependencies* which exist between features, which is the analysis part of establishment. Here are some examples:

(1) The structure of the base set *Pts* of any complex object X necessarily *follows Pts* itself. Consequently any change to *Pts* must affect its structure. On the other hand, a change in the structure of *Pts* need not affect this set.

(2) The fact that the value map of X is independent of the structure of *Pts,* at least in our models, means that these two features may be handled independently of each other, *once the base set Pts has been fixed.* This greatly simplifies the establishment (specification and analysis) of operations in particular.

(3) Pointers necessarily follow the base set *Pts* of X and its structure. This suggests that pointers should be operated on *after* the base set and its structure have been fixed. This is the essence of navigation operations. Also the fact that pointers are not directly related to the value map means that these two features may be handled totally independently of each other. The consequence again is simplified establishment of operations.

Note that it would be wrong to conclude that any change in the base set of X or its structure must necessarily affect its pointers. On the contrary, in all our list and tree models, the primitive base set transformation operations are defined in such a way that the pointers are not themselves affected. This again simplifies the establishment of operations quite considerably.

These observations apply not only to lists and trees but also to all other classes of objects described similarly.

3 We are often led, given a certain object X (list, tree, and so on), to identify and operate on complex subobject(s) of X, rather than just individual points. In fact operations on subobjects are usually the most interesting! Moreover, the type of a subobject may well be different from that of the main one. Three typical examples are (a) the children of a point in an ordered tree, which form a list, (b) the path leading from the root of a tree to any other point, which is also a list essentially, and (c) the subobject of a tree induced by any subset of its base points, which in general is a forest. It turns out that our unified approach makes it much easier to describe such subobjects.

For instance, consider the set *Chis*(i) of children of a point i in an ordered tree T. The fact that T is ordered means that we must also describe these children as a list. Because we allow the base set of a list to be any set, we may take *Chis*(i) itself as the base set of this list; all we have to do is add a successor function. This is conceptually both simple and entirely natural.

In contrast, the definition of this list as a standard list is much more cumbersome. It must be defined as a function $L\colon \mathrm{Pos}_n \to \mathit{Chis}(i)$, which means bringing in the set Pos_n with n specified as equal to $\mathrm{Num}(\mathit{Chis}(i))$. This is not the end of the story, because L specified in this way does not necessarily define a total order of *Chis*(i): in addition, we must require that L be *injective.* Draw a diagram to see what happens when this condition is not satisfied, taking a set *Chis*(i) of, say, five members.

10.2 Feature Notation for complex models

Theoretical models developed in practice to represent 'realistic' (distant) systems tend to be 'complex', in the sense that they may involve multiple sets and multiple relations on these sets. Moreover, as these models represent 'concrete' systems, for example actual organizations or actual physical systems, these multiple features generally need to be named individually. Consequently, we may expect models of 'real' objects to have many named features. In practice, tens and even hundreds of features are not unusual even for relatively simple models. Note that often a model is called 'complex' because it has many features, although *conceptually* it may be relatively simple. In such cases, the term 'large-scale', which we also use, may be a more accurate description.

In view of the proliferation of features which we may expect of complex models, a systematic method of naming features is clearly necessary. The Feature Notation now to be introduced is designed to meet this need. It is mainly an extension of traditional mathematical notation. We first present a critique of the latter, which provides the motivation for the new notation. We then introduce the basic elements of Feature Notation by means of the example given in Section **10**.1A. This is done in Section **10**.2A. In Section **10**.2B, we discuss some implications of this first model and give further examples. In Section **10**.2C, basic rules are given for creating names of features. In Section **10**.2D, it is shown by an example that the basic notation rules induce a tree structure on the set of features of a model.

Models established in Feature Notation are naturally modular. This property of the notation is due to its tree structure, and is further enhanced by a rule on model extension given in Section **10**.3. This aspect cannot be well illustrated by simple examples, but it is abundantly illustrated by the applications of Chapters **11** and **12** and Part **5**.

The basic 'modules' making up a model are represented in a standard 'Feature Notation format' which is described in Section **10**.2A. There is similarity between Feature Notation formats and the schemas of the specification language Z. However, there are also important differences between these two notations. A Feature Notation format gives a name to a class of objects, as a Z schema does, but also makes a clear distinction between (a) the name of the class and (b) the names of *variables* ranging on the specified class, of which there may be many. Thus, a variable is always symbolically distinct from the class over which it ranges. This distinction is not so clearly emphasized in Z case studies, where the prevalent method is to interpret a schema name as both a certain class and an object in this class.

10.2A Basic notation

Consider again the example of a complex model given in Section **10**.1A. This describes an organization as an object O with four features: two sets A (people) and B (resources), and two relations R and U on these sets.

Critique of the mathematician's notation

A mathematician would typically rephrase this original description in the following terms:

"An organization is an object $O =_d (A, B, R, U)$ where A, B, R and U are defined as follows:

(1) A and B are two disjoint sets (of people and resources respectively).

(2) R is a relation on A, that is, both its domain Dom(R) and its codomain Cod(R) are equal to A. ('$p\ R\ q$' means that p reports to q.)

(3) U is a relation between A and B, that is, Dom(U) $=_d A$ and Cod(U) $=_d B$. ('$p\ U\ r$' means that p uses resource r.)"

What is the intention behind this model? It is to introduce a *class* of objects called organizations, by describing any member in this class. For clearly we are not interested in any specific organization here, but the *concept* of an organization, in other words a certain class of organizations. Any member in this class, that is any organization, is described as an object O with four features: A, B, R, and U. Each feature or component is a more elementary object, with its own features. For instance, R and U are relations, so each has a domain, a codomain, a graph, and so on. The first step in Feature Notation is to give a name to the *class* introduced, say Organization in this example. Thus, any organization we wish to consider is introduced as a member of this class. This is done as usual by writing O: Organization.

Next, in the above definition O is clearly a variable ranging over Organization, that is, designed to represent any member of Organization. What about the other names, A, B, R and U? A is the first feature of the organization O, B the second, and so on. This notation is fine as long as we do not need to refer to more than one organization at a time. However, in reality we often do need to refer to several organizations simultaneously, which we do by introducing the corresponding number of variables, for example P, $O1$ and $O2$: Organization. In this case the usual mathematical notation lets us down: how do we refer to the features of P, $O1$, $O2$, and so on, corresponding to A, B, and so on in O? A common practice in mathematics is to give different names to features of different variables: for example, to introduce P by stating: 'Consider the organization $P =_d (C, D, S, V)$' or, which is a little better, 'Consider the organization $P =_d (A', B', R', U')$'. The reader is implicitly left to identify the features of P by matching (C, D, S, V) or (A', B', R', U') with (A, B, R, U) componentwise.

Feature Notation format

The main purpose of Feature Notation is to provide a more systematic method of naming objects and their features. The main rule is to name any feature of a specific object O by suffixing O with the general name of the feature. Thus, an organization is now introduced as an object O:Organization with four features OA, OB, OR and OU, each as defined above. This immediately introduces the features of, say, P:Organization, which are PA, PB, and so on.

Actually, more meaningful names are used. Instead of resorting to single letters as feature names, we mainly use *word prefixes* starting with an upper-case letter. Such names are called *elementary names* or *identifiers*. Variants of this basic rule for forming elementary names are discussed in Section **10**.2C.

Thus in the present example, we rename A as *Mems*, for 'set of members', and B as *Res*, for 'set of resources'. Likewise, we rename the two relations R an U as *Rep* for 'reports to' and *Use* for 'uses' respectively. With this convention, for an organization named O the four features of O become *OMems*, *ORes*, *ORep* and *OUse*. (Note that as a rule we use 's' as a suffix in a name to indicate that this name denotes a set, as in *OMems* and *ORes*. This is no more than a stylistic convention.)

In any O:Organization, the four features we have just named are *variable*, as they vary from organization to organization. O has a further explicitly stated feature, namely the property that the two sets *OMems* and *ORes* are disjoint. We may express this with the predicate

IsDisjoint(*OMems*, *ORes*)

This is a *fixed* feature, as it must be true in any O:Organization. All the same, it is a feature, and we also give it a name for reference purposes, namely *OCond1* (for 'condition 1').

The introduction of a concept is done in a standard format. For instance the above informal description of an organization, using the suggested more meaningful feature names, is formally established as follows:

O:Organization	
OMems: Set	Set of members
ORes: Set	Set of resource units
OCond1 .: IsDisjoint(*OMems*, *ORes*)	
ORep: *OMems* ↔ *OMems*	Authority relation
p *ORep* q: Bool	True iff p reports to q
(p, q: *OMems*)	
OUse: *OMems* ↔ *ORes*	Resource usage relation
p *OUse* r: Bool	True iff p uses resource r
(p: *OMems*, r: *ORes*)	

To sum up, this format should be read thus: A class called 'Organization' is established as follows. Any member O:Organization is an object with four *variable features*: *OMems*, *ORes*, *ORep* and *OUse*, specified as indicated. In addition, *O* must satisfy the condition named *OCond1*, that *OMems* and *ORes* are disjoint. This condition is a *fixed feature* of *O*, as it must be satisfied by *every* member *O* of Organization. It is indicated by the special symbol '.:' between '*OCond1*' and its definition. (Recall that for any sets *A* and *B*, '$A \leftrightarrow B$' denotes the set of all relations *R* with $\text{Dom}(R) =_{\text{d}} A$ and $\text{Cod}(R) =_{\text{d}} B$.) In this format '*O*' is the *example variable.*

The purpose of this format is also to indicate how *any name* denoting a member of Organization is introduced, that is, any variable ranging over this class. For instance, the *introduction* or *declaration*

O1: Organization

means, as usual, that *O1* is a member of Organization. In addition, it means that *O1* has the features *O1Mems*, *O1Res*, *O1Rep*, *O1Use* and *O1Cond1*. Their respective definitions are obtained by substituting '*O1*' for '*O*' wherever this occurs as the first component of a name in the above definition of Organization.

10.2B Discussion and further examples

To illustrate how the notation works in the case of Organization, suppose two persons, Albert and Beth, are members of both *O1* and *O2*: Organization. *O1* is a business company, and *O2* is a parachute-jumping club. Albert and Beth's membership of *O1* and *O2* is expressed by

Albert ∈ *O1Mems* and Beth ∈ *O1Mems*
Albert ∈ *O2Mems* and Beth ∈ *O2Mems*

Next, suppose that in *O1* Beth reports to Albert, but in *O2* it is the reverse. We express these two facts by

Beth *O1Rep* Albert

and

Albert *O2Rep* Beth

Thus, the notation is very precise. *p O1Rep q* indicates that *p* reports to *q within organization O1*, and the example shows that in general this qualification is indeed necessary.

For any *O*: Organization, the condition *OCond1* is not absolutely essential. Whether it is imposed or not is a modelling choice. It is also important to see what this condition does *not* imply. Consider again *O1* and *O2*: Organization. *O1Cond1* states that *O1Mems* and *O1Res* are disjoint, and *O2Cond1* that this is also true of *O2Mems* and *O2Res*. However, no constraints directly relate the features of *O1* to those of *O2*. Therefore, some elements of *O1Mems* may belong to *O2Res*, and similarly *O1Res* and *O2Mems* may have common elements. It is for the modeller (a) to see these consequences (the analysis part of the job) and (b) to decide whether they are acceptable or not (specification). Note there are various ways of preventing such 'unexpected features'.

Relations in Feature Notation

By way of further simple applications of Feature Notation, we now describe relations and functions in this notation. Consider (binary) relations first. Let Relation denote the class of all such objects. We want to state that any *R*: Relation is an object with the following primary features: a *domain*, a *codomain* and a *graph*. In Feature Notation, these are denoted by *RDom*, *RCod* and *RGr* respectively.

These three features are sets – that is, members of Set. Therefore, they are introduced by '*RDom*: Set', and so on. Moreover, they are *variable* features of *R*, as in general they vary as *R* varies over Relation. *RDom* and *RCod* may be any set, but the graph *RGr* depends on the other two sets: it must be a subset of the cartesian product $RDom \times RCod$:

$$RGr \subseteq RDom \times RCod$$

This completes the description of Relation, using *R* as example variable. The Feature Notation format is as follows:

<u>*R*: Relation</u>

RDom: Set	Domain of relation *R*
RCod: Set	Codomain of *R*
RGr: Set	Graph of *R*
RCond1 .: $RGr \subseteq RDom \times RCod$	

Notes

1 The introduction of *RGr* could be combined with condition *RCond1*, giving the equivalent definition shown below. In this alternative, the old condition *RCond1* still holds, but implicitly.

<u>*R*: Relation (Alternative)</u>

RDom: Set	Domain of relation *R*
RCod: Set	Codomain of *R*
$RGr \subseteq_d RDom \times RCod$	Graph of *R*

---

2 Given the above definition of Relation, the subsequent introduction of R: Relation is not the same as writing $R: A \leftrightarrow B$, where A and B are two predefined sets. The latter declaration may be rendered by

$$R\text{: Relation with } RDom =_{\mathrm{d}} A \text{ and } RCod =_{\mathrm{d}} B$$

for instance. Other methods will be introduced in due course.

3 In Chapter **3**, the domain, codomain and graph of a relation R have been denoted as functions Dom(R), Cod(R) and Gr(R) respectively. This notation is still valid, as an alias for *RDom*, *RCod* and *RGr*. However, in the sequel we shall generally use the latter, for two reasons. First, it emphasizes that *RDom* and so on are main features of R, that is, somewhat more closely connected to R than other functions of it. Second, this alternative is more consistent with the Feature Notation form of the other models we shall establish. ■

Functions in Feature Notation

Functions are special members of Relation. Therefore, we may introduce the class Function of all (possibly partial) functions in the same way as Relation. Simply add the functionality condition. In Feature Notation format, using F as an example variable, the definition is as shown below. Alternatively, Function may be introduced as an extension or, more precisely, a specialization of Relation. This is done in Section **10**.3D.

<u>F: Function</u>

$FDom$: Set	Domain of function F
$FCod$: Set	Codomain of F
FGr : Set	Graph of F

$FCond1 .. : FGr \subseteq FDom \times FCod$

$FCond2 .. : \forall\, x : FDom,\ y_1,\ y_2 : FCod \cdot$

$$[(x, y_1) \in FGr \wedge (x, y_2) \in FGr] \Rightarrow y_1 = y_2$$

10.2C Feature names

An *elementary name* or *identifier* is defined as a string of characters made up of an upper-case letter followed by zero or more lower-case letters, digits or other visible characters. The other visible charaters are mainly decorations like '′' (prime) or '″' (double prime). Digits are often used to distinguish different versions. They must not be confused with subscripts. Decorations tend to be used to name related objects in the same class, for example the argument and the result of an operation. For instance, an operation AddMember to insert a new member into an organization typically takes an organization as argument and returns a *different* organization as a result. It is convenient to introduce these two objects as O and O' : Organization respectively.

A *compound* name is a concatenation of one or more elementary identifiers. The rule on the formation of elementary names guarantees that any compound identifier may be decomposed in only one way into elementary components (unique readability).

Consider any definition of a class of objects in Feature Notation, such as O : Organization. The reference to a feature of O obtained by extending this name with a feature name is called a *feature extension.* For instance, *OMems* is a feature extension of O.

As a rule, only elementary identifiers should be used as feature names. If this recommendation is fully adhered to then any concatenation of elementary names indicates an explicit feature extension. This discipline lends great clarity to the system (tree) of feature names obtained. In practice, this rule is relatively easy to apply in most cases, but may have to be broken occasionally. When a feature is given a compound name, then the modeller should at least seek to justify this as an implicit feature extension.

The main method of constructing an elementary name is to take the prefix of the corresponding natural-language word. This rule establishes a simple and close connexion between the formal model and its natural-language counterpart. The rule on compound identifiers means that prefixes of different lengths may be used. This lends flexibility to the notation. Digits and decorations sould normally be used only as suffixes of elementary names. Recall also that in general we use the suffix '*s*' in an elementary name to indicate that this denotes a set.

A few exceptions to the main name formation rule may be tolerated for feature names which occur very frequently and therefore should be kept short. For instance we often use the name *Pts* to denote a *set of points.* This feature occurs in all the list, tree and related models developed in the next two chapters.

10.2D Implied tree structure

The basic rules of Feature Notation imply that in general the system of names making up a model has a tree structure. We shall now illustrate this property by a simple example.

Consider again the definition of Organization (Section **10**.2A). This format gives the first two levels of the total tree of feature names of O, which we call the *feature tree* of O. We develop the tree laterally, with the children of any point listed in the column on the right of their parent. Also, at each point we give only the name of the feature extension, or name *increment.* The first two levels are shown in Figure **10**.2D.1.

This initial tree gives the *direct* features of O. Two of these are themselves complex objects, with their own features. They are the relations *Rep* and *Use.* Consider *Rep* in particular. Using the first definition of Relation given in Section

O : Organization	
$OMems$: Set	Set of members
$ORes$: Set	Set of resource units
$OCond1$.: IsDisjoint($OMems$, $ORes$)	
$ORep$: $OMems \leftrightarrow OMems$	Authority relation
p $ORep$ q : Bool (p, q : $OMems$)	True iff p reports to q
$OUse$: $OMems \leftrightarrow ORes$	Resource usage relation
p $OUse$ r : Bool (p : $OMems$, r : $ORes$)	True iff p uses resource r

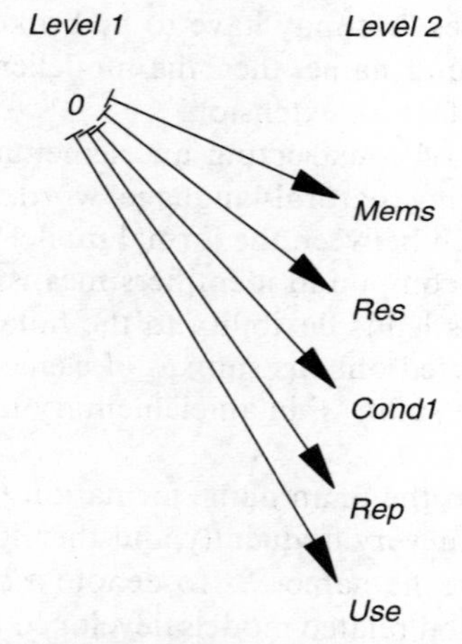

Figure 10.2D.1 Direct features of O : Organization.

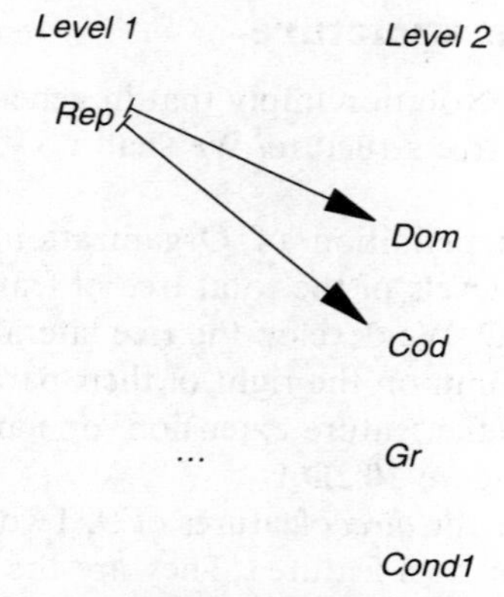

Figure 10.2D.2 Features of *Rep*.

10.2B, the feature tree of this object is given in Figure **10**.2D.2. (The ellipsis represents further arrows not explicitly shown.)

A similar tree may be obtained for *Use*. Now again consider O : Organization specifically. The features of *ORep* and *OUse* are *ORepDom*, *ORepCod*, and so on. These are also features of O and are called its *indirect* or *inherited* features.

We may now expand the initial tree of O : Organization by grafting the two feature trees of *Rep* and *Use* on these two points respectively. The result is shown in Figure **10**.2D.3. This gives the totality of O's features named so far, direct and inherited, in incremental form. Each full feature name is obtained by concatenating the increment names on a path leading from O.

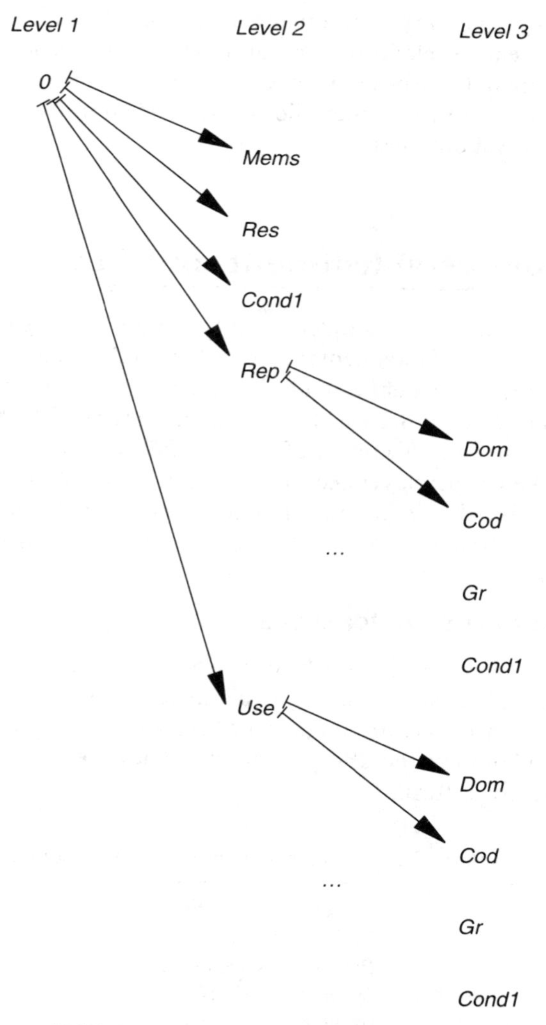

Figure 10.2D.3 Feature expansion of O : Organization.

Note the fundamental property of this tree. For each point, the incremental names of its children are all distinct and elementary. Consequently *all the full feature names of O, direct or indirect, are distinct from one another.* For instance, three features of *O* finish with '*Cond1*', but this causes no confusion, because the full names of these features are *OCond1*, *ORepCond1* and *OUseCond1*.

If compound names are used as (incremental) feature names, then the rule which ensures unambiguity of full feature names must be generalized a little. It becomes: for any two different children i, j of a given point, the incremental name of i must not be a prefix, proper or not, of the incremental name of j. Here by prefix of a compound name v we mean the subname made up of the first k elementary components of v, where $k \geqslant 1$.

The full Feature Notation tree of a system also reflects the hierarchic modular structure of this object in a clear way. Each subtree describes a distinct module. This shows how each module is a subsystem in its own right, with its own hierarchy of submodules.

10.3 Model establishment and Feature Notation

The features of a theoretical model fall into a number of general categories. This taxonomy plays a fundamental role in the establishment of such models. It seems appropriate to define it at this stage, as it is reflected in Feature Notation. This is done in Section **10**.3A, which elaborates on the introduction to establishment given in Section **1**.2F. This is followed, in Sections **10**.3B and **10**.3C, by a few key principles concerning the establishment of models in Feature Notation, based on this taxonomy. Finally, Section **10**.3D presents a further notation rule to enable the construction of models by successive 'extensions'.

10.3A Taxonomy of features

The taxonomy of features of an object consists of a number of classification dimensions. By 'dimension' we mean a partition of features into pairwise disjoint classes. (Partitions are defined in Section **3**.4D.) These partitions are combined 'freely' to form the whole taxonomy. They are listed in Table **10**.3A.1 and then described in turn.

Table 10.3A.1 Dimensions of feature taxonomy.

Direct	vs inherited
Variable	vs fixed
Primary	vs secondary
Specified	vs derived
Implicit	vs explicit

Direct versus inherited features

We have already made the distinction between direct and indirect, or inherited, features of an object. It is restated here for completeness.

Variable versus fixed features

Any feature of an object X in a class C is either *variable* or *fixed*. A feature of X is *variable* if it varies with X over C. More precisely, C must contain at least two objects differing at least by this feature.

For instance, in any O:Organization, *OMems* is a variable feature of O because there are many other O':Organization such that *OMems* $\neq$ *O'Mems*. Note that we are *not* saying that two different O and O':Organization must necessarily have different sets *OMems* and *O'Mems*; they may differ by other features. What we are saying is that as we vary O over the whole of Organization, there must come a point when *OMems* changes with O.

On the other hand, a feature of an object $X:C$ is *fixed* if it is constant *over the class C*. More precisely, for any two objects in C, the feature must be the same in both of them. A fixed feature is also called a *property* or *invariant* of the members of C. The standard way of defining a fixed feature is to give a predicate which is true for all objects in the class under consideration.

For instance in O:Organization, *OCond1* is a fixed feature. It is the property that *OMems* and *ORes* are disjoint. It is true of every member O of Organization (by definition of this class).

Whether a feature is variable or fixed depends on the class under consideration. A feature may be variable in a given class C and fixed in a subclass of C. For instance let Club $=_d$ {Albert, Beth, Cathy}. We may form the subclass of Organization consisting of all O:Organization in which *OMems* $=_d$ Club. This is obtained by adding the condition (predicate) *OMems* $=_d$ Club to the definition of Organization. Then clearly over this subclass, *OMems* is a fixed feature of O: it is always equal to Club. In Section **10**.3D we shall give a Feature Notation format for defining a subclass in this way, which we call *specialization* of the original class.

Primary versus secondary features

When we introduce a class C of objects, like Organization, we *specify* a number of features of its members. In general many more features of any $X:C$ may then be *derived by analysis*. We call the specified features *primary* and the others *secondary*. This distinction is fundamental. In other words, a feature of an object X is called primary if it plays an 'essential role' *in the definition of the class C* to which the object belongs, in the following sense.

The *variable* primary features of X are such that when all of them are fixed, X is *entirely* or *uniquely determined*. For instance for any O:Organization, the four variable features *OMems*, *ORes*, *ORep* and *OUse* are labelled primary features of O because when all of them are fixed, O is uniquely determined.

The *fixed* primary features of X form a set sufficient to determine the *class* C of X entirely. For instance, in the definition of O: Organization, there are one *explicit* and two *implicit* primary fixed features. The explicit property is condition *OCond1*, IsDisjoint(*OMems*, *ORes*). The implicit ones are

(a) $ORep \in$ Relation, $ORepDom = OMems$ and $ORepCod = OMems$.
(b) $OUse \in$ Relation, $OUseDom = OMems$ and $OUseCod = ORes$.

These are implied by the introduction of *ORep* and *OUse*, namely

$$ORep : OMems \leftrightarrow OMems$$
$$OUse : OMems \leftrightarrow ORes$$

respectively. These state that *ORep* and *OUse* are two relations whose domains and codomains are as specified, and this clearly restricts the class Organization.

The *secondary features* of an object X (in a class C) are all the features *implied* by the primary ones, those which can be derived from the latter by analysis. These again are either variable or fixed.

A *secondary variable* feature of X is any variable feature entirely determined by the primary ones. It is fixed once all the latter have been fixed. For instance, consider O: Organization again. This object has many variable features in addition to the primary ones mentioned so far, and each one of these is *secondary*. Here is an example. For each member $p : OMems$, we may define the set of all the resources used by p. This is

$$\{r : ORes \mid (p, r) \in OUseGr\}$$

This set is a *function* of p. Clearly this function is entirely determined once the primary variable features of O, namely *OMems*, *ORes*, *ORep* and *OUse*, have been fixed. Therefore it is a secondary feature of O. Many other examples could be given.

A *secondary fixed* feature of an object X (in class C) is any property implied by the primary ones. Like any fixed feature, it is true of all the members X of C. However, it is not part of the definition of C; it is a consequence of this definition.

For instance, any O: Organization has many properties implied by its primary features. A simple example is the following:

Property 10.3A.1

The two graphs *ORepGr* and *OUseGr* are disjoint. ■

Proof This is implied by the definition of the two relations *ORep* and *OUse*, as well as condition *OCond1*. If in any O: Organization, *ORepGr* and *OUseGr* were not disjoint, then there would be a couple $(p, x) \in ORepGr \cap OUseGr$. This would imply $x \in ORepCod \cap OUseCod = OMems \cap ORes \neq \varnothing$, which contradicts *OCond1*. ■

In the terminology of logic, the primary fixed features of a class of objects are the *axioms* defining this class, and the secondary fixed features are its *theorems*.

Specified versus derived features

The distinction between primary and secondary features is close to another distinction, which is that between *specified* and *derived*, or *implied*, features of an *individual* object. Suppose we have defined a class C of objects. The next step typically is to define *operations* on C. In order to define an operation, we must give a rule specifying one or more objects to be returned, usually depending on one or more arguments. Thus we face the general problem of specifying individual members of C, that is, determining them completely.

As already stated, given a class C, in order to specify a member X of C completely, all we need to do is ensure that all its *primary* variable features are fixed, consistently with the primary fixed features of the members of C. However, this does not mean that we must explicitly specify each primary variable feature and only such features. In some cases, X is entirely determined by explicitly fixing only a subset of its primary variable features. In other cases, it may be more convenient to fix explicitly a mixture of primary and *secondary* variable features. The primary features are then determined *by implication.*

Here is a simple example. An O: Organization may be entirely 'empty' – void of members and void of resources. In order to specify O, which incidentally is unique, all we need to do is set $OMems =_{\mathrm{d}} \varnothing$ and $ORes =_{\mathrm{d}} \varnothing$. The two relations $ORep$ and $OUse$ are then entirely determined: their graphs must be empty. Therefore there is no need to impose $ORepGr =_{\mathrm{d}} \varnothing$ and $OUseGr =_{\mathrm{d}} \varnothing$ explicitly: these conditions are implied by $OMems = \varnothing$ and $ORes = \varnothing$. Many other examples will be given later.

To sum up, what matters is to ensure that whatever method is used to specify an individual member X of a given class C, every *primary* variable feature of X is fixed, consistently with the primary properties of the members of C, *either directly or by implication.* Consequently, the distinction between specified and derived features must not be confused with that between primary and secondary features, even though they may coincide, at least partly.

Implicit versus explicit features

A final distinction is between implicit and explicit features of an object. Often a condition may be imposed on a feature of an object by the manner in which it is introduced, rather than by an explicit predicate. Such a condition is implicit. The two implicit fixed features of any O: Organization mentioned earlier are examples. They illustrate the fact that there is often a choice between imposing a condition implicitly or doing it explicitly. Alternatively, we may say that a feature is explicit iff it is given a name.

10.3B Principle of minimal specification

Specification of a class

In a theoretical model, the distinction between primary and secondary features is *arbitrary*: it is a matter of choice on the part of the model builder. Thus, it is generally possible to specify the same class of objects in several different ways, with some features, variable or fixed, labelled primary in one definition and secondary in the other. However, the selection of primary features should be guided by one fundamental rule, which we shall call the *principle of minimal specification*. This is as follows:

Principle of minimal specification of a class

In the definition of a class of objects, the set of features labelled primary, variable or fixed, should be minimal. ■

In other words, the set of features chosen as primary should be such that the elimination of any primary feature from it would modify the class of objects defined, by extending it or reducing it or both.

The number of primary features needed to specify a theoretical model completely is usually quite small by comparison with the number of secondary features one may be interested in. The reasons for applying the principle of minimal specification are as follows.

First, given a class C of objects, in order to specify any member X of C, all we have to do is ensure that all the *primary* variable features of X (a) are fixed and (b) satisfy the conditions (*primary* fixed features) imposed on all the members of C. Clearly, the smaller the set of primary features, the lesser the burden of specification and proof.

Second, if the set of primary features is not minimal, at least one of its members is either redundant, that is, implied by the others, or inconsistent with the others. In either case, the establishment of the class is at fault: the analysis part is deficient. Of course, the second case is more serious as it means that the class is incorrectly defined.

Even if the principle of minimal specification is followed, it is in general possible to define the same class C of objects in several different ways. However, suppose for instance that C is given by two different definitions *D1* and *D2*. In this case, there must be at least one feature primary in *D1* and secondary in *D2*, and another feature primary in *D2* and secondary in *D1*. Examples will be given in subsequent chapters.

In the light of these comments, we now add a further notation rule. It is sometimes convenient to include in the Feature Notation format defining a class some secondary features, for clarity. These are usually variable features. In such cases, *the primary variable features are marked with an asterisk (*) to distinguish them from the secondary ones.*

Specification of an individual member of a class

Subject to a minor qualification, the principle of minimal specification also holds for the specification of an *individual* member X of a class C, for example in the description of the result of an operation on C.

Principle of minimal specification of an element

An individual member X of a class C should be specified by fixing a *minimal* set of variable features. This set should be just sufficient to determine, *either directly or by implication, all the primary* variable features of X. ■

The reasons for this principle are similar to those given for the establishment of a class.

10.3C Specification of relations; secondary features

In Chapter **3**, the standard method of introducing a total function in mathematics was given. It is to write $f: A \rightarrow B$, which indicates that f is a member of the class of all total functions with domain A and codomain B. Possibly partial functions and relations are declared in the same way, using the symbols '$\nrightarrow$' and '$\leftrightarrow$' respectively. Note that the introduction '$f: A \rightarrow B$' does not specify f *fully*; it only fixes its domain and codomain and imposes on it the conditions which any total function must satisfy (fixed features).

We continue to use this notation, but only occasionally, whenever we wish to emphasize the limited information it conveys. The reason for this is as follows. In general, it is often necessary or at least natural to focus on the *members* of the sets (domain, codomain) involved in the specification of a relation (or function). If we do so, it is highly advisable to indicate, for each element referred to, the set (domain or codomain) to which it belongs. Likewise, the description must also make it clear whether the object described is a general relation, or a function, or a total function. This means that a proper 'element-oriented' description must contain all the information given by the standard introductory notation, and the latter may be dispensed with.

For instance, consider the specification of any O: Organization. The feature *ORep* is introduced as a relation between *OMems* and *OMems*. The key idea is that for any two members p and q of *OMems*, the notation 'p *ORep* q' states that p reports to q, which is either true or false. The natural way to express this is to write

ORep
  p *ORep* q: Bool True iff p reports to q
    (p, q: *OMems*)

in the definition of O: Organization. This clearly indicates that *ORep* is a binary relation with domain and codomain *OMems*. Therefore the introduction

$$ORep : OMems \leftrightarrow OMems$$

may be dispensed with.

Groups of secondary features

Consider the specification of any theoretical model given in Feature Notation format. The next step in the establishment of this model is to determine some of its secondary features, those which are likely to serve a useful purpose. As we proceed, we generally identify multiple groups of further features. It is convenient to represent each of these groups in a format similar to the original specification. We shall do so with an indication in the heading of each group that the features listed form a family of related secondary features.

For instance, a first group of secondary features of an O: Organization would be put in the form

O: Organization	Secondary Features I
...	...

Subsequent groups would be represented similarly.

10.3D Extension and specialization AT

The essence of modular design is to define object units which are then used as building blocks of more complex units. In Section 1.2C, we pointed out that this construction mode is universal. Its aim may also be described as the principle of *separation of concerns*: in constructing a system, the modeller should seek to treat its various features in isolation first, and then to combine them as simply as possible. The various complex models we shall develop in subsequent chapters will be built in this way. Feature Notation is well suited to this method, owing to its tree structure. However, the basic notation as described so far has a shortcoming, which we now make good.

This shortcoming may be illustrated by the following simple example. Consider again the concept of an organization, as modelled by O: Organization. Suppose that instead of allowing at once for both the human and the resource aspects of this notion, we decide to model these two features in two successive steps.

First, we define a simpler concept, say the notion of a human group, in which physical resources have no role to play. Let Group be the class of all such groups. In keeping with the original definition of Organization, any

G: Group is defined as an object with two features: (a) a set *GMems* of members (people); and (b) an authority relation *GRep* on *GMems*. The Feature Notation format (obtained by deleting three features of Organization) is as follows:

G: Group	
GMems: Set	Set of members
GRep	Authority relation
p GRep q: Bool	True iff *p* reports to *q*
(*p*, *q*: *GMems*)	

Second, we seek to define the full concept of an organization *by building on* Group. We shall call the new class to be defined Organization2. Using the basic Feature Notation rules, we may specify it by the following argument. An *O*: Organization2 is an object with the following features: (a) a group *OGr*: Group; (b) a set *ORes*: Set of resources; (c) the condition *OCond1* that *OGrMems* and *ORes* are disjoint; and (d) the relation *OUse* such that for any *p*: *OGrMems* and any *r*: *ORes*, *p OUse r* iff member *p* uses resource *r*. The format is as follows:

O: Organization2	
OGr: Group	Authority-structured membership
ORes: Set	Set of resource units
OCond1 .: IsDisjoint(*OGrMems*, *ORes*)	
OUse	Resource usage relation
p OUse r: Bool	True iff *p* uses resource *r*
(*p*: *OGrMems*, *r*: *ORes*)	

This construction is straightforward and gives another illustration of the ease of modularization in Feature Notation. However, compare the feature trees of Organization and Organization2, as given in Figure **10**.3D.1. It can be seen that the tree of Organization2 is slightly skewed, in comparison with that of Organization. It is 'deeper' at one end, owing to the additional point representing *OGr*: Groups.

The derivation of Organization2 may be regarded as an *extension* of Group. In practice we are often led to build models by repeated extensions of an initial core model. The shortcoming illustrated by one such extension soon becomes significant: each additional extension adds an extra level to part of the tree. The final result may be very lopsided. Moreover the compound feature names at the deep end of the tree are correspondingly long and hence unwieldy.

This example shows that in practice we need to be able to exercise more control over the tree structure of a model resulting from successive extensions.

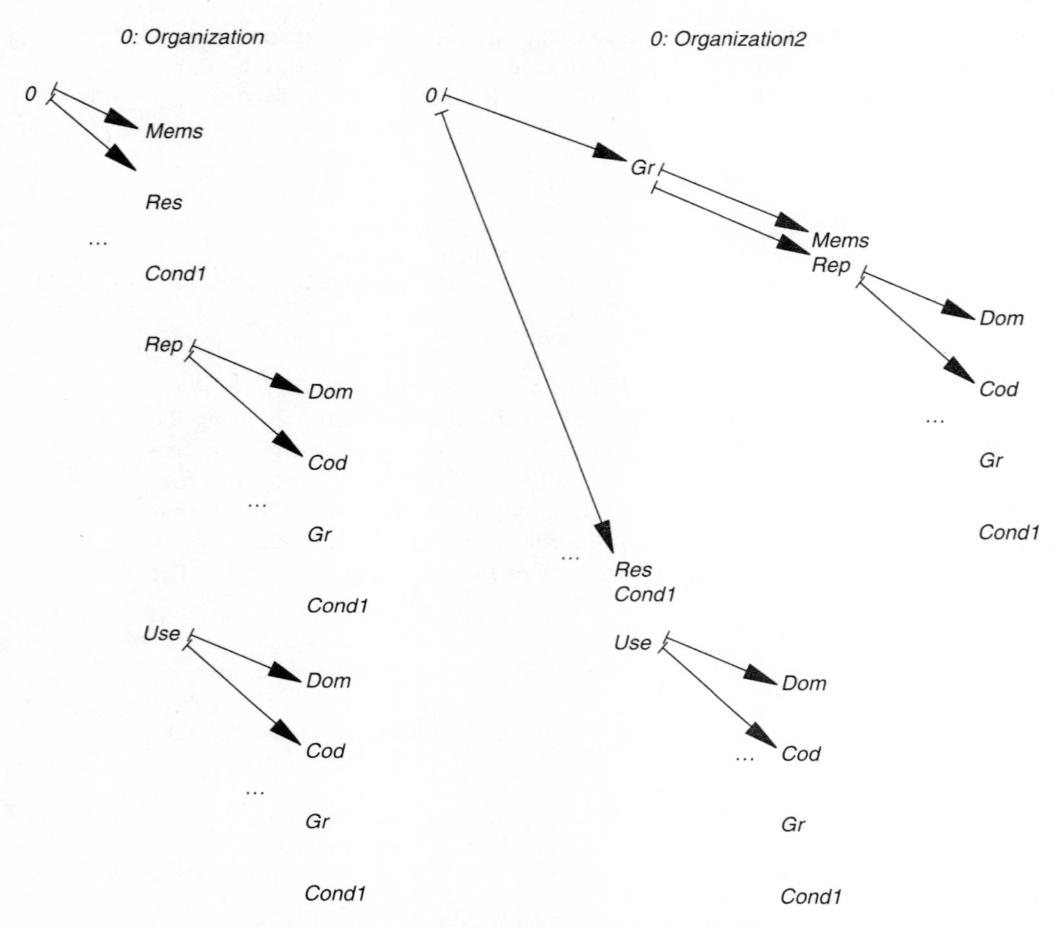

Figure 10.3D.1 Organization versus Organization2.

In particular, we should be able control its balance and depth. There is a simple method to do this. This is to make some intermediate points of the tree optional or, as we shall say, *dispensable*, in a sense we shall now define by means of an example.

Consider again O: Organization2. We now label the increment feature name '*Gr*' as *dispensable*. This is done in the Feature Notation format by enclosing '*Gr*' in square brackets. The meaning of this step is to indicate that '*Gr*' *must be eliminated in any compound name of a feature of OGr*. For instance, the two direct features of *OGr* are *OGrMems* and *OGrRep* in O: Organization2. With '*Gr*' cast as *dispensable*, these two features are renamed *OMems* and *ORep* respectively, and consequently become *direct* features of *O* in their own right.

The new format, which we shall name Organization3, is

O: Organization3	
O[*Gr*]: Group	Authority-structured membership
...	(Remainder as in Organization2)

This format states that the *direct* features of *O*: Organization3 are *OGr*: Group, together with *OMems*, *ORep*, *ORes*, *OCond1* and *OUse*, the latter defined as in Organization. That is, they are the same as in Organization, *with the addition of OGr*. The first two levels of the feature tree are as in Figure **10**.3D.2. In *O*: Organization3, we also call *OGr* a *group feature*, as it may be regarded as a name for a subgroup of *direct* features of *O*.

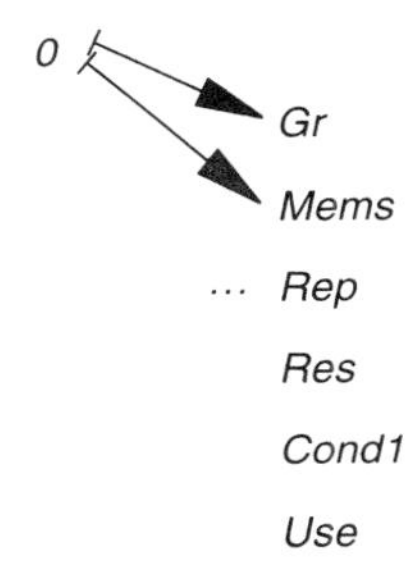

Figure 10.3D.2 Part of the feature tree of *O*: Organization3.

To sum up, in the definition of a model in Feature Notation format, any direct feature *F* may be cast as *dispensable* by enclosing its name in square brackets. This means that *the direct features of F are now also regarded as direct features of the object specified*. A feature whose name is dispensable is called a *group feature* as it names a subset of direct features of the specified object.

A format constructed in this way is called an *extension* of the group feature(s) it contains. Most extensions we shall develop contain only one group feature, but we shall give examples of extensions based on several group features simultaneously.

In practice, a useful sylistic convention is to name a group feature after the class to which it belongs. Thus instead of using *Gr*: Group in the above example, we would use *Group*: Group. This rule is an effective way of curbing the proliferation of names. It makes sense, as the class of a group feature cannot occur more than once in the format. Likewise, we find it convenient to separate the group features from the additional ones in the format by inserting a local heading with the class name prefixed with 'Δ'. This heading may also be used as the group feature name. The final version of Organization, incorporating these various ideas, is as follows:

O: Organization4	
$O[Group]$: Group	Authority-structured membership
ΔOrganization4	
$ORes$: Set	Set of resource units
$OCond1$.: IsDisjoint($OMems$, $ORes$)	
$OUse$	Resource usage relation
p $OUse$ r: Bool (p: $OMems$, r: $ORes$)	True iff p uses resource r

This again is an extension of Group. It combines the advantage of Organization with that of Organization2. The advantage of Organization is its flat, balanced feature tree, which implies *shorter compound feature names*. The advantage of Organization2 is its greater modularity, i.e. *enhanced separation of concerns*. In constructing Organization2, we really consider one group of features at a time: first, human aspects and then resources and relations between members and resources. To put it another way: *the construction of* Organization2, *hence* Organization4, is *incremental.*

Incremental definition of operations

Group features have proved to be very convenient modelling concepts. Consider a specification X: $C1$, built by extension of a more elementary class C. By our conventions, X has a feature XC: C which is a group feature. Having established $C1$, our next main step is to define operations on this class, or at least involving it. It is frequently convenient to construct such operations *in terms of operations on the more elementary class* C. By definition, such functions operate on objects in the class C, either as arguments or as results. The group feature XC is just the operand needed in these cases!

To sum up: our general approach to model building is highly *incremental*. We build models by successive extensions of an initial core, each extension bringing in only one or a small set of new related features. In parallel, we define at each stage a collection of operations involving the class being specified. The form of the successive extensions means that *the operations too are defined incrementally*, those on the more complex objects in terms of the functions defined on the simpler objects. We use this approach systematically in all the advanced applications of Chapters **11** and **12** and Part **5**.

Specialization

In general, an extension adds new primary variable and fixed features to the features of the members of a given class. Exceptionally, the only additional primary features are fixed features – that is, they are extra conditions. In this case, the formal extension only means that the new class is a subclass of the original one. The term extension then is a misnomer, and we call this construction a *specialization.*

An example of specialization has been given in Section **10**.3A . It consists of adding the rule $OMems =_d$ Club to the definition of O: Organization, where Club is the predefined set equal to {Albert, Beth, Cathy}. This subclass – call it Collegium – is introduced as follows:

O: Collegium (Specialized Organization4)

O[*Organization4*]: Organization4
ΔCollegium
OClubCol1 .: $OMems =_d$ Club

Another example is the definition of Function as a specialization of Relation:

F: Function (Specialized Relation)

F[*Relation*]: Relation
ΔFunction
FFunCol1 .: $\forall\, x : FDom,\ y_1,\ y_2 : FCod \cdot$
$$[(x, y_1) \in FGr \wedge (x, y_2) \in FGr] \Rightarrow y_1 = y_2$$

Aliases

Occasionally we shall introduce a long name together with a shorter alias. This applies in particular to class names, which are normally not abbreviated. For instance 'Organization' might usefully be introduced with the alias 'Org', which proves more convenient as group feature name.

11 Families and Lists

In Section **10**.1B we introduced the standard concept of a list as a function $L : \text{Pos}_n \rightarrow \textit{Vals}$ and pointed out that this concept is too restrictive. Often the only feature that matters is the value map. The total order of the base set may be the wrong structure or may be irrelevant. Further restrictions should be mentioned. First, in a finite list, there is no reason why the base set should necessarily be the set Pos_n for some $n : \text{Nat}$. There are advantages in allowing *any* finite set as base set. Second, in addition to finite lists, it is useful to define infinite lists, in the sense that the base set is infinite.

In this chapter, we first develop two preliminary concepts, the notions of *family* and *distributed* family. These were initially introduced in Section **3**.4C; our purpose now is to redefine them in a Feature Notation form consistent with our subsequent establishment of lists. The corresponding classes are called Family, alias Fam, and FamDist respectively.

Recall that a family is a total function whose domain members, often called *indexes*, have little or no relevance as individuals; the only property that matters is that they are distinct from one another. Furthermore, the domain has no structure. In this context, the domain of a family F is called the base set of F, and its members simply points. The base set of F is denoted by *FPts*. The codomain of F is called the *value set* and denoted by *FVals*.

A family F is *distributed* if, for each base point i, the corresponding value $F(i)$ is drawn from a value set which is itself a function of i. It is a family with multiple value sets or codomains.

Next, we introduce our main concept of a list, essentially as an extension of a family. This is done in two stages. First, we introduce the class List of *unvalued* lists. A member L: List is just a base set *LPts* of points in *sequence*, that is, totally ordered by a 'successor function'. Second, we introduce the class ListV of *valued* lists. An L: ListV is a total function from its base set *LPts* to a value set *LVals*, where *LPts* is in sequence. Thus, an L: ListV may be described either as an unvalued list augmented with a value map *LPts* → *LVals*, or as a family whose base set *LPts* is in sequence. Our formal definition of ListV reflects this double description. The value map itself is denoted by L in compliance with standard notation, or by *LV* to avoid ambiguity.

The standard concept of a list as a function $L: \mathrm{Pos}_n \to Vals$ is a special case of ListV. A valued list L: ListV is more general than the standard concept in two ways. First, we allow any set as base set *LPts*, and the successor function by which *LPts* is ordered is not necessarily the successor function of the natural numbers. Second, *LPts* may be finite or (countably) infinite. The case of an infinite list is allowed for mainly because of its theoretical importance. In this book, we are mainly concerned with finite lists.

In the remaining sections of this chapter, we describe some basic properties of lists and operations on lists. We terminate with a description of *pointed lists*. Essentially, a pointed list is a valued list augmented with 'cursors' or pointers to some of its base points. These pointers model the cursor and other markers of common screen text editors.

Our approach to lists has three main advantages. First, the description of some operations on lists is simplified. For instance, the concatenation of two lists L and *L1* is obtained quite naturally by merging their base sets and their successor functions, and making the first element of *L1* the successor of the last element of L. As for the value maps, these are simply merged. Second, lists described in this way arise naturally as 'subobjects' of other similar structures, such as other lists or trees. Third, our description of lists is in fact very close to an important *computer* representation of lists, namely the concept of a *linked list*, described for instance in Aho, Hopcroft and Ullman (1974). Thus, far from widening the gap between conceptual models and computer representations, or 'implementation features', our approach actually reduces it.

Recall the main taxonomy of generalized lists described in

Chapter **10**; it is restated here, in Table **11.1**. This taxonomy will be expanded to some extent.

Table 11.1 Main classes of generalized lists.

Family alias Fam
Class of all families, i.e. '*unordered valued* lists'
List
Class of '*unvalued*' lists, i.e. sequenced sets
ListV (etc.)
Class of valued lists, including *standard* lists
ListPTd0 (etc.)
Class of *pointed* lists (valued)

11.1 Families

We first define the class Family, alias Fam. The aim of our definition is to provide a first core of primary features common to all the types of list we shall consider later: any other list will be defined by *extension* of the concept of a family, that is, by adding further variable features and conditions.

Second, we introduce two extensions of the concept of family: a parametrized form, in which the value set is a parameter or argument of the class, and the distributed family mentioned above.

11.1A Definition of Family

A family F: Family consists of two sets *FPts* and *FVals* together with a total function or value map, also denoted by F, from *FPts* to *FVals*. Thus,

$$F: FPts \rightarrow FVals$$

FPts is the *base set* and *FVals* the *value set* of F. Either feature may be any set, and any structure it may have is ignored. *FVals* must not be empty. The formal definition in Feature Notation is given below. In this description, the three variable features are primary, which is indicated by the asterisk '*'. This means that a family F is entirely determined iff all three features are fixed, as with any function with specified domain and codomain. The new terms 'base' and 'value set' are introduced to harmonize our description with subsequent models. This does not mean the standard terminology is obsolete. We still regard any F: Fam as a function with a domain *FDom* ($=_d$ *FPts*), a codomain *FCod* ($=_d$ *FVals*), a graph *FGr*, and so on.

F: Fam alias Family (Specialized Function)

* *FPts*: Set	Base set of *F*, or set of 'points'. May be empty
* *FVals*: Set	Value set
* *F*(*i*): *FVals*	Value of point *i*
(*i*: *FPts*)	
FCoFam1 .: *FVals* $\neq_d \varnothing$	

Note that condition *FCoFam1* is *not* absolutely essential. It is there for 'good order'. We could allow a family to have an empty value set, but this would imply that the base set *FPts* too must be empty, as any *total* function with empty codomain must have an empty domain! To allow such a special case would be a potential source of errors for no apparent benefit. Therefore, we rule it out by condition *FCoFam1*.

11.1B Families with parameters AT

In any application, for any F: Family, the nature of the base points i: *FPts* usually does not matter: *FPts* is essentially an *index set*. In contrast, the nature of the values v: *FVals* is usually important. Moreover, *FVals* is often a *predefined* set and must be common to all the families considered in the application.

For this reason we introduce a class related to Family and denoted by Fam(*Vals*). This construction turns Family into a function of *Vals*. The latter is now treated as a parameter, a local variable in the definition of Family, to be replaced by a specific set in an application of this function. Specifically, for any given nonempty set *Vals'*, any F: Fam(*Vals'*) is an $F \in$ Family such that *FVals* $=_d$ *Vals'*. Note that for any *Vals*: Set, Fam(*Vals*) is a subclass of Family. More precisely, it is easy to see that, as a function of *Vals*, Fam(*Vals*) defines a *partition* of Family. The formal definition of Fam(*Vals*) follows.

F: Fam(*Vals*) (Specialized Family)

* *F*[*Fam*]: Family

ΔFam(*Vals*)

* *Vals*: Set

ValsCo .: *Vals* $\neq_d \varnothing$

FCoFamV1 .: *FVals* $=_d$ *Vals*

This description must be read as follows. Any object F in the class Fam(*Vals*) has all the features of an ordinary family: *FPts*, *FVals*, the function from *FPts* to *FVals* also denoted by F and the condition *FCoFam1*. All these features, inherited from Family, form the group named *FFam*. In addition, given the parameter *Vals*, F must satisfy the condition *FCoFamV1*. Therefore, Fam(*Vals*) is a *specialization* of Family, as the only additional feature is a constraint or fixed feature.

The condition *ValsCo* imposed on the parameter *Vals* is necessary to ensure that any member F of Fam(*Vals*) is indeed a member of Family, which requires that $FVals \neq \emptyset$.

Note the advantage of using the variable F as an 'example variable' in the definition. The full name of the feature *FVals* of F is distinct from the increment name *Vals*. Consequently the latter may be used as parameter name.

Example 11.1B.1

Suppose we wish to define three families *F1*, *F2* and *F3*, all with the same value set *Char*, here equal to {'a', 'b', ..., 'z'}. We introduce or declare these three families by

$$F1, F2, F3 : \text{Fam}(Char)$$

We may now legitimately perform any operation requiring *Char* as common value set with these three objects. For instance, we may test whether $F1(i) = \text{'a'}$ or $F1(i) = F2(j)$, where i is any member of *F1Pts* and j any member of *F2Pts*. We may also impose additional constraints – for example, $F1(i) \neq F3(k)$, where $k : F3Pts$. The set *Char* which is substituted for the argument *Vals* ensures that $F1Vals = F2Vals = F3Vals = Char$. Note that the same effect would be achieved by declaring

$$F1, F2, F3 : \text{Family where } F1Vals =_{\text{d}} F2Vals =_{\text{d}} F3Vals =_{\text{d}} Char$$

precisely. Thus the parametrized version of Family is mainly a syntactic convenience. ■

11.1C Distributed families AT

We now turn to a generalization of Family, the class FamDist of distributed families. Any F : FamDist has a base set *FPts* and a value $F(i)$ for each point i : *FPts*, like any ordinary family. The distinctive feature of F is that for any point i : *FPts*, the associated value $F(i)$ is drawn from a value set $FDistVals(i)$ which is a *function* of i. Thus, F is a family with multiple value sets or 'distributed values'. This concept was introduced in Section 3.4E. As an important example, recall that an n-tuple $(a_1, a_2, \ldots, a_n) \in A_1 \times A_2 \times A_n$ may be described as a distributed function or family, with domain $\{1, 2, \ldots, n\}$.

F: FamDist (Extended Family)

  * $F[Fam]$: Fam
  ΔFamDist
  * $FDistVals(i)$: Set — Value set of point i
    $(i: FPts)$
    $FCoDist1 .: \forall\, i: FPts \cdot FDistVals(i) \neq_d \varnothing$
    $FCoDist2 .: FVals =_d \cup \{FDistVals(i) \mid i: FPts\}$
    $FCoDist3 .: \forall\, i: FPts \cdot F(i) \in FDistVals(i)$

In this definition, an F: FamDist is described as an ordinary family with one additional variable feature, the function *FDistVals* from *FPts* to Set. This associates a set of values with each point i: *FPts*. The commanding condition is *FCoDist3*, which states that for each i: *FPts*, the associated value $F(i)$ must be a member of *FDistVals*(i). This in turn implies that each such set should be nonempty, which is condition *FCoDist1*.

Another consequence is that the set *FVals* cannot be left independent of the various sets *FDistVals*(i). As F is a family in its own right, each value $F(i)$ must also be a member of *FVals* by the definition of Family. Therefore we should have $FDistVals(i) \subseteq FVals$, and a reasonable way of ensuring this is to impose condition *FCoDist2*.

Again, neither condition *FCoDist1* nor *FCoDist2* is absolutely essential, but failing to enforce them would produce a very messy situation and could be a source of errors.

Note that FamDist is *not* a subclass of Family. The reason is that an F: FamDist has one *variable* feature more than an ordinary family, namely the function *FDistVals*. Moreover, it is a primary characteristic, as it is not determined by the other features of F. Thus, FamDist is a proper extension of Family.

It is also possible to define a distributed family F in which the function *FDistVals* is specified by a parameter. This will not be done here.

11.2 Lists

A standard list $L: \mathrm{Pos}_n \to Vals$ has two main features: (a) its base set Pos_n, which is the finite set $\{1, 2, \ldots, n\}$ totally ordered by the successor function S of Nat; and (b) the function L itself from Pos_n to *Vals*. In our approach to lists, we separate these two features, and the full concept of a list is established in two stages. First, we introduce the class List of *unvalued* lists. An L: List is a set *LPts* together with a successor function *LS* which imposes a total order on *LPts*. Second, we add a value map, a total function from *LPts* to a nonempty set *LVals* of 'values'. This map is also denoted by *L*, which is the standard notation, or by *LV* to avoid ambiguity. The resulting objects form the class ListV. Standard lists belong to this more general class.

11.2A Unvalued lists

We begin with the precise definition of the class List. First, the set *LPts* may differ from the base set Pos_n of a standard list in two ways: (a) *LPts* may be any set and (b) *LPts* may be either finite or (countably) infinite. Second, in order to define any *L*: List, the main task is to define the *successor function LS*. The main instance of a successor function is the function *S* of the set Nat of natural numbers. Therefore, we define *LS* in the way in which we have defined the Peano system (Nat, 0, *S*). All we have to do is relax Peano's postulates slightly in order to allow the base set *LPts* to be either finite or infinite. The reader should refer to Definition **4**.1A.1 before proceeding. A list is represented in Figure **11**.2A.1.

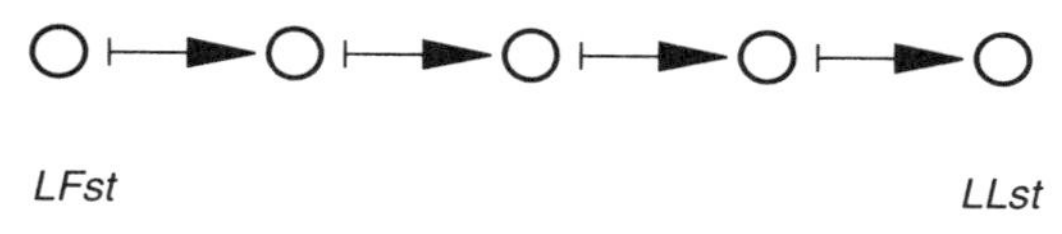

Figure 11.2A.1 A (finite, nonempty) list *L*: List.

We amend Peano's postulates in two ways. First, we allow *LPts* to be empty. In this case, *LPts* has no members, hence no *first* member. This is a partial relaxation of Peano's postulate (1). Second, we state that *LS* may be either *partial* or *total*. This is a partial relaxation of Peano's postulate (2), which requires *S* to be a *total* function. *LPts* is finite iff $LPts = \varnothing$ or *LS* is partial. (If $LPts = \varnothing$ then *LS* is a *total* function, vacuously!) If $LPts \neq \varnothing$ then there is a first point in *LPts*, which we denote by *LFst*. This first point is 0 in the case of (Nat, 0, *S*).

In conclusion, an (unvalued) list *L*: List is defined as an object *L* with three variable features: a set *LPts*, an element *LFst* and a (possibly partial) function $LS: LPts \nrightarrow LPts$. These are subject to the following additional conditions (fixed features of *L*):

LCo1 If *LPts* is nonempty then *LFst* is a member of *LPts* lying outside the range of *LS*, that is, $LFst \in LPts - LSRan$. This makes *LFst* the first point of *LPts*. *LFst* is treated as a *secondary* variable feature, as it is entirely determined by *LS* and the conditions imposed on this function.

LCo2 *LS* is injective. We state this by writing IsInjective(*LS*), where for any relation *R*, the predicate IsInjective(*R*) is true iff

$$\forall j: RRan\ \exists 1\ i: RDef \cdot i\ R\ j$$

LCo3 *LS* satisfies the induction principle (Peano's fifth postulate), which we restate as follows. For any set *A*, let '*A* ClosedBy *LS*' be the predicate true iff *A* is closed by *LS*: that is, for any points *i* and *j* such that $j =_{\mathrm{d}} LS(i)$, iff $i \in A$ then $j \in A$. Formally:

$$A \text{ ClosedBy } LS \text{ iff } \quad \forall i : A \cap LSDef \cdot LS(i) \in A$$

Now we define any set *A* to be *inductive* with respect to *LFst* and *LS* iff (a) $LFst \in A$ and (b) *A* ClosedBy *LS* (see Chapter **4**). The induction principle states that for any inductive subset $A \subseteq_{\mathrm{d}} LPts$, $A = LPts$. In other words, *LPts* is the smallest inductive set. We put these features together in the following definition.

<u>*L*: List</u>

* *LPts*: Set	Base set (of 'points')
LFst: *LPts*	First member of *L* (defined iff $LPts \neq \varnothing$)
* $LS: LPts \leftrightarrow LPts$	Successor function
$LS(i): LPts$ $(i: LPts)$	Successor of point *i* (may be undefined)

LCo1 .: If $LPts \neq \varnothing$ then $LFst \in LPts - LSRan$
LCo2 .: IsInjective(*LS*)
LCo3 .: *Induction principle*
$\forall A \subseteq_{\mathrm{d}} LPts \cdot$
If (a) $LFst \in A$
(b) *A* ClosedBy *LS*
then $A = LPts$

Notes

1 The definition of *L*: List means that *LPts* is either empty or the set *inductively generated* by *LFst* (regarded as a nullary function) and *LS*. Moreover, *LPts* is *freely generated* by *LFst* and *LS*, on account of *LCo1* and *LCo2*. Consequently, we may define recursive functions $h: LPts \rightarrow V$, where *V* is any set, on this basis.

2 For any *L*: List, if we impose $LPts \neq \varnothing$ and $LSDef =_{\mathrm{d}} LPts$ (i.e. *LS* is total), then *L* is a Peano system – the system (*LPts*, *LFst*, *LS*) in the notation of Chapter **4**.

3 In a standard list, the base set is the set Pos_n where *n* is any natural number. Pos_n may be described as the *L*: List where $LPts =_{\mathrm{d}} \{1, 2, \ldots, n\}$, and the successor function *LS* is the function *S* restricted to Pos_n, i.e. $LS =_{\mathrm{d}} \mathrm{Pos}_n \diamond S$. *n* may be equal to 0, in which case $LPts = \varnothing$ and *LFst* is undefined. Otherwise *LFst* is defined and equal to 1. Note that the notation Pos_n in itself is incomplete, as it represents only a set, not the successor function on it. The notation L and its feature extensions $LPts$ and LS capture all the essential elements of a sequence. ■

11.2B Basic secondary features of lists

Any list L: List is entirely determined by its primary variable features, $LPts$ and LS. These two features imply a number of secondary features. We have already introduced one, namely $LFst$. We now define a few more. First, note two elementary properties of L.

Property 11.2B.1

If $LPts$ is not empty then $LPts - LSRan$ has exactly one member, namely $LFst$. ■

Proof This follows from the induction principle, $LCo3$. In outline, if $LPts - LSRan$ had a member $i \neq LFst$, then $A =_{\mathrm{d}} LPts - \{i\}$ would be an inductive proper subset of $LPts$, contradicting $LCo3$. ■

Property 11.2B.2

If $LPts = \varnothing$ or $LPts$ is infinite then $LPts = LSDef$. Otherwise, the set $LPts - LSDef$ has *exactly one* member. ■

This should be intuitively clear. We now turn to variable secondary features of L.

LLst If $LPts \neq \varnothing$ and $LPts$ is finite, then by Property **11**.2B.2 there is exactly one point in $LPts$ with no successor. This is the *last* element of L; it is named $LLst$. It is determined by the relation

$$\{LLst\} =_{\mathrm{d}} LPts - LSDef$$

LPre Any injective function has a unique inverse (Section **3**.6E). The inverse of the successor function LS is called $LPre$. It is determined by $LPre =_{\mathrm{d}} \mathrm{Inv}(LS)$. Recall that this implies $LPreDom =_{\mathrm{d}} LSCod = LPts$, $LPreCod =_{\mathrm{d}} LSDom = LPts$ and

$$LPreGr =_{\mathrm{d}} \{(j, i) \mid (i, j) : LSGr\}$$

Two further obvious properties are $LPreDef = LSRan$ and $LPreRan = LSDef$. Moreover, an alternative specification of $LPre$ is $LPre: LPts \nrightarrow LPts$, $LPreDef =_{\mathrm{d}} LSRan$ and

$$\forall\, i: LSDef \cdot LPre(LS(i)) =_{\mathrm{d}} i$$

Here is a summary of these secondary features.

L: List Secondary Features I: Definitions	
$LLst: LPts$	Last element in the list (defined iff $LPts \neq \varnothing \wedge \text{IsFinite}(LPts)$)
$LDef1.: LPts \neq \varnothing \wedge \text{IsFinite}(LPts) \Rightarrow (\{LLst\} =_d LPts - LSDef)$	
$LPre(i): LPts$ $(i: LPts)$	Immediate predecessor of point i (may be undefined)
$LDef2.: LPreGr =_d \{(j, i) \mid (i, j): LSGr\}$ Equivalently: $LDef2'.: (1)\ LPreDef =_d LSRan$ $(2)\ \forall\, i: LSDef \cdot LPre(LS(i)) =_d i$	

11.2C Basic order properties of lists

In any L: List, the successor function LS determines a *total order* on the points $i: LPts$, which is precisely defined in Section **11**.2D. We shall now describe various basic secondary features of L associated with this order. Several of these features are sets. This is indicated by the suffix '*s*' in their names.

LAncs For any point $j: LPts$, consider the points $LPre(j)$, $LPre(LPre(j))$, $\ldots, LFst$. These points are the *ancestors*, or predecessors, of j in L. They form a finite set, which is denoted by $LAncs(j)$. This set is illustrated in Figure **11**.2C.1.

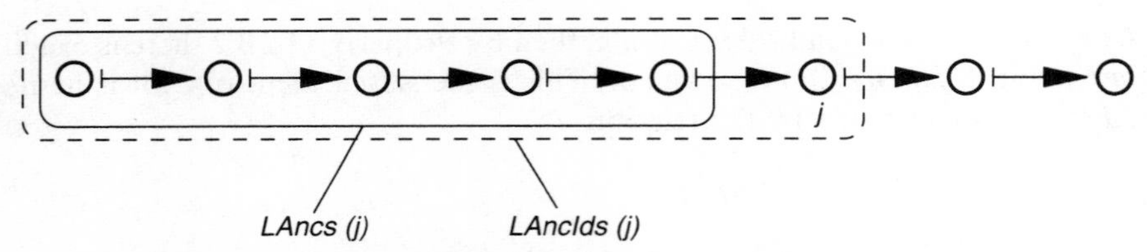

Figure 11.2C.1 Sets $LAncs(j)$ and $LAncIds(j)$ of point $j: LPts$.

The set $LAncs(j)$ is a subset of $LPts$. It is recursively defined for any $j: LPts$ by

(1) $LAncs(LFst) =_d \varnothing$

(2) $\forall\, i: LSDef \cdot LAncs(LS(i)) =_d LAncs(i) + \{i\}$

We thus have a total function

$$LAncs: LPts \to \text{Pow}(LPts)$$

where $\text{Pow}(LPts)$ is the powerset of $LPts$, $\{A \mid A \subseteq LPts\}$. The function $LAncs$ is well defined as a consequence of the recursion theorem and the fact that $LPts$

is freely generated by *LFst* and *LS*, as mentioned at the end of Section **11**.2A. Note the elementary

Property 11.2C.1

For any L: List and any $j: LPts$, $j \notin LAncs(j)$. ■

This property justifies the use of '+' in '$LAncs(i) + \{i\}$'. It can be proved by induction on L.

The next three features are similarly total functions from *LPts* to Pow(*LPts*).

LAncIds For any point $i: LPts$, we may form the set $LAncIds(i)$, defined as $LAncs(i)$ augmented with i itself:

$$LAncIds(i) =_{d} LAncs(i) + \{i\}$$

The name component '*Id*' stands for *identity*. See Figure **11**.2C.1.

LDescs For any point $i: LPts$, consider the set of points following i in L, that is, $LS(i)$, $LS(LS(i))$, and so on. We call these points the *descendants*, or successors, of i. Clearly any $j: LPts$ is a descendant of i iff i is an ancestor of j. Consequently the descendants of i form a set $LDescs(i)$ defined by

$$LDescs(i) =_{d} \{j: LPts \mid i \in LAncs(j)\}$$

The two functions *LAncs* and *LDescs* are symmetric and entirely determined by each other.

LDescIds For any point $i: LPts$, the set $LDescIds(i)$ is defined as $LDescs(i)$ augmented with i itself:

$$LDescIds(i) =_{d} LDescs(i) + \{i\}$$

The reader may verify that an equivalent definition of this function is

$$LDescIds(i) =_{d} \{j: LPts \mid i \in LAncIds(j)\}$$

This shows that *LAncIds* and *LDescIds* are symmetric and entirely determined by each other.

LDepth For any point $i: LPts$, $LDepth(i)$ is defined as the number of ancestors of i in L. Thus *LDepth* is a function $LPts \rightarrow$ Nat defined by

$$LDepth(i) =_{d} \text{Num}(LAncs(i))$$

for any $i: LPts$. Equivalently, we may define *LDepth* recursively by

(1) $LDepth(LFst) =_d 0$

(2) $\forall\, i: LSDef \cdot LDepth(LS(i)) =_d LDepth(i) + 1$

LBef The successor function *LS* defines a total order on *LPts*. This relation is denoted by *LBef* for 'before'. We use this name in preference to '<' in order to emphasize the existence of different total orders even on the same set; the overloading of '<' may be a cause of confusion. For any two points $i, j: LPts$, we write

$$i\ LBef\ j$$

to indicate that i is an ancestor of j in L. Therefore, $i\ LBef\ j$ is true iff $i \in LAncs(j)$; formally:

$$\forall\, i, j: LPts \cdot i\ LBef\ j \Leftrightarrow_d i \in LAncs(j)$$

LBef= For any $i, j: LPts$, we also write $i\ LBef{=}\ j$ to state that i is either before or equal to j in L. Thus, $i\ LBef{=}\ j$ is true iff $i\ LBef\ j$ or $i = j$; formally:

$$\forall\, i, j: LPts \cdot i\ LBef{=}\ j \Leftrightarrow_d (i\ LBef\ j \lor i = j)$$

L: List   Secondary Features II: Definitions

$LAncs(j) \subseteq_d LPts$	Set of ancestors, alias predecessors,
$(j: LPts)$	of point j
LDefAn1 .:	
(1) $LAncs(LFst) =_d \varnothing$	
(2) $\forall\, i: LSDef \cdot$	
$LAncs(LS(i)) =_d LAncs(i) + \{i\}$	
$LAncIds(j) \subseteq_d LPts$	Extension of $LAncs(j)$
$(j: LPts)$	
LDefAn2 .: $\forall\, j: LPts \cdot LAncIds(j) =_d LAncs(j) + \{j\}$	
$LDescs(i) \subseteq_d LPts$	Set of descendants, alias successors,
$(i: LPts)$	of point i
LDefAn3 .: $\forall\, i: LPts \cdot$	
$LDescs(i) =_d \{j: LPts \mid i \in LAncs(j)\}$	
$LDescIds(i) \subseteq_d LPts$	Extension of $LDescs(i)$
$(i: LPts)$	
LDefAn4 .: $\forall\, i: LPts \cdot LDescIds(i) =_d LDescs(i) + \{i\}$	
Equivalently:	
LDefAn4' .: $\forall\, i: LPts \cdot$	
$LDescIds(i) =_d \{j: LPts \mid i \in LAncIds(j)\}$	

$LDepth(i)$: Nat — Depth of point i

(i: $LPts$)

$LDefAn5$.: $\forall\, i{:}\, LPts \cdot LDepth(i) =_{\mathrm{d}} \mathrm{Num}(LAncs(i))$

Equivalently:

$LDefAn5'$.:

(1) $LDepth(LFst) =_{\mathrm{d}} 0$

(2) $\forall\, i{:}\, LSDef \cdot$

$LDepth(LS(i)) =_{\mathrm{d}} LDepth(i) + 1$

$i\ LBef\ j$: Bool — True iff i precedes j in L

(i, j: $LPts$)

$LDefAn6$.: $\forall\, i, j{:}\, LPts \cdot i\ LBef\ j \Leftrightarrow_{\mathrm{d}} i \in LAncs(j)$

$i\ LBef{=}\ j$: Bool — True iff i precedes j or $i = j$ in L

(i, j: $LPts$)

$LDefAn7$.: $\forall\, i, j{:}\, LPts \cdot i\ LBef{=}\ j \Leftrightarrow_{\mathrm{d}} (i\ LBef\ j \vee i = j)$

11.2D Trichotomy law

For any L: List, the function *LAncs* and the relation *LBef* are closely related. They are in fact equivalent. Given *LAncs*, we obtain *LBef* by the simple property used to define this relation. Conversely, given *LBef*, *LAncs* is determined by

$$LAncs(j) = \{i \mid i\ LBef\ j\}$$

for all j: *LPts*. Consequently, for any property of *LAncs*, there is a corresponding property of *LBef* and vice versa.

One such property is fundamental. It is the so-called *trichotomy* law, usually defined primarily as a feature of *LBef*. It is on account of this law that *LBef* is called a *total order*.

Theorem 11.2D.1 (trichotomy law)

For all i, j: *LPts*, exactly one of the following is true:

(1) $i\ LBef\ j$

(2) $i = j$

(3) $j\ LBef\ i$ ■

Corollary 11.2D.2

For all i, j: *LPts*, exactly one of the following is true:

(1) $i \in LAncs(j)$

(2) $i = j$

(3) $j \in LAncs(i)$ ■

Clearly the fact (Property **11**.2C.1) that, for any $j: LPts$, $j \notin LAncs(j)$ is a consequence of this corollary. The equivalence of the theorem and its corollary is obvious.

Corollary 11.2D.3
For all $i: LPts$, the three sets $LAncs(i)$, $\{i\}$ and $LDescs(i)$ are pairwise disjoint. ■

11.3 Basic operations on List

We now establish various basic operations on the class List of unvalued lists. These operations will mainly be used as 'building blocks' in subsequent developments. We first define two initialization operations, which return an empty list and a list of one element respectively. Then, we introduce two major operations: Concat, which concatenates two lists, and Split, which splits a list into two parts. Finally, we establish another two operations: Ins, which inserts a list within another one, and Rem, which removes a sublist from a given list.

Recall that any function may be *partially defined* on its domain. This applies in particular to list operations. If an operation is partial, its domain of definition is determined by conditions imposed on its domain elements. These are called *preconditions* of the operation. They are generally labelled (Pre 1), (Pre 2), ..., in the formal establishment of operations.

Whenever possible, an operation is defined so as to be fully *invertible*, and its inverse is developed in parallel with it. Concat and Split on the one hand, and Ins and Rem on the other, are established in this way.

This strategy, whenever appropriate, has several advantages. First, it clarifies the nature of both the original operation and its inverse. Second, the inverse operation may be established systematically by inverting the specification details of the original in reverse order, as an almost entirely mechanical exercise. Consequently, the specification of the original provides a tight guide in the development of the inverse and, reciprocally, the development of the inverse provides a second check of the original. Third, pairs of full inverses turn out to be particularly useful as components of more complex operations. One reason is that such operations often involve the composition of several more elementary functions, some of which are the inverses of some of the others. Another reason is that a complex operation is often needed with its inverse. If the former is a composite of invertible functions, the latter is automatically obtained as the composite of the corresponding inverses in reverse order. Many examples will be given.

11.3A Initialization operations

We begin with two very simple operations. The first is called EmpList. It returns an empty list, that is, a list L' such that $L'Pts =_{\mathrm{d}} \varnothing$. Its specification is immediate:

EmpList

Return the empty list.
EmpList $=_d L'$ where L' : List and
(1) $L'Pts =_d \varnothing$

The second operation, called InitList, does a little more. It returns a list L' with just one element. This element may be named at once, as it must necessarily be $L'Fst$. The specification of InitList is also immediate:

InitList

Create a one-point list L'.
InitList $=_d L'$ where L' : List and
(1) $L'Pts =_d \{L'Fst\}$

Notes

1 Both EmpList and InitList are nullary operations: they have no arguments.

2 In both specifications, only the minimum necessary information is given – see Section **10**.3B. Thus, the successor function $L'S$ is *not* explicitly specified. It need not be, because it is entirely determined by the specification of $L'Pts$. If $L'Pts = \varnothing$, as in the case of $L' =$ EmpList, $L'SGr$ is necessarily empty, as $L'SDef = L'Pts$ in this case. Likewise, if $L'Pts = \{L'Fst\}$, as in the case of $L' =$ InitList, $L'SGr$ is also necessarily empty, but for a different reason. In this case, $L'Pts$ is finite and nonempty, hence it must have a last element $L'Lst$ by Property **11**.2B.2, and $L'Lst = L'Fst$. Consequently $L'SDef = L'Pts - \{L'Lst\} = \varnothing$, and $L'SGr = \varnothing$.

3 InitList is *underspecified*: nothing in the establishment of this operation indicates what the element $L'Fst$ actually is. Consequently, $L'Fst$ may be any element which may be a member of a set $L'Pts$. The reason for not specifying $L'Fst$ is that *at this stage, the identity of the base points of a list does not concern us.* Therefore our strategy is to separate this matter from those features which we currently regard as essential. This is not to say that the identity of base points, $L'Fst$ in particular, is unimportant, because at some stage this issue must be settled. However, our strategy signifies that this matter must be dealt with *separately*, typically as an 'implementation feature'. We shall come back to the general question of the specification of base points at the end of this section. ■

11.3B Concatenation and splitting operations

The next two operations are Concat and Split. Given two lists L and $L1$: List satisfying appropriate conditions, the main result of Concat(L, $L1$) is a new list

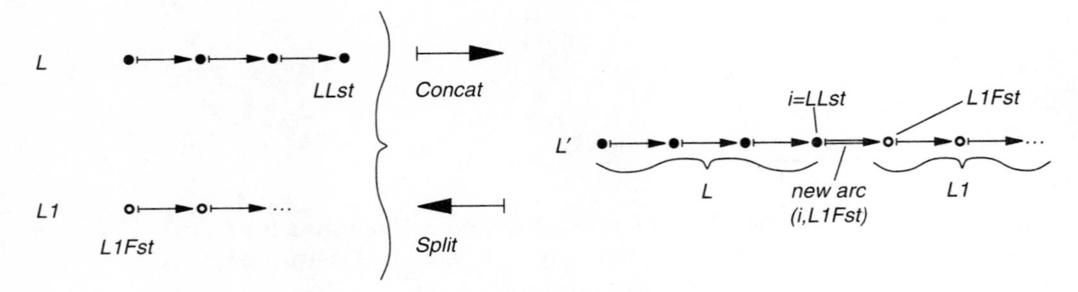

Figure 11.3B.1 Effect of Concat and Split.

L' consisting of L followed by $L1$. Split is the inverse of Concat. Given a list L' and a point $i\!:\!L'Pts$, Split returns two sublists of L'. These are L, which extends from $L'Fst$ to i *inclusive*, and $L1$, the remainder. If L' is the result of Concat(L, $L1$) then the application of Split to L' returns the original lists L and $L1$. These two operations are illustrated in Figure **11**.3B.1

The specification of Concat and Split gives a first illustration of the reasoning involved in the construction of a pair of fully inverse operations. We could define the result of Concat(L, $L1$) simply as the list L'. However, this would not do, for the following reason. From its outline description, Split requires *two* arguments: a list L' and a point $i\!:\!L'Pts$. If Concat returned L' only, a slight loss of information would be incurred, namely the identity of i. As a result, Concat would not be the exact inverse of Split. It is easy to see how Concat must be specified to make it a full inverse of Split. The second argument i of Split must be the last element of L. Therefore, we define the result of Concat(L, $L1$) as the couple (L', i) where $i =_{\mathrm{d}} LLst$.

Likewise, we could define the result of Split as either L or $L1$. This again would cause a loss of information and Split would not be the full inverse of Concat. This is why we stated at once that Split returns the couple (L, $L1$). To sum up, Concat has two arguments, L and $L1$, and returns Concat(L, $L1$) $=_{\mathrm{d}}$ (L', i) where $i =_{\mathrm{d}} LLst$. Split takes L' and $i\!:\!L'Pts$ as arguments, and returns Split(L', i) $=_{\mathrm{d}}$ (L, $L1$). The rule is simple: the couple of arguments of one operation is the result of the other.

This is not the end of the reasoning. The specification of Concat and Split side by side also immediately reveals that these operations are well defined only if certain preconditions are satisfied. If Concat must return $i = LLst$, then it immediately follows that $LPts$ must be *nonempty* and *finite*, for otherwise $LLst$ would not exist. Conversely, the argument L' of Split must not be empty, lest i be undefined. One more precondition is needed for Concat, namely that $LPts$ and $L1Pts$ be disjoint. The identification of these preconditions is another important consequence of establishing Concat and Split simultaneously. We now give the details of these operations in turn.

Concat

As already stated, given L and $L1$: List, Concat(L, $L1$) = (L', i) is defined iff three preconditions are satisfied:

(Pre 1) $LPts$ is finite.
(Pre 2) $LPts$ is not empty.
(Pre 3) $LPts$ and $L1Pts$ are disjoint.

We have already justified (Pre 1) and (Pre 2). The reason for (Pre 3) is closely linked to the definition of (L', i). Therefore, let us develop this definition first. The point i has already been defined as $LLst$:

$$i =_{\mathrm{d}} LLst$$

As for L', we can see from Figure **11**.3B.1 that if (Pre 3) is satified, concatenating L and $L1$ is easy. We take as base set of L' the union of $LPts$ and $L1Pts$. Likewise, the graph of the successor function $L'S$ is naturally given as the union of the graphs of LS and $L1S$, plus the arrow ($LLst$, $L1Fst$) to connect the two lists. This arrow is defined (and is needed) iff $L1Fst$ exists, that is, iff $L1Pts$ is not empty. Therefore L' is given by

$$L'Pts =_{\mathrm{d}} \quad LPts + L1Pts$$
$$L'SGr =_{\mathrm{d}} \quad LSGr \text{ if } L1Pts = \varnothing$$
$$\qquad LSGr + \{(i, L1Fst)\} + L1SGr \quad \text{otherwise}$$

This defines L' completely, as the two primary variable features of this list are $L'Pts$ and the function $L'S$, and the latter is entirely determined, like any function, by fixing its domain $L'SDom$, codomain $L'SCod$ and graph $L'SGr$. $L'SGr$ is given explicitly. $L'SDom =_{\mathrm{d}} L'SCod =_{\mathrm{d}} L'Pts$ by the definition $L'S: L'Pts \leftrightarrow L'Pts$.

We must satisfy ourselves that $L'Pts$ and $L'SGr$ are indeed well defined, given that the set operation + is defined only if its operands are disjoint. This disjointness condition holds for $LPts$ and $L1Pts$, by (Pre 3), so $L'Pts$ is defined. Now (Pre 3) also clearly implies that $LSGr$, $L1SGr$ and $\{(i, L1Fst)\}$ are pairwise disjoint. Therefore $L'SGr$ is defined in all cases. There remains one final task. At this point, all we have established is that $L'S$ is well defined *as a relation*. We must verify that $L'S$ is indeed a *successor function* – that is, that all three conditions $L'Co1$ to $L'Co3$ are satisfied. This should be intuitively clear. The full specification of Concat is given below.

We can see now why precondition (Pre 3) is essential. If it were not satisfied, we could of course define $L'Pts$ and $L'SGr$ as above, but using the ordinary union operation $\cup$. However, the relation $L'S$ would not be a successor function, which only a careful verification of conditions $L'Co1$ to $L'Co3$ would reveal. An example is given in Figure **11**.3B.2. Note that precondition (Pre 3) is often treated implicitly, being 'obvious'. This is a mistake. This condition is clearly essential to the success of Concat and any essential property should be handled explicitly.

Concat

Concatenate lists L and $L1$.
Given L, $L1$: List such that
(Pre 1) IsFinite($LPts$)
(Pre 2) $LPts \neq \varnothing$
(Pre 3) IsDisjoint($LPts$, $L1Pts$)
Concat(L, $L1$) $=_d$ (L', i) where L': List, i: $L'Pts$ and
(1) $i =_d LLst$
(2) $L'Pts =_d LPts + L1Pts$
(3) $L'SGr =_d LSGr$ if $L1Pts = \varnothing$
$LSGr + \{(i, L1Fst)\} + L1SGr$ otherwise

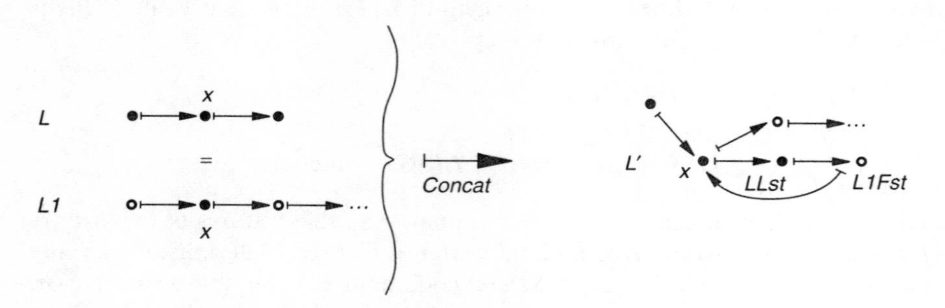

Figure 11.3B.2 Effect of Concat(L, $L1$) when $LPts \cap L1Pts =_d \{x\}$.

The standard concatenation operation of list processing is slightly different, in that it returns only L' as a result, with the loss of the junction point. This simpler version is also useful in some cases. Therefore, we introduce it now. It is represented by the infix operator '$+\!\!\!+$'.

$+\!\!\!+$

Concatenate lists L and $L1$ with loss of junction point.
Given L, $L1$: List such that
(Pre 1) IsFinite($LPts$)
(Pre 2) $LPts \neq \varnothing$
(Pre 3) IsDisjoint($LPts$, $L1Pts$)
(1) $L +\!\!\!+ L1 =_d L'$ where $(L', i) =_d$ Concat(L, $L1$)

Split

The definition of Split has been outlined above. The details are as follows. First, recall that this operation takes two arguments, L' : List and $i : L'Pts$, and returns Split$(L', i) =_d (L, L1)$ where $L, L1$: List. Split(L', i) has one precondition, namely $L'Pts \neq \varnothing$. However, we do not express this explicitly as it is implied by the very fact that $i \in L'Pts$.

Our next task is to define the two lists L and $L1$, given the information provided by the arguments L' and i. We must define the primary variable features of these two lists: $LPts$ and LS on the one hand, $L1Pts$ and $L1S$ on the other. Refer to Figure **11**.3B.1 above.

Informally, L is the sublist of L' which extends from $L'Fst$ to i inclusive. Therefore $LPts$ is the set of ancestors of i in L' together with i itself, that is:

$$LPts =_d L'AncIds(i)$$

As for LS, this is clearly equal to $L'S$ restricted to $LPts$:

$$LS =_d LPts \diamond L'S$$

Recall that by Definition **3**.6C.3 of $\diamond$, $LS =_d LPts \diamond L'S$ means that

(1) $LSDom =_d LPts \cap L'SDom$

(2) $LSCod =_d LPts \cap L'SCod$

(3) $LSGr =_d (LSDom \times LSCod) \cap L'SGr$

The second list $L1$ is defined in a similar way. Its base set is the set of descendants of i, that is:

$$L1Pts =_d L'Descs(i)$$

This set could be empty. As for $L1S$, this is defined in the same way as LS:

$$L1S =_d L1Pts \diamond L'S$$

This completes our establishment of Split, which is clearly the inverse of Concat.

Split

Split nonempty list L' after point $i : L'Pts$. Split $=_d$ Inv(Concat).
Given L' : List and $i : L'Pts$, Split$(L', i) =_d (L, L1)$, where $L, L1$: List and

(1) (a) $LPts =_d L'AncIds(i)$
    (b) $LS =_d LPts \diamond L'S$

(2) (a) $L1Pts =_d L'Descs(i)$
    (b) $L1S =_d L1Pts \diamond L'S$

11.3C Insert and remove

The last two list operations are similar to Concat and Split: they are denoted by Ins and Rem respectively, and are inverses of each other (see Figure **11**.3C.1). Ins takes four arguments: a main list L: List, two points i, j: $LPts$ such that j is the immediate successor of i in L, and a second list $L1$. It returns three objects: a list L': List and the two original points i and j. Thus, Ins$(L, i, j, L1) =_{\mathrm{d}} (L', i, j)$. L' is the list obtained by inserting $L1$ between i and j in L. The two points i and j are included in the result in order to make Ins fully invertible.

Rem is the inverse operation. It takes as arguments a list L': List and points i and j: $L'Pts$ such that $i\, L'Bef\, j$. The result is $(L, i, j, L1)$ where $L1$ is the sublist occurring between i and j *exclusive* in L', i and j are as in the argument list and L is the sublist 'surrounding' $L1$ in L'. Therefore, Rem$(L', i, j) =_{\mathrm{d}} (L, i, j, L1)$. Note that $L1$ may be empty.

We construct Ins and Rem using Concat and Split. As Rem is to be defined as the full inverse of Ins, we establish the former by inverting the latter systematically, taking advantage of the fact that Concat and Split are themselves mutual inverses. This provides a good illustration of the point made in the introduction about the usefulness of inverses. We now describe Ins and Rem in turn.

Ins

The operation Ins has three explicit preconditions:

(Pre 1) j must be the successor of i, that is, $LS(i) =_{\mathrm{d}} j$.
(Pre 2) $L1Pts$ must be finite.
(Pre 3) $LPts$ and $L1Pts$ must be disjoint.

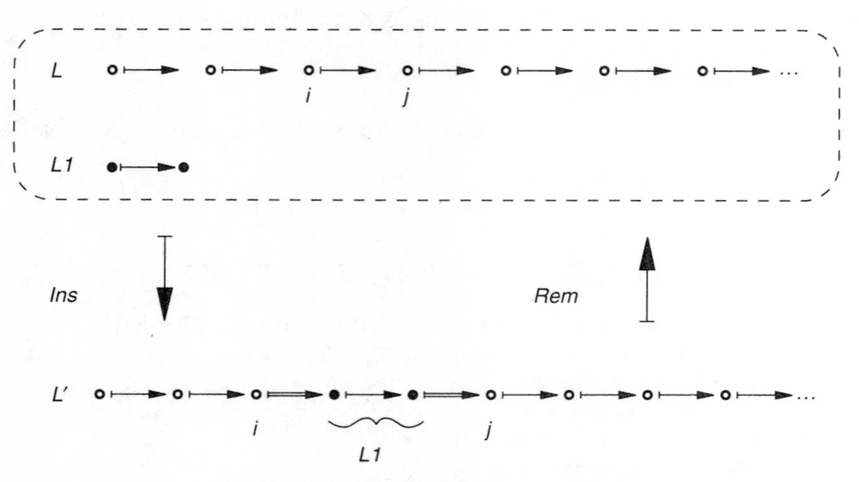

Figure 11.3C.1 Effects of Ins and Rem.

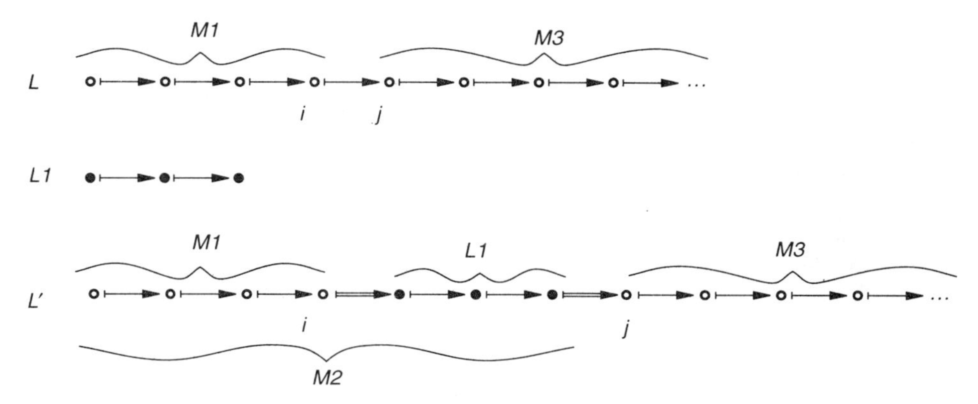

Figure 11.3C.2 Description of Ins(L, i, j, $L1$).

(Pre 1) implies that $LPts$ must contain at least two members, namely i and j which are necessarily distinct as $LS(i) = j$. We leave this precondition implicit.

The reason for (Pre 1) is that in the result L', $L1$ is to follow i and to precede j. Moreover, the target position of $L1$ within L must be uniquely defined, which it is iff no other points occur between i and j in L. The reason for (Pre 2) is that if $L1Pts$ were infinite, it could not be 'followed' by j (and $LDescs(j)$) in L'. (Pre 3) is needed for the same reasons as in Concat.

In order to describe the effect of Ins(L, i, j, $L1$), we introduce three local variables $M1$, $M2$, $M3$: List. These represent intermediate lists. We obtain L' from (L, i, j, $L1$) as follows. First, we split L at i into two parts, $M1$ and $M3$, using Split. Then we concatenate $M1$ and $L1$ giving $M2$. Finally, we concatenate $M2$ and $M3$. This process is illustrated in Figure **11**.3C.2. The formal description of Ins is given below.

The three 'local' lists $M1$, $M2$ and $M3$ are not absolutely necessary. We use them to name each intermediate result of an elementary application either of Split or Concat. This will clarify the derivation of Rem as a systematic inversion of these applications.

Ins

Insert list $L1$ between i and j in L. $L1$ may be empty.
Given L, $L1$: List, i, j: $LPts$ such that

(Pre 1) $LS(i) =_{\mathrm{d}} j$
(Pre 2) IsFinite($L1Pts$)
(Pre 3) IsDisjoint($LPts$, $L1Pts$)

Ins(L, i, j, $L1$) $=_{\mathrm{d}}$ (L', i, j) where L': List. Let $M1$, $M2$, $M3$: List.

(1) $(M1, M3) =_{\mathrm{d}}$ Split(L, i)
(2) $M2 =_{\mathrm{d}} M1 \mathbin{+\!\!+} L1$
(3) $L' =_{\mathrm{d}} M2 \mathbin{+\!\!+} M3$

Rem

The operation Rem takes as arguments L': List, i, j: $L'Pts$. These must satisfy one explicit precondition, namely:

(Pre 1) i is before j in L', that is, $i\ L'Bef\ j$

The result of this operation is $\text{Rem}(L', i, j) =_d (L, i, j, L1)$ where L, $L1$: List. The two lists L and $L1$ are derived from L', i and j by inverting the description of $\text{Ins}(L, i, j, L1)$, as mentioned. To do this, we use the same local variables as in Ins, that is, $M1$, $M2$, $M3$: List. Before reading on, the reader should seek to work out this derivation, bearing in mind that *intermediate results are obtained in the reverse order of Ins.*

The steps of Ins and the corresponding steps of Rem are shown side by side in Table **11**.3C.1, in both natural and formal language. The reader will notice that the derivation of Rem from Ins is a purely mechanical process.

Table 11.3C.1 Derviation of Rem from Ins.

Ins	Rem
(1) Split L at i into two parts, $M1$ and $M3$. $(M1, M3) =_d \text{Split}(L, i)$	(3) Concatenate $M1$ and $M3$, giving L. $L =_d M1 +\!\!+ M3$
(2) Concatenate $M1$ and $L1$, giving $M2$. $M2 =_d M1 +\!\!+ L1$	(2) Split $M2$ at i into two parts, $M1$ and $L1$. $(M1, L1) =_d \text{Split}(M2, i)$
(3) Concatenate $M2$ and $M3$, giving L'. $L' =_d M2 +\!\!+ M3$	(1) Split L' at $L'Pre(j)$ into two parts, $M2$ and $M3$. $(M2, M3) =_d \text{Split}(L', L'Pre(j))$

Our establishment of Rem is now complete. The full formal specification of Rem is as follows:

Rem

Remove $L1$ from L', where $L1$ is the sublist occurring between i and j in L'. $L1$ may be empty (iff i and j are adjacent).

Given L': List, i, j: $L'Pts$ such that

(Pre 1) $i\ L'Bef\ j$

$\text{Rem}(L', i, j) =_d (L, i, j, L1)$ where L, $L1$: List. Let $M1$, $M2$, $M3$: List.

(1) $(M2, M3) =_d \text{Split}(L', L'Pre(j))$

(2) $(M1, L1) =_d \text{Split}(M2, i)$

(3) $L =_d M1 +\!\!+ M3$

Several different versions of Ins and Rem will be introduced in subsequent subsections, operating on other classes of objects. Thus these two operators are heavily overloaded. Of course, in each application the intended operation will always be determined without ambiguity by the class of its arguments.

11.3D Isomorphism and base set conversion

Consider the two lists L and L': List shown in Figure **11**.3D.1. The points of the first are represented by small solid circles and those of the second by open ones. Clearly *LPts* and *L′Pts* are disjoint.

In a certain sense, which is made precise below, L and L' are *equivalent*. They have the same structure, and we also say they are *isomorphic*. This word is from Greek and means that they have the same ('iso') form ('morphism'). Consequently, for most purposes it does not matter which of these two lists we use. For instance, if we are interested in their properties, these are essentially the same: both are finite, have a first and a last element, and a base set of five points.

This is why we have adopted the point of view that, for most of our present purposes, the *identity* of the base points of a list is irrelevant. Therefore this matter is to be dealt with *separately*, typically as an 'implementation feature'. As far as we are concerned, the base set of a list L should be considered only to the extent that it affects the structure of L. It is clear that two unvalued lists have the same structure iff they have the same number (finite or countably infinite) of points.

This principle has several consequences. First, when we define a list in any way, for example by application of any operation like InitList, Concat or Ins, we should leave the identity of the base points unspecified. More precisely, we should postulate that they are determined by a separate agency.

Second, given any list L, we may always change the base points of L while keeping the structure of L. This will be called a *base set conversion*. One main reason for making such a change is this. The two operations Concat and Ins both require that the base sets *LPts* and *L1Pts* of their arguments be disjoint. In order to apply either operation when this condition is not satisfied, we would first have to convert one of them, say *L1*, to an equivalent list *L1′* such that *LPts* and *L1′Pts* are disjoint. This can always be done, which implies that the disjointness condition of Concat and Ins may be circumvented.

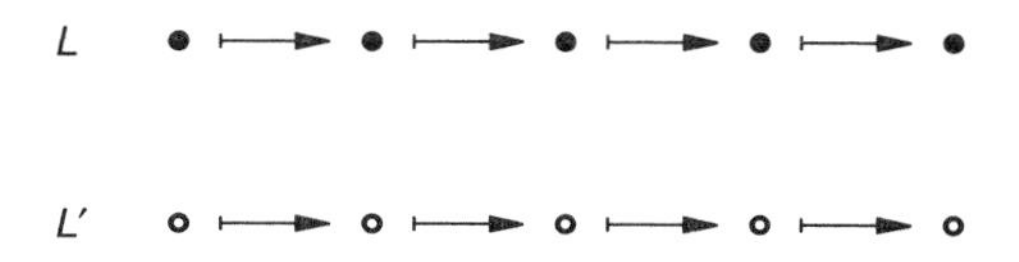

Figure 11.3D.1 Two equivalent lists L and L'.

We must establish what a base set conversion exactly means. It must be an operation which transforms a given L: List into a new L': List such that $L'Pts$ may differ from $LPts$. Moreover, this transformation is suitable for our purposes iff the new list L' is isomorphic to the original L. Therefore, we must now define exactly what we mean by two isomorphic lists.

Isomorphism of lists

Consider Figure **11**.3D.1 again. We can see intuitively that L and L' are equivalent, because for each point $i: LPts$ there is a corresponding point in $L'Pts$ which we denote by $\varphi(i)$, and this correspondence is such that the following conditions are satisfied:

(1) If $i = LFst$ then $\varphi(i) =_d L'Fst$.

(2) For all $i, j: LPts$, if $LS(i) = j$ then $L'S(\varphi(i)) =_d \varphi(j)$.

This correspondence is represented by vertical arrows in Figure **11**.3D.2. It is clearly a *bijection* (one–one correspondence) $\varphi: LPts \rightarrow L'Pts$.

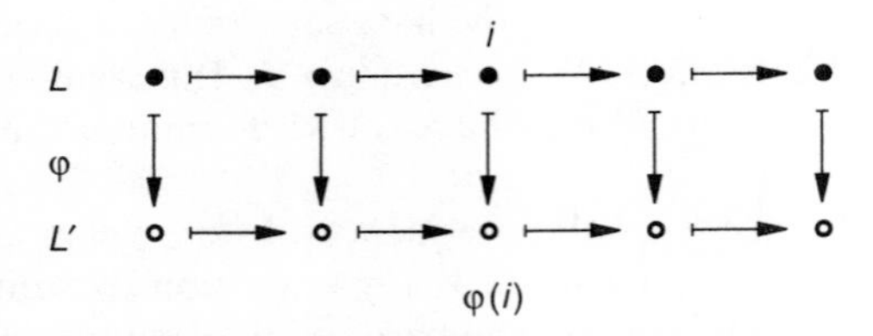

Figure 11.3D.2 Isomorphism between L and L'.

Note that φ is more than a mere bijection $LPts \rightarrow L'Pts$; it satisfies the two conditions (1) and (2) given above. For this reason, φ is called an *isomorphism* (of List). To sum up:

Definition 11.3D.1 (isomorphism of List)

(1) Given any two lists L and L': List, an isomorphism between L and L' is a bijection

$$\varphi: LPts \rightarrow L'Pts$$

such that

(a) $\varphi(LFst) =_d L'Fst$

(b) $\forall\, i: LSDef \cdot \varphi(LS(i)) =_d L'S(\varphi(i))$

(2) L and L' are *equivalent* or *isomorphic* iff there exists an isomorphism between them. In this case we also write

$$L \cong L'$$

■

Notes

1 We shall later specify another type of isomorphism between valued lists. Different isomorphisms must be carefully distinguished. For instance, two valued lists may be isomorphic as *unvalued* lists, that is, ignoring their value maps, and not as valued lists.

2 It is easy to see that the identity function Id : $LPts \to LPts$ is an isomorphism. Moreover, if $\varphi : LPts \to L'Pts$ is an isomorphism then, being a bijection, it has an inverse $\varphi^{-1} : L'Pts \to LPts$, and it is clear that φ^{-1} itself is an isomorphism. Finally, given three lists $L1$, $L2$ and $L3$: List such that there are isomorphisms $\rho : L1Pts \to L2Pts$ and $\varphi : L2Pts \to L3Pts$, the composite $\varphi \circ \rho$ itself is an isomorphism between $L1$ and $L3$.

These properties of isomorphisms imply corresponding properties of the relation $\cong$ on List. First, the fact that Id : $LPts \to LPts$ is an isomorphism implies that $\cong$ is *reflexive*: that is, $L \cong L$ for any L : List. Second, that the inverse of an isomorphism is an isomorphism means that $\cong$ is *symmetric*: that is, $L \cong L' \Rightarrow L' \cong L$. Third, the fact that the composite of two isomorphisms is an isomorphism implies that $\cong$ is *transitive*: that is, if $L1 \cong L2$ and $L2 \cong L3$ then $L1 \cong L3$. Therefore, $\cong$ is an *equivalence*. ■

BaseConv

We now establish an operation BaseConv to convert an L : List to a new L' : List such that $L \cong L'$, and L' satisfies some additional required property. Usually the property needed is that $L'Pts$ be disjoint from a specified set C. Thus, we define BaseConv as taking two arguments, L : List and C : Set, and returning an L' : List such that C and $L'Pts$ are disjoint and $L \cong L'$.

BaseConv

Convert the base set of L : List, that is, create a list L' : List isomorphic to L and with IsDisjoint(C, $L'Pts$).

Given L : List and C : Set, BaseConv(L, C) $=_d L'$ where L' : List and

(1) IsDisjoint(C, $L'Pts$)

(2) $L' \cong_d L$

Note that BaseConv is *underspecified*. The set $L'Pts$ is determined only to the extent that it must be disjoint from C. Likewise, no method or algorithm is given here actually to construct L' from L. This is in keeping with the principle of separation of concerns. The main purpose of BaseConv is just to indicate to the 'implementor' the essential properties required of L'.

Ins1

Using BaseConv, we may now establish an insertion operation Ins1 which is defined even if its arguments L and $L1$ have common base points:

Ins1

Insert list $L1$ between i and j in L. $LPts$ and $L1Pts$ need *not* be disjoint.
Given $L, L1$: List, $i, j: LPts$ such that
(Pre 1) $LS(i) = j$
(Pre 2) IsFinite($L1Pts$)
Ins1$(L, i, j, L1) =_d (L', i, j)$ where L': List and
(1) $(L', i, j) =_d$ Ins(L, i, j, BaseConv($L1, LPts$))

Discussion

The reader may feel that the above developments are rather theoretical and remote from 'real life' – ultimately, the job of implementing specifications as programs in a computer-executable language. This would be a mistake. The above considerations are entirely relevant, for they describe precisely what has to be done in practice. They constitute the proper introduction to the very practical tasks that the implementor has to carry out, yet without unduly restricting his or her freedom of action.

Specifically, suppose the implementor chooses to represent lists as so-called *linked lists* in a language like Pascal. This data structure is very close to our own model of lists, and this consistency in itself is precious. Now consider the task of implementing Concat (or Ins). It is clear that all the above developments are entirely relevant. The implementor must first realize that two linked lists L and $L1$ may be concatenated as described in the specification of Concat only if their base sets are disjoint. Moreover, if a version of Concat is required in which the base sets of the operands are not necessarily disjoint, the implementor must conclude that first a 'copy' $L1'$ of $L1$ (say), with $L1'Pts$ disjoint from $LPts$, must be created, and that it is this copy which must be appended to L. Now the concept of a 'copy' of an object must be defined exactly, and the proper way of defining a copy L' of an L: List is to state that L' is a list *isomorphic to* L, that is, $L \cong L'$. Furthermore, the operation BaseConv defined above is an exact description of what the implementor has to do in order to obtain the desired result.

These considerations are not restricted to unvalued lists. They apply *mutatis mutandis* to all the classes of objects we have already introduced or shall develop later, such as valued lists, pure trees, ordered and/or valued trees. In each case, all the above principles hold with only minor adjustments.

11.4 Valued lists and related operations

The standard concept of a list is valued: a list is usually defined as a function from a finite ordered set, namely Pos_n, to some set of elements called 'values'. We call such lists *valued* to distinguish them from members of List.

This section first defines valued lists in general. The class of such lists is denoted by ListV. It also introduces a subclass of ListV, namely the class ListV1 of finite valued lists, and a parametrized version of ListV1. Then operations on ListV1 are established. These are obtained by extending the List operations to allow for the assignment of values to base points. An additional function SetV is also introduced, whose purpose is to reset the value of a base point. Finally, the concepts of isomorphism and base set conversion on ListV1 are defined.

11.4A Valued lists

Recall the description of a family given in Section **11**.1. An F: Family has been defined there as a function $F: FPts \rightarrow FVals$, where $FPts$ is any (unstructured) set and $FVals$ any nonempty set. There are therefore two ways of describing an L: ListV. One is to define L as a member of List augmented with a value map, also called $L: LPts \rightarrow LVals$. The other is to define L as a member of Family augmented with a successor function LS. In fact, we can do even better and assert that an L: ListV is an object which combines the features of members of List and those of members of Family, alias Fam.

In addition, we also denote the value map by LV in order to distinguish it from the list L as a whole. A second reason for introducing this alias is to harmonize our list notation with that of valued forests and trees established in Chapter **12**. This completes our description of a valued list L: ListV. Accordingly, the formal definition is as follows:

<u>L: ListV</u>

   * $L[List]$: List
   * $L[Fam]$: Fam
     <u>ΔListV</u>
     $LV_i : LVals\ (i : LPts)$ — LV_i is an alias for L_i (value map)
        $LCoV1 .: \forall\, i : LPts \cdot LV_i =_{\mathrm{d}} L_i$

This definition may be read thus: any L: ListV is an object with the following features:

(1) <u>Inherited from List</u>

Variable features: $LPts$, $LFst$, LS
Fixed features or conditions: $LCo1$, $LCo2$, $LCo3$

This group is represented by $LList$, which is a *group* feature.

(2) <u>Inherited from Fam</u>

Variable features: $LPts$, $LVals$, $L: LPts \to LVals$
Fixed feature: $LCoFam1$

This group is represented by $LFam$ (group feature).

(3) <u>Own features</u>

Variable feature: $LV: LPts \to LVals$ (alias for L)
Fixed feature: $LCoV1$

Notes

1 This definition is slightly redundant: $LPts$ is implicitly listed twice as a feature of L. There is no harm in this, as $LPts$ is introduced as a set in the definition of both List and Fam. It is understood that $LPts$ inherited from List is the same feature as $LPts$ inherited from Fam.

2 As LV is an alias for $L: LPts \to LVals$, it is entirely determined by the latter. Therefore, LV is listed as secondary.

3 Further features of L: ListV may be mentioned, in addition to the main ones set out above. Briefly, these are:

(a) Variable features *indirectly* inherited, such as $LSDom$, $LSGr$, etc. via List and $LDom$, LGr, etc. via Fam

(b) Fixed features or conditions *indirectly* inherited, such as $LSGr \subseteq LSDom \times LSCod$, etc.

(c) Secondary features (implied by primary ones), variable or fixed, inherited from List or Fam, such as $LLst$, $LDef1$, $LPre$, etc.

(d) Any secondary features depending on LV ■

In conclusion, the definition of L: ListV is another illustration of the two related principles of *separation of concern* and *modularity*, as these are understood in this book – see Section **1**.2C. First, two classes of theoretical objects are defined separately, namely Family and List. The explicit theory of both classes is already fairly complex, especially that of List. Then the definitions of List and Family are combined to form a third class, namely ListV. This

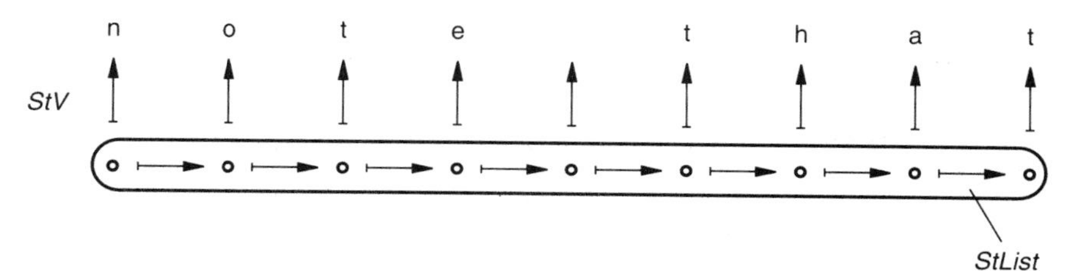

Figure 11.4A.1 A string *St*: String.

combination is very simple. Moreover, the theory of ListV is also a natural combination of the theories of Family and List, and there is no need to develop it explicitly. These features are characteristic of good modular design.

Example: String

Finite lists of characters are the most common examples of lists. They are called *strings*. Any piece of text may be described as a string. We shall denote the class of all strings by String.

A precise specification of String first requires the selection of a common set of characters, say $Char =_d \{\text{'a'}, \text{'b'}, \ldots, \text{'z'}, \ldots, \}$. Such a set is also called an *alphabet*. A member of String is then defined as a list *St*: ListV such that $StVals =_d Char$. By way of concrete example, the string 'note that' regarded as a member of String is illustrated in Figure **11**.4A.1. In this example the base elements are represented by circles.

Note that the class String varies with the underlying alphabet *Char*. Therefore, *Char* may be regarded as an implicit parameter of String. We shall shortly establish a version of the subclass of finite valued lists in which the value set is specified by an explicit parameter. ■

The classes ListV1 and ListV1(Vals)

As we are mainly concerned with finite lists, we now introduce the subclass of ListV which these form. This subclass is denoted by ListV1. An *L*: ListV1 has all the features of members of ListV, plus the property that its base set *LPts* is finite. Thus, ListV1 is a specialization of ListV. The formal definition is straightforward:

L: ListV1 (Specialized ListV)

* *L*[*ListV*]: ListV

ΔListV1

LCo11.: IsFinite(*LPts*)

We also introduce a parametrized version of ListV1, in which the value set *LVals* of an *L*: ListV1 is defined by a parameter *Vals*. This version is denoted by ListV1(*Vals*), which represents the subclass of *L*: ListV1 such that *LVals* $=_d$ *Vals*. The formal establishment of ListV1(*Vals*) is as follows:

L: ListV1(*Vals*) (Specialized ListV1)

* *L*[*ListV1*]: ListV1
  ΔListV1
* *Vals*: Set
  ValsCo .: *Vals* $\neq_d \varnothing$
  LCo12 .: *LVals* $=_d$ *Vals*

This definition is to be read as follows. Given any predefined nonempty set *Vals'*, an *L*: ListV1(*Vals'*) is a member of ListV1 such that *LVals* $=_d$ *Vals'*. We also make the convention that, given *L*: ListV1 in a context in which *LVals* = *Vals'*, *L* is regarded as having been introduced by *L*: ListV1(*Vals'*). This will make it possible to leave the parameter *Vals* implicit in most operation specifications. The condition '*ValsCo* .: *Vals* $\neq_d \varnothing$' is necessary to ensure that '*LCoFam1* .: *LVals* $\neq_d \varnothing$' is satisfied.

11.4B Initialization operations

The two initialization operations of List are EmpList and InitList. We now extend them to operations returning an *L'*: ListV1.

The first operation is denoted by EmpListV1 and has one argument, a nonempty set *Vals*. It produces the empty list *L'* with value set *L'Vals* equal to *Vals*. The formal definition is immediate. Note that in the specification of EmpListV1, the condition *L'Vals* $=_d$ *Vals* is not explicitly stated, as it is implied by the declaration *L'*: ListV1(*Vals*).

EmpListV1

  Return the empty list of ListV1(*Vals*).
  Given *Vals*: Set such that
(Pre 1) *Vals* $\neq \varnothing$
  EmpListV1(*Vals*) $=_d$ *L'* where *L'*: ListV1(*Vals*) and
(1) *L'Pts* $=_d \varnothing$

The second operation is InitListV1. It has two arguments: a nonempty set *Vals* and a value *v*: *Vals*. It returns the list *L'* of exactly one element *L'Fst*, such that *L'Vals* $=_d$ *Vals* and the value *L'V*(*L'Fst*) $=_d$ *v*. In this definition, we do not impose *Vals* $\neq \varnothing$ as an explicit precondition on the parameter *Vals*, as it is implied by $v \in$ *Vals*.

<u>InitListV1</u>

Create a one-point valued list L'.
Given $Vals$: Set and v: $Vals$, InitListV1($Vals$, v) $=_d L'$ where
L': ListV1($Vals$) and
(1) $L'Pts =_d \{L'Fst\}$
(2) $L'V(L'Fst) =_d v$

11.4C Concatenation and splitting operations

Next, consider the extension of Concat and Split to ListV1. As for Concat, this is done in a very natural way. First, we allow the concatenation of two lists L and $L1$ only if they have the same value set – that is, $LVals = L1Vals$. This is imposed as a new precondition. Accordingly, the value set $L'Vals$ of the result is set to $LVals$. Second, we require that any point j: $L'Pts$ keeps its original value: if $j \in LPts$, then $L'V(j) =_d LV(j)$, and if $j \in L1Pts$, then $L'V(j) =_d L1V(j)$. This rule is consistent in view of $LVals = L1Vals = L'Vals$ and the precondition that $LPts$ and $L1Pts$ must be disjoint.

Recall that for any L: ListV1, we denote by $LList$ the underlying pure list of L, that is, the result of 'forgetting' the value map of L. More precisely, $LList$ is a group feature of L. It contains all the features of L inherited from List. Consequently, $LList \in$ List, and $LList$ may be used in any operation requiring a member of List as operand. We exploit this property to define all the List features of the result L', that is, $L'List$, by the single equation

$$(L'List, i) =_d \text{Concat}(LList, L1List)$$

where Concat is the List operator defined earlier. Thus, our specification of Concat on ListV1 is truly incremental, and the extension of Concat closely reflects the extension of List to ListV1.

<u>Concat</u>

Concatenate lists L and $L1$.
Given L, $L1$: ListV1 such that
(Pre 1) $LPts \neq \varnothing$
(Pre 2) IsDisjoint($LPts$, $L1Pts$)
(Pre 3) $LVals = L1Vals$
Concat(L, $L1$) $=_d (L', i)$ where L': ListV1, i: $L'Pts$ and
(1) $(L'List, i) =_d \text{Concat}(LList, L1List)$
(2) (a) $L'Vals =_d LVals$
(b) $\forall j: LPts \cdot L'V(j) =_d LV(j)$
(c) $\forall j: L1Pts \cdot L'V(j) =_d L1V(j)$

Note that as any L: ListV1 is finite, the original precondition (Pre 1) of Concat, namely IsFinite(*LPts*), is no longer needed explicitly.

With this second definition, Concat is overloaded. As applied to *LList* and *L1List*, Concat is clearly a List operator, as *LList* and *L1List* $\in$ List. As applied to L and $L1$, it is obviously a ListV1 operator, as L and $L1 \in$ ListV1. Therefore the effect of Concat and the class of its result (L', i) is unambiguous. Note that overloading could be avoided by using a different name, such as ConcatV1 for the ListV1 version of Concat.

The simplified concatenator $+\!\!+$ is derived from Concat in the same way as in List.

$+\!\!+$

Concatenate lists L and $L1$ with loss of junction point.
Given $L, L1$: ListV1 such that

(Pre 1) $LPts \neq \varnothing$
(Pre 2) IsDisjoint($LPts$, $L1Pts$)
(Pre 3) $LVals = L1Vals$
(1) $L +\!\!+ L1 =_d L'$ where $(L', i) =_d$ Concat $(L, L1)$

The extension of Split to ListV1 is equally natural. Split is again defined as the full inverse of Concat. This implies the following additional features of the new version. First, the value sets of the two resulting lists L and $L1$ must be equal to $L'Vals$. Second, each point $j : L'Pts$ keeps its original value: that is, $LV(j) =_d L'V(j)$ if $j \in LPts$, and $L1V(j) =_d L'V(j)$ if $j \in L1Pts$.

The pure List features of the two resulting lists L and $L1$: ListV1 are simply given by

$$(LList, L1List) =_d \text{Split}(L'List, i)$$

where Split is the List operator. Like Concat, Split is overloaded: it is both a List and a ListV1 operator.

Split

Split nonempty list L' after point $i : L'Pts$. Split $=_d$ Inv(Concat).
Given L': ListV1 and $i : L'Pts$, Split$(L', i) =_d (L, L1)$, where $L, L1$: ListV1 and

(1) $(LList, L1List) =_d \text{Split}(L'List, i)$
(2) (a) $LVals =_d L1Vals =_d L'Vals$
(b) $\forall j : LPts \cdot LV(j) =_d L'V(j)$
(c) $\forall j : L1Pts \cdot L1V(j) =_d L'V(j)$

It is important to realize the full role of equation (1) in this definition. This rule defines all the pure List features of L and $L1$. Thus, it is this equation which ensures that $LPts$ and $L1Pts$ are well defined in the specification of LV and $L1V$, on lines 2(b) and 2(c).

11.4D Insert and remove

The two List operations Ins and Rem are extended to ListV1 functions in the same way as Concat and Split have been. All the comments made on Concat and Split in Section **11**.4.C apply *mutatis mutandis* to Ins and Rem. Therefore, the formal definitions of these two operations are given without more ado.

Ins

Insert list $L1$ between i and j in L. $L1$ may be empty.
Given $L, L1$: ListV1, $i, j : LPts$ such that

(Pre 1) $LS(i) = j$
(Pre 2) IsDisjoint($LPts$, $L1Pts$)
(Pre 3) $LVals = L1Vals$

Ins($L, i, j, L1$) $=_d$ (L', i, j) where L' : ListV1 and

(1) ($L'List, i, j$) $=_d$ Ins($LList, i, j, L1List$)
(2) (a) $L'Vals =_d LVals$
(b) $\forall j : LPts \cdot L'V(j) =_d LV(j)$
(c) $\forall j : L1Pts \cdot L'V(j) =_d L1V(j)$

Rem

Remove $L1$ from L', where $L1$ is the sublist occurring between i and j in L'. $L1$ may be empty (iff i and j are adjacent).
Given L' : ListV1, $i, j : L'Pts$ such that

(Pre 1) $i\ L'Bef\ j$

Rem(L', i, j) $=_d$ ($L, i, j, L1$) where $L, L1$: ListV1 and

(1) ($LList, i, j, L1List$) $=_d$ Rem($L'List, i, j$)
(2) (a) $LVals =_d L1Vals =_d L'Vals$
(b) $\forall j : LPts \cdot LV(j) =_d L'V(j)$
(c) $\forall j : L1Pts \cdot L1V(j) =_d L'V(j)$

11.4E Resetting a value

To the above operations, we add one function specific to ListV1, namely SetV. Given an L : ListV1, a point $i : LPts$ and a value $v : LVals$, SetV returns a new list L' : ListV1 which differs from L only by the fact that $L'V(i) =_d v$.

In order to specify the result $L' =_d \mathrm{SetV}(L, i, v)$ we may write

$$L'List =_d LList$$

as the pure List features of L are identical in L'. So all we have to do of any substance is to indicate how the function $LV: LPts \to LVals$ is converted to $L'V: L'Pts \to L'Vals$. This may be done using the function-overriding operation of Section **3**.6C:

$$L'V =_d (LV \mid i \mapsto v)$$

Recall the meaning of this notation. First, $L'VDom =_d LVDom$ $(=_d LPts = L'Pts)$ and $L'VCod =_d LVCod$ $(=_d LVals = L'Vals)$. Second, $L'VDef =_d LVDef \cup \{i\}$, and for all $j: L'VDef$

$$L'V(j) =_d \begin{cases} LV(j) & \text{if } j \neq i \\ v & \text{otherwise} \end{cases}$$

SetV

Set the value of point $i: LPts$ to v.
Given L: ListV1, $i: LPts$ and $v: LVals$, $\mathrm{SetV}(L, i, v) =_d L'$ where L': ListV1 and

(1) $L'List =_d LList$
(2) $L'V =_d (LV \mid i \mapsto v)$

11.4F Isomorphism and base set conversion AT

Finally, what has been said in Section **11**.3D about isomorphism and base set conversion in List holds for ListV1, *mutatis mutandis*. All we have to do now is extend these two concepts to ListV1.

Isomorphism in ListV1

Recall that two lists L and L': List are isomorphic iff there exists a bijection $\varphi: LPts \to L'Pts$ which *preserves* the structure of L, in the sense that

(1) $\varphi(LFst) =_d L'Fst$.

(2) $\forall i: LSDef \cdot \varphi(LS(i) =_d L'S(\varphi(i))$.

For two lists L and L': ListV1, these conditions must also be satisfied. In addition, any isomorphism $\varphi: LPts \to L'Pts$ must also preserve the value map

LV. This means that *L′Vals* must be equal to *LVals*, and the values of corresponding points must be equal.

Definition 11.4F.1 (isomorphism of ListV1)

Two lists L and L': ListV1 are *equivalent* or *isomorphic*, written $L \cong L'$, iff $LVals = L'Vals$ and there exists a bijection $\varphi : LPts \rightarrow L'Pts$ with the following properties.

(1) φ is an isomorphism of List, i.e.

(a) $\varphi(LFst) =_d L'Fst$
(b) $\forall\, i : LSDef \cdot \varphi(LS(i)) =_d L'S(\varphi(i))$

(2) φ preserves the values of L, i.e.

$$\forall\, i : LPts \cdot LV(i) =_d L'V(\varphi(i))$$

The function φ is called isomorphism of ListV1. ■

This property is illustrated in Figure **11**.4F.1, assuming $LVals =_d L'Vals =_d Char$. Note that $L \cong L'$ implies $LList \cong L'List$, but the converse is not true.

The properties of isomorphisms in List given in the notes of Section **11**.3D also hold for isomorphisms in ListV1. In fact, they hold for any type of isomorphism.

BaseConv

The base set conversion BaseConv defined on List extends naturally to ListV1. All we need to do is substitute 'ListV1' for 'List' in the definition.

The comments made on the List version of BaseConv also apply to its ListV1 extension. Consequently, we may also define an insertion Ins1 on ListV1

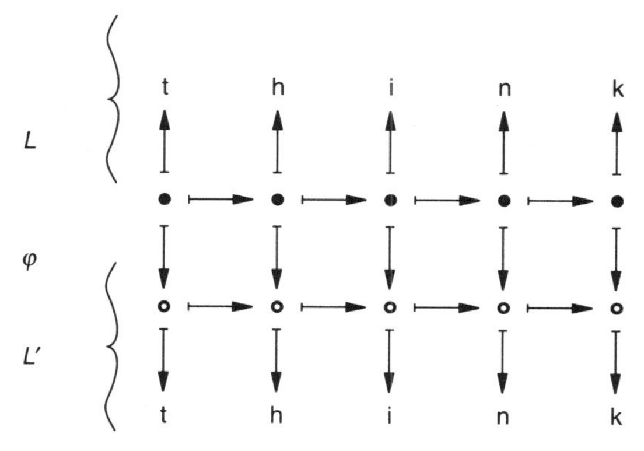

Figure 11.4F.1 Isomorphism between L and L': ListV1.

in which the disjointness precondition is relaxed. This is obtained by substituting 'ListV1' for 'List' in the original definition of Ins1.

BaseConv

Convert the base set of L: ListV1, i.e. create a list L': ListV1 isomorphic to L and with IsDisjoint(C, $L'Pts$).
Given L: ListV1 and C: Set, BaseConv(L, C) $=_d L'$ where L': ListV1 and

(1) IsDisjoint(C, $L'Pts$)
(2) $L' \cong_d L$

11.5 Pointed lists and related operations

A natural extension of a list L: List is to add one or more pointers to the base points of L. In its simplest definition, a pointer is a nullary function P to $LPts$ or, equivalently, an element $P \in LPts$. By adding one or more pointers to L, we create a new object which we call a *pointed list*. Note that the addition of pointers is largely 'orthogonal' to the other extensions of List defined so far. Thus, we may have pointed valued lists, parametrized pointed valued lists, and so on.

To simplify, we do not consider all these possible combinations, but only a simple extension of the class ListV1 and its parametrized version. These are denoted by ListPtd0 and ListPtd0(*Vals*) respectively. A list L: ListPtd0 is very simple. It has all the features of a member of ListV1, plus just one pointer, also called a *cursor*. This is an element of $LPts$ denoted by LC; it is a new primary variable feature of L. The class ListPtd0 will serve as a basis for the specification of a class of *pointed trees* in Chapter **12**. There are more general definitions of 'pointers'. However, the description of suitable pointers greatly depends on the application, and it seems difficult to define a general class of 'pointed lists', suitable for all applications.

The addition of pointers to lists makes it possible to define a wider range of operations on these objects. However, they also impose the introduction of further, auxiliary functions, concerned with the definition of the pointers themselves. These 'pointer operations' are often referred to as *navigation operations*.

The simplest concrete example of a pointed list is the *logical* concept of a piece of text in a word processor, as mentioned in Chapter **10**. Recall that this is a finite list of characters, a *string*, together with a pointer, or cursor, to one element in the list. It indicates the position of the next input character, or of the character which would be removed by inputting backspace. The cursor may be moved forward and backward on the text. These steps are the navigation operations referred to above. There are two other functions, namely the insertion of a new character at the position indicated by the cursor, and the deletion of the character preceding the cursor. These will be called *list transformation* operations.

Consequently, by combining navigation and list transformation operations, the user may insert additional characters or delete existing ones *anywhere* in the text. Note that in this description, we ignore the *physical representation* of the text, in particular that it must be split into lines and that at any time only part of it may be displayed on the computer screen. 'Logically' or 'conceptually', a text is nothing more than a finite sequence of characters with a cursor and the operations outlined.

11.5A Pointed lists

As stated, a list L: ListPtd0 has all the features of a member of ListV1, plus a selected point LC: $LPts$ called the cursor. This extra feature is primary and variable. Therefore, ListPtd0 is a proper extension of ListV1.

The cursor LC is always defined. This implies the added constraint on L that $LPts \neq \varnothing$. This condition need not be stated explicitly. The formal definition of ListPtd0 is immediate.

L: ListPtd0	(Extented ListV1)
* $L[ListV1]$: ListV1	
ΔListPtd0	
* LC: $LPts$	Cursor

The parametrized version of this class is ListPtd0($Vals$), where the parameter $Vals$ stands for a nonempty set and has the same meaning as in ListV1($Vals$): for any L: ListPtd0($Vals$), $LVals =_d Vals$. This version may be established in three ways. One method is to extend ListV1($Vals$), by adding LC as an extra feature. This parallels the above derivation of ListPtd0 from ListV1. The second method is to extend ListPtd0 by adding the parameter $Vals$, in the same way as ListV1($Vals$) is obtained from ListV1. The third method is simply to merge the features of ListV1($Vals$) and ListPtd0. All three routes lead to the same result. The third approach has the merit of simplicity and symmetry, but is redundant. This situation is similar to the derivation of ListV from Family and List in Section **11**.4A. The first and third constructions are as follows:

L: ListPtd0($Vals$)	(Extended ListV1($Vals$))
* $L[ListV1]$: ListV1($Vals$)	
ΔListPtd0	
* LC: $LPts$	Cursor

L: ListPtd0(*Vals*) (Alternative derivation)

* *L*[*ListV1*]: ListV1(*Vals*)
* *L*[*ListPtd0*]: ListPtd0

These definitions are to be read as follows. Given any predefined nonempty set *Vals*′, an L: ListPtd0(*Vals*′) is a member of ListPtd0 such that $LVals =_{d} Vals'$. We repeat the convention that given L: ListPtd0, in a context in which $LVals = Vals'$, L is regarded as having been introduced by L: ListPtd0(*Vals*′). Consequently, operations established in ListPtd0, with the parameter *Vals* left implicit, automatically hold in any subclass ListPtd0(*Vals*′).

Full expansion of ListPtd0(Vals)

The various list classes developed so far have been built in small increments, each corresponding to a distinct concern. It seems appropriate at this stage to summarize the development path we have followed from Family and List to ListPtd0(*Vals*), and to show the full list of primary features of an L: ListPtd0(*Vals*) resulting from this process. This full list is called the *feature expansion* of L.

The successive extensions of Family and List are given in Figure **11**.5A.1. This figure summarizes the taxonomy of the group of list classes defined so far.

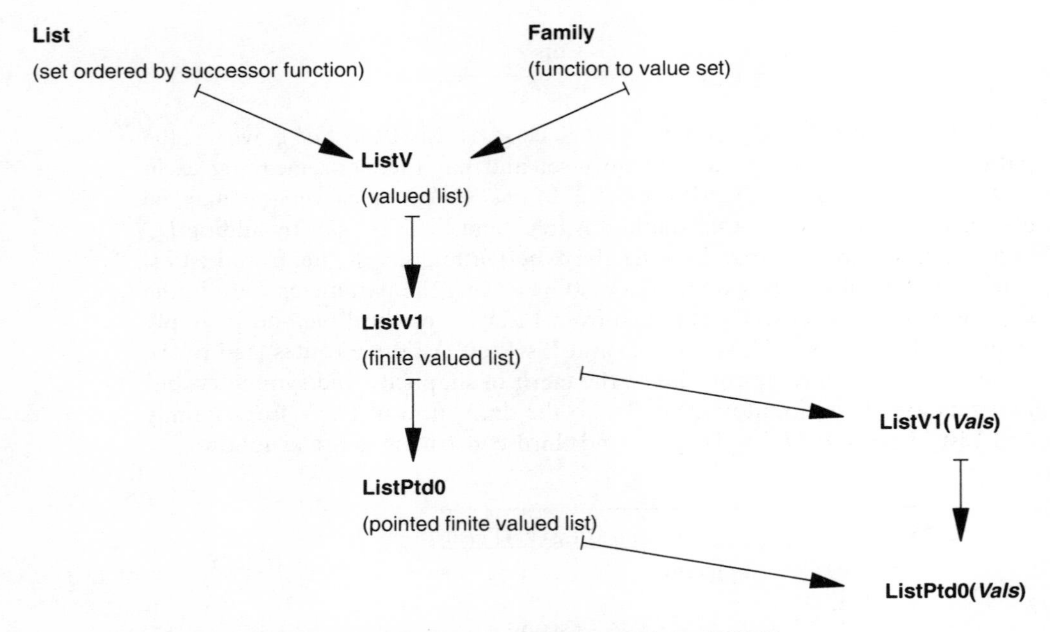

Figure 11.5A.1 Development of ListPtd0(*Vals*).

Here first are the *group* features of L: ListPtd0($Vals$):

$L[List]$: List
$L[Fam]$: Family
$L[ListV]$: ListV
$L[ListV1]$: ListV1($Vals$)
$L[ListPtd0]$: ListPtd0

The feature expansion of L: ListPtd0 follows, given with only the first two group features.

L: ListPtd0($Vals$) (Feature Expansion)	
$L[List]$: List	
* $LPts$: Set	Base set of L. Set of 'points'
$LFst$: $LPts$	First member of list (defined iff $LPts \neq \varnothing$)
* LS	Successor function
$LS(i)$: $LPts$	Successor of point i
(i : $LPts$)	(may be undefined)
$LCo1$.: If $LPts \neq \varnothing$ then $LFst \in LPts - LSRan$	
$LCo2$.: IsInjective(LS)	
$LCo3$.: *Induction principle*	
$\forall A \subseteq_d LPts \cdot$	
If (a) $LFst \in A$	
(b) A ClosedBy LS	
then $A = LPts$	
$L[Fam]$: Family	
(* $LPts$: Set	Base set of L. Set of 'points')
* $LVals$: Set	Value set
* $L(i)$: $LVals$	Value of point i
(i : $LPts$)	
$LCoFam1$.: $LVals \neq_d \varnothing$	
ΔListV	
LV_i : $LVals$ (i : $LPts$)	LV_i is an alias for L_i (value map)
$LCoV1$.: $LV_i =_d L_i$	
(i : $LPts$)	
ΔListV1	
$LCo11$.: IsFinite($LPts$)	
* $Vals$: Set	
$ValsCo$.: $Vals \neq_d \varnothing$	
$LCo12$.: $LVals =_d Vals$	
ΔListPtd0	
* LC : $LPts$	Cursor

11.5B Navigation operations

We now turn to operations on ListPtd0, starting with navigation operations. A *navigation operation* in ListPtd0 is an operation which, given any L: ListPtd0, modifies the cursor LC only. More precisely, it produces a *new* list L' which can differ from L only by the value of $L'C$.

We establish just two navigation operations on ListPtd0. These automatically apply to any subclass ListPtd0(*Vals*). They are the *minimum operations*, taking only L as argument, needed to make LC point to any base element in L. The following developments will give a further illustration of the process of systematic object establishment as a combination of specification and analysis.

MoveFwd

Given L: ListPtd0, MoveFwd 'moves' LC to the next element in $LPts$, if possible. This at any rate is our *intention*. We shall first establish the effect of MoveFwd formally. Then we shall determine the *minimum* or *weakest* precondition which must be satisfied for this operation to be well defined. This derivation will form the *analysis* part of our establishment.

From this informal definition, it is clear that the result of MoveFwd(L) must be the list L': ListPtd0 satisfying the following conditions. First, all the features of L different from LC must be preserved in L'. These features are represented as a group by $LListV1$. Consequently, their preservation is expressed by

(1) $L'ListV1 =_d LListV1$

Second, the cursor $L'C$ must be defined. This is obviously achieved by

(2) $L'C =_d LS(LC)$

The effect of this operation is illustrated in Figure 11.5B.1.

Note that we could also express the definition of $L'C$ by $L'C = L'S(LC)$, as the successor function $L'S = LS$. As a rule, when such a choice arises we give priority to expressions in the arguments rather than the results of the operation defined, unless the alternative is simpler.

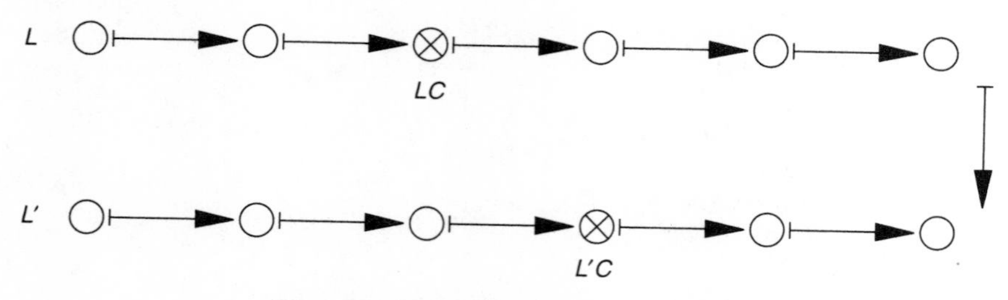

Figure 11.5B.1 Effect of MoveFwd(L).

The above definition of MoveFwd(L) is only an *initial approximation*, a statement of intent, and must be refined. We must verify that in all cases the result L' is a member of ListPtd0, and is entirely defined.

(a) As the only modified feature of L is LC, we need only consider the conditions imposed on $L'C$. More precisely, as L is *given* as a member of ListPtd0, $LListV1$ is a member of ListV1 and consequently so is $L'ListV1$ by (1).

(b) Consider now the cursor $L'C$. This is well defined iff $LS(LC)$ is well defined in L. Two cases must be considered.

Case 1 $LC \neq LLst$ In this case, $LC \in LSDef$, i.e. $LS(LC)$ is well defined.
Case 2 $LC = LLst$ In this case, $LC \notin LSDef$, i.e. $LS(LC)$ is not defined.

In concrete terms, in case 1 the pointer LC has a successor to move to in L. Therefore in this case MoveFwd(L) is well defined. In case 2, on the other hand, LC is at the end of L, so it is clearly impossible to 'move it forward' any further, at least without changing the list itself. Therefore, MoveFwd(L) itself is *undefined.* In conclusion, given L, the result $L' =$ MoveFwd(L) is well defined iff $LC \neq LLst$. This is the minimum precondition we need to impose on L.

The final definition of MoveFwd thus reads:

MoveFwd

Given L: ListPtd0 such that
(Pre 1) $LC \neq LLst$
MoveFwd (L) $=_d L'$ where L': ListPtd0 and
(1) $L'ListV1 =_d LListV1$ (The 'list itself' does not change)
(2) $L'C =_d LS(LC)$

MoveBack

MoveBack is the inverse of MoveFwd: that is, it 'moves' the cursor LC back one position (Figure **11**.5B.2). In order to establish MoveBack, we could follow

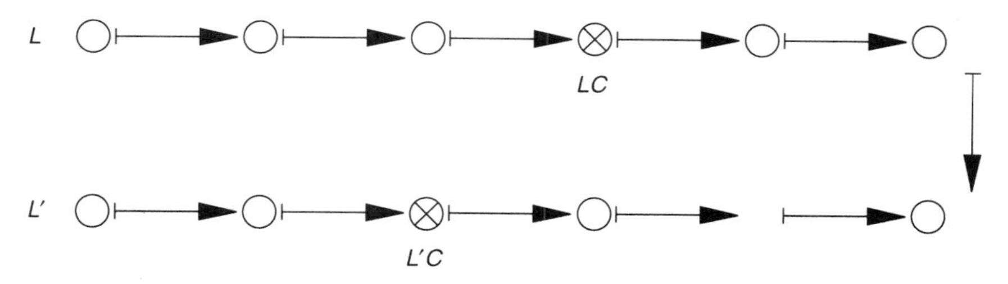

Figure 11.5B.2 Effect of MoveBack(L).

Table 11.5B.1 Derivation of MoveBack from MoveFwd.

MoveFwd	MoveBack
Given L: ListPtd0 such that (Pre 1) $LC \neq LLst$ MoveFwd(L) $=_d L'$ where L': ListPtd0 and (1) $L'ListV1 =_d LListV1$ (2) $L'C =_d LS(LC)$	Given L: ListPtd0 such that (Pre 1) $LC \neq LFst$ MoveBack(L) $=_d L'$ where L': ListPtd0 and (1) $L'ListV1 =_d LListV1$ (2) $L'C =_d LPre(LC)$

the same reasoning as for MoveFwd. However, we shall take another route, which is to derive the former by inverting the specification of the latter formally. We do this by applying the following rules:

(1) Replace 'MoveFwd' by 'MoveBack'.

(2) Replace the successor function *LS* by its inverse *LPre*.

(3) Swap *LLst* for *LFst*.

Now let us apply these substitutions *textually* in the definition of MoveFwd. We first show the two specifications side by side (Table **11**.5B.1). It can be seen that the derivation of MoveBack from MoveFwd again is an entirely mechanical *symbolic* transformation process. It is clear that MoveBack is well defined, for exactly the same reasons that MoveFwd is, *mutatis mutandis*.

MoveBack

Given L: ListPtd0 such that
(Pre 1) $LC \neq LFst$
MoveBack(L) $=_d L'$ where L': ListPtd0 and
(1) $L'ListV1 =_d LListV1$ (The 'list itself' does not change)
(2) $L'C =_d LPre(LC)$

Recall that, unlike *LS*, the function *LPre* is a *secondary* feature of *L*. We may therefore wish to remove it from the specification of MoveBack, in order to describe this function entirely in terms of primary features. This can be done using definition *LDef2* of *LPre*. The result is as follows:

MoveBack (Alternative)

Given L: ListPtd0 such that
(Pre 1) $LC \neq LFst$
MoveBack (L) $=_d L'$ where L': ListPtd0 and
(1) $L'ListV1 =_d LListV1$
(2) $LS(L'C) =_d LC$

In the above derivations of MoveFwd and MoveBack, we have shown the *soundness* of the definitions arrived at. This demonstration was carried out *interactively* with the specification of these operations, which is typical of concept establishment.

Another feature to verify is the *completeness* of this pair of operations, in the following sense. Consider any L:ListPtd0 in which LC may be *any* point in $LPts$. The question is: 'Can we obtain the L':ListPtd0 with $L'ListV1 =_d LListV1$ and $L'C$ equal to *any* other point $j{:}LPts$, by applying MoveFwd or MoveBack a finite number of times to L?' Intuitively, the answer is obviously 'yes'. If $j\ LBef\ LC$ then apply MoveBack until $L'C = j$; if $LC = j$ then do nothing; and if $LC\ LBef\ j$ then apply MoveFwd until $L'C = j$. A formal proof by induction may be given. It is also obvious that MoveFwd and MoveBack are 'minimum' operations, in the sense that both of them are needed to meet this completeness requirement.

These are examples of the type of questions one should seek to answer when developing systems.

11.5C List transformation operations

A word processor requires three editing functions: (a) to create an initial empty text; (b) to insert a character on the left of the cursor and (c) to delete the character to the left of the cursor. In this section, we model these three functions as operations in ListPtd0. They are called InitListPtd0, InsPt and RemPt respectively, and are derived from our list transformation functions on ListV1.

InitListPtd0

In ListPtd0, we cannot define a nullary function EmpListPtd0, as any L:ListPtd0 must be nonempty by $LC \in LPts$. We need an operation which returns a list, call it L', with *exactly one* base point. This is the aim of InitListPtd0. It is established in the same way as InitListV1.

InitListPtd0

Create a one-point valued list L'.
Given $Vals$:Set and $v{:}\ Vals$, InitListPtd0($Vals$, v) $=_d L'$ where L': ListPtd0($Vals$) and

(1) $L'Pts =_d \{L'Fst\}$
(2) $L'V(L'Fst) =_d v$

Note that this definition is obtained by replacing every occurrence of 'ListV1' by 'ListPtd0' in the specification of InitListV1, as a purely symbolic transformation.

Now the reader may well ask: 'How is the cursor $L'C$ defined?' The answer is that in this operation there is no need to specify $L'C$ explicitly. As $L'Pts$ is the singleton $\{L'Fst\}$, $L'C$ must necessarily be equal to $L'Fst$. Any attempt to specify $L'C$ explicitly would be either redundant or inconsistent (minimality principle).

InsPt

Given any L: ListPtd0, the purpose of InsPt is to insert a new base point p and its associated value in L, giving a new list L': ListPtd0. The position of p in L' is to be determined by the cursor LC. This is the initial intention. We must transform this (somewhat vague) statement into a full and consistent establishment of InsPt.

First, the arguments of InsPt must be specified. We take as arguments the initial list L and the value $v: LVals$ to be assigned to p. The new base point p is left *implicit*. All we need to stipulate at this stage is that p is not a member of $LPts$; the full specification of p is a separate concern, typically a matter of 'implementation'.

Second, the position of p in L' must be specified. There are two obvious candidates: immediately *before* LC or immediately *after* LC in L'. We choose the first solution, which reflects the practice of writing from left to right. Think of applying the operation repeatedly!

Third, the new cursor $L'C$ must be specified. We adopt the minimalist solution of no change: $L'C =_d LC$. This completes the informal establishment of InsPt.

It remains to establish InsPt formally, using the ListV1 operations available. A one-point auxiliary list $L1$: ListV1 is first defined, with the value of its single point equal to v. Then $L1$ is 'inserted' in L. Here, two cases must be distinguished:

Case 1 $LC = LFst$ Then the new list is obtained by applying Concat to $L1$ and $LListV1$.

Case 2 $LC \neq LFst$ Then the new list is obtained by inserting $L1$ between $LPre(LC)$ and LC in L, using Ins.

The formal specification is given below and illustrated in Figure **11**.5C.1. Note that the need to enforce $L1Fst \notin LPts$ in InsPt prevents us from invoking InitListV1 in this definition without taking some precautions. We may use this operation, but in conjunction with BaseConv. This alternative solution is shown without further comments.

InsPt

Insert a new point valued with v on the left of LC in pointed list L.
Given L: ListPtd0 and $v: LVals$, InsPt(L, v) $=_d L'$ where L': ListPtd0.
Let $L1$: ListV1. $L1$ is an intermediate variable.

Definition of $L1$

(1) (a) $L1Pts =_d \{L1Fst\}$
(b) $L1Fst \notin_d LPts$
(c) $L1Vals =_d LVals$
(d) $L1V(L1Fst) =_d v$

Definition of L proper

(2) *Case 1* $LC = LFst$
$L'ListV1 =_d L1 \mathbin{+\!\!+} LListV1$
Case 2 $LC \neq LFst$
$(L'ListV1, i, j) =_d$ Ins($LListV1$, $LPre(LC)$, LC, $L1$)
where $i, j: LPts$ (dummies)

(3) $L'C =_d LC$

InsPt (Alternative)

Insert a new point valued with v on the left of LC in pointed list L.
Given L: ListPtd0 and $v: LVals$, InsPt(L, v) $=_d L'$ where L': ListPtd0.
Let $L1 =_d$ BaseConv(InitListV1($LVals$, v), $LPts$).

(1) *Case 1* $LC = LFst$
$L'ListV1 =_d L1 \mathbin{+\!\!+} LListV1$
Case 2 $LC \neq LFst$
$(L'ListV1, i, j) =_d$ Ins($LListV1$, $LPre(LC)$, LC, $L1$)
where $i, j: LPts$ (dummies)

(2) $L'C =_d LC$

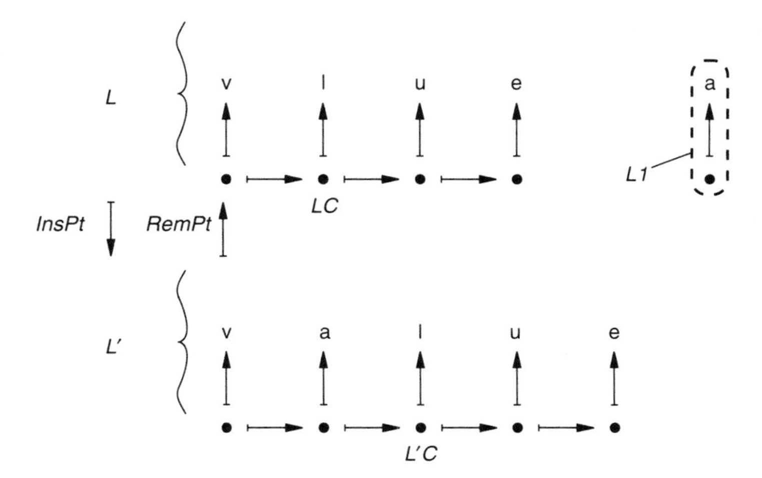

Figure 11.5C.1 Effect of InsPt and RemPt.

RemPt

The aim of RemPt is to reverse the effect of InsPt. However, as the present operations are meant to model the features of a simple word processor, we do not define RemPt as a full inverse of InsPt. (A full inverse would be necessary to model a more sophisticated word processor equipped with an *undo* command.)

Consequently, RemPt is defined as follows. It takes as argument a list L': ListPtd0 and returns L: ListPtd0 such that (a) the element to the left of $L'C$ is removed from L' and (b) all the other features of L are left unchanged.

We now transform this loose specification into a precise one. First, it is clear that RemPt must be subject to one precondition, namely $L'C \neq L'Fst$. Otherwise there would be no element to the left of $L'C$ to remove from L'. Second, if this condition is satisfied, $L =_d \text{Rem}(L')$ is defined by inverting condition (2) of InsPt, and setting $LC =_d L'C$. Here is the result:

<u>RemPt</u>

Remove the predecessor of $L'C$ from pointed list L' if possible.

Given L': ListPtd0 such that

(Pre 1) $L'C \neq L'Fst$

RemPt(L') $=_d L$ where L: ListPtd0. Let $L1$: ListV1, $i, j : L'Pts$.

(1) *Case 1* $L'Pre(L'C) = L'Fst$

$(L1, LListV1) =_d \text{Split}(L'ListV1, L'Fst)$

Case 2 $L'Pre(L'C) \neq L'Fst$

$(LListV1, i, j, L1) =_d \text{Rem}(L'ListV1, i, j)$

where $i =_d L'Pre(L'Pre(L'C))$, and $j =_d L'C$

(2) $LC =_d L'C$

This completes our simple pointed list model.

12 Forests and Trees

Recall from Section **10**.1C that a tree is a conceptual model of a hierarchy, a set on which a 'parenthood' relation is defined. The example of a book has already been given. Many other examples could be offered. Indeed, trees are objects of fundamental importance in computing, both as abstract models and as a basis for representing data efficiently.

There are several ways of defining trees. For instance, one book on graph theory lists six equivalent definitions of finite trees (Berge 1962). The main definition adopted here was chosen for the following reasons.

1 This definition is simple and directly captures the key property of hierarchies, namely the parent relation and the fact that each element has exactly one parent, except for the root, which has none.

2 The definition is expressed as a subset of Peano's postulates. This immediately establishes a close connection between lists and trees. The latter generalize the former: lists may be described as a subclass of the class of trees. Equivalently, the properties common to all lists include the properties common to all trees: anything that is true of any tree is also true of any list. Therefore, our theory of trees closely mirrors our theory of lists.

3 As with lists, our definition covers both finite and infinite trees uniformly. Although we are mainly interested in finite trees in this book, infinite trees also have their applications, so a theory that covers both is useful.

Forests

The concept of a tree is closely related to another notion, that of a *forest*. The connection is so tight that we develop the theory of these two concepts simultaneously. A forest may be viewed as a set of trees. However, this is not our definition, because it would prevent us from extending to one concept the features of the other. Our strategy is to take the notion of forest as a starting point. A forest F is defined like a tree, except that it may have any number of roots (parentless points) instead of just one. A tree, then, is a forest with just one root. While a tree must have at least one point, namely its root, a forest F may be 'empty' in the sense that $FPts = \emptyset$. (This of course is true iff F has no roots.) The class of forests is denoted by Forest, and that of trees by Tree.

One key reason for working with forests is that in general, for any tree T with base set $TPts$, a subobject of T induced by a subset $A \subseteq TPts$ is a forest, not a tree. A related reason is that an important operation on a tree T is the insertion of a forest F immediately below a point $p: TPts$, as well as the inverse function, the removal of a subforest F from T.

Accordingly, our primary aim is to develop a theory of forests. This automatically extends to trees. Special features defined for trees only will be added whenever needed. The reader should bear in mind that anything said about forests holds for trees as well.

Like a list, a forest F is described as an object which has a structured base set and is susceptible of various extensions: addition of a value map, etc. The base set $FPts$ may be any set. We may now reap one benefit of allowing lists with any base set. Such lists occur naturally as subobjects of a forest F – objects defined as restrictions induced by a subset of $FPts$. The description of such lists is simplified and, in a sense, safer.

Taxonomy of forests and trees

As with families and lists, subsequent developments are based on a taxonomy of forests and trees similar to that of lists. This taxonomy consists of various classes of forests obtained from Forest by successive *extensions* and one *specialization*. In parallel, for each class of forests a corresponding class of trees is derived, always by applying the specialization criterion stated above. The classes defined in this chapter are reproduced in Table **12**.1.

Table 12.1 Taxonomy of forests and trees.

Forest Classes	*Tree Classes*
Forest alias For Basic class of forests, unordered and unvalued	Tree Basic class of trees, i.e. forests with one root
ForOrd Class of *ordered* forests (Extension of Forest)	TreeOrd Class of *ordered* trees
ForV Class of *valued* forests (Extension of Forest)	TreeV Class of *valued* trees
ForOV Class of *ordered valued* forests (Extension of ForOrd)	TreeOV Class of *ordered valued* trees
ForOV1 Class of *finite, ordered valued* forests (Specialization of ForOV)	TreeOV1 Class of *finite, ordered valued* trees
	TreePtd0 Class of *pointed, finite, ordered valued* trees (Extension of TreeOV1)

The initial class is Forest. This is the class of all forests as outlined above. ForOrd is a proper extension of Forest. In any ordinary forest F, the parent relation implies a secondary variable feature, namely the set $FChis(i) \subseteq_d FPts$ of points with a common parent i, for any $i: FPts$. The members of any set $FChis(i)$ are the 'children' of i. In an ordinary forest, this set is unstructured. In an ordered forest $F: ForOrd$, $FChis(i)$ is structured as an unvalued *list*. The roots themselves are ordered in a similar way. Thus, ordered forests are extensions of ordinary forests obtained by imposing a second (partially linear) structure on the base set. TreeOrd is defined similarly as the class of all ordered trees.

In our theory of lists in Chapter **11**, the base structure was clearly distinguished from the value map, in accordance with the principle of separation of concerns. We first introduced the class List of all *unvalued* lists, and then extended it to ListV by adding a value map. The class ForV is derived from Forest in exactly the same way.

Any F: ForV is a forest together with such a map, i.e. a function from *FPts* to a nonempty set *FVals* of values.

The next class is ForOV. This is the class of valued, ordered forests obtained by combining the two extensions leading from Forest to ForOrd and ForV respectively. Finally ForOV1 is a specialization of ForOV. It is derived by adding the constraint (fixed feature) that for any F: ForOV1, *FPts* is finite. We also define a parametrized version of ForOV1, with the value set passed as a parameter.

As already mentioned, each class of forests gives rise to a corresponding class of trees, by the specialization rule stated above. Only one class of trees is specified in a different way. This is the class TreePtd0 of *pointed trees*, derived by extension from TreeOV1. A pointed tree T: TreePtd0 is a finite, valued ordered tree together with a 'cursor', or pointer, *TC* to an element of *TPts*. TreePtd0 is derived from TreeOV1 because we do not define the concept of pointed forest.

This taxonomy could be extended by adding some of the distinctions introduced in Chapter **11**, in particular the concept of distributed values. This is not done here. In Chapter **16**, we shall introduce an alternative class of pointed trees called TreePtd1 and a further specialization of ForOV1.

This taxonomy determines the structure of the present chapter. For each forest class, we establish the features of its members in some detail, as well as operations on the class. The operations are established by successive extensions closely shadowing the above taxonomy.

The distinction is again made between the primary and the secondary features (variable or fixed) of an object. Recall that the latter are those characteristics entirely determined by the former, and that the distinction is relative to the chosen definition.

12.1 Pure forests and trees

We begin with the establishment of Forest, the class of 'pure' – that is, unordered, unvalued – forests, and of the subclass Tree of pure trees. As for Tree, the specification below is mainly a restatement in Feature Notation of the definition given in Section **10**.1C. Recall that in a feature name, the suffix '*s*' means the feature is a set.

12.1A Definition of forests and trees

Definition of Forest

A forest F:Forest is an object with the following primary variable features: a base set *FPts* and a relation *FParentOf* with graph $FParentOfGr \subseteq FPts \times FPts$. For any two points i, j:*FPts*, 'i *FParentOf* j' means that i is the parent of j in F. An example is given in Figure **12**.1A.1.

The figure illustrates the following defining properties of an F:Forest. First, the set of points j which have a parent is the range of *FParentOf*, that is, *FParentOfRan*. A point j with *no* parent is called a *root*. The set of roots is denoted by *FRoots*. It is determined formally by the condition

$$FRoots =_d FPts - FParentOfRan$$

Second, for any point j:*FParentOfRan*, there is exactly one i such that i *FParentOf* j. This means that *FParentOf* is injective. We express this by

IsInjective(*FParentOf*)

where for any relation R, the predicate IsInjective(R) is true iff

$$\forall y : RRan\ \exists 1\ x : RDef \cdot x\ R\ y$$

Third, F satisfies a certain *induction principle*. The purpose of this condition is to ensure that any point j:*FPts* is reachable from some root by a 'path' determined by *FParentOf*. In other words there must be a sequence

(1) $(r = i_0, i_1, \ldots, i_n = j)$

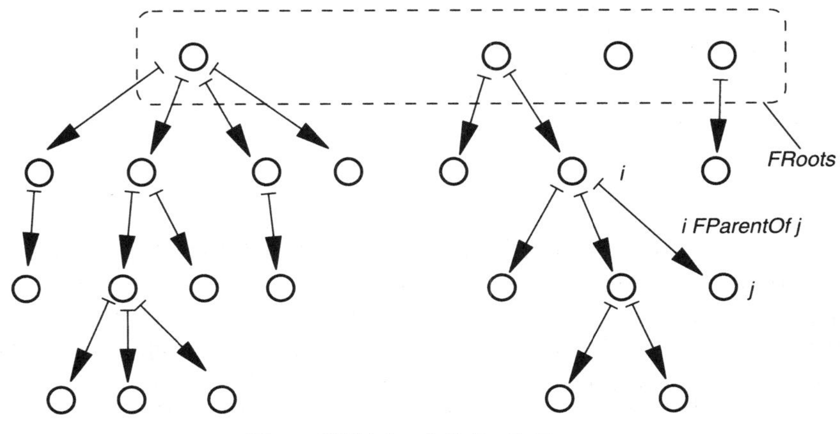

Figure 12.1A.1 A finite F:Forest.

where r is a root ($r \in FRoots$), $i_1, \ldots, i_n \in FPts$ and

$$i_0 \; FParentOf \; i_1, \quad i_1 \; FParentOf \; i_2, \quad \ldots, \quad i_{n-1} \; FParentOf \; i_n$$

This condition is formally expressed as the induction principle first defined for natural numbers (Peano's fifth postulate). We now restate it as follows. For any relation R and any set A, let 'A ClosedBy R' be the predicate true iff A is closed by R, that is, for any points x, y such that $x \; R \; y$, if $x \in A$ then $y \in A$.

A ClosedBy R iff
$$\forall x : A \cap RDef, \; y : RRan \cdot x \; R \; y \Rightarrow y \in A$$

Now we say (see Chapter 4) that any set A is *inductive* with respect to *FRoots* and *FParentOf* iff (a) $FRoots \subseteq A$ and (b) A ClosedBy *FParentOf*. Thence, the induction principle for F: Forest reads: for any inductive subset $A \subseteq_d FPts$, $A = FPts$. In other words, *FPts* is the smallest inductive set.

This completes our description. We gather these various features in the following definition, where '*' indicates a primary variable feature.

F: For alias Forest

*	$FPts$: Set	Base set of F
	$FRoots \subseteq_d FPts$	Set of roots of F (parentless points)
*	$FParentOf: FPts \leftrightarrow FPts$	Parent relation
	$i \; FParentOf \; j$: Bool $(i, j : FPts)$	True iff i is the parent of j in F

$FCo1$.: $FRoots =_d FPts - FParentOfRan$

$FCo2$.: IsInjective($FParentOf$)

$FCo3$.: *Induction Principle*

$\forall A \subseteq_d FPts \cdot$

If (a) $FRoots \subseteq A$

(b) A ClosedBy $FParentOf$

then $A = FPts$

Notes

1 The set *FRoots* is a *secondary* feature of F : Forest, as it is entirely determined by the relation *FParentOf*. It is included in the definition of Forest for clarity.

2 The conditions imposed on any F : Forest are a subset of Peano's postulates for the definition of the natural numbers (Definition **4**.1A.1). Consequently, the system (Nat, 0, S) is a special case of a forest. In this system there is one root, namely 0, and the relation *FParentOf* is the successor function S, which is a total function. Thus an F : Forest may be described as a *relaxed* Peano system.

3 For any F:Forest, the induction principle *FCo3* means that *FPts* is the (unique) set inductively generated by *FRoots*, regarded as a unary relation, and *FParentOf*. Conditions *FCo1* and *FCo2* mean that each point i:*FPts* is generated in exactly *one* way. If $i \in FRoots$ then i has no parent and so is not generated by *FParentOf* from any other point. If $i \notin FRoots$, then it is generated by *FParentOf* from exactly one other point p, as *FParentOf* is injective. Consequently *FPts* is *freely generated*, and total functions $h: FPts \rightarrow V$, where V is any set, may be defined recursively on this basis. Several examples will be given later. Conditions *FCo1* and *FCo2* correspond to Peano's postulates 3 and 4 in the special case of Nat.

4 One key consequence of conditions *FCo1* to *FCo3* is that for each point i:*FPts*, there is *exactly one* sequence (1) from a root r to i. A corollary is that F may not contain any circuits. These are essential properties in all applications of forests and trees. ■

Definition of Tree

The definition of the class Tree of pure trees follows immediately. A tree T: Tree is defined as a forest with exactly one root. This point is given the name *TRoot*. This must not be confused with the *set TRoots*, which is also a feature of T, as of any other forest. Obviously

$$TRoots =_{\mathrm{d}} \{TRoot\}$$

T: Tree (Specialized Forest)	
* $T[Forest]$: Forest	
ΔTree	
$TRoot: TPts$	Root of T
$TCoTr1 .: TRoots =_{\mathrm{d}} \{TRoot\}$	T is a forest with one root

Notes

1 The definition of a T:Tree is obtained by adding the extra constraint *TCoTr1*. The point *TRoot* then is entirely determined by *TCoTr1*. Therefore, it is a *secondary* feature of T, and Tree is a *specialization* of Forest.

2 Recall that *TForest*: Forest is a *group feature* of T. It is the set of all the features, variable or fixed, inherited by T from Forest, and to which *TRoot* and *TCoTr1* are added. Thus, the total set of features of T named so far consists of *TPts*, *TRoots*, *TParentOf*, *TCo1*, ..., *TCo3*, *TRoot* and *TCoTr1*.

3 As *TRoot* is always defined for any T:Tree, *TPts* cannot be empty: it contains at least *TRoot*. Therefore, the condition $TPts \neq \varnothing$ is a secondary feature of T, implied by *TCoTr1*. No such condition is imposed on an F: Forest, and indeed *FPts* may be empty. Clearly $FPts = \varnothing$ iff $FRoots = \varnothing$. ■

12.1B Basic secondary features of forests

Any F: Forest is entirely determined by fixing *FPts* and *FParentOf*. These two primary variable features imply a variety of secondary features in addition to *FRoots*, some of which are formally defined below.

FParent The opposite relation of *FParentOf* is denoted by *FParent*. It is defined formally by

$$FParent =_{\mathrm{d}} \mathrm{Opp}(FParentOf)$$

Recall from Section **3**.6E that this means

$$FParentDom =_{\mathrm{d}} FParentOfCod =_{\mathrm{d}} FPts$$
$$FParentCod =_{\mathrm{d}} FParentOfDom =_{\mathrm{d}} FPts$$
$$FParentGr =_{\mathrm{d}} \{(j, i) | (i, j) : FParentOfGr\}$$

Hence, $FParentDef = FParentOfRan = FPts - FRoots$. Furthermore, the condition IsInjective(*FParentOf*) implies that *FParent* is a partial function

$$FParent : FPts \nrightarrow FPts$$

Hence, for any point $j : FPts - FRoots$, the parent of j is written $FParent(j)$.

Note that the two features *FParentOf* and *FParent* are entirely determined by each other. Therefore they can be used interchangeably. For instance, we could give an alternative definition of F: Forest, in which *FParent* is primary and *FParentOf* secondary. This would be equivalent to the original definition. Accordingly, in the establishment of operations on forests, we sometimes use *FParent* instead of *FParentOf*.

FChis This is the total function $FChis : FPts \to \mathrm{Pow}(FPts)$ already mentioned. For each $i : FPts$, $FChis(i)$ is the set of 'children' of i. It is defined by

$$FChis(i) =_{\mathrm{d}} \{j : FPts | i \ FParentOf \ j\}$$

FLeafs A *leaf* of F is a childless element, that is, a point $i : FPts$ such that $FChis(i) = \varnothing$. The set of leaves of F is denoted by *FLeafs*. Thus,

$$FLeafs =_{\mathrm{d}} \{i : FPts | FChis(i) = \varnothing\}$$

Using this secondary feature, we may now write

$$FParentRan = FParentOfDef = FPts - FLeafs$$

These results are grouped together and illustrated in Figure **12**.1B.1.

F : Forest Secondary Features I: Definitions	
$FParent(j): FPts$	Parent of point j in F
$(j: FParentOfRan)$	
$FDef1 .: FParent =_d \mathrm{Opp}(FParentOf)$	
$FChis(i) \subseteq_d FPts$	Set of children of point i
$(i: FPts)$	
$FDef2 .: \forall\, i: FPts \cdot FChis(i) =_d \{j \mid i\ FParentOf\ j\}$	
$FLeafs \subseteq_d FPts$	Set of leaves of F
$FDef3 .: FLeafs =_d \{i: FPts \mid FChis(i) = \varnothing\}$	

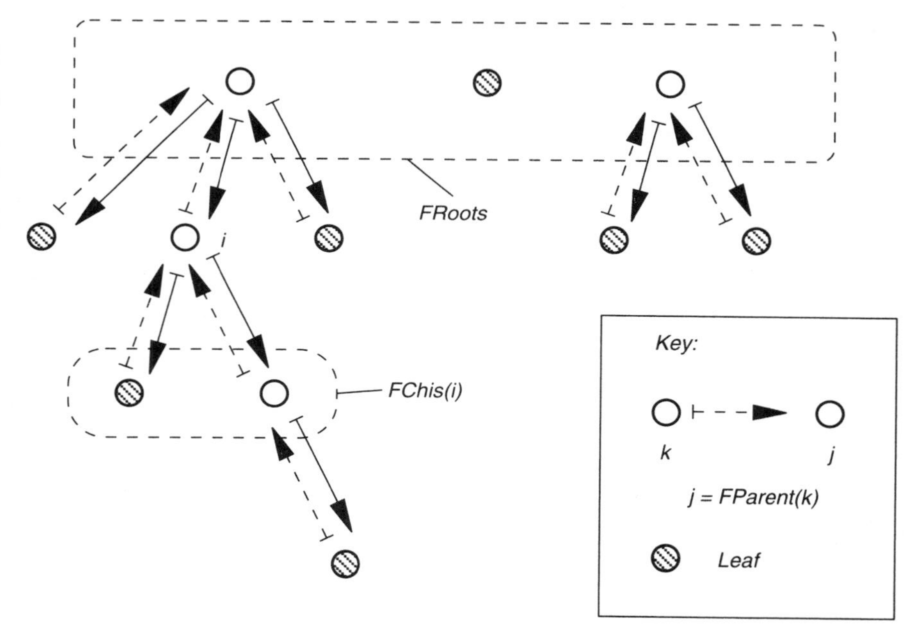

Figure 12.1B.1 Secondary features of *F* : Forest.

12.1C Order properties of forests

In any *F* : Forest, the relation *FParentOf* defines a *strict partial order* on the points of *F* (Section **3**.6F). A number of basic secondary properties of *F* are associated with this partial order. These are described below.

FAncs For any point *j* : *FPts*, consider the points *FParent*(*j*), *FParent* (*FParent*(*j*)), and so on. These various elements are the *ancestors* of *j*. It is easy to see intuitively that if *j* is not a root, they form a finite set which contains exactly one root of F. This set is denoted by $FAncs(j)$ and illustrated in Figure **12**.1C.1. It is a total function

$$FAncs: FPts \to \text{Pow}(FPts)$$

and is defined recursively by

(1) $\forall\, r: FRoots \cdot FAncs(r) =_{\text{d}} \varnothing$

(2) $\forall\, i: FPts, j: FChis(i) \cdot FAncs(j) =_{\text{d}} FAncs(i) + \{i\}$

The fact that the function *FAncs* is well-defined follows from the recursion theorem and the property that *FPts* is freely generated by *FRoots* and *FParentOf*. Two related elementary properties of *FAncs* may be stated:

Property 12.1C.1

For any F: Forest and any $i: FPts$,

(1) There exists exactly one root $r: FRoots$ such that either $r = i$ or $r \in FAncs(i)$.

(2) $i \notin FAncs(i)$. ■

Thus Property **12**.1C.1(2) justifies the use of '$+$' in '$FAncs(i) + \{i\}$'.

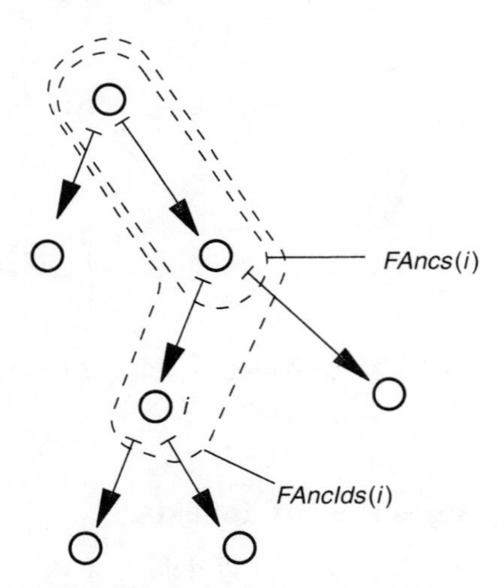

Figure 12.1C.1 Functions *FAncs* and *FAncIds*.

FAncIds This is an extension of *FAncs*. It is the function $FAncIds$: $FPts \to \text{Pow}(FPts)$ defined for all $i: FPts$ by

$$FAncIds(i) =_{\text{d}} FAncs(i) + \{i\}$$

In other words, *FAncIds*(i) is the set of ancestors of i augmented with i. '*Id*' stands for *identity*.

FDescs For any $i: FPts$, the set of 'descendants' of i is defined as

$$FDescs(i) =_{d} \{j: FPts \mid i \in FAncs(j)\}$$

for all $i: FPts$. Thus, any j is a descendant of i iff i is an ancestor of j, and *FDescs* is a total function $FPts \rightarrow \mathrm{Pow}(FPts)$.

FDescIds This is an extension of *FDescs*. It is the function $FDescIds$: $FPts \rightarrow \mathrm{Pow}(FPts)$ defined for all $i: FPts$ by

$$FDescIds(i) =_{d} FDescs(i) + \{i\}$$

The reader may verify that this definition is equivalent to

$$FDescIds(i) =_{d} \{j: FPts \mid i \in FAncIds(j)\}$$

FDepth This is the function $FDepth: FPts \rightarrow \mathrm{Nat}$ defined by

$$FDepth(i) =_{d} \mathrm{Num}(FAncs(i))$$

for all $i: FPts$. $FDepth(i)$ is the 'distance' from *FRoots* to i in F. An equivalent recursive definition of *FDepth* is

(1) $\forall r: FRoots \cdot FDepth(r) =_{d} 0$

(2) $\forall i: FPts, j: FChis(i) \cdot FDepth(j) =_{d} FDepth(i) + 1$

F: Forest Secondary Features II: Definitions

$FAncs(j) \subseteq_{d} FPts$ — Set of ancestors of points j
$(j: FPts)$
$FDefAn1$.:
(1) $\forall j: FRoots \cdot FAncs(j) =_{d} \varnothing$
(2) $\forall i: FPts, j: FChis(i) \cdot FAncs(j) =_{d} FAncs(i) + \{i\}$

$FAncIds(j) \subseteq_{d} FPts$ — Extension of $FAncs(j)$
$(j: FPts)$
$FDefAn2$.: $\forall j: FPts \cdot FAncIds(j) =_{d} FAncs(j) + \{j\}$

$FDescs(i) \subseteq_{d} FPts$ — Set of descendants of point i
$(i: FPts)$
$FDefAn3$.: $\forall i: FPts \cdot FDescs(i) =_{d} \{j: FPts \mid i \in FAncs(j)\}$

$FDescIds(i) \subseteq_{d} FPts$ — Extension of $FDescs(i)$
$(i: FPts)$

$FDefAn4 .: \forall i: FPts \cdot FDescIds(i) =_d FDescs(i) + \{i\}$
Equivalently:
$FDefAn4' .: \forall i: FPts \cdot FDescIds(i) =_d \{j: FPts \mid i \in FAncIds(j)\}$

$FDepth(i)$: Nat — Depth of i
$(i: FPts)$
$FDefAn5 .: \forall i: FPts \cdot FDepth(i) =_d \mathrm{Num}(FAncs(i))$
Equivalently:
$FDefAn5' .:$
(1) $\forall r: FRoots \cdot FDepth(r) =_d 0$
(2) $\forall i: FPts, j: FChis(i) \cdot FDepth(j) =_d FDepth(i) + 1$

12.1D Quadrichotomy law AT

The trichotomy law of List has a corresponding property in Forest. The latter is a generalization of the former. We call it the *quadrichotomy law*, as it involves four mutually exclusive cases. It is established in the same way as trichotomy.

Consider any F: Forest. There is an obvious 'ancestor–descendant' relation on *FPts*. This relation is satisfied by any $i, j: FPts$ iff i is the ancestor of j in F. It is a *strict partial order*, denoted by *FAnBef*. Formally:

$$\forall i, j: FPts \cdot i \ FAnBef \ j \Leftrightarrow_d i \in FAncs(j)$$

The relation *FAnBef* corresponds to the order *LBef* of a list L: List. It is given a rather long name to distinguish it from other orders which will be defined later on ordered trees. As usual, $i \ FAnBef\!= j$ means $i \ FAnBef \ j$ or $i = j$; or, equivalently, $i \in FAncIds(j)$. Also, we define

$$FAnUnrel(i, j) \Leftrightarrow_d$$
$$(i \neq j) \wedge \neg (i \ FAnBef \ j) \wedge \neg (j \ FAnBef \ i)$$

Thus $FAnUnrel(i, j)$ means that i and j are not related either by *FAnBef* (either way) or by equality.

F: Forest Secondary Features III: Definitions

$i \ FAnBef \ j$: Bool — True iff i is an ancestor of j
$(i, j: FPts)$
$FDefAn6 .: \forall i, j: FPts \cdot i \ FAnBef \ j \Leftrightarrow_d i \in FAncs(j)$

$i \ FAnBef\!= j$: Bool — True iff i is an ancestor of j or $i = j$
$(i, j: FPts)$
$FDefAn7 .: \forall i, j: FPts \cdot i \ FAnBef\!= j \Leftrightarrow_d i \in FAncIds(j)$

$FAnUnrel(i, j)$ — True iff i and j are 'unrelated'
$FDefAn8 .: \forall i, j: FPts \cdot FAnUnrel(i, j) \Leftrightarrow$
$(i \neq j) \wedge \neg (i \ FAnBef \ j) \wedge \neg (j \ FAnBef \ i)$

Theorem 12.1D.1 (quadrichotomy law)

For all $i, j: FPts$, *exactly one* of the following propositions is true:

(1) $i \; FAnBef \; j$

(2) $i = j$

(3) $j \; FAnBef \; i$

(4) $FAnUnrel(i, j)$ ■

This theorem is formulated in this way in order to establish and explicitly label the four cases which may obtain for any $i, j: FPts$. These four cases are reflected in the following properties of *FAncs* and *FDescs*, all fairly obvious.

Corollary 12.1D.2

For all $i: FPts$, the three sets $FAncs(i)$, $\{i\}$ and $FDescs(i)$ are pairwise disjoint. (The corresponding property of List is Corollary **11**.2D.3.) ■

Corollary 12.1D.3a (FAncIds)

$\forall \; i, j: FPts \cdot$

(1) $i \; FAnBef \; j \Leftrightarrow FAncIds_i \subset FAncIds_j$

(2) $i = j \Leftrightarrow FAncIds_i = FAncIds_j$ ■

Corollary 12.1D.3b (FDescIds)

$\forall \; i, j: FPts \cdot$

(1) $i \; FAnBef \; j \Leftrightarrow FDescIds_j \subset FDescIds_i$

(2) $i = j \Leftrightarrow FDescIds_i = FDescIds_j$

(3) $FAnUnrel(i, j) \Leftrightarrow \text{IsDisjoint}(FDescIds_i, FDescIds_j)$ ■

One consequence of Corollary **12**.1D.3b(3) is

Corollary 12.1D.4

(1) (a) For all $j, k: FRoots$ with $j \neq k$, $FDescIds_j$ and $FDescIds_k$ are disjoint.

(b) For all $i: FPts$, j, $k: FChis_i$ with $j \neq k$, the following are pairwise disjoint: $\{i\}$, $FDescIds_j$ and $FDescIds_k$.

(2) $\forall \; i: FPts \cdot FDescIds_i = \{i\} + \Sigma \; \{FDescIds_j | j: FChis_i\}$ ■

The practical consequence of this property is important. Consider any F: Forest such that $FPts$ is finite. Suppose we want to apply an operation Op which requires selecting each point $i: FPts$ *exactly once*; for example, we wish to count the members of $FPts$. We may apply the following rule:

For each $r: FRoots$

(1) apply Op to r;
(2) for each $j: FChis_r$, apply Op to each $k: FDescIds_j$.

Part (1) of Corollary **12**.1D.4 guarantees the *nonredundancy* of the process; no $k: FPts$ is selected more than once. Part (2) guarantees the *completeness* of the process, namely that every $k: FPts$ must be selected. Note that this process is implicitly recursive, but on a different induction base.

Corollary 12.1D.5

(1) For all $i: FPts$,
  (a) $FChis_i \subseteq FDescs_i$.
  (b) $\{i\}$ and $FChis_i$ are disjoint.
(2) For all $i: FPts$, $FRoots$ and $FChis_i$ are disjoint.
(3) For all $i, j: FPts$ with $i \neq j$, $FChis_i$ and $FChis_j$ are disjoint. ■

12.1E Three sets of subobjects of F: Forest AT

Consider any F: Forest and any subset $A \subseteq_d FPts$. The *subobject of F induced by A* is defined as the object X with the following features:

(1) $XPts =_d A \subseteq FPts$
(2) $XR =_d A \diamond FParentOf$

Recall that for any set A and any relation R, $R' =_d A \diamond R$ is the *restriction* of R defined by $R'Dom =_d A \cap RDom$, $R'Cod =_d A \cap RCod$, and $R'Gr =_d (A \times A) \cap RGr$.

It can be shown that in general X is a forest. (Specifically: there exists an F': Forest with $F'Pts =_d XPts$ and $F'ParentOf =_d XR$.) However, for some sets A, X may be more special: for example, it may determine a sublist or a subtree of F. We now consider three special cases.

FAn For any $i: FPts$, let FAn_i be the subobject of F induced by the set $FAncIds_i$. It is a list, which we define by posing FAn_i: List, where

$FAn_iPts =_d FAncIds_i$

$FAn_iS =_d FAncIds_i \diamond FParentOf$

This determines a function *FAn* from *FPts* to the set of all lists L: List with $LPts \subseteq FPts$. For any i: *FPts*, FAn_i is necessarily finite. FAn_i is illustrated in Figure **12**.1E.1. The fact that it is a list is clear, although this should be proved, by verifying that conditions FAn_iCo1 to FAn_iCo3 of the definition of List are satisfied. FAn_i is also called a *path* from the unique point $r: FRoots \cap FAncIds_i$ to i in F. $FDepth_i$ is the *length* of this path. The existence and uniqueness of FAn_i for any point i is important. It is a fundamental property of forests, as mentioned in Section **12**.1A.

FTr For any i: *FPts*, let FTr_i be the subobject of F induced by $FDescIds_i$. We make FTr_i a member of Tree by stipulating FTr_i: Tree where

$$FTr_iPts =_d FDescIds_i$$
$$FTr_iParentOf =_d FDescIds_i \diamond FParentOf$$

(See Figure **12**.1E.1.) It is easy to see that FTr_i is indeed a member of Tree, although this fact should be proved formally. This determines a function *FTr* from *FPts* to the set of trees T: Tree such that $TPts \subseteq FPts$.

F: Forest Secondary Features IV: Definitions		
FAn_i: List (i: *FPts*)		List of ancestors of i, including i
FDefSub1.: (1)	$FAn_iPts =_d FAncIds_i$	
(2)	$FAn_iS =_d FAncIds_i \diamond FParentOf$	
FTr_i: Tree (i: *FPts*)		Subtree of descendants of i, including i
FDefSub2.: (1)	$FTr_iPts =_d FDescIds_i$	
(2)	$FTr_iParentOf =_d FDescIds_i \diamond FParentOf$	

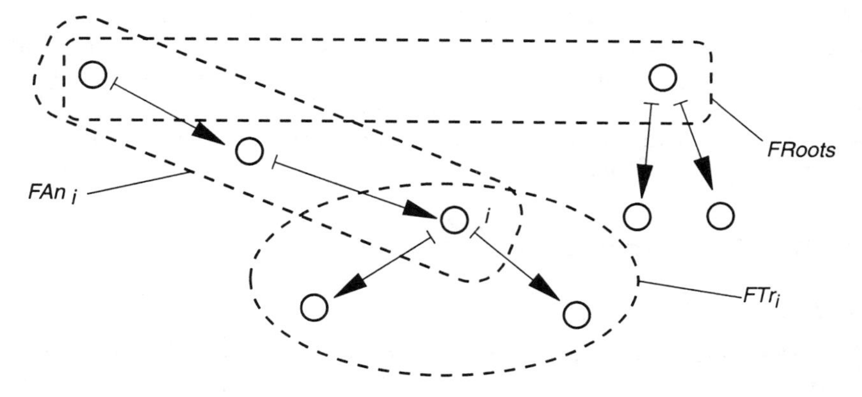

Figure 12.1E.1 Path FAn_i and tree FTr_i in F.

In any F: Forest, FTr_i is called the *subtree of F rooted at i.* It has all the secondary features of any instance of Tree. For example we may write: $FTr_iRoot = i$, $FTr_iParent = FDescIds_i \diamond FParent$, and so on. We may also define exactly what we mean by the forest F *regarded* as a set of trees. This is the set $\{FTr_i | i : FRoots\}$; it is not the same as F. Note that the correspondence between features of FTr_i and features of F is not always that simple. For instance, the *function* FTr_iChis is *not* simply given by $FDescIds_i \diamond FChis$, because the codomain of $FChis$ is not $FPts$ but Pow($FPts$). The reader should establish the proper correspondence as an exercise.

FChis For any $i : FPts$, it is also interesting to consider the subobject of F induced by $FChis_i$. It is obvious that this is just an unstructured set. This is because, for any $j : FChis_i$, $FParent_j = i \notin FChis_i$ by Corollary **12**.1D.5(1). Consequently, $(FChis_i \diamond FParentOf)Gr = \varnothing$. Like rests in music, the *absence* of structure in a subobject may be just as important as the existence of structure.

12.2 Operations on forests and trees

We now define some elementary operations on trees and forests. Our purpose is not to devise a complete system of functions on these objects, but to establish a few basic operations which will serve as 'building blocks' in later constructions.

First, we establish three functions: InitTree, Ins and Rem. InitTree is a nullary operation which returns a tree of just one point. Ins is a ternary operation which inserts a given forest F in a given tree T 'immediately below' a given point p of T, giving a new tree T'. Rem is the inverse operation. These are the topics of Section **12**.2A.

Second, we discuss a somewhat more technical issue, namely the conversion of the base set of a forest or a tree. Such a transformation is necessary because if we wish to insert a forest F into a tree T, their respective base sets $FPts$ and $TPts$ must be disjoint. If this condition is not met and the insertion is nevertheless required, it is necessary first to convert, say, F to a new forest F' equivalent to F in some sense and such that $TPts$ and $F'Pts$ are disjoint. We also say that F and F' must be *isomorphic*. Our aim in Section **12**.2B is to define the notion of equivalence or isomorphism of forests, and then to establish an operation BaseConv to convert F to F'.

12.2A Basic operations

InitTree

The first operation on trees is InitTree. This returns a tree T': Tree with just one point, the root $T'Root$. There cannot be a smaller tree, as any tree must contain at least a root. The specification is immediate.

InitTree

Create a one-point tree T'.
InitTree $=_d T'$ where T': Tree and
(1) $T'Pts =_d \{T'Root\}$

InitTree is a nullary operation. It is *underspecified* in that its definition does not state what $T'Root$ is. Therefore $T'Root$ may be any element which may be the member of a set, more specifically of the set $T'Pts$. This underdetermination of InitTree reflects our view that the identity of base points is a matter which should not concern us at this stage. Thus, our strategy is a signal that the identity of $T'Root$, like that of any other base point, should be dealt with separately, typically as an 'implementation feature'. This is discussed further in Section **12**.2B.

Ins

The next two operations are central to all subsequent developments on trees. They are defined as inverses of each other. The first function, Ins, takes as input a tree T: Tree, a point p: $TPts$ and a forest F: Forest. It returns two objects: a new T': Tree, the result of *inserting* F in T immediately below p, that is, with p the parent of the members of $FRoots$ in T'; and a set A, equal to $FRoots$. Thus, Ins$(T, p, F) =_d (T', A)$.

The reason for returning $A =_d FRoots$ is to make Ins invertible. In order to reverse the effect of Ins, we need two pieces of information: first, the tree T' itself, and second, some subset $A \subseteq T'Pts$ necessary to identify F within T'. A simple solution is to take $A =_d FRoots$. The inverse of Ins is then defined as the operation Rem, which removes from T' the subforest whose roots make up A. Again, for full inversion of Ins, Rem must return all three arguments of Ins; that is, we must have Rem$(T', A) =_d (T, p, F)$.

This, however, imposes a small penalty: the operation Ins(T, p, F) cannot be allowed if $FPts = \varnothing$. If Ins(T, p, F) were defined with $FPts = \varnothing$ then we would have $A = FRoots = \varnothing$, and consequently a small loss of information would be incurred when applying Ins: the point p could not be retrieved by Rem from T'. We could, of course, make p a third argument of Rem and allow $FPts = \varnothing$, but this seems an unnecessary complication. We prefer making $FPts \neq \varnothing$ a precondition of Ins.

Given T, p and F, the definition of T' should be clear from Figure **12**.2A.1. First, the base set $T'Pts$ must be the union of $TPts$ and $FPts$. Second, the graph of the relation $T'ParentOf$ must include the graphs of $TParentOf$ and $FParentOf$. In addition, it must contain every couple (p, r) with r: $FRoots$, to 'bind' F to T.

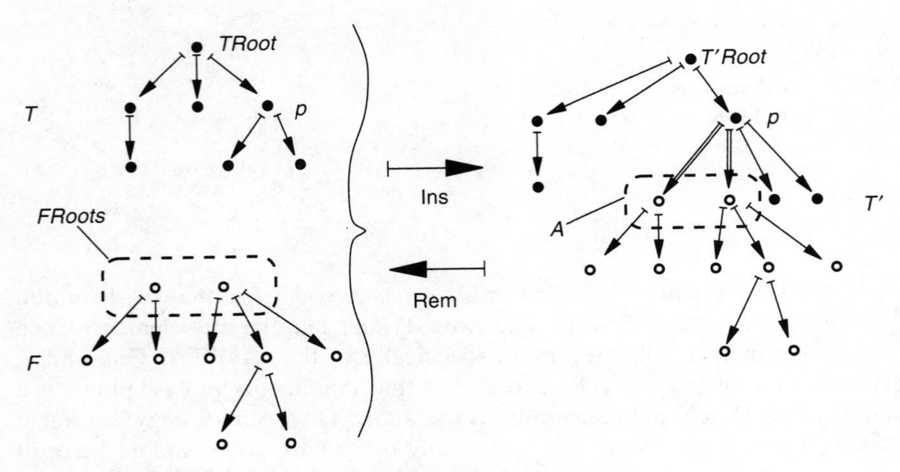

Figure 12.2A.1 Insertion and removal of forest F in tree T.

The result T' of Ins(T, p, F) is well defined, that is, satisfies all the defining conditions $T'Co1, \ldots, T'CoTr1$ iff $TPts$ and $FPts$ are disjoint. For if $TPts$ and $FPts$ had some points in common, the union of $TParentOfGr$ and $FParentOfGr$ would not in general be the graph of a parent function, as Figure **12**.2A.2 illustrates. (The reader should construct other examples.) Therefore we impose a second precondition on Ins(T, p, F), namely IsDisjoint($TPts$, $FPts$). The full specification of Ins may now be given without more ado.

Ins

Insert F: Forest below p: $TPts$ in T: Tree, where $FPts$ and $TPts$ are disjoint and $FPts$ is not empty.

Given T: Tree, p: $TPts$ and F: Forest with

(Pre 1) $FPts \neq \varnothing$

(Pre 2) IsDisjoint($TPts$, $FPts$)

Ins(T, p, F) $=_d (T', A)$ where T': Tree, $A \subseteq_d T'Pts$ and

(1) $A =_d FRoots$

(2) (a) $T'Pts =_d TPts + FPts$

(b) $T'ParentOfGr =_d TParentOfGr + FParentOfGr + \{(p, r) \mid r : FRoots\}$

Rem

Given T': Tree and a nonempty subset $A \subseteq_d T'Pts$ such that all the points in A have a common parent in T', the operation Rem returns three objects: the common parent p of the members of A in T'; the subforest F of T' such that $FRoots =_d A$; and the tree T resulting from removing F from T'. Thus, we define

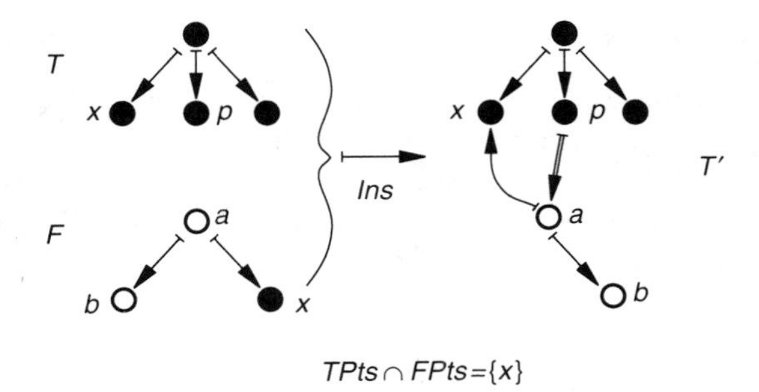

Figure 12.2A.2 Application of Ins when $FPts \cap TPts \neq \varnothing$.

Rem(T', A) $=_d$ (T, p, F). Moreover, Rem is the inverse of Ins, as Figure **12**.2A.1 clearly illustrates: Rem = Inv(Ins).

Rem has two preconditions. The first is that A must not be empty, for the reason given above. The second is that the points in A must have a common parent: that is, there must be a point $p' : T'Pts$ such that $A \subseteq T'Chis(p')$. This constraint is needed to ensure that Rem is the inverse of Ins; clearly the set A returned by Ins(T, p, F) satisfies this property in T'.

The definition of Rem is obtained by inverting that of Ins systematically. The point p is the parent of any $r : A$. The set $FPts$ is obtained as the union of the descendant sets of the members of A. $FParentOf$ is the restriction of $T'ParentOf$ induced by $FPts$. $TPts$ is the relative complement of $FPts$ in $T'Pts$ and, finally, $TParentOf$ is the restriction of $T'ParentOf$ induced by $TPts$. The definition is as follows:

Rem

Remove subforest F : Forest from T' : Tree, where F is given by $FRoots =_d A$ and $FPts$ must not be empty. Rem $=_d$ Inv(Ins).

Given T' : Tree and $A \subseteq_d T'Pts$ with

(Pre 1) $A \neq \varnothing$

(Pre 2) $\exists\, p' : T'Pts \cdot A \subseteq T'Chis(p')$

Rem(T', A) $=_d$ (T, p, F) where T : Tree, p : $TPts$, F : Forest and

(1) $\forall\, r : A \cdot p = TParent(r)$.

(2.1) (a) $FPts =_d \Sigma\, \{T'DescIds(r) | r : A\}$

(b) $FParentOf =_d FPts \diamond T'ParentOf$

(2.2) (a) $TPts =_d T'Pts - FPts$

(b) $TParentOf =_d TPts \diamond T'ParentOf$

12.2B Isomorphism and base set conversion

Consider the two forests F and F': Forest represented in Figure **12**.2B.1. To emphasize that they are distinct objects, the points of F are represented as solid circles and those of F' as open ones. Thus *FPts* and *F′Pts* clearly are disjoint.

Now in a certain sense (to be made precise shortly), F and F' are *equivalent*. They clearly have the same structure, and we also say they are *isomorphic*. Consequently, for most purposes it does not matter which one we use. For instance, if we wish to determine some of their properties, for example the size of their base set or the maximum depth of a point, we can study either of them: the observations will be identical.

This shows that for most purposes the identity of the base points of a forest or a tree is irrelevant. This matter should therefore be dealt with separately, typically as an 'implementation feature'. As far as we are concerned, the base set of a forest F should be considered only to the extent that it affects the structure or 'shape' of F determined by its parent relation. This point has already been made about lists in Chapter **11**. It is another application of the principle of separation of concerns.

This principle has several consequences. First, when we define a forest in any way, for example by application of any operation, we should leave the identity of the base points unspecified. More precisely, we should postulate that each point is determined by what we may call a *choice function*, that is, a function which returns an arbitrary element determined by a *separate agency* (the 'implementor').

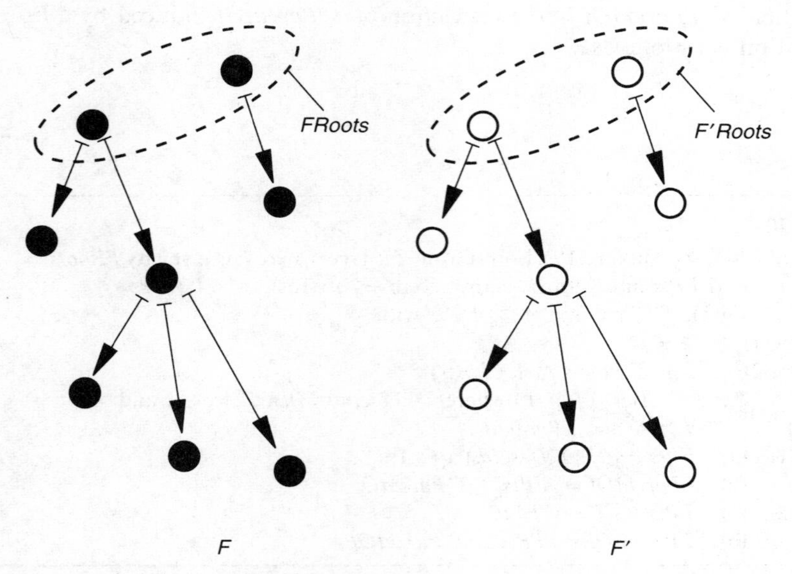

Figure 12.2B.1 Two equivalent forests F and F'.

Second, given any forest F, we may always change the base points of F while keeping the structure of F. This is called a *base set conversion.* One main reason for making such a change has already been given in the introduction of Section **12**.2: it is to make it possible to apply the operation Ins to a T: Tree and an F: Forest even when *TPts* and *FPts* are not disjoint.

We must establish what a base conversion exactly means. Obviously it must be an operation which transforms a given F: Forest into a new F': Forest such that *F′Pts* may differ from *FPts*. However, we must be more specific. From the above remarks, this transformation is suitable for our purposes iff the new forest F' is isomorphic to F. Therefore, we must now state precisely when two forests are isomorphic.

Isomorphism of forests

Consider Figure **12**.2B.1 again. We can see intuitively that F and F' are equivalent because for each point i: *FPts* there is a corresponding point i': *F′Pts* and this correspondence is such that for all i, j: *FPts*,

(1) $\quad i\ FParentOf\ j \Leftrightarrow i'\ F'ParentOf\ j'$

This correspondence is represented by broken arrows in Figure **12**.2B.2.

The correspondence $i \mapsto i'$ must clearly be a *bijection* (one–one correspondence) from *FPts* to *F′Pts*, which we denote by φ. This bijection is called

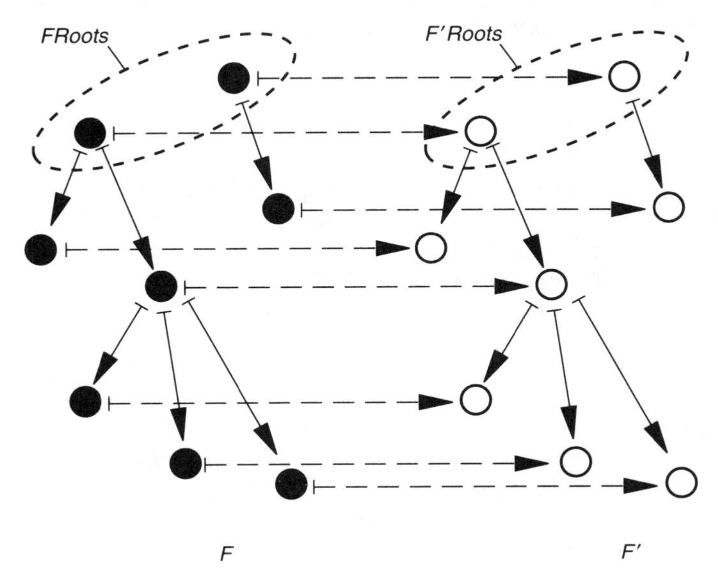

Figure 12.2B.2 Isomorphism between F and F'.

an *isomorphism* as it satisfies condition (1). To sum up:

Definition 12.2B.1 (isomorphism of forests)

(1) Given any two forests F and F' : Forest, an isomorphism between F and F' is a *bijection* $\varphi : FPts \to F'Pts$ such that for all $i, j : FPts$,

$$i \; FParentOf \; j \Leftrightarrow \varphi(i) \; F'ParentOf \; \varphi(j)$$

(2) F and F' are *equivalent* or *isomorphic* iff there exists an isomorphism between them. In this case we also write

$$F \cong F'$$

■

Notes

1 Later on, we shall specify other types of isomorphism between forest extensions, such as ordered or valued forests. These must be carefully distinguished. For instance, two valued forests may be isomorphic as pure forests, that is, ignoring their value maps, and not as valued forests.

2 Clearly the identity function Id : $FPts \to FPts$ is an isomorphism. Moreover, if $\varphi : FPts \to F'Pts$ is an isomorphism, then, being a bijection, it has an inverse $\varphi^{-1} : F'Pts \to FPts$, and it is clear that φ^{-1} itself is an isomorphism. Finally, given three forests $F1$, $F2$ and $F3$: Forest such that there are isomorphisms $\rho : F1Pts \to F2Pts$ and $\varphi : F2Pts \to F3Pts$, the composite $\varphi \circ \rho$ itself is an isomorphism between $F1$ and $F3$. It follows that, as with lists, the relation $\cong$ on Forest is *reflexive*, *symmetric* and *transitive*, that is, it is an *equivalence*. See Sections **3**.6F and **11**.3D. Actually, these properties are enjoyed by any type of isomorphism. ■

BaseConv

We now define an operation BaseConv to convert the base set of an F : Forest in a suitable way. Usually the aim is to convert F to a new F' : Forest such that $F'Pts$ is disjoint from a specified set C and $F' \cong_{\text{d}} F$. Thus, BaseConv takes as argument F and C and returns F', as specified.

BaseConv

Convert the base set of F : Forest, that is, create a forest F' : Forest isomorphic to F and with IsDisjoint(C, $F'Pts$).

Given F : Forest and C : Set, BaseConv(F, C) $=_{\text{d}}$ F' where F' : Forest and

(1) IsDisjoint(C, $F'Pts$)

(2) $F' \cong_{\text{d}} F$

Note that BaseConv is underspecified. The set $F'Pts$ is only determined to the extent that it must be disjoint from C. This is in keeping with the principle of separation of concerns.

Ins1

Using BaseConv, we may now establish an insertion operation Ins1 which is defined even if its arguments T and F have common base points. The application of BaseConv means that the second precondition of Ins is satisfied. If appropriate, this version may be used instead of the original function Ins.

Ins1

Insert F:Forest below p:$TPts$ in T:Tree, where $FPts$ and $TPts$ need not be disjoint. $FPts$ may not be empty.

Given T:Tree, p:$TPts$ and F:Forest with

(Pre 1) $FPts \neq \varnothing$

Ins1$(T, p, F) =_d (T', A)$ where T':Tree, $A \subseteq_d T'Pts$ and

(1) $(T', A) =_d$ Ins$(T, p, \text{BaseConv}(F, TPts))$

12.3 Ordered forests and trees

Although a tree T:Tree (or a forest) is often the natural model of a given object to be described, in practice the fact that the sets $TChis(i)$ are not ordered may be inconvenient. The reason is that the points of T are only partially ordered, which means that in general there is no concrete, deterministic method of accessing a particular point: whenever we reach a point i with more than one child, nothing tells us which child of i to access next or, more generally, in which order the members of $TChis(i)$ should be taken.

The basic method of making the points of a set 'accessible' is to put them in a *sequence* based on some suitable criterion. Once this is done, each member may be accessed by the simple deterministic method: 'Take the first element; after each selected element, take its successor (if any) in the defined order'. This is the method used in directories, dictionaries and countless other applications. If we apply this ordering principle to the root and child sets of forests and trees, we obtain *ordered* forests and trees. Thus, an ordered forest is a forest F with the added feature that the set $FRoots$ is in sequence and so is $FChis(i)$ for each i:$FPts$. Ordered trees are then derived from ordered forests by specialization, in the same way as pure trees are derived from pure forests.

12.3A Definition of ordered forests and trees

The class ForOrd

The class of ordered forests we establish is called ForOrd. What we must consider now is the means by which the set of roots and the child sets of a forest are ordered, which determines the members of ForOrd. We have here another good illustration of the principle of modularity as understood in this book. We have already developed a theory of lists. Our strategy then is to try to 'weld' this theory to that of forests.

This can be done easily by the method of extension. A member F of ForOrd is defined as an object with all the characteristics of any member of Forest, plus the following features:

(1) A list FR: List

(2) For each i: $FPts$, a list FL_i: List

These are additional *variable* features. Furthermore, they must satisfy the following conditions or *fixed* features:

(3) The base points of FR must be the members of $FRoots$:

$$FRPts =_{\mathrm{d}} FRoots$$

(4) For each i: $FPts$, the base points of FL_i must be the members of $FChis_i$:

$$FL_iPts =_{\mathrm{d}} FChis_i$$

This completes our definition of an ordered forest F: ForOrd.

The rationale of this construction should be clear. The purpose of the list FR is to impose a total order on the roots of F. Likewise, the purpose of each list FL_i is to impose a total order on the set $FChis_i$ of children of i.

This is a good example of 'modular construction' by combination of two different concepts: List and Forest. The coupling of these two concepts is minimal and entirely straightforward. Yet the result is substantially more complex than a pure forest or a pure list. In addition to all the properties of any forest, each set $FRoots$ or $FChis_i$ of F also has all the properties of a list. For instance, for any i: $FPts$, if $FChis_i$ is not empty then i has a first child FL_iFst and if in addition $FChis_i$ is finite then i has a last child FL_iLst. The order of $FChis_i$ is determined by the successor function FL_iS, and there is no need to respecify all the conditions which this function must satisfy, including the induction principle for lists.

This advantage is also reflected in the ease with which operations on ordered forests may be defined. These are naturally established in terms of operations on forests and lists, a strategy which reflects the very definition of ForOrd. As a result, all the properties of operations on forests and lists (well-definedness, and so on) are automatically inherited by operations on ordered forests; there is no need to provide fresh proofs of such properties.

The full specification of ForOrd is as follows:

F: ForOrd (Extended Forest)	
* $F[Forest]$: Forest	
ΔForOrd	
* FR: List	Total order imposed on $FRoots$
$FCoOrd1 .: FRPts =_d FRoots$	
* FL_i: List ($i: FPts$)	Total order imposed on $FChis_i$ for each point i
$FCoOrd2 .: \forall\, i: FPts \cdot FL_i Pts =_d FChis_i$	

In this specification, *FForest* is the underlying pure forest of F, that is, the set of all features inherited by F from Forest: *FPts*, *FRoots*, *FParentOf*, *FCo1*, and so on, as well as all the secondary features of members of Forest. The association of FL_i: List with each $i: FPts$ may be described as a function FL from *FPts* to the set of all lists with base points in *FPts*. Both FR and FL are primary features as they vary over ForOrd (even with *FForest* fixed). Therefore, ForOrd is a proper extension of Forest. The various lists FR and FL_i are called *the sibling lists* of F.

The class TreeOrd

As already stated, ordered trees are derived from ordered forests in the same way as pure trees are from pure forests: an ordered tree is an ordered forest with exactly one root. The class of ordered trees is called TreeOrd. We establish it as follows:

T: TreeOrd (Specialized ForOrd)
* $T[ForOrd]$: ForOrd
$T[\Delta Tree]$: ΔTree

In this description, $T\Delta Tree$ is the set of all additional features of members of Tree. These are listed under the heading ΔTree in the definition of Tree. Therefore, any T: TreeOrd has the following primary features:

(1) From ForOrd:
 (a) From Forest: *TPts*, *TRoots*, . . . , *TCo3*
 (b) From ΔForOrd: *TR*, *TCoOrd1*, TL_i for each $i: TPts$, *TCoOrd2*

(2) From ΔTree: *TRoot*, *TCoTr1*

In addition, T has the following group features:

$$TForest: \text{Forest} \qquad TTree: \text{Tree} \qquad T\Delta Tree: \Delta\text{Tree}$$
$$TForOrd: \text{ForOrd} \qquad T\Delta ForOrd: \Delta\text{ForOrd}$$

Each represents a group of basic features of T and may be used in the same way as any member of the associated class. For instance, *TForest* is the underlying pure forest of T or T 'regarded as' a pure forest, and so on.

12.3B Secondary features of ordered forests

For any F: ForOrd, the secondary features of F fall into two main groups. First, there is the set of all features inherited from Forest and from List. As far as the latter are concerned, they are, more precisely, features of the sibling lists of F. Second, there is the set of all additional secondary features, which are called 'own features' of F.

Here is a first example of an own feature of F. Consider the successor functions of the sibling lists of F, namely FRS and FL_iS, $i: FPts$. Clearly we may take the 'union' of all these functions. This is defined as the partial function

$$FSibNex: FPts \nrightarrow FPts$$

which associates with each $i: FPts$ its 'next sibling', the successor of i in the sibling list in which it occurs. At point level, *FSibNex* is defined as follows: (a) for each $r: FRoots$, $FSibNex(r) =_d FRS(r)$; (b) for each $i: FPts$, $j: FChis_i$, $FSibNex(j) =_d FL_iS(j)$.

Equivalently, we may complete the formal definition of *FSibNex* by specifying its graph *FSibNexGr*. This is defined as the union of the graphs of the various functions FRS and FL_iS. Obviously these are pairwise disjoint, by Corollary **12**.1D.5. Therefore we may write

$$FSibNexGr =_d FRSGr + \Sigma\,\{FL_iSGr \mid i: FPts\}$$

It is easy to see that either way, *FSibNex* is a well-defined partial function.

A second example is the 'sibling order' induced by the various sibling lists. This is denoted by *FSibBef*. Informally, for any two points $i, j: FPts$,

$$i\ FSibBef\ j$$

iff i and j are siblings, that is, belong to the same sibling list, and i precedes j in this list. Formally, *FSibBef* is defined by

$$\begin{aligned} i\ FSibBef\ j \Leftrightarrow_d\ & (i, j \in FRoots \wedge i\ FRBef\ j) \\ & \vee (\exists\, p: FPts \cdot i, j \in FChis_p \wedge i\ FL_pBef\ j) \end{aligned}$$

Here is a short list of secondary features of F: ForOrd, including *FSibNex* and *FSibBef*. They are all derived in the same way as these two features and are given without further explanations.

F: ForOrd Secondary Features I: Definitions

$FSibNex(i): FPts$ — Next sibling of point i
  $(i: FPts)$ — (may be undefined)
  $FDefOrd1 .: (1)\ \forall\ i: FRoots \cdot FSibNex(i) =_d FRS(i)$
  $(2)\ \forall\ i: FPts,\ j: FChis_i \cdot FSibNex(j) =_d FL_iS(j)$

$FSibPre(i): FPts$ — Previous sibling of point i
  $(i: FPts)$ — (may be undefined)
  $FDefOrd2 .: (1)\ \forall\ i: FRoots \cdot FSibPre(i) =_d FRPre(i)$
  $(2)\ \forall\ i: FPts,\ j: FChis_i \cdot FSibPre(j) =_d FL_iPre(j)$

$FChiFst(i): FPts$ — First child of point i
  $(i: FPts)$ — (may be undefined)
  $FDefOrd31 .: \forall\ i: FPts \cdot FChiFst(i) =_d FL_iFst$

$FChiLst(i): FPts$ — Last child of point i
  $(i: FPts)$ — (may be undefined)
  $FDefOrd32 .: \forall\ i: FPts \cdot FChiLst(i) =_d FL_iLst$

$FIsSib(i, j)$: Bool — True iff $i = j$ or i is a sibling of j
  $(i, j: FPts)$
  $FDefOrd4 .: \forall\ i, j: FPts \cdot FIsSib(i, j) \Leftrightarrow_d (i, j \in FRoots) \vee (\exists\ p: FPts \cdot i, j \in FChis_p)$

$i\ FSibBef\ j$: Bool — True iff i is a sibling preceding j
  $(i, j: FPts)$
  $FDefOrd51 .: \forall\ i, j: FPts \cdot i\ FSibBef\ j \Leftrightarrow_d (i, j \in FRoots \wedge i\ FRBef\ j)$
  $\vee\ (\exists\ p: FPts \cdot i, j \in FChis_p \wedge i\ FL_pBef\ j)$

$i\ FSibBef\!=\ j$: Bool — True iff i is a sibling preceding j or $i = j$
  $(i, j: FPts)$
  $FDefOrd52 .: \forall\ i, j: FPts \cdot i\ FSibBef\!=\ j \Leftrightarrow_d i\ FSibBef\ j \vee i = j$

Note

There is a small price to pay for taking Forest as the initial concept from which Tree is then derived. In several specifications of features of an F: ForOrd, a certain rule has to be stated twice, once for the set *FRoots* and once for each set $FChis_i$. This duplication could be avoided if we took Tree as the initial concept and defined a forest as an F: Tree in which *FRoot* is 'forgotten' in some appropriate sense. This alternative was rejected as it appears to be a source of confusion. ■

12.3C Operations on ordered forests and trees

We now extend the various Forest and Tree operations of Section **12**.2A to ordered forests and trees. We begin with InitTreeOrd, which creates an ordered tree of one point.

<u>InitTreeOrd</u>

Create a one-point ordered tree T'.

InitTreeOrd $=_d T'$ where T' : TreeOrd and

(1) $T'Pts =_d \{T'Root\}$

Note there is no substantial difference between $T1 =_d$ InitTree and $T2 =_d$ InitTreeOrd. $T2Tree \cong T1$ and all the additional features of $T2$ are entirely determined by $T2Tree$. For instance, $T2R$ is the list with a single base point, namely $T2Root$. Therefore this list is uniquely defined: the graph of its successor function $T2RSGr = \emptyset$, $T2RFst = T2RLst = T2Root$, and so on. However, *formally* we must make the distinction between $T1$ and $T2$, because characteristics like $T2R$ and so on are defined for $T2$ but *not* for $T1$: there are no objects $T1R$, $T1RS$, and so on.

Ins

Next, we extend the two main operations Ins and Rem to ForOrd. Note that as this extension is repeated for all remaining classes For—, we use the same names Ins and Rem for all extensions. Likewise, we use the operations Ins and Rem defined for List in Chapter **11**. Thus 'Ins' and 'Rem' are overloaded, and for each application of either function the exact class of the result must be determined by the class of its arguments. This solution seems acceptable, given the close connection existing between the various versions of Ins and Rem.

Ins takes as input a tree T:TreeOrd, two points i, j: $TPts$ such that $j =_d TSibNex(i)$, and a forest F:ForOrd. It returns three objects: a new T':TreeOrd, i and j. T' is defined as the result of inserting F in T between i and j. Thus, Ins$(T, i, j, F) =_d (T', i, j)$. As T is a tree and i and j are different siblings, these two points must necessarily be different from $TRoot$. The reason for returning i and j is to make Ins invertible, as in the case of Forest. These two points replace the set A as part result of Ins. We continue to impose $FPts \neq \emptyset$ as a precondition of Ins in order to be able to invoke the Forest version of Ins in the specification.

There are altogether four preconditions in the ForOrd version of Ins. First, j must be the sibling immediately following i in T, so that the insertion point is unambiguously defined. Second, $FPts \neq \emptyset$ as mentioned. Third, the set $FRoots$ must be finite, for otherwise the list containing i and j in T' could not be defined with all the roots of F preceding j. Fourth, $TPts$ and $FPts$ must be disjoint, as in the Forest version.

The specification of Ins$(T, i, j, F) =_d (T', i, j)$ is in two parts. First, the effect on T and F regarded as unordered is defined by

$$(T'Tree, A) =_d \text{Ins}(TTree, p, FForest)$$

using the Forest version of Ins, where p is the common parent of i and j. Then the various sibling lists of T' are defined. $T'L_p$ is obtained by inserting FR between i and j using the List version of Ins. Every other list $T'L_k$ is a list of either T or F. In the specification, p and A are local variables needed by the application of the Forest version of Ins and the definition of sibling lists.

Ins

Insert F: ForOrd between i and j: $TPts$ in tree T: TreeOrd. $FPts$ may *not* be empty.

Given T: TreeOrd, i, j: $TPts$ and F: ForOrd with

(Pre 1) $j = TSibNex(i)$ (implying $\exists\, p' : TPts \cdot p' = TParent(i)$)

(Pre 2) $FPts \neq \varnothing$

(Pre 3) IsFinite($FRoots$)

(Pre 4) IsDisjoint($TPts$, $FPts$)

$\text{Ins}(T, i, j, F) =_d (T', i, j)$ where T' : TreeOrd. Let $p =_d TParent(i) = TParent(j)$ and $A \subseteq_d T'Pts$.

(1) $(T'Tree, A) =_d \text{Ins}(TTree, p, FForest)$

(2) (a) $(T'L_p, i, j) =_d \text{Ins}(TL_p, i, j, FR)$ (List insertion)

(b) $\forall\, k : TPts - \{p\} \cdot T'L_k =_d TL_k$ (Conservation of all other sibling lists)

(c) $\forall\, k : FPts \cdot T'L_k =_d FL_k$

Note that there is redundancy in this specification. For each $i : T'Pts$, the set $T'Chis_i = T'L_iPts$ is determined by both (1) and (2). However, the two definitions of each $T'Chis_i$ are clearly consistent so the operation is obviously well defined.

Rem

Given T': Tree and two points i, j: $T'Pts$ such that $i\; T'SibBef\; j$ and $T'SibNex(i) \neq j$, Rem returns four objects: the subforest F of T' such that $FRoots$ are the points occurring between i and j in T'; the two points i and j; and the tree T resulting from removing F from T'. The constraint imposed on i and j is the sole precondition of Rem. It corresponds to the two preconditions of the Forest version. It also implies that i and j have a parent p in T. We define $\text{Rem}(T', i, j) =_d (T, i, j, F)$. Furthermore, Rem is the inverse of Ins, as in the Forest version: $\text{Rem} =_d \text{Inv}(\text{Ins})$.

The definition of Rem is obtained by inverting that of Ins systematically. The two local variables p and A are again introduced, for the same reasons as in Ins. The point p is the parent of i, etc. and A the set of points occurring between i and j. First, the underlying unordered tree and forest of T and F respectively are redefined using the Forest version of Rem. Second, the sibling lists of T and F are redefined or retrieved from T', using the List version of Rem for TL_p and FR.

Rem

Remove F: ForOrd from tree T': TreeOrd, where F is the subforest with *FRoots* between i and j. *FPts* must *not* be empty (that is, i and j may not be adjacent).

Given T': TreeOrd, $i, j: T'Pts$ with

(Pre 1) $i\ T'SibBef\ j \wedge T'SibNex(i) \neq j$

Rem$(T', i, j) =_d (T, i, j, F)$ where T: TreeOrd and F: ForOrd. Let $p: T'Pts$ and $A =_d \{k: T'Pts \mid i\ T'SibBef\ k\ T'SibBef\ j\}$.

(1) $(TTree, p, FForest) =_d$ Rem$(T'Tree, A)$

(2) (a) $(TL_p, i, j, FR) =_d$ Rem$(T'L_p, i, j)$ (Two lists defined)

(b) $\forall k: TPts - \{p\} \cdot TL_k =_d T'L_k$

(c) $\forall k: FPts \cdot FL_k =_d T'L_k$

12.3D Isomorphism and base set conversion

As with Forest, we need to define when two F, F': ForOrd are isomorphic and to establish the corresponding base conversion operation BaseConv.

Isomorphism of ForOrd

Given any F, F': ForOrd, we again write $F \cong F'$ to state that these two objects are isomorphic *as members of ForOrd*. The definition of equivalence or isomorphism on ForOrd is a straightforward extension of isomorphism on Forest: $F \cong F'$ iff there exists a bijection $\varphi: FPts \to F'Pts$ such that (a) φ is an isomorphism of Forest (between *FForest* and *F'Forest*) and (b) for each sibling list, φ is an isomorphism of List. The latter condition means that for all $i, j: FPts$, $FSibNex(i) = j$ iff $F'SibNex(\varphi(i)) = \varphi(j)$. Note that for any F: ForOrd, the order of F is entirely determined by the function *FSibNex*.

Definition 12.3D.1 (isomorphism of ForOrd)

(1) Given any two forests F and F': ForOrd, an isomorphism between F and F' is a bijection $\varphi: FPts \to F'Pts$ such that

(a) φ is an isomorphism between *FForest* and *F'Forest* i.e. for all $i, j: FPts$,

$$i\ FParentOf\ j \Leftrightarrow \varphi(i)\ F'ParentOf\ \varphi(j)$$

(b) For all $i, j: FPts$, $FSibNex(i) = j \Leftrightarrow F'SibNex(\varphi(i)) = \varphi(j)$.

(2) F and F' are *equivalent* or *isomorphic* iff there exists an isomorphism of ForOrd between them. In this case we write

$$F \cong F'$$

■

BaseConv

The base set conversion operation on ForOrd is essentially the same as on Forest. It is obtained formally by substituting 'ForOrd' for 'Forest' in the latter.

BaseConv

Convert the base set of F : ForOrd, i.e. create an ordered forest F' : ForOrd isomorphic to F and with IsDisjoint(C, $F'Pts$).
Given F : ForOrd and C : Set, BaseConv(F, C) $=_d F'$ where F' : ForOrd and
(1) IsDisjoint(C, $F'Pts$)
(2) $F' \cong_d F$

12.4 Valued (ordered) forests and trees

12.4A Valued forests and trees

In most applications, we use a valued version of forests and trees. These are derived from Forest as in the case of List. A valued forest is a forest F together with a value map FV from the base set $FPts$ to some value set $FVals$. Valued trees are defined similarly. The class of valued (unordered) forests is called ForV, and that of valued trees TreeV. The definition of these two classes is immediate.

F : ForV (Extended Forest)

* $F[Forest]$: Forest
ΔForV
* $FVals$: Set — Set of values
* $FV(i)$: $FVals$ — Value of point i
(i : $FPts$)
$FCoVal1$.: $FVals \neq_d \varnothing$

T : TreeV (Specialized ForV)

* $T[ForV]$: ForV
$T[\Delta Tree]$: ΔTree

In the definition of an F:ForV, the only condition imposed on *FVals* is that this set be nonempty. This is done as in ListV in order to ensure that the total function $FV : FPts \to FVals$ can be defined in all cases.

Example Feature Notation trees

The main idea at the basis of the Feature Notation used in this book is that object features have a naturally hierarchical structure, which should be reflected in the names given to features. Therefore, whenever we specify a certain class C of objects and introduce a variable object $X : C$, we assign to X a whole hierarchy of features, directly and indirectly. This hierarchy may be regarded as a valued tree, in which the values are the feature name increments specified at each level of the introduction of X. Trees of this type are called *feature trees*.

It has already been mentioned that the total orders imposed on sets – child sets of trees in particular – are often not essential. Feature trees provide a good illustration of this fact. In the written representation of such a tree, each child set must obviously be listed in some order. However, in general this order is irrelevant: what matters is the feature name increments specified at each level, which should all be different. By way of concrete example, Figure **12**.4B.1 shows part of the Feature Notation tree for F:ForOrd with some comments. It is expanded laterally for convenience, and only some of the *FParentOf* arrows are represented. Note that at each level, only feature name *increments* are indicated. In actual specifications the full name expansion for each feature is given, as this seems to be clearer.

Recall the discussion of Section **10**.2. It may again be observed that even for elementary constructions, the number of features or attributes of an object grows rapidly. A feature tree provides an effective and flexible way of organizing these features systematically. In particular, all the incremental feature names are simple identifiers, with one exception, namely *ParentOf*, as this must be distinguished from the function *Parent*. Such departures should be exceptional.

Another property of the tree is that on any path from the root each step takes us from a complex object to a more elementary one. This simple rule mirrors the hierarchical partition of a class into smaller and smaller subclasses, as in any taxonomy. Whenever we move from one class to a subclass, we do so (typically) by fixing a further feature of the class members. ■

12.4B Operations on valued forests and trees

We briefly specify operations on ForV which are natural extensions of the operations on Forest given in Section **12**.2. In addition we establish a function SetV which sets the value of a given point in a given forest.

We begin with the initialization operation InitTreeV. This is a simple extension of InitTree. It returns a one-point tree T' in which the value set and the value of the root are determined by arguments of the operation.

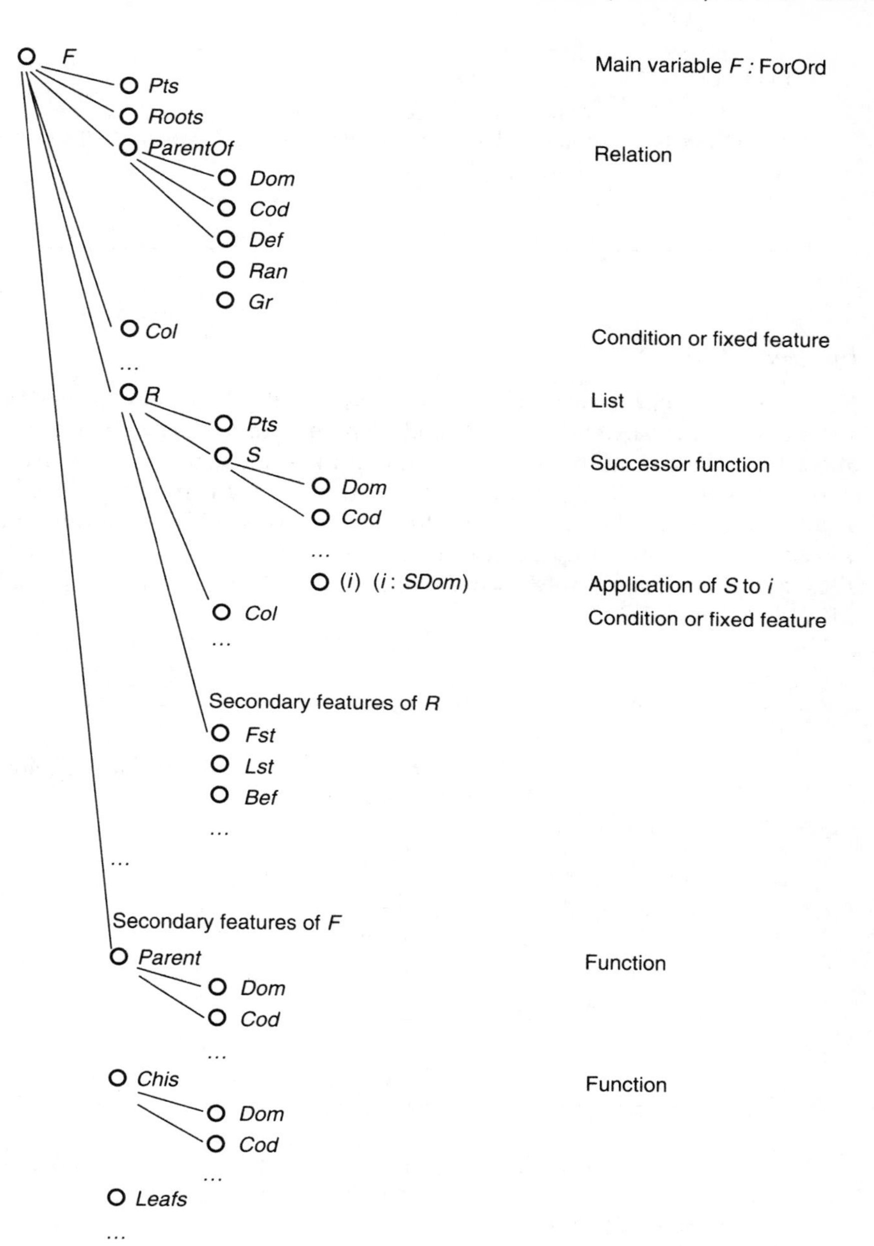

Figure 12.4B.1 Part of Feature Notation tree for F: ForOrd.

InitTreeV

Create a one-point valued tree T'.

Given $Vals$: Set and v: $Vals$, InitTreeV($Vals$, v) $=_d T'$ where T': TreeV and

(1) $T'Pts =_d \{T'Root\}$

(2) (a) $T'Vals =_d Vals$

(b) $T'V(T'Root) =_d v$

Ins and Rem

Next, we establish the twin operations of Ins and Rem on ForV. These again are straightforward extensions of Ins and Rem on Forest. The distinctive feature of the ForV version of Ins is the definition of the value map $T'V$. It is given by stating that its graph is the union of the graphs of TV and FV, which are disjoint on account of (Pre 2). Clearly Rem is the inverse of Ins. The value maps TV and FV are obviously defined as domain-restrictions of $T'V$ induced by $TPts$ and $FPts$ respectively – see Definition **3**.6C.1. Note that this implies $TVals = FVals = T'Vals$.

Ins

Insert F: ForV below p: $TPts$ in tree T: TreeV. $FPts$ must not be empty.

Given T: TreeV, p: $TPts$ and F: ForV with

(Pre 1) $FPts \neq \emptyset$

(Pre 2) IsDisjoint($TPts$, $FPts$)

(Pre 3) $TVals = FVals$

Ins(T, p, F) $=_d (T', A)$ where T': TreeV, $A \subseteq_d T'Pts$ and

(1) $(T'Tree, A) =_d$ Ins($TTree$, p, $FForest$)

(2) (a) $T'Vals =_d TVals$

(b) $T'VGr =_d TVGr + FVGr$

Rem

Remove the subforest F : ForV from tree T': TreeV, where F is given by $FRoots =_d A$ and $FPts$ may not be empty. Rem $=_d$ Inv(Ins).

Given T': TreeV and $A \subseteq_d T'Pts$ with

(Pre 1) $A \neq \emptyset$

(Pre 2) $\exists\, p' : T'Pts \cdot A \subseteq T'Chis(p')$

Rem(T', A) $=_d (T, p, F)$ where T: TreeV, p: $TPts$, F: ForV and

(1) $(TTree, p, FForest) =_d$ Rem($T'Tree$, A)

(2) (a) $TV =_d TPts \langle T'V$

(b) $FV =_d FPts \langle T'V$

Setting a point value

The next operation is SetV. Given an F:ForV, a point i:*FPts* and a value v:*FVals*, SetV returns a new F':ForV which differs from F only by the fact that $F'V(i) = v$. This condition is expressed by means of the function-overriding operation. Recall that by this definition $F'V$ has the same domain and codomain as FV. Moreover, $F'V(j) = FV(j)$ for all j:*FPts* with $j \neq i$, while $F'V(i) = v$.

SetV

Set the value of point i:*FPts* to v.
Given F : ForV, i : *FPts* and v : *FVals*, SetV(F, i, v) $=_{\mathrm{d}}$ F' where F' : ForV and
(1) $F'Forest =_{\mathrm{d}} FForest$
(2) $F'V =_{\mathrm{d}} (FV \mid i \mapsto v)$

12.4C Valued ordered forests and trees

If we combine the two extensions of Forest to ForOrd and ForV respectively, we obtain the class ForOV of valued ordered forests. The corresponding tree class is TreeOV. The definition of these two classes is immediate.

F:ForOV (Extended ForOrd)

* $F[ForOrd]$: ForOrd
* $F[\Delta ForV]$: ΔForV

T:TreeOV (Specialized ForOV)

* $T[ForOV]$: ForOV
* $T[\Delta Tree]$: ΔTree

Finite valued forests and trees

In any application in which trees are constructed primarily by repeated insertion of new individual points, the operands (trees and forests) are necessarily finite. Moreover, the trees and forests to be considered usually have the same value set. Therefore, we now specialize ForOV to the class ForOV1 by adding the condition that for any F:ForOV1, *FPts* is finite. In addition, we introduce a parametrized version of ForOV1, in which the value set of a member F is specified by an argument or parameter of ForOV1. The associated tree class is TreeOV1.

The main version of ForOV1 is given below. In this version, for any F:ForOV1, *FVals* may be any nonempty set, by definition of ForOV. *FVals* may be determined by any additional rule.

F: ForOV1 (Specialized ForOV)

* $F[ForOV]$: ForOV
ΔForOV1
$FCo11$.: IsFinite($FPts$)

The parametrized version of ForOV1 follows. It is denoted by ForOV1(*Vals*), where *Vals* is a parameter, a name standing for any nonempty set. This means that we in effect introduce a family of forest classes, one for each nonempty set *Vals*.

F: ForOV1($Vals$) (Specialized ForOV1)

* $Vals$: Set
$ValsCo$.: $Vals \neq \varnothing$
* $F[ForOV1]$: ForOV1
ΔForOV1
$FCo12$.: $FVals =_d Vals$

This definition is to be read as follows. Given any predefined nonempty set $Vals'$, an F: ForOV1($Vals'$) is a member of ForOV1 with $FVals = Vals'$. As with ListV1, we also make the convention that given any F: ForOV1, in a context in which $FVals = Vals'$, F is regarded as having been introduced by F: ForOV1($Vals'$).

For instance, let *Char* be any set of characters, for example {'A', 'B', ..., 'Z'}. Then for any F: ForOV1(*Char*), $FVals =_d Char$ and so for any $i: FPts$, $FV(i) \in Char$. Moreover, F is a member of both ForOV1(*Char*) and ForOV1. Conversely, the introduction of F: ForOV1 combined with the equation $FVals =_d Char$ in a given context is equivalent to the introduction of F: ForOV1(*Char*).

As usual, each version of ForOV1 gives rise to a corresponding tree version. For the parametrized case:

T: TreeOV1($Vals$) (Specialized ForOV1($Vals$))

* $T[ForOV1]$: ForOV1($Vals$)
$T[\Delta Tree]$: ΔTree

The parameterless version is obtained by eliminating '(*Vals*)' in this definition.

12.4D Operations on finite valued ordered forests and trees

We now establish operations on valued ordered forests and trees, based on the operations defined for ForOrd and ForV. To simplify, we restrict our definitions to members of ForOV1 and TreeOV1. These constructions are similar to previous ones. Note that they may be applied to operands F (T) of both the parametrized and the parameterless versions of ForOV1 (TreeOV1).

One minor adjustment may be mentioned. In the establishment of Ins, it is no longer necessary to impose IsFinite(*FRoots*) on the argument F: ForOV1 as a precondition, as this is implied by *FColl*. The operations are given below without further comments.

<u>InitTreeOV1</u>

Create a one-point finite valued ordered tree T'.
Given *Vals*: Set and v: *Vals*, InitTreeOV1(*Vals*, v) $=_d T'$ where T': TreeOV1(*Vals*) and
(1) $T'Pts =_d \{T'Root\}$
(2) $T'V(T'Root) =_d v$

<u>Ins</u>

Insert F: ForOV1 between i and j: *TPts* in tree T: TreeOV1. *FPts* must *not* be empty.
Given T: TreeOV1, i, j: *TPts* and F: ForOV1 with
(Pre 1) $j = TSibNex(i)$ (Implying $\exists\, p: TPts \cdot p = TParent(i)$)
(Pre 2) $FPts \neq \varnothing$
(Pre 3) IsDisjoint(*TPts*, *FPts*)
(Pre 4) $TVals = FVals$
Ins(T, i, j, F) $=_d (T', i, j)$ where T': TreeOV1.
(1) $(T'TreeOrd, i, j) =_d$ Ins($T'TreeOrd, i, j, FForOrd$)
(2) (a) $T'Vals =_d TVals$
(b) $T'VGr =_d TVGr + FVGr$

<u>Rem</u>

Remove F: ForOV1 from tree T': TreeOV1, where F is the subforest with *FRoots* between i and j. *FPts* must *not* be empty (i.e. i and j must not be adjacent).
Given T': TreeOV1, i, j: $T'Pts$ with
(Pre 1) $i\ T'SibBef\ j \ \wedge\ T'SibNex(i) \neq j$
Rem(T', i, j) $=_d (T, i, j, F)$ where T: TreeOV1 and F: ForOV1.
(1) $(TTreeOrd, i, j, FForOrd) =_d$ Rem($T'TreeOrd, i, j$)
(2) (a) $TV =_d TPts \langle T'V$
(b) $FV =_d FPts \langle T'V$

SetV

Set the value of point $i: FPts$ to v.
Given F: ForOV1, $i: FPts$ and $v: FVals$, SetV(F, i, v) $=_d F'$ where F': ForOV1 and
(1) $F' ForOrd =_d F ForOrd$
(2) $F'V =_d (FV|i \mapsto v)$

12.4E Isomorphism and base set conversion

As with Forest and ForOrd, we need to define when two F, F': ForV (F, F': ForOV1) are isomorphic and to establish the corresponding base conversion operation BaseConv.

Isomorphism of ForV

Given any F, F': ForV, $F \cong F'$ means that F and F' are isomorphic as members of ForV. The definition of isomorphism on ForV is an obvious extension of isomorphism on Forest. $F \cong F'$ iff there exists a bijection $\varphi: FPts \to F'Pts$ such that (a) φ is an isomorphism of Forest (between *FForest* and *F'Forest*) and (b) $FVals = F'Vals$ and elements corresponding by φ have equal value. In other words, for all $i: FPts$, $F'V(\varphi(i)) = FV(i)$.

Definition 12.4E.1 (isomorphism of ForV)

(1) Given any two forests F and F': ForV, an isomorphism between F and F' is a bijection $\varphi: FPts \to F'Pts$ such that

(a) φ is an isomorphism between *FForest* and *F'Forest*; that is, for all $i, j: FPts$,

$$i\ FParentOf\ j \Leftrightarrow \varphi(i)\ F'ParentOf\ \varphi(j)$$

(b) $FVals = F'Vals$ and for all $i: FPts$, $F'V(\varphi(i)) = FV(i)$.

(2) F and F' are *equivalent* or *isomorphic* iff there exists an isomorphism of ForV between them. In this case we write

$$F \cong F'$$

■

As with ForOrd, for any F, F': ForV, $F \cong F'$ implies $FForest \cong F'Forest$, but the converse is not true.

BaseConv on ForV

The base set conversion operation on ForV is essentially the same as on Forest. It is obtained formally by substituting 'ForV' for 'Forest' in the latter.

BaseConv

Convert the base set of F: ForV, that is, create a valued forest F': ForV isomorphic to F and with IsDisjoint(C, $F'Pts$).
Given F: ForV and C: Set, BaseConv(F, C) $=_d F'$ where F': ForV and
(1) IsDisjoint(C, $F'Pts$)
(2) $F' \cong_d F$

Isomorphism of ForOV1

Finally, we define isomorphisms on the class ForOV1 and the corresponding base set conversion. Given any F, F': ForOV1, $F \cong F'$ means that F and F' are isomorphic as members of ForOV1 in the following sense. $F \cong F'$ iff there exists a bijection $\varphi: FPts \to F'Pts$ such that (a) φ is an isomorphism of ForOrd (between *FForOrd* and *F'ForOrd*) and (b) $FVals = F'Vals$ and elements corresponding by φ have equal value.

Definition 12.4E.2 (isomorphism of ForOV1)

(1) Given any two forests F and F': ForOV1, an isomorphism between F and F' is a bijection $\varphi: FPts \to F'Pts$ such that

(a) φ is an isomorphism between *FForOrd* and *F'ForOrd*; that is, for all $p, i, j: FPts$,

(i) $p\ FParentOf\ i \Leftrightarrow \varphi(p)\ F'ParentOf\ \varphi(i)$
(ii) $FSibNex(i) = j \Leftrightarrow F'SibNex(\varphi(i)) = \varphi(j)$.

(b) $FVals = F'Vals$ and for all $i: FPts$, $F'V(\varphi(i)) = FV(i)$.

(2) F and F' are *equivalent* or *isomorphic* iff there exists an isomorphism of ForOV1 between them. In this case we write

$$F \cong F'$$

■

BaseConv on ForOV1

The base set conversion operation is derived as in the previous extensions.

BaseConv

Convert the base set of F: ForOV1, that is, create a valued forest F': ForOV1 isomorphic to F and with IsDisjoint(C, $F'Pts$).
Given F: ForOV1 and C: Set, BaseConv(F, C) $=_d F'$ where F': ForOV1 and
(1) IsDisjoint(C, $F'Pts$)
(2) $F' \cong_d F$

12.5 Pointed trees

As with finite lists, a natural extension of a tree T: TreeOV1 is to add pointers to the base points of T, giving a *pointed tree*. Such pointers are defined in the same way as list pointers. The introduction of pointers on trees extends the range of operations definable on these objects. However, pointers must also be supplemented with their own definition functions, or *navigation operations*.

Again, we do not attempt formally to define a general class of pointed trees. Only a simple example is presented in this section. This example is elaborated on in a modified form in Chapter **16** as part of the establishment of a general-purpose tree editor.

The present construction of pointed trees generalizes the definition of pointed lists given in Section **11**.5. A pointed tree is specified here as a finite valued ordered tree T together with a point $TC: TPts$ called a *cursor* on T. The purpose of TC is to serve as argument in any operation on a pair (T, i) with $i: TPts$. The class of pointed trees obtained in this way is denoted by TreePtd0, the suffix '0' distinguishing it from a variant to be introduced in Chapter **16**. Formally, TreePtd0 is established as an extension of TreeOV1. We also introduce a parametrized version TreePtd0(*Vals*) corresponding to TreeOV1(*Vals*).

The present example has two didactic aims. The first is to show how the operations on TreePtd0 may be derived from those of TreeOV1 on the one hand and ListPtd0 on the other. In other words, we again seek to combine the theories of two different classes. The second didactic aim is to contrast two different solutions to a given problem. The model established in this section is relatively complex and somewhat messy. The one developed in Chapter **16** is more powerful: it solves a more general problem. The paradox is that this second model is also substantially simpler and more elegant than the first.

12.5A The class TreePtd0 of pointed trees

The definition of the parametrized version of TreePtd0 is immediate. The parameterless version is obtained by erasing every occurrence of '(*Vals*)' in this definition.

T: TreePtd0(*Vals*) (Extended TreeOV1(*Vals*))

* $T[TreeOV1]$: TreeOV1(*Vals*)

ΔTreePtd0

* $TC: TPts$ Cursor

The theory of ListPtd0 readily applies to TreePtd0. Informally, for any T: TreePtd0 and any $p: TPts$, recall that the 'children' of p form a list TL_p: List, with base set $TL_pPts =_d TChis_p$. If the cursor $TC \in TChis_p$, we may describe the list TL_p augmented with TC in the same way as a member of ListPtd0($TVals$). Formally, the connection is as follows. We extend TL_p to an L: ListPtd0($TVals$) defined by $LList =_d TL_p$, $LV =_d TChis_p \langle TV$ and $LC =_d TC$. Then the theory of L: ListPtd0 is 'inherited' by T. We use this principle to guide our construction of operations on TreePtd0.

12.5B Navigation operations in TreePtd0

In TreePtd0, a navigation operation is a function which takes a T: TreePtd0 as argument and 'modifies' the cursor TC. More precisely, it returns a new T': TreePtd0, which may differ from T only by the value of $T'C$. Note that these operations apply to operands of both TreePtd0 and TreePtd0($Vals$), as a declaration T: TreePtd0($Vals$) implies T: TreePtd0.

Navigation operations in TreePtd0 fall into two natural groups. First, there are two operations 'inherited' from ListPtd0, namely those which leave $TParent(TC)$ unchanged, in the sense that TC and $T'C$ are siblings in $TTreeOV1$. These two operations are obvious translations of their ListPtd0 analogues, MoveFwd and MoveBack. They are called MoveToSibNex and MoveToSibPre, and defined only if $TC \neq TRoot$.

MoveToSibNex

Given T: TreePtd0 where
(Pre 1) $TC \neq TRoot$
(Pre 2) $TC \neq TChiLst_p$ where $p =_d TParent(TC)$
MoveToSibNex(T) $=_d T'$ where T': TreePtd0 and
(1) $T'TreeOV1 =_d TTreeOV1$
(2) $T'C =_d TSibNex(TC)$

MoveToSibPre

Given T: TreePtd0 where
(Pre 1) $TC \neq TRoot$
(Pre 2) $TC \neq TChiFst_p$ where $p =_d TParent(TC)$
MoveToSibPre(T) $=_d T'$ where T': TreePtd0 and
(1) $T'TreeOV1 =_d TTreeOV1$
(2) $T'C =_d TSibPre(TC)$

These two operations are illustrated in Figure **12**.5B.1. The various comments made in Section **11**.5 about MoveFwd and MoveBack apply *mutatis mutandis*.

The navigation operations in the second group have no strict analogues in ListPtd0, although they bear some similarity to MoveBack and MoveFwd. Their purpose is to move the cursor TC from its current list TL_p to $TRoot$ or

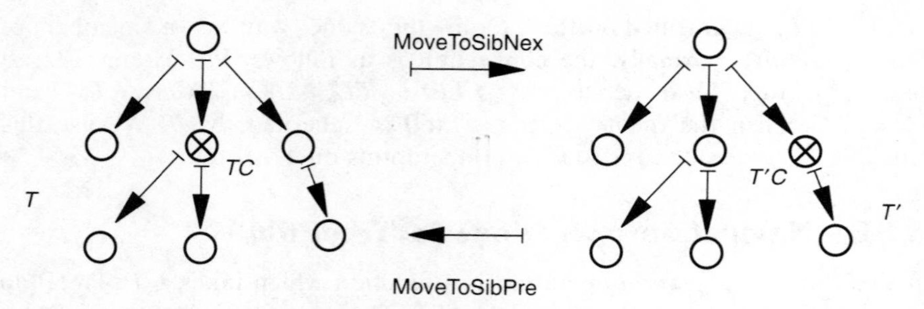

Figure 12.5B.1 Effects of MoveToSibNex and MoveToSibPre.

to any other list TL_i, $i : TPts$. This requirement is met by two basic operations: (a) MoveToParent, which moves TC to its parent in T; and (b) MoveToChiFst, which moves TC to its first child.

MoveToParent

Given T : TreePtd0 where
(Pre 1) $TC \neq TRoot$
MoveToParent(T) $=_{\mathrm{d}} T'$ where T' : TreePtd0 and
(1) $T'TreeOV1 =_{\mathrm{d}} TTreeOV1$
(2) $T'C =_{\mathrm{d}} TParent(TC)$

MoveToChiFst

Given T : TreePtd0 where
(Pre 1) $TChis(TC) \neq \varnothing$
MoveToChiFst(T) $=_{\mathrm{d}} T'$ where T' : TreePtd0 and
(1) $T'TreeOV1 =_{\mathrm{d}} TTreeOV1$
(2) $T'C =_{\mathrm{d}} TChiFst(TC)$

These last two operations are illustrated in Figure **12**.5B.2. We leave it to the reader to prove that our four navigation operations are *sound*, using the method applied to the derivation of MoveFwd and MoveBack in Section **11**.5. Likewise, the reader should verify that these operations are *complete*, in the sense that, given any T : TreePtd0 with TC on any point in $TPts$, we may 'move' TC in $TTreeOV1$ to any other point $j : TPts$ in a finite number of navigation steps.

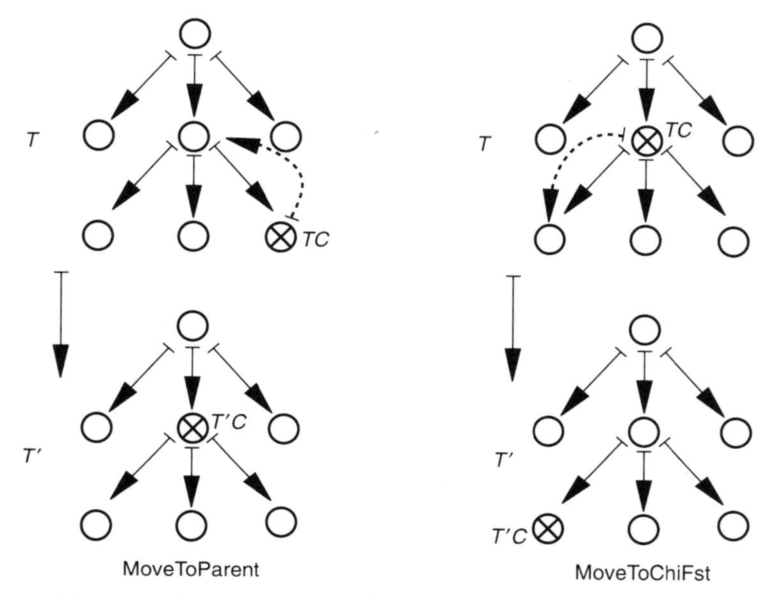

Figure 12.5B.2 Effects of MoveToParent and MoveToChiFst.

12.5C Tree transformation operations

We specify six basic tree transformation operations in TreePtd0: the initialization function InitTreePtd0; the 'first child' insertion function InsChiFst and its inverse RemChiFst; the 'next sibling' insertion function InsSibNex and its inverse RemSibNex; and SetV, which redefines $TV(TC)$. These operations make it possible in particular to move a subtree between two points in a tree. Again, they apply to operands of both TreePtd0 and TreePtd0(*Vals*). They are based on the operations Ins and Rem on ForV and the List transformation operations $+\!\!+$, Split, Ins and Rem.

InitTreePtd0

Recall that in TreeOV1, given *Vals*: Set and v: *Vals*, InitTreeOV1(*Vals*, v) returns the one-point tree T': TreeOV1 with $T'Pts =_{\mathrm{d}} \{T'Root\}$, $T'Vals =_{\mathrm{d}} Vals$ and $T'V(T'Root) =_{\mathrm{d}} v$. InitTreePtd0 is specified in exactly the same way. InitTreePtd0(*Vals*, v) $=_{\mathrm{d}} T'$, where T': TreePtd0 is entirely determined by this rule, as the cursor $T'C$ must necessarily equal $T'Root$, the unique member of $T'Pts$. Also recall that the precondition $Vals \neq \varnothing$ is left implicit, as it is implied by $v \in Vals$. The operation is illustrated in Figure **12**.5C.1.

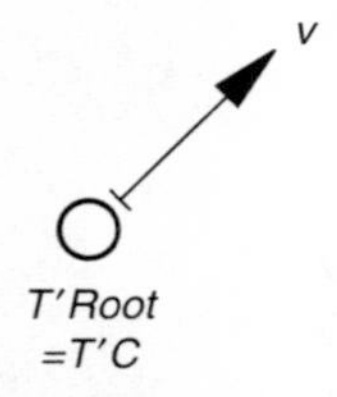

Figure 12.5C.1 InitTreePtd0($Vals$, v).

InitTreePtd0

Create a one-point pointed tree T', with value $T'V(T'Root) =_d v$. The cursor $T'C$ is necessarily equal to $T'Root$.

Given $Vals$: Set and v: $Vals$, InitTreePtd0($Vals$, v) $=_d T'$ where T': TreePtd0 and

(1) $T'TreeOV1 =_d$ InitTreeOV1($Vals$, v)

InsChiFst and RemChiFst

Given a main tree T: TreePtd0 and a second tree $T1$: TreeOV1, InsChiFst inserts $T1$ in T so that the root of $T1$ is the new first child of TC. The cursor itself is left unchanged.

InsChiFst

Insert $T1$ in T, with the root of $T1$ as the new first child of TC.

Given T: TreePtd0 and $T1$: TreeOV1 where

(Pre 1) IsDisjoint($TPts$, $T1Pts$)

(Pre 2) $TVals = T1Vals$

InsChiFst(T, $T1$) $=_d T'$ where T': TreePtd0. Let $p =_d TC$ and $A \subseteq_d T'Pts$.

(1) $(T'TreeV, A) =_d$ Ins($TTreeV$, p, $T1ForV$)

(2) (a) $T'L_p =_d T1R \mathbin{+\!\!\!+} TL_p$ (List insertion)

(b) $\forall k: TPts - \{p\} \cdot T'L_k =_d TL_k$

(c) $\forall k: T1Pts \cdot T'L_k =_d T1L_k$

(3) $T'C =_d TC$

The effect of this operation is illustrated in Figure **12**.5C.2. Note that the second operand $T1$ is specified as an unpointed tree. Had $T1$ been specified as a member of TreePtd0, the operation would have resulted in a loss of information as either TC or $T1C$ would have to be forgotten in T'. Consequently, although RemChiFst is defined as the inverse of InsChiFst, it could not be an exact one.

Given a T': TreePtd0 in which $T'C$ has a child, RemChiFst removes the subtree $T1$ rooted at the first child of $T'C$. It is obtained by inverting the definition of InsChiFst systematically.

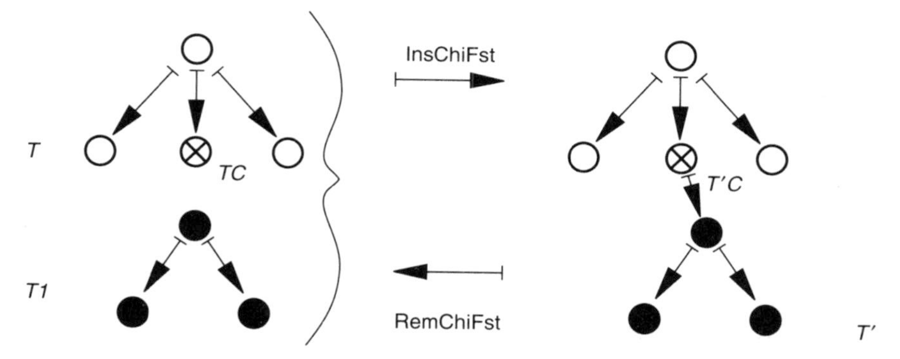

Figure 12.5C.2 Effects of InsChiFst and RemChiFst.

RemChiFst

Remove *T1* from *T'*, where *T1* is the subtree whose root is the first child of *T'C*.

Given *T'*: TreePtd0 where

(Pre 1) $T'Chis(T'C) \neq \varnothing$

RemChiFst(T') $=_d (T, T1)$ where T: TreePtd0 and $T1$: TreeOV1.

Let $i =_d T'ChiFst(T'C)$, $A =_d \{i\}$ and $p: T'Pts$.

(1) $(TTreeV, p, T1ForV) =_d$ Rem$(T'TreeV, A)$ (This implies $p = TC$)

(2) (a) $(T1R, TL_p) =_d$ Split$(T'L_p, i)$ (Two lists defined)

(b) $\forall k: TPts - \{p\} \cdot TL_k =_d T'L_k$

(c) $\forall k: T1Pts \cdot T1L_k =_d T'L_k$

(3) $TC =_d T'C$

InsSibNex and RemSibNex

The next two operations, InsSibNex and RemSibNex, are similar to InsChiFst and RemChiFst (Figure 12.5C.3). Given a main tree T: TreePtd0 and a second

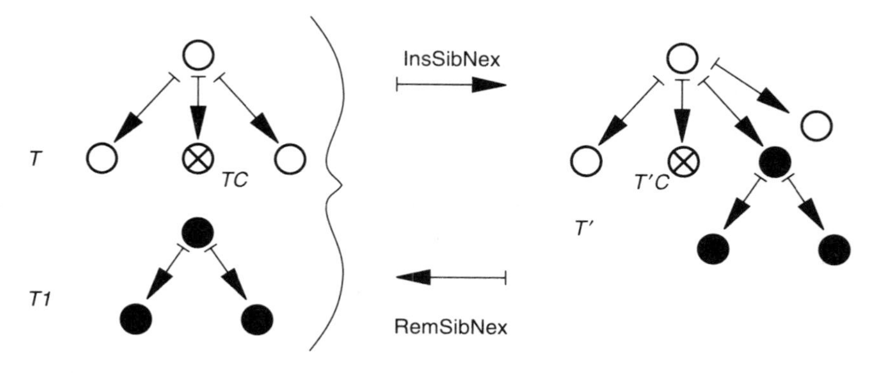

Figure 12.5C.3 Effects of InsSibNex and RemSibNex.

tree $T1$: TreeOV1, InsSibNex inserts $T1$ in T so that the root of $T1$ is the new next sibling of TC. The cursor is left unchanged. A special precondition of InsSibNex is that $TC \neq TRoot$, as the root cannot be followed by a sibling in a tree.

<u>InsSibNex</u>

Insert $T1$ in T, with the root of $T1$ immediately after TC.
Given T: TreePtd0 and $T1$: TreeOV1 where

(Pre 1) IsDisjoint($TPts$, $T1Pts$)
(Pre 2) $TC \neq TRoot$
(Pre 3) $TVals = T1Vals$

InsSibNex(T, $T1$) = T' where T': TreePtd0. Let $i =_d TC$, $p =_d TParent(i)$ and $A \subseteq_d T'Pts$.

(1) $(T'TreeV, A) =_d \text{Ins}(TTreeV, p, T1ForV)$
(2) (a) (i) *Case* $i = TChiLst(p)$ (List insertion)
$T'L_p =_d TL_p \mathbin{+\!\!+} T1R$
(ii) *Case* $i \neq TChiLst(p)$
$(T'L_p, i, j) =_d \text{Ins}(TL_p, i, j, T1R)$
where $j =_d TSibNex(i)$
(b) $\forall k : TPts - \{p\} \cdot T'L_k =_d TL_k$
(c) $\forall k : T1Pts \cdot T'L_k =_d T1L_k$
(3) $T'C =_d TC$

RemSibNex is the inverse of InsSibNex. Given T': TreePtd0, it removes the subtree $T1$ rooted at the next sibling of $T'C$. It is obtained by inverting the definition of InsSibNex systematically.

<u>RemSibNex</u>

Remove $T1$ from T', where $T1$ is rooted at the next sibling of $T'C$.
Given T': TreePtd0 where

(Pre 1) $\exists r : T'Pts \cdot r = T'SibNex(T'C)$

RemSibNex(T') $=_d$ (T, $T1$) where T: TreePtd0 and $T1$: TreeOV1. Let $i =_d T'C$, $r =_d T'SibNex(i)$, $A =_d \{r\}$ and $p : T'Pts$.

(1) $(TTreeV, p, T1ForV) =_d \text{Rem}(T'TreeV, A)$ (This defines p)
(2) (a) (i) *Case* $r = T'ChiLst(p)$ (Two lists defined)
$(TL_p, T1R) =_d \text{Split}(T'L_p, i)$
(ii) *Case* $r \neq T'ChiLst(p)$
$(TL_p, i, j, T1R) =_d \text{Rem}(T'L_p, i, j)$
where $j =_d T'SibNex(r)$
(b) $\forall k : TPts - \{p\} \cdot TL_k =_d T'L_k$
(c) $\forall k : T1Pts \cdot T1L_k =_d T'L_k$
(3) $TC =_d T'C$

SetV

The last operation resets the value of TC in a tree T to a specified value v. It is defined in the same way as SetV on ForOV1.

SetV

Set the value of TC in the pointed tree T to v.
Given T:TreePtd0 and $v: TVals$, SetV$(T, v) =_{\mathrm{d}} T'$ where T':TreePtd0 and

(1) $T'TreeOrd =_{\mathrm{d}} TTreeOrd$
(2) $T'V =_{\mathrm{d}} (TV|TC \mapsto v)$
(3) $T'C =_{\mathrm{d}} TC$

This completes our model of pointed trees, with associated navigation and tree transformation operations. By applying these functions repeatedly, the modeller may build any finite tree and modify the structure of a given tree by relocating any *subtree* within it. We thus have a first model of a tree editor. A more advanced and more 'concrete' model is developed in Chapter **16**.

It may be observed that the four main tree transformation operations (InsChiFst, etc.) are rather complex. In each of them we cannot invoke TreeOV1 functions: the list transformation operations must be carried out separately from the transformation of other features, and in two cases they require a case analysis which is not so straightforward. Yet at first sight this model seems quite reasonable, given the basic operations available: it is not easy to see how it could be any simpler.

The tree editor of Chapter **16** operates on pointed trees equipped with two cursors instead of one. Their purpose is to delimit a *subforest* to be used as operand in some functions. Thus, this model is more advanced and its navigation operations slightly more complex. The paradox is that the introduction of two pointers actually leads to a significant *simplification* of our initial model: only two of the four main tree transformation operations are needed, and their establishment is significantly simpler. Thus, the establishment of the second model will illustrate an important modelling technique, which it will be useful to contrast with the 'obvious' approach used above.

Part 5

Application Case Studies

13 Introduction to Application Case Studies

13.1 Aim of Part 5

Parts **2** and **3** were devoted to the principles and methods of set theory and logic. Part **4** introduced two classes of 'complex' models, namely lists and trees, and related concepts. The establishment of these theoretical models gave a first illustration of the *practice* of modelling, including the modular definition of multiple classes of objects by successive extensions, and the corresponding establishment of operations by parallel successive extensions. However, lists and trees are still relatively abstract; they are halfway between the basic set-theoretical notions of sets, relations and functions for instance, and models of concrete 'distant systems', objects or situations like organizations, projects or complex physical products.

The aim of Part **5** is to develop theoretical models of such concrete aspects of the 'real world'. The establishment of such models involves a new range of difficulties: how to relate our basic conceptual models, which are closed systems, to the concrete 'distant' systems we are interested in, which are often open, moving targets of infinite variety and complexity. This is what distinguishes *modelling*, as a *practice* or an art, the production of models of 'real life' systems, from the construction of models as pure theory.

Each of the applications developed in Part **5** may be regarded as a case study in modelling a *type* of concrete object. In each case, we start with a number of familiar instances of the concrete system to be modelled, be it a group of people, a dictionary, a book, a stock of spare parts, a lending library, and so on. The aim usually is to describe how any object of the type considered evolves in time. For example: how a population evolves through the arrival and departure of its members; how a dictionary is created, maintained by inserting new entries and deleting existing ones, and consulted by users; how a library purchases, lends, receives and disposes of books, and the role played by employees and users in this process; and so on.

In each case, the reader has a concrete situation to refer to. This situation may be relatively simple or complex, but it is realistic and general. Consequently, the reader is likely to be familiar with it, as it is part of common general culture. Likewise, the practical relevance of the situation is readily apparent, which is another motivating factor.

In each application, the aim is to build a *theoretical model* of the object under study and of the rules determining its evolution. The theoretical model captures a few essential elements of the concrete situation, that is, it is a highly simplified picture of the reality described. This is the essence of *abstraction*, properly understood. The method used to build the model is very much the same as in Part **4**. It always involves (a) establishing a certain class or classes of objects by describing the common features, fixed and variable, of their respective members, and (b) establishing a number of operations on the classes defined. The model is expressed both in natural language, English, and in Feature Notation. The reader is constantly encouraged to translate from one into the other. The formulation of the model makes it possible to *reason* about the concrete objects it represents – that is, to identify, analyse and express all their relevant properties in a systematic fashion.

Overview of case studies

Part **5** contains four models of progressively increasing complexity. They fall into two groups. Each model is very general, that is, represents a wide class of concrete applications. The more advanced models are developed in a modular fashion, by successive extensions of classes of objects of increasing complexity. These models are as follows:

Group I: Simple Applications

1. An evolving set model
2. An evolving dictionary model

Group II: Advanced Applications

3. A tree editor
4. A general resource allocation model

These applications are introduced in turn.

13.2 Simple applications

13.2A An evolving set model

Many objects arising in practice may be described as finite *sets* or *collections* of more elementary objects *evolving in time*. Here are some examples:

- A human group or population
- A dictionary, viewed as a set of entries
- A stock of parts in a maintenance shop
- The stock of books of a lending library
- The set of spare seats on an airline flight
- The set of rules of a legislative code

In each case, there is a certain set of elements. This set goes through successive states according to a certain discipline: it is an *evolving* set or system. In other words, it may be described as a *sequence of states*, each of which is a *static set* in its own right.

In the history of an evolving set, each state S' is related to its predecessor S, if any, by some law or operation. In this model, three basic laws determine the state S' obtaining at any time:

Emp: S' is the empty set (first state of the system)
Ins: S' is the result of inserting a new element in the previous set S
Rem: S' is the result of removing an element from its predecessor S

These three transformation rules are the *operations* of the model. They form an adequate description in most cases. For instance, a human group such as a club C may be described as follows. First C is created, and at this stage it is empty. Then, as time unfolds, C acquires new members and loses old ones, and this process goes on until C is wound up. There is no harm in assuming that members join and leave *one at a time*. If several people join or leave C simultaneously, we may always twist reality slightly and assume that they do so one at a time.

The other examples may be similarly described. When a dictionary is first conceived, it contains no entries. Then entries are added to the dictionary, or removed from it, one at a time. When a library is built, initially it is empty. Then books are purchased, lent, returned and finally disposed of. Each such transformation of the book stock may be described as 'a certain book in' or 'a certain book out'.

It is easy to see that this description applies to all the other above examples, and countless more instances could be given. In each case the situation is the same: there is an evolving set undergoing a sequence of transformations, and at each stage of the process, the transformation is described by one of the three operations Emp, Ins or Rem. It is important to make the distinction between a set as an *evolving object*, which is modelled as a *sequence* of states, and the various *static sets* which make up its possible states. *Only the latter are proper sets in our theoretical model.*

We have just completed an informal description of what is clearly a universal phenomenon. Our first model is the formal set-theoretical counterpart of this description. This model is *generic* in that the class of *possible* members of the evolving set is open, that is, varies with the application. Thus in each application the first step to take is to specify this class: it may be people, books, engineering parts, dictionary entries, and so on. It is precisely the possibility of varying this class which makes the model universal. This model is established in Chapter **14**.

13.2B An evolving dictionary model

This model may be regarded as an extension of the previous one. As already mentioned, a dictionary is an evolving set subject to the three operations Emp, Ins and Rem. However, a dictionary has a number of additional properties. First, each entry consists of a *couple* of elements: (a) a *word* and (b) a corresponding *definition*. Second, each word must have only *one* definition. The operations Ins and Rem must preserve these properties.

In addition, further operations are provided, to model the way a dictionary is *consulted by users*. Such functions are called *retrieve operations*; they return information without altering the dictionary. A typical example is the looking up of a word. Given (a) a dictionary and (b) a certain word occurring in it, this operation produces the corresponding definition.

Our second model is the set-theoretical counterpart of this description. It is built as an implicit refinement of the previous model. It is generic, and may be applied in its own right to a wide range of cases. Indeed, any *information table* may be regarded as a dictionary as defined above, subject to the same operations. Different applications are obtained by varying the class of possible words and the class of possible definitions. This model is developed in Chapter **15**.

13.3 Advanced applications

13.3A A tree editor

As we have seen in Chapters **10** and **12**, a tree is a model of a hierarchy, that is, of a set on which a 'parenthood' relation is defined. The third model is a generic 'tree editor', which we call *TEd*. This may be used to represent finite valued trees of any type, and involves a number of operations to create, transform and use the variety of trees represented.

Recall that in our theoretical model a tree is described essentially as a set of elements (base points) with the following properties: (a) with one exception, each point has *exactly one* 'parent' in the set; (b) the exception has no parent and is called the *root* of the tree; and (c) the root is an 'ancestor' of every other element. This is the primary concept; it is extended in various ways.

Trees are universal; instances occur, implicitly or explicitly, in all walks of life. Examples were given in Chapter **12**. These are expanded below, in order to demonstrate the importance of this notion.

Concrete examples of trees

1 Any piece of text, ranging from a simple sentence or a simple mathematical formula to a whole encyclopaedia, has a tree structure. A sentence may be decomposed into propositions, propositions into phrases, phrases into words and words into more elementary word components and ultimately characters. The key property of the sentence is that any unit at any level occurs in *exactly one* unit of the previous level, its 'parent'. A mathematical formula may be decomposed in the same way. The result is a *parse tree*, and we have seen in Part **3** the fundamental role played by such trees in logic and, more generally, the description of languages. The tree structure of Feature Notation is a third example. An encyclopaedia is a fourth example. It is a set of books; these are broken down into parts, parts into chapters, chapters into sections, sections into paragraphs and paragraphs into sentences. Again, any unit at any level occurs in exactly one unit of the previous level.

2 In any well-established field of science, art or philosophy, the *classification* or *taxonomy* of the objects under study is a major feature. To classify a set of objects is to partition them into disjoint subgroups and to repeat the process with each subgroup, up to a point. The result is a hierarchy, as each identified subgroup is an immediate subclass of exactly one larger group, its 'parent'. See also Section **1**.2B.

The universality of taxonomy may be explained as follows. Whenever we are presented with a large class of objects of any type, we are almost inevitably led to organize these into coherent groups and subgroups according to appropriate classification criteria. The reason for doing so is twofold: first, it is to reduce the complexity of the overall unorganized class; second, it is to gain insight into the relationships existing between the various objects under consideration. This insight is provided by the very classification criteria found to be appropriate. This holds for any kind of object. Typical examples include:

- Ideas or concepts in any discursive field
- Mineral, vegetable and animal species
- The set of tasks making up a project
- The set of parts of a complex engineering product (car, machine, etc.)
- Geopolitical groupings: districts, towns, counties, states, countries, continents
- The units, departments, divisions, etc. making up any human organization

3 Any computer program or system has a hierarchic structure: like any text, it consists of parts and subparts. This is a necessity. The main import of concepts such as *structured programming*, *modular design*, *structured system design* etc. has perhaps been not so much to impose a hierarchic structure on systems as to make this necessary structure apparent.

4 Users of interactive personal computer systems are well aware of the hierarchic structure of directories in operating systems like MS-DOS, and the hierarchic structure of command menus. The hierarchic structure of directories is designed precisely to enable the user to organize information into coherent groups and subgroups, as in any discursive field.

These examples could be multiplied and demonstrate the universality of hierarchic structures. A main task in computing is to learn to identify hierarchic structures whenever they arise logically, and to develop suitable methods of establishing such structures in all potential application areas.

Two remarks are in order at this point.

1 Although tree structures are universal, they are *not* unique in modelling. They often arise in conjunction with other types of structure, such as general relations or graphs. It is wrong to seek to reduce all structures to trees, just as it is wrong to deny the presence of a hierarchic structure where it logically occurs.

2 There is a tendency in computer science to present trees primarily as *implementation* data structures. For instance, a tree is one of the main methods of representing a *set* in computer storage, and is often presented as such in books on data structures. This may be misleading. The concept of a tree is just as important at all levels of abstraction, in particular as part of the user's view of a system, as the previous examples clearly demonstrate.

TEd

In view of the universality of trees, it is clear that a tree editor such as TEd is of wide applicability. TEd is a generic editor in the sense that the type of tree the modeller may construct is open, that is, it may vary with the application. The type of a tree is determined by the set of values which may be assigned to its points. These values may be characters, strings of characters, persons, concrete objects, sets or classes – in fact any objects, structured or unstructured.

The main object on which TEd operates is an evolving ordered valued tree T, together with a couple of pointers on two of its base points, TE_1 and TE_2. At any time, these two points must be siblings and TE_1 must precede TE_2 in their sibling list. The modeller may create, expand and modify T by applying various functions similar to those of the one-cursor pointed tree model of Section **12**.5.

The operations of TEd fall into two main groups. The first consists of navigation operations, namely functions to 'move' the cursors about the tree. The second comprises operations which modify the tree in various ways: they insert a new element, remove or copy an element or a subforest, reinsert a previously removed subforest, possibly at a new location in the tree, and so on. In each case, the location of the second operand within T is determined by the cursors, as in the model of Section **12**.5.

This model is established in Chapter **16**.

13.3B A resource allocation model

The last model is concerned with another universal problem, the efficient management and use of fixed resources. More precisely, it is concerned with the allocation of resources to competing uses or tasks, or *resource allocation* for short. This model is highly generic. Its aim is to capture the features common to all resource allocation problems.

In any such problem, we find the following elements:

First, there is a collection of *tasks* to be executed by some individual or organization. This set may be fixed or may evolve in time like any *evolving* set.

Second, there is a collection of *resources* or *physical units* of various types 'controlled' by the organization: tools, machines, facilities, workers, space units, and so on. Each unit is *fixed* in the sense that it is not absorbed or destroyed by use, and thus may be used repeatedly.

Third, the execution of any task requires a number of resources of various types. The resources needed by any task are required *jointly*. Therefore at any time a task is either *active*, i.e. being executed, or *inactive*, i.e. suspended; if it is active then it is allocated all the resources it needs, otherwise no resources are allocated to it.

The problem is to decide at any time (a) which tasks should be active and (b) how the resources available should be allocated to the active tasks in order to enable their execution. The aim of the model is *not* to solve this problem optimally, but *to represent its various constituent elements and to analyse their implications*, as a first step towards an adequate (if not optimal) solution. The situation may also involve the various *agents* or 'stakeholders' interested in the execution of the tasks or somehow connected with them: for example, employees or users of the organization's services.

The model describing this situation is called *ResAll*. The main difference between the previous models and ResAll is that the latter involves many sets: collections of tasks, active or inactive, of resources and agents of various types, and so on. In particular, it involves an explicit *set of resource types*, themselves represented as disjoint sets. In addition, it involves multiple relations between all its constituent sets, such as 'task Ta requires n units of resource type r' or 'agent Ag is the client for task Ta'. These relations may express either obvious *facts* or physical constraints, such as 'at any time, no resource unit may be allocated to more than one task', or *decision rules*, such as 'at any time, the resources allocated to (the needs of) a single client must not exceed certain limits'. It is the collection of all these sets and relations which defines the class of objects represented by the model.

The basic principles established in the simpler models are still entirely valid. Specifically, each set or relation is again expected to evolve in time through the application of various operations such as Emp, Ins and Rem on elementary sets. The resource allocation process itself is entirely captured by the operations which activate and deactivate tasks – that is, transfer them between the two subsets of active and inactive tasks.

To sum up, the various objects of the model, each characterized by the sets and relations mentioned, are viewed as the possible *states* of an *evolving system*, and the operations form the *evolution laws* of the system. However, these operations are more complex then simple set functions, as they must preserve the essential relations of the model's objects (the possible system states), as in the dictionary model. In addition, there are a number of *retrieve operations*, which return information on an object without transforming it, as in the dictionary model. An evolving system of the type just described is called a *ResAll system.*

Two special cases

Two typical applications of ResAll are (a) the description of a *lending library* and (b) the representation of a *conference centre.* Models for both systems have been published, in the specification language Z in particular; see, for instance, Hayes (1987) and McDermid (1989). We outline these two applications in turn.

The resources managed by a library are *book copies.* Each book is a resource *type* and a copy of a book is a resource (unit) of this type. The 'tasks' are the uses to which library users put the books they borrow. They are explicitly accounted for in the model. This is somewhat unusual, but it may be useful if, for instance, the lending rules allow for different purposes or 'projects' which the books are to serve.

Any book copy is bought and later disposed of by the library. Between these two events, it is repeatedly lent to users and returned by them. A loan of a copy is its allocation to the user's task for which the copy is required. When the copy is returned, it again becomes free for further allocation.

Book loans must conform to certain rules, for example, 'at any time, the number of books lent to a user must not exceed a certain limit'. Thus book lending is a resource allocation process subject to physical constraints and decision rules, exactly as described in ResAll.

A conference centre owns a set of rooms and other facilities: overhead projectors, video tape recorders, and so on. These form its 'resources'. The centre is used for events such as lectures and seminars. Each event is a 'task' requiring some of the centre's resources in adequate quantities. At any time, such a task is either simply 'planned' or being held. In the first case, it is an inactive task, and obviously requires no resources; in the second case, it is an active task and must be allocated the types of resource it needs, in the quantities required.

Consequently, a conference centre may be described as a ResAll system. Each state is a 'snapshot' of the centre at a certain point in time. It is characterized by the set of resources owned by the centre at this point, the set of inactive (planned) events, the set of active events, and so on. Furthermore, the possible successive states of the system are governed by ResAll operations. For instance, each event is first planned, that is inserted into the set of tasks to be performed; then activated, that is held; and finally, deactivated. Likewise, each resource is first acquired, then repeatedly allocated to active events and deallocated, and finally disposed of. Although most events are held once, an event may involve a series of separate sessions. This is naturally modelled by activating and deactivating the event several times.

The general model is established in Chapter **17**.

14 An Evolving Set Model

14.1 Introduction

As stated in Section **13**.2A, many practical objects or situations may be represented as finite *evolving sets* of more elementary objects. The examples given were a population, a book stock, a dictionary, and so on. An evolving set is *not* a proper set in its own right. It is a *sequence* of proper, i.e. static sets, its successive *states*. Each state S' is related to its immediate predecessor S by one of the three operations or laws

Emp: S' is the empty set (with no predecessor S)
Ins: S' results from inserting a new element in S
Rem: S' results from removing an element from S

We have seen how these assumptions fit such diverse cases as a club, a dictionary or a stock of books. In each case the situation is the same: there is a finite evolving set S undergoing successive transformations, each of which is described by one of the three rules Emp, Ins or Rem.

Now we must refine this initial description somewhat. In each case, the evolving set S must be a finite subset of *another set*, the class of potential or actual members of S. This larger set varies with the application, and consequently we call it the *application domain*. For instance, in the case of a club, the application domain is the set of all people, past present and future, whether actually members of the club or not. In the case of a library book stock, it is the set of all possible book copies, whether currently held by the library or not, in existence or still to be made. Note that in most cases the application domain is a matter of choice on the part of the modeller.

The purpose of the evolving set model established in this chapter is formally to represent the situation just described. As the given examples suggest, this is a very simple model. It involves one main class, the set of all finite subsets of a given application domain, and the operations outlined above.

We develop our set model in two stages. First, we give a formal description of its objects. This is done in general terms, that is, without specifying the application domain. Consequently, the application domain is treated as an implicit parameter. To keep matters concrete, we also simultaneously illustrate developments with the two applications of a club and a library book stock. Second, the operations are established formally in general terms and illustrated by an example. At the end of the chapter, we introduce a parametrized version of the model in which the application domain is treated as an explicit parameter.

Preconditions of operations Recall that operations are just functions on the class of objects represented by the model, here the finite subsets of the application domain. In general, a function may be partial, defined for only some of the objects in its domain. When this is the case, the definition domain is usually determined by a set of conditions which must be satisfied by any object for which the function is defined. These conditions are called *preconditions* and labelled (Pre 1), (Pre 2), and so on in the specification of operations.

14.2 Model definition

14.2A Application domain and objects

In any application, the class of objects of the model is defined in two stages. First, an application domain is selected. Second, the class itself is established.

The *application domain* is a set of objects of some type. It is denoted by *Domain*. in the case of a club, *Domain* is the set of all persons, past present or future, as a member of a club must necessarily be a person. In the case of a book stock, *Domain* is the set of all book copies which are or *may* possibly be held in stock. This includes all the book copies which have existed in the past, which currently exist but are not held in stock, which are held in stock, or which will exist in future.

Note that is both cases, *Domain* could be defined in many other ways. For instance, in the case of a club, *Domain* could be restricted to all the people satisfying certain conditions of age, domicile, and so on. In the case of a book stock, *Domain* could be restricted to certain type(s) of book. The appropriate application domain is a purely *modelling* matter.

Only one condition is imposed on *Domain*: this set must be nonempty, in order to avoid the trivial case which an empty set would imply. We introduce *Domain* by

---

Domain: Set	Set of objects under consideration, potential or actual
$Domain \neq \varnothing$	

The objects of the model are all the *finite subsets* of *Domain*. They form a set, which we generically name SetStates. In the case of a club, a set S: SetStates is a *possible* state of the club's membership, and SetStates is the set of all such possible states. In the case of a book stock, a set S: SetStates is any finite set of actual book copies, that is, a possible state of the stock.

The reason for the name 'SetStates' is that in any application, the aim is to describe a certain entity which *evolves* in time. Therefore, this entity goes through successive states. The purpose of SetStates is to describe *the set of all the possible states of the entity*. However, for the moment there is no reference to time nor to the way the successive states of the entity are related. The possible sequences of states are determined by the operations Emp, Ins and Rem on SetStates formally established in Section **14**.3.

The set SetStates is defined as follows in Feature Notation:

S: SetStates

$SCond1 .: S \subseteq_{\mathrm{d}} Domain$
$Scond2 .: \mathrm{IsFinite}(S)$

In this definition, S is a variable representing any member of SetStates. It is specified as a finite subset of *Domain*. Observe that, unlike other objects, any S: SetStates has no *variable* features distinct from itself. This, of course, is exceptional. The condition IsFinite(S) is not essential. It is there to emphasize that it is a necessary consequence of generating members S: SetStates by means of the three operations Emp, Ins and Rem only.

The set SetStates may also be defined in standard set-theoretical notation. It is *not* the powerset Pow(*Domain*), unless *Domain* itself is finite, but it may be specified by

$$\mathrm{SetStates} = \{S \mid S \subseteq_{\mathrm{d}} Domain \wedge \mathrm{IsFinite}(S)\}$$

or

$$\mathrm{SetStates} =_{\mathrm{d}} \mathrm{Powf}(Domain)$$

using the operation Powf given in Definition **2**.2F.2.

14.2B Example: a stock of books

As in any application, the first task is to specify the set *Domain*. This example gives a good illustration of the care with which this must be done. The term 'book' is often used in two different ways. In one sense, a book is an abstract object with a title, text, and so on, and which may exist in several physical copies. In this sense, it is what is common to all its copies. In a second sense, a book is just *one specific copy* of an abstract book. To distinguish these two meanings, we use the terms 'book' and 'book copy' (or simply 'copy') respectively. Clearly in this application, our purpose is to describe the stock of book *copies* of a library.

Let the various possible book copies be identified by names like A, Aa, Ab, B, Ba, Baa, etc. Consequently, we may write semiformally:

$$\mathit{Domain} =_{\mathrm{d}} \{\mathrm{A}, \mathrm{Aa}, \mathrm{Ab}, \mathrm{B}, \mathrm{Ba}, \mathrm{Baa}, \ldots\}$$

Our aim is to describe a certain book stock as an evolving entity. At any time, the state S of the stock may be, for instance:

$S = \varnothing$	The empty stock
$S = \{\mathrm{A}\}$	A stock of one copy
$S = \{\mathrm{A}, \mathrm{Aa}\}$	A stock of two copies

Consequently, the set SetStates of all possible states of the stock is

$$\mathrm{SetStates} = \{\varnothing, \{\mathrm{A}\}, \{\mathrm{A}, \mathrm{Aa}\}, \{\mathrm{B}\}, \{\mathrm{A}, \mathrm{B}\}, \{\mathrm{A}, \mathrm{Aa}, \mathrm{B}\}, \ldots\}$$

Each member of SetStates is a finite set of book copies.

14.3 Operations on SetStates

14.3A Definitions

We now formally define the three operations Emp, Ins and Rem mentioned in Section **14**.1. These are operations on SetStates.

Emp

The first operation returns the empty set. This is a nullary function, and its definition is immediate.

Emp

Return the empty set.
Emp : SetStates and

(1) $\mathrm{Emp} =_{\mathrm{d}} \varnothing$

Ins

Recall the purpose of Ins. Given an S: SetStates and an element x: *Domain*, this operation returns a new set S': SetStates defined as the union of S and $\{x\}$.

We impose one precondition on this operation: x must not already be a member of S, i.e. $x \notin S$. This restriction is not absolutely necessary. We impose it in order to reflect the natural view that an object x 'cannot' be added to a set if it is already a member of it. In other words, we postulate that attempting to 'insert' an element in a set of which it already is a member is likely to be an error, and this assumption is explicit in the model. These are purely *modelling* considerations.

With this precondition, the result S' may be defined by

$$S' =_d S + \{x\}$$

where $+$ is the union of *disjoint* sets.

The full formal definition of Ins is as follows:

Ins

Insert object x in set S.
Given S: SetStates and x: *Domain* where
(Pre 1) $x \notin S$
Ins(S, x) $=_d S'$ where S': SetStates and
(1) $S' =_d S + \{x\}$

Rem

The operation Rem reverses the effect of Ins. Given a set S': SetStates and an object x: *Domain*, Rem returns the set $S =_d S' - \{x\}$.

This operation has one precondition, namely $x \in S'$. (This is why we use '$-$' to denote the relative complement.) The reason for this precondition mirrors the justification for (Pre 1) in Ins: we postulate that attempting to remove an element x from a set of which x is not a member is probably an error.

In the formal definition of Rem, x is introduced as a member of *Domain*, and the precondition $x \in S'$ is stated explicitly. We could also have introduced x by x: S' and left $x \in S'$ as an implied property. As it is, our specification of Rem matches that of Ins more closely.

Rem

Remove x from S'.
Given S': SetStates and x: *Domain* where
(Pre 1) $x \in S'$
Rem(S', x) $=_d S$ where S: SetStates and
(1) $S =_d S' - \{x\}$

On model adequacy

In our set model, we assume that elements are inserted in a main set S: SetStates or removed from it *one at a time*. This is a simplifying assumption which is likely to be acceptable in most applications, and which is typical of the art of modelling. If in reality a whole (finite) set of elements can be added to or removed from the main set, then either operation may be represented as a repetition of Ins or Rem.

Note that this equivalence between a single *set* operation and the repetition of an *element* operation is valid here because there is no reference to *time* in our model. Should time be a concern, in particular the 'speed of execution of operations', then the above equivalence might be invalid.

Clearly, Ins and Rem are full inverse operations. The first argument of Rem is named S' to emphasize this fact.

14.3B Example: book stock operations

Consider again the book stock example of Section **14**.2B. Recall that in this case,

$$Domain =_{\mathrm{d}} \{\mathrm{A, Aa, Ab, B, Ba, Baa, \ldots}\}$$

We now simulate a possible sequence of states of the stock resulting from the application of the three operations Emp, Ins and Rem. The resulting successive sets are indexed with 0, 1, 2, ... ; that is, they are named $S_0, S_1, S_2, \ldots, S_i, \ldots$. For each i: Nat, S_i: SetStates.

(0)	$S_0 = \mathrm{Emp} = \varnothing$	Initial stock
(1)	$S_1 = \mathrm{Ins}(S_0, \mathrm{Aa}) = \{\mathrm{Aa}\}$	Insert Aa in S_0
(2)	$S_2 = \mathrm{Ins}(S_1, \mathrm{Ababa}) = \{\mathrm{Aa, Ababa}\}$	Insert Ababa
(3)	$S_3 = \mathrm{Ins}(S_2, \mathrm{Cb}) = \{\mathrm{Aa, Ababa, Cb}\}$	Insert Cb
(4)	$S_4 = \mathrm{Rem}(S_3, \mathrm{Aa}) = \{\mathrm{Ababa, Cb}\}$	Remove Aa
(5)	$S_5 = \mathrm{Ins}(S_4, \mathrm{Dac}) = \{\mathrm{Ababa, Cb, Dac}\}$	Insert Dac
(6)	$S_6 = \mathrm{Rem}(S_5, \mathrm{Ababa}) = \{\mathrm{Cb, Dac}\}$	Remove Ababa

The successive sets S_i are clearly all members of SetStates. Note that the above sequence is only *one* of all possible 'histories' of a book stock.

14.4 Parametrized version of the model AT

In the above set model, every nonempty set *Domain* defines a different set SetStates and *different* associated operations Emp, Ins and Rem. We now develop an extension of this model in which *Domain* occurs as an explicit parameter. One advantage of this extension is that it is then possible to operate simultaneously on several sets SetStates, each corresponding to a different application domain. We first define the objects of the model. Then we define its operations.

14.4A Objects

We adapt the initial definition of the set SetStates in two stages. As a first step, we introduce a new class SetStates1, which may be regarded as an extension of SetStates. An S: SetStates1 now has two variable features: first, a set *SDomain*, again called the application domain of S; second, a finite subset of *SDomain*, also named S. Thus the application domain is now made a feature of S. Consequently, different S: SetStates1 may have different application domains. For variety, we combine the introduction of S, as a subset of *SDomain*, with the condition that S must be a subset of *SDomain* (condition *SCond1* in SetStates).

S: SetStates1

  * *SDomain*: Set
     SCond1 .: $SDomain \neq \emptyset$
  * $S \subseteq_d SDomain$
     SCond2 .: IsFinite(S)

Note that the feature *SDomain* of any S: SetStates1 is similar to the value set *FVals* of a family F: Family, for instance; see Section **11**.1A.

Now that different objects S: SetStates1 may have different application domains *SDomain*, there remains the task of coordinating this feature. We do that by adding a parameter *Domain* to SetStates1. This gives the class SetStates1(*Domain*), which follows:

S: SetStates1(*Domain*) (Extended SetStates1)

  * S[*SetStates1*]: SetStates1
    ΔSetStates1
  * *Domain*: Set — Parameter
     DomCo .: $Domain \neq_d \emptyset$
     SCond3 .: $SDomain =_d Domain$

This specification should be read thus: Given any set *Domain′*, any S: SetStates1(*Domain′*) is a member of SetStates1 such that $SDomain = Domain'$. We also make the convention that given S: SetStates1, in any context in which $SDomain = Domain'$, S is regarded as having been introduced by

S:SetStates1(*Domain'*). This makes it possible to treat the parameter *Domain* implicitly in most operations.

14.4B Operations

We now convert the three set operations Emp, Ins and Rem in turn to functions on SetStates1. Emp is renamed Emp1, as the original version is nullary. Ins and Rem are overloaded.

Emp1

The difference between Emp and Emp1 is that the latter returns an object S':SetStates1 such that $S'Domain$ is determined by an argument.

Emp1

Return the empty set, with associated application domain specified.
Given *Domain*:Set such that

(Pre 1) $Domain \neq \varnothing$

Emp1(*Domain*) $=_d S'$ where S':SetStates1 and

(1) $S'Domain =_d Domain$

(2) $S' =_d \varnothing$

Ins

The operation Ins is upgraded as follows. First, its two arguments now are S:SetStates1 and an element x to insert in S, and the result is S':SetStates1. Second, x is constrained to be a member of *SDomain*. Third, the feature $S'Domain$ of the result is equated to *SDomain*.

Ins

Insert object x in set S.
Given S:SetStates1 and x:*SDomain* where

(Pre 1) $x \notin S$

Ins(S, x) $=_d S'$ where S':SetStates1 and

(1) $S'Domain =_d SDomain$

(2) $S' =_d S + \{x\}$

Rem

The operator Rem is adapted in the same way as Ins. Again clearly Rem is the full inverse of Ins.

<u>Rem</u>

Remove x from S'.
Given S' : SetStates1 and $x : S'Domain$ where
(Pre 1) $x \in S'$
Rem(S', x) $=_d S$ where S : SetStates1 and
(1) $SDomain =_d S'Domain$
(2) $S =_d S' - \{x\}$

This completes the establishment of the parametrized evolving set model.

15 An Evolving Dictionary Model

15.1 Introduction

Consider an ordinary dictionary. How can we describe its essential features? Anyone familiar with dictionaries and the use for which they are intended will probably agree with the following description. A dictionary is a set of objects of a certain type. Each object is in two parts. The first part is a *word* to be defined and the second part is the corresponding *definition*. Thus, each object is a *couple* (w, d), where w is a word and d a definition. Moreover, any word occurs in at most *one* couple in the dictionary. This implies that all the couples are different, and so form a *set* of couples in the mathematical sense of the term 'set'.

What is the main purpose of a dictionary? Simply, to provide the definition of each word it contains. In order to use a dictionary we must (a) know a word and (b) need or wish to obtain the corresponding definition. Accordingly, the main use of a dictionary is to *look up the definition of a known word.*

This initial description leads at once to the following observations. First, we can see why each word should occur only once. If a word w occurred as the first component of several couples, the look-up operation would not be well defined: would it return just one definition selected at random or by some other rule, or would it return all the definitions of w? It could be argued that in practice words often have several definitions. But this is not a reason for allowing several couples (w, d) with the same first component w. The proper way to model multiple definitions of a word is to group them into a single compound definition occurring in a single couple. We return to this point at the end of the section.

Second, the rule that no word may occur in several couples implies more than the fact that a dictionary is a set of couples. It implies that a dictionary is essentially (the graph of) a *finite, partial function*. Indeed, by definition we have a partial function whenever we have a set of couples such that no object – here, a word – occurs as the first component in more than one couple. The function is partial because in general, of all *possible* words, only some are defined in the dictionary. It is also finite, in the sense that its graph (a certain set) is finite.

Third, we may wonder whether our description of a dictionary as a *set* (of couples) is sufficient. If we consider a 'real' dictionary – a book – we know that in such a dictionary words are sorted in alphabetical order (also called *lexicographic order*). Is this order not essential, and should we not regard a dictionary as a *list* of couples? The answer is no. In an ordinary dictionary words are listed in alphabetical order to enable the user to carry out searches efficiently. Thus the order of words is a *means* to an *end*, and we are only interested in the end – that is, given a word, return the corresponding definition. At this level of abstraction the order of the words is irrelevant. Indeed, in a computerized dictionary the user is not even aware of the order in which words are stored. Consequently the description of a dictionary as a set (which is essentially unordered) and not a list is the correct model.

Fourth, a remark should be made about the nature of words and definitions. We want to take these two terms in the broadest possible sense, so as to come up with a very general definition of a dictionary. Thus by 'word' we mean any type of symbol which may be used to refer to (or name) any type of object. For instance, a word could consist of a number (think of a part code in manufacturing industry) or even a combination of letters, digits and non-alphanumeric symbols such as '+', '@', etc. For this reason we may prefer the term 'entry' to 'word', which is more general. Likewise by 'definition' we mean *any type of information* about the corresponding entry.

With such a general definition we may regard as 'dictionaries' numerous types of object which are not usually so called. For instance:

- An address book
- A birthday book
- A telephone directory
- A symbol table in a book
- A subject index in a book
- An author index

In every case, or *application*, the object is the same: it is a set of couples making up a finite partial function.

Note that in each application, for any dictionary, *the entries and the definitions must belong to certain predefined sets.* For instance, in a birthday book each entry must be the name of a person and the associated 'definition' must be a birthday, that is, a date. In a telephone directory, each entry must be the name of a person or an organization, and the corresponding 'definition' a telephone number.

For any application, we denote the set of all possible entries by *Words*, and the set of all possible definitions by *Definitions*. These two sets must be carefully specified in each case, though this is a purely modelling task. Any application gives rise to a certain class of dictionaries. As mentioned above, these may be described as all the finite partial functions from the set *Words* to the set *Definitions* of the application. Consequently, different applications differ precisely by their respective sets *Words* and/or *Definitions*.

Finally, in any application, we often mean by 'dictionary' not a specific or static object, but *an entity evolving in time*, as in the set model of Chapter **14**. In other words, it is an object going through successive states. The two fundamental sets *Words* and *Definitions* of the application must first be selected, and an initial dictionary created. To simplify, we again assume that this is the empty dictionary, one with no entries and no definitions. Then from time to time new couples (word, definition) are inserted in the dictionary and old ones removed from it.

From this outline, it is apparent that a dictionary as an entity evolving in time may be described as a special case of the set model of Chapter **14**. Indeed, the latter may be applied to dictionaries with only minor adjustments, which is precisely the method we follow. Consequently, a dictionary as an evolving entity will be described as progressing according to the same three laws that were defined for general sets: Emp, which produces the empty set; Ins, which inserts a new member (a couple (word, definition)) in the current set; and Rem, which removes a member from the set. In the following sections, a dictionary specifically regarded as an object evolving in time is called an *evolving dictionary*, in order to emphasize that it is distinct from its successive states.

The aim of this chapter is to establish a formal definition of a dictionary along the lines just indicated. To simplify we continue to call its members 'couples of the form (w, d)', where w is a 'word', that is, any entry, and d a 'definition'. We first formalize the definition of a dictionary as a finite partial function from a given set *Words* to a given set *Definitions*. This is done in Section **15**.2. Then, in Section **15**.3, we define the three operations Emp, Ins and Rem determining the possible evolution of a dictionary, and a new function Redef which combines Rem and Ins. In addition, we introduce various so-called *retrieve* or *query* operations. A retrieve function simply returns a feature of a dictionary without transforming it. Finally, in Section **15**.4, we allow for the fact that in reality operations on a dictionary are the result of 'decisions' or 'commands', and must produce related information in addition to their main effect. The model is extended accordingly.

In most applications, the assumption of one definition per word is appropriate. However, there may be cases where any word may have many definitions. In such applications, treating the *set* of definitions of a word as a single compound 'definition' is not wholly satisfactory, as this implies that the whole set must be redefined every time a member needs updating. Consequently, in Section **15**.3C, we briefly outline an extension of the model in which the components of compound definitions may be handled individually.

The model we develop is *generic* in the sense that it describes *any* application. This means that in this model the two sets *Words* and *Definitions* are regarded as implicit parameters. They are two sets which vary with the application, but are fixed before any other features of the model. A parametrized version of the model could be established as in Chapter **14** with *Words* and *Definitions* passed as parameters of the class of dictionaries. This extension seems straightforward, and we do not develop it.

15.2 Model definition: objects

Any type of dictionary is specified by giving two sets: the set *Words* of all *possible* entries, and the set *Definitions* of all possible definitions. Given these two sets, a dictionary is a finite partial function D from *Words* to *Definitions*. The class of all dictionaries in a particular application is denoted by Dictionary.

First some examples of the sets *Words* and *Definitions* are given. Then we study a concrete example of a dictionary. Finally, the formal definition of Dictionary is given in full.

15.2A Instances of dictionaries

Table **15**.2A.1 describes various types of dictionary, giving the sets *Words* and *Definitions* for each type. Note that these definitions are very abstract: in each case, the members of *Words* and *Definitions* would have to be specified in much greater detail. However, the level of specification of these examples is enough for our present purpose, which is to illustrate the variety of dictionaries which arise in practice. It must also be emphasized that in each case both sets, *Words* and *Definitions*, could be defined in many other ways.

Example A telephone directory

The following example of a dictionary is the internal telephone directory of a very small organization. The entries are surnames of individuals, and the 'definitions' are four-digit telephone extension numbers. Thus in this case *Words*

Table 15.2A.1 Various types of dictionary

Dictionary	*Words*	*Definitions*
Language dictionary	Words (†)	Definitions or sets of definitions
Address book	Personal names	Addresses
Birthday book	Personal names	Birthdays
Telephone directory	Personal or organization names	Telephone numbers
Symbol table in a book	Special symbols	Definitions
Subject index in a book	Subject names	Definitions
Author index in a book	Authors' names	Publication lists

(†) For 'Words' read 'Class of all possible words', etc.

is the set of all possible surnames and *Definitions* the set of all four-digit numbers. This defines the set Dictionary of all possible dictionaries in this application. A first instance D: Dictionary is as follows, in tabular form:

Surname	Extension
Carey	2692
Fenshaw	3778
Irvin	6945

This table is of course the *graph* of the dictionary D as a partial function from *Words* to *Definitions*. Note that, although the entries are shown in alphabetic order, this is not an essential feature of D.

Another example is D': Dictionary, with graph $D'Gr$ given by

Surname	Extension
Carey	2692
Fenshaw	3778
Irvin	6945
Walter	7392

This differs from the previous one by the insertion in D of one more couple (word, definition), namely (Walter, 7392). A third example is the dictionary D'' with no entries, that is, with graph

$$D''Gr =_{\mathrm{d}} \varnothing$$

15.2B Formal definition of a dictionary

We now turn to the formal definition of our dictionary model. This consists of any two sets *Words* and *Definitions*, and the associated class Dictionary.

Words is the set of all possible entries. Only one condition is imposed on *Words*: this set may not be empty. This constraint is designed to rule out the trivial class of only one member, the 'empty' dictionary.

Words: Set   Total set of words, potential or actual

$Words \neq_d \emptyset$

Definitions is the set of all the possible definitions which may correspond to members of *Words*. This set is also constrained to be nonempty, for the same reason that *Words* is nonempty.

Definitions: Set   Total set of definitions, potential or actual

$Definitions \neq_d \emptyset$

Finally, Dictionary is defined as the class of all possibly partial and finite functions *D* from *Words* to *Definitions*. The finiteness of *D* is secured by making the definition domain of *D* finite.

D: Dictionary

* $D: Words \nrightarrow Definitions$

$DCond1$.: IsFinite($DDef$)

This specification means that a *D*: Dictionary is a special type of function, one for which $DDom =_d Words$, $DCod =_d Definitions$ and $DDef$ is finite. As *D* is a function, IsFinite($DDef$) implies IsFinite(DGr).

15.3 Operations on dictionaries

Operations on the class Dictionary fall into two groups. First, *transformation operations* either create a dictionary or convert a dictionary to a new one. Second, *retrieve operations* return a feature of a given dictionary without defining a new dictionary. These two groups are now established in turn.

15.3A Dictionary transformation operations

We define three basic transformation operations on Dictionary: Emp, Ins and Rem. These are very similar to their counterparts in the set model. The differences are entirely due to the special nature of the elements of a dictionary, i.e. couples (w, d). In addition, we establish an operation Redef which updates the definition of a word. This function is constructed by composition of Ins and Rem.

Emp

Emp returns the empty dictionary, that is, the D' : Dictionary whose definition domain (and consequently graph) is empty:

Emp

Return the empty Dictionary.
Emp $=_d D'$ where D' : Dictionary and
(1) $D'Def =_d \varnothing$

Ins

The function Ins has the same purpose as in the evolving set model. Given a D : Dictionary, a word w : *Words* and a definition d : *Definitions*, Ins returns D' : Dictionary, which is the result of inserting (w, d) in D. Thus, the graph $D'Gr$ is defined as the union of DGr and $\{(w, d)\}$.

One precondition is imposed on this operation. This is that w is not already defined in D, i.e. $w \notin DDef$. This restriction is adopted in order to preserve the functionality of D. It also reflects the assumption that attempting to define a word which is already defined is probably an error. The specification of Ins is as follows:

Ins

Insert new word–definition couple (w, d) in dictionary D.
Given D : Dictionary, w : *Words* and d : *Definitions* where
(Pre 1) $w \notin DDef$
Ins$(D, w, d) =_d D'$ where D' : Dictionary and
(1) $D'Gr =_d DGr + \{(w, d)\}$

Note that in (1) the + operator (union of disjoint sets) is proper, as (Pre 1) implies $(w, d) \notin DGr$.

Rem

The operation Rem reverses the effect of Ins. It takes two arguments: a D' : Dictionary and a word w : *Words* defined in D'. This means that the graph of D' contains a couple (w, d), where d : *Definitions* is the definition of w in D'.

Given D' and w, Rem returns D: Dictionary, which is the result of removing (w, d) from D'. In other words, the graph DGr is defined as $D'Gr - \{(w, d)\}$.

From this outline definition, we can see that Rem has one precondition. This is that w is defined in D', i.e. $w \in D'Def$. This reflects the assumption that attempting to remove an undefined word from D' is probably an error.

Note that the dictionary definition of w, referred to as d above, is denoted by $D'(w)$ in standard functional notation. Thus in the formal definition of Rem the variable d is not used.

Rem

Remove word–definition couple $(w, D'(w))$ from dictionary D'.
Given D': Dictionary and w: *Words* where
(Pre 1) $w \in D'Def$
Rem$(D', w) =_d D$ where D: Dictionary and
(1) $DGr =_d D'Gr - \{(w, D'(w))\}$

Redef

In addition to inserting a new entry w and a corresponding definition in a dictionary D, we may also want to *update* a definition, that is, replace the definition $D(w)$ of a word w by a new one, giving D': Dictionary. This may be achieved by first removing $(w, D(w))$ from D and then inserting a new couple (w, d). Therefore, we express this operation as the composition of Ins and Rem. The precondition must obviously be as in Rem. This construction illustrates the establishment of a complex function in terms of more elementary operations, and is fairly elegant. However, Redef could also be described more directly with the function-overriding operation defined in Section 3.6C.

Redef

Redefine a word w in dictionary D.
Given D: Dictionary, w: *Words* and d: *Definitions* where
(Pre 1) $w \in DDef$
Redef$(D, w, d) =_d D'$ where D': Dictionary and
(1) $D' =_d$ Ins(Rem(D, w), w, d)

15.3B Retrieve operations

In addition to the dictionary transformation operations described above, we may also want to test whether a word w is defined in a dictionary D, and to look up the definition of w if this definition exists. As already mentioned, operations of this kind are called *retrieve* or *query* operations.

The first function is very simple and is named IsEntry. Given D: Dictionary and w: *Words*, IsEntry returns the boolean value true if $w \in DDef$ and false if $w \notin DDef$. Thus IsEntry is a predicate, a boolean function of D and w which 'does a little more' than $\in$. Note that this function is total, that is, it is defined everywhere on its domain Dictionary $\times$ *Words*.

IsEntry

Test whether a word w is defined in the dictionary.
Given D: Dictionary and w: *Words*
(1) IsEntry(D, w) $=_d$ true if $w \in DDef$;
false otherwise

The second retrieve operation is called Lookup. It represents the main use of a dictionary D, namely to look up the definition of a word w in D. It is defined iff w is an entry in D, that is, $w \in DDef$. Thus, unlike IsEntry, Lookup is a partial operation.

Lookup

Look up definition of word w.
Given D: Dictionary and w: *Words* where
(Pre 1) $w \in DDef$
Lookup(D, w) $=_d d$ where d: *Definitions* and
(1) $d =_d D(w)$

15.3C Dictionaries with compound definitions

As pointed out in the introduction, while there are good reasons for allowing only one definition per word in a dictionary, this may prove inconvenient in any application in which any word may have many different definitions. The main drawback of our solution in this case is that, whenever a member is to be added to, or removed from, the set of elementary definitions of a word, the whole set must be replaced. We now briefly discuss how this shortcoming may be made good. The new class of dictionaries is called Dictionary1.

1 For any D: Dictionary1 and w: $DDef$, the associated 'definition' must be established explicitly as a finite subset of *Definitions*. We leave open the question as to whether $D(w)$ should be allowed to be empty or not; either alternative has some advantages. The formal definition is:

D: Dictionary1

* D: *Words* ↔ Powf(*Definitions*)
DCond1 .: IsFinite(*DDef*)

---

where Powf(*Definitions*) is the set of finite subsets of *Definitions* (see Definition 2.2F.2).

2 The operation Ins must be modified so as to allow the insertion of an additional word–definition couple (w, d) for any word w in a dictionary D, giving D' as a result. The main question is what the precondition should be in this case. Obviously w must belong to *Words* and d to *Definitions*. In addition, should w have to belong to $DDef$? It seems reasonable to answer *no*: if $w \notin DDef$ then the natural effect of Ins is to make w a member of $D'Def$ at the same time as adding (w, d).

Another possible precondition is that $d \notin D(w)$ if $D(w)$ is defined. This is justified on the ground that attempting to insert the same definition twice in $D(w)$ is likely to be an error. We are thus led to the following definition of Ins. The function-overriding operation proves particularly convenient here (Definition 3.6C.4).

Ins

Insert new word–definition couple (w, d) in dictionary D.
Given D: Dictionary1, w: *Words* and d: *Definitions* where
(Pre 1) $w \in DDef \Rightarrow d \notin D(w)$
Ins$(D, w, d) =_d D'$ where D': Dictionary1 and
(1) $D' =_d$ $(D \mid w \mapsto \{d\})$ if $w \notin DDef$;
$(D \mid w \mapsto D(w) + \{d\})$ otherwise

---

3 By a similar reasoning, we obtain the definition of Rem:

Rem

Remove word–definition couple (w, d) from dictionary D'.
Given D': Dictionary1, w: *Words* and d: *Definitions* where
(Pre 1) $w \in D'Def \wedge d \in D'(w)$
Rem$(D', w, d) =_d D$ where D: Dictionary1 and
(1) $D =_d (D' \mid w \mapsto D'(w) - \{d\})$

This is a simple solution which leaves w in $DDef$ when $D'(w) = \{d\}$, implying $D(w) = \varnothing$. We could also remove w from $DDef$ in this case. Note that in this version of Rem, the definition d to be removed must be specified as an argument of the operation, as it is not completely determined by D and w – compare this case with the previous definition of Rem.

The other operations of Dictionary must be adjusted in a similar way.

15.4 Commands, errors and reports

So far, our dictionary model describes the way in which a dictionary of some type may evolve in time and how information may be retrieved from it. In reality, the changes which an evolving dictionary undergoes do not occur spontaneously. They are the results of *decisions* made by agents who have control of the dictionary – its editors typically. We now enlarge our model to take this fact into account. We assume a specific evolving dictionary D to be given, and all the operations considered below are understood to be applied to a state of D. We also use D (possibly decorated) to denote a particular state of the dictionary, typically the 'current' one.

15.4A General definition of commands

To start with, what is a decision? Let us call *primary* the operations on Dictionary we have described so far: Emp, Ins, Rem, Redef, IsEntry and Lookup. A decision may be described as a *command* to apply any primary operation to the current state of D. So a command is an operation in its own right, as it is intended to bring about a new state of D. It is an *extension* of the primary operation it invokes, and we assume that it has the same arguments as the latter.

For instance, we describe the decision to insert a new word–definition couple (w, d) in D as the command to apply Ins to (D, w, d). We denote this command by ComIns(D, w, d). Other commands are named similarly from the primary operation they invoke, whenever appropriate.

Given a primary operation Op and the corresponding command ComOp, we must now establish the effect of ComOp. It is natural to derive this definition from the specification of Op itself, by *analysing* the essential differences between these two operations.

1 A *command* is always understood to be applied to a specific *state* D of an evolving dictionary. This state must be followed by a new state D'. Thus for any command ComOp, it is natural to regard the new state D' as part of the result of ComOp, even if D' is not an output of the corresponding operation Op. For instance, we have defined the retrieve operation Lookup as returning the definition $D(w)$ of its second argument w. The result of the corresponding command ComLookup must include the new state D', which we naturally equate to D, as Lookup is defined as a retrieve function.

2 A primary operation may be partial. For instance, Ins(D, w, d) is not defined if w is already a member of *DDef*. In contrast, we must assume that, at any time, any command can be invoked. This is not to say that a command can always be applied *successfully*, but simply that it can always be invoked at least tentatively. Moreover, we must specify the effect of the command under all circumstances. Consequently, the second difference between any operation Op and the corresponding command ComOp is this: whereas Op may be partial, ComOp must be total; the effect of ComOp must be fully defined for every possible combination of values of its arguments.

For any primary operation Op, let the arguments of Op be denoted by (D, —). Thus, D is the main argument and '—' represents all the other arguments; for example, 'w, d' in the case of Ins(D, w, d). In order to define the corresponding command ComOp(D, —), we must distinguish two cases.

Case 1 Op(D, —) is defined. Then in this case ComOp(D, —) must be regarded as successful, and its result include Op(D, —) itself (at least). We also say that in this case the command is *correct*. For instance, if $w \notin DDef$. then Ins(D, w, d) is defined, and the new state D' resulting from ComIns(D, w, d) must naturally be equal to Ins(D, w, d).

Case 2 Op(D, —) is *not* defined. In this case, ComOp(D, —) is unsuccessful and is called *incorrect*. What should be the new state D' in this case? The natural answer is to rule that an incorrect command has 'no effect', that is, it leaves the dictionary unchanged. Consequently, in this case we let $D' =_d D$. For instance, if $w \in DDef$, then Ins(D, w, d) is not defined. However, the result of ComIns(D, w, d) *is* defined. It includes (at least) the new state D', which is equal to D. This is quite different from saying that D' is undefined!

3 By definition, a dictionary is there to meet certain information requirements of certain agents, its users to be precise. These are catered for by the provision of retrieve operations. Now we have identified further information needs. If a command has been issued, the author should certainly know whether it has been successful or not, and if not, why. Therefore, we further enlarge our model to cater for these additional requirements.

We do so by postulating that in addition to its normal effect, determined by Op, a command ComOp produces a message or *report*. The purpose of this report is to indicate whether the command has been successful or not. We assume that there is a set *Reps* of possible reports, and any command always returns one report *Rep* : *Reps*. We further assume that *Reps* has two members: the strings 'OK' and 'ERROR'. This second assumption is made only to provide a simple illustration of the reporting mechanism, and is open to variation. The choice of the proper contents of *Reps* is highly application-dependent, and should be dealt with separately. More advanced reporting mechanisms are developed as part of the tree editor and the resource allocation model described in Chapters **16** and **17** respectively.

To sum up: for any primary operation Op(D, —), the corresponding command ComOp(D, —) is defined as follows.

Case 1 Op is a dictionary transformation function If Op(D, —) is defined, then ComOp(D, —) returns $D' =_d$ Op(D, —) together with $Rep =_d$ 'OK'. Otherwise, ComOp(D, —) returns $D' =_d D$ together with $Rep =_d$ 'ERROR'.

Case 2 Op is a retrieve function If Op(D, —) is defined, then ComOp(D, —) returns Op(D, —), $D' =_d D$ and $Rep =_d$ 'OK'. Otherwise, ComOp(D, —) returns $D' =_d D$ and $Rep =_d$ 'ERROR'.

This construction is generic: for any primary operation Op, it gives a corresponding command ComOp in general terms. (This is a kind of higher-order function, as it sends operations to operations.) Next, we apply this construction formally to each of our six primary operations.

15.4B Dictionary transformation commands

The dictionary transformation commands are established below without further comments. Note that ComEmp (re)initializes D and as Emp has no preconditions, the report is necessarily 'OK'.

ComEmp

Return the empty Dictionary.

(1) ComEmp $=_d$ (Emp, 'OK')

ComIns

Insert new word–definition couple (w, d) in dictionary D.
Given D: Dictionary, w: *Words* and d: *Definitions*

(1) ComIns(D, w, d) $=_d$ (Ins(D, w, d), 'OK') if $w \notin DDef$;
(D, 'ERROR') otherwise

ComRem

Remove word–definition couple (w, $D(w)$) from dictionary D.
Given D: Dictionary and w: *Words*

(1) ComRem(D, w) $=_d$ (Rem(D, w), 'OK') if $w \in DDef$;
(D, 'ERROR') otherwise

ComRedef

Redefine a word w in dictionary D.
Given D: Dictionary, w: *Words* and d: *Definitions*

(1)	ComRedef(D, w, d) $=_d$	(Redef(D, w, d), 'OK')	if $w \in DDef$;
		(D, 'ERROR')	otherwise

15.4C Retrieve commands

Recall that if Op is a retrieve operation, it does not return a member of Dictionary. However ComOp does: it returns the initial state D, together with some information about D.

ComIsEntry

Test whether a word w is defined in the dictionary.
Given D: Dictionary and w: *Words*

(1) ComIsEntry(D, w) $=_d$ (D, IsEntry(D, w), 'OK')

This command cannot fail as IsEntry itself is total.

ComLookup

Look up definition of word w.
Given D: Dictionary and w: *Words*

(1)	ComLookup(D, w) $=_d$	(D, Lookup(D, w), 'OK')	if $w \in DDef$;
		(D, 'ERROR')	otherwise

There is a slight discrepancy between ComLookup and the other commands. In all other cases, whether the command is successful or not, the result has the same format. For instance, ComIns always returns a couple (D', *Rep*) where D': Dictionary and *Rep*: *Reps*. In the case of ComLookup, as defined above, the result is either a triple (D', d, *Rep*) or a couple (D', *Rep*), where D': Dictionary, d: *Definitions* and *Rep*: *Reps*. This is not fundamentally wrong but may make the identification of result components more difficult.

An alternative is to impose an extra constraint on the set *Definitions*, namely that it contain a special element *Undef* for 'undefined'. Then if Lookup(D, w) is undefined by its original specification (when $w \notin DDef$), we let Lookup(D, w) return *Undef*. The revised version of ComLookup is as follows:

ComLookup′

Look up definition of word w.
Given D : Dictionary and w : *Words*

(1) ComLookup(D, w) $=_d$ (D, Lookup(D, w), 'OK') if $w \in DDef$;
(D, *Undef*, 'ERROR') otherwise

16 A Tree Editor (TEd)

16.1 Introduction

The universality of (ordered, valued) trees means that there is a general need for a tool to construct and 'manipulate' trees with any type of value. A first theoretical model of such an editor has been established in Section **12**.5. In this chapter we build a second model which we call TEd. This model is also generic, in the sense that the value set is treated as an implicit parameter, assumed given beforehand. It is more advanced and more realistic than the first model. Note that the reason for providing two models of essentially the same object, a tree editor, is to illustrate two solutions to essentially the same problem. The comparison between these two approaches is instructive. Both models are entirely 'reasonable'. Yet the paradox is that, although the second one is more powerful, it is substantially simpler than the first one in some respects. The main differences between these two models are in outline as follows:

1 In the model of Section **12**.5, the objects considered are finite valued ordered trees T with one pointer, or cursor, TC. Their class is called TreePtd0. TEd operates on a new class of pointed trees, called TreePtd1. A tree T: TreePtd1 is a finite valued ordered tree with *two* pointers, denoted by TE_1 and TE_2. They are always siblings, and TE_1 always precedes TE_2. Their main purpose is to delimit a *subforest* of T, which is used as an operand in various operations. The cost of replacing the original single cursor TC by the couple $TE = (TE_1, TE_2)$ is not very high: the navigation operations are a little harder to establish, which actually makes them more interesting, as they must differentiate between the first and the second cursor.

2 In TEd, the tree transformation operations are significantly simpler. Recall that in Section **12**.5, we had to define *four* main tree transformation operations: two to insert a second tree $T1$ with its root $T1Root$ as new first child of TC, and to reverse this operation (InsChiFst, RemChiFst); and two to insert $T1$ with $T1Root$ as new next sibling of TC, and to reverse this operation (InsSibNex, RemSibNex). Their establishment was complicated by the case analysis needed in each of them. In TEd, only two operations are needed instead of the four mentioned. These are (a) the insertion of a subforest between TE_1 and TE_2 (if these are adjacent), and (b) the removal of the subforest delimited by TE_1 and TE_2. Moreover, their establishment is simpler as the case analyses of the original four operations are no longer necessary.

There is a small price to pay for this strategy. The base set $TPts$ must be partitioned into two groups: (a) a subset of *main points*, and (b) a disjoint subset of *auxiliaries*, also called *sentinels*. Each main point must have a first and a last child, both of which must be sentinels. Conversely, a sentinel must necessarily be the first or the last child of a main point and must be childless.

This additional feature may seem to be a serious complication, but in fact it is not. On the contrary, it turns out to be entirely natural, almost a necessary implication of the introduction of the twin cursors $TE = (TE_1, TE_2)$. These must be definable in any T: TreePtd1, and the sentinels automatically ensure that this condition is satisfied. Furthermore, there is no need to impose these sentinels as *explicit* features of operands T: TreePtd1. This is because we may easily ensure that they are present in every tree generated by the operations of the editor: all we have to do is qualify slightly *one* of them, namely the generation of a one-point tree. Sentinels are modelling devices arising in data structure theory (although one might argue that 0 in Nat, for instance, is essentially a sentinel); see, for example, Wirth (1976). The use of these humble auxiliaries here is another example of cross-fertilization between computing and mathematics.

3 The third main difference between our initial pointed tree model and TEd is that the latter is more 'concrete', that is, closer to the interactive computer program it is meant to model. A tree editor as a computer program involves two interacting agents: the computer itself and the user. At any time, the state of the computer represents a certain fixed pointed tree, possibly augmented with some auxiliary information still to be established. Like any evolving object, the computer goes through successive states representing successive trees, etc. These successive states are determined by commands input by the user. Any command typically invokes a tree operation and may be incorrect, if the operands (the 'current state' of the computer) do not satisfy the operation's preconditions. Finally, the user may require more information than that represented by the current state of the edited tree. For instance, various messages confirming the execution of operations or warning of errors may be needed. These additional features are allowed for in the final version of TEd.

In Section **16**.2, we define the class TreePtd1 of pointed trees used in TEd. This is established as an extension of the class TreeOV1 of finite ordered valued trees, and we derive some interesting secondary features of its members. In Section **16**.3, we define navigation operations on TreePtd1, and in Section **16**.4, tree transformation functions. User–machine interaction features are incorporated in the model as a final extension in Section **16**.5.

16.2 Pointed trees in TEd: the class TreePtd1

16.2A Definition of TreePtd1

The class TreePtd1 of pointed trees used as main operands in TEd is defined in much the same way as TreePtd0 was in Section **12**.5. We first introduce a value set *Vals*, which is treated as an implicit parameter. We impose on *Vals* the requirement that it contain a special value *Undef*, standing for 'undefined' but 'different from the normal values in *Vals*'. This is the 'value' which must logically be assigned to sentinels, for instance, as these are not supposed to represent any 'normal' values. This condition implies $Vals \neq \varnothing$.

Vals : Set	Set of values
* *Undef*: *Vals*	

Next, we turn to the establishment of the class TreePtd1 itself. As stated, this class is specified as an extension of TreeOV1 defined in Section **12**.4C. We begin with the analysis motivating the introduction of the twin cursors TE_1 and TE_2. TEd is to be equipped with the two general operations Ins and Rem defined for TreeOV1 in Section **12**.4D. In TEd, these two operations are converted to functions on pointed trees, also named Ins and Rem respectively. Recall that both Ins and Rem on TreeOV1 require a tree T and *two* points i and $j : TPts$ as operands, with i $TSibBef$ j. Our design decision is to represent these two points as the two cursors TE_1 and TE_2 (see Figure **16**.2A.1). Consequently, a pointed tree T in TEd is defined as a tree T^- : TreeOV1 together with the couple $TE = (TE_1, TE_2)$. TE_1 is called the *first external cursor* and TE_2 the *second external cursor* of T. They satisfy the condition

$$TE_1 \ TSibBef \ TE_2$$

More generally, the main purpose of $TE = (TE_1, TE_2)$ in T is to replace the two points i and j in *any* operation taking as arguments a tree T^- : TreeOV1 and $i, j: T^-Pts$ with $i\ T^-SibBef\ j$. In conclusion, TreePtd1 is defined as follows. See also Figure **16**.2A.1

T: TreePtd1 (Extended TreeOV1)

* $T[TreeOV1]$: TreeOV1
ΔTreePtd1
    $TCoPtd1 .: TVals =_d Vals$
  TE
  * $TE_1 : TPts$ — First external cursor
  * $TE_2 : TPts$ — Second external cursor
    $TCoPtd2 .: TE_1\ TSibBef\ TE_2$

As usual, given T: TreePtd1, the asterisk (*) indicates the primary variable features of T. *TTreeOV1* denotes the underlying valued ordered tree of T, the object denoted by 'T^-' above. And also as usual, $T[TreeOV1]$ means that the incremental feature name '*TreeOV1*' is dispensable, hence T has all the features of any member of TreeOV1 : *TPts*, etc. *TTreeOV1* is also regarded as a group feature. It is used as an operand in the various operations we shall define as extensions of TreeOV1 functions.

Alternatively, we may define *TTreeOV1* as a member of TreeOV1(*Vals*). In this case, *TCoPtd1* is no longer needed. The above description is more explicit.

In addition to trees, several functions of TEd take as second operands forests F: ForOV1(*Vals*). Note that, to simplify, we do not use the parameter *Vals* whenever the context implies $FVals = Vals$: we introduce F by F : ForOV1.

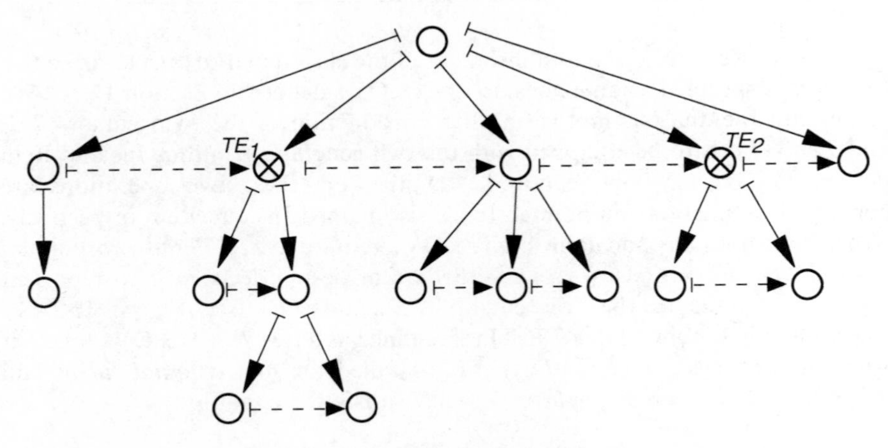

Figure 16.2A.1 Pointed Tree T: TreePtd1.

Value set Vals

The value set *Vals* may be any predefined set containing the special element *Undef.* Typical examples of *Vals* are a set *Char* of characters, or the set of strings on *Char*, all suitably augmented with *Undef.*

In this chapter, we make almost no explicit reference to the value map $TV: TPts \rightarrow Vals$ of any T:TreePtd1. When a value $v: Vals$ is needed as, say, an 'input' argument, we assume that v is supplied by some separate process: this could be as simple as a keystroke or as complex as a text subeditor. This is another application of the principle of *separation of concerns.*

16.2B Secondary features of TreePtd1

The definition of a T:TreePtd1 implies a number of interesting secondary features of T, some of which are now reviewed.

Internal cursor pair TI; boundaries defined by TE

Consider any T:TreePtd1 and its external cursor pair $TE = (TE_1, TE_2)$. We introduce a second couple $TI = (TI_1, TI_2): TPts^2$ of so-called *internal cursors.* These are defined symmetrically from TE by the following equations:

(1) (a) $TI_1 =_d TSibNex(TE_1)$

(b) $TI_2 =_d TSibPre(TE_2)$

This second pair mirrors TE and is illustrated in Figure **16**.2B.1. Three cases may be distinguished; they are illustrated in the figure.

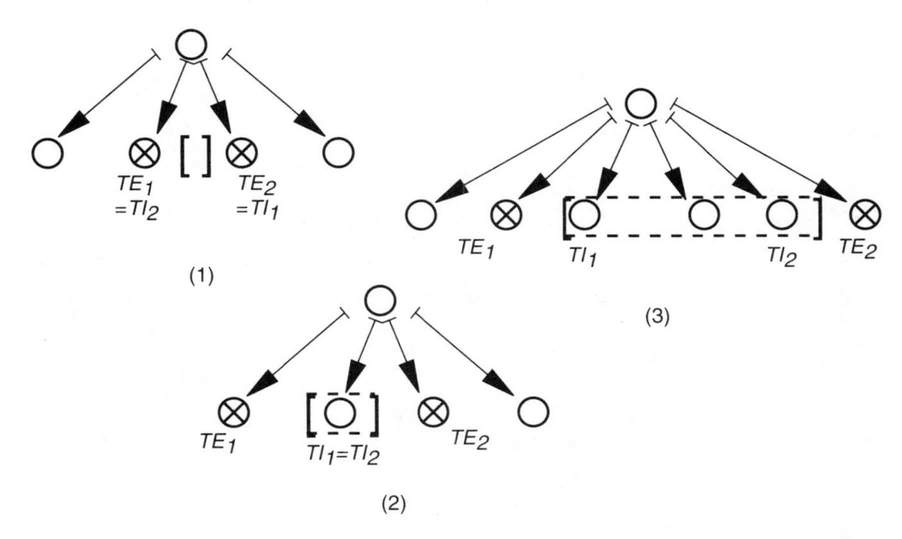

Figure 16.2B.1 External and internal cursor pairs in T.

In case 1, there are *no* points between TE_1 and TE_2. As a result, TI_1 and TI_2 are in *reverse order*. In case 2, there is just one point between TE_1 and TE_2, i.e. $TI_1 = TI_2$. In case 3, a list of several points occurs between TE_1 and TE_2, and TI_1 precedes TI_2.

The couple $TI = (TI_1, TI_2)$ is exactly determined by *TE*, hence it is a secondary variable feature of *T*. It is defined for *all* T: TreePtd1, as by definition of any such *T*, TE_1 is always followed by at least one sibling and TE_2 is always preceded by at least one sibling.

There is a certain view of the cursor couple *TE* which it is also useful to bear in mind. This is that *TE* defines a *couple of boundaries* between adjacent elements on the sublist TL_p of *T* such that $p =_d TParent(TE_1)$. The first boundary is between TE_1 and TI_1, the second between TI_2 and TE_2. When TE_1 and TE_2 are *adjacent*, i.e. $TSibNex(TE_1) = TE_2$, these two boundaries coincide. Otherwise, they are separated by the points occurring between TE_1 and TE_2. These boundaries are indicated by '[' and ']' in Figure **16**.2B.1.

Subforest TF

An important concept related to *TE* is the subforest *TF*: ForOV1 occurring between TE_1 and TE_2. It is illustrated in Figure **16**.2B.2.

Recall that, by definition of an ordered forest, *TF* has a top list *TFR*: List whose points are the roots of *TF*. Within *T*, these are the siblings occurring between TE_1 and TE_2. The three cases of *TE* illustrated in Figure **16**.2B.1 extend to *TF*:

Case 1 TE_1 *and* TE_2 *are adjacent, that is* $TSibNex(TE_1) = TE_2$. In this case *TFR* is empty, and so is the whole of *TF*: $TFRPts = \varnothing$ and $TFPts = \varnothing$.

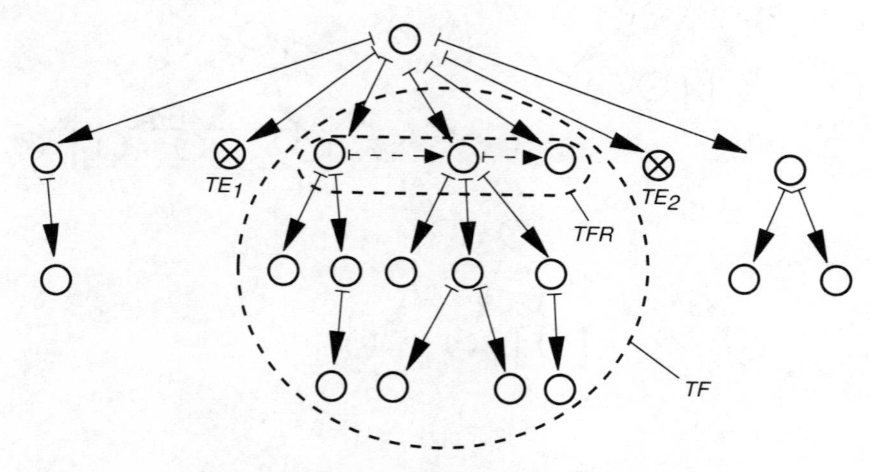

Figure 16.2B.2 Subforest *TF* delimited by *TE*.

Case 2 *TE_1 and TE_2 are separated by one point: $TI_1 = TI_2$*. In this case TF consists of exactly one tree, the subtree of T rooted at $TI_1 = TI_2$.

Case 3 *TE_1 and TE_2 are separated by several points, that is TI_1 $TSibBef$ TI_2*. In this case TF forms an ordered subforest of several trees.

In cases 2 and 3, the top list TFR has a first point $TFRFst$ and a last point $TFRLst$. These are equal to TI_1 and TI_2 respectively:

$$TFRFst = TI_1 \quad \text{and} \quad TFRLst = TI_2$$

Note however that TI_1 and TI_2 are *always defined*, whereas $TFRFst$ and $TFRLst$ are *not* defined in case 1.

The subforest TF must be formally defined. There are two ways to do this. The first method is to work out the definition 'from scratch', that is, to state that TF is a member of ForOV1 satisfying the following conditions (work them out by yourself before reading on):

(1) The set of roots of TF is the set of points occurring between TE_1 and TE_2. It is given by

$$TFRoots =_d \{r : TPts \mid TE_1 \; TSibBef \; r \; TSibBef \; TE_2\}$$

Note that TE_1 and TE_2 are excluded from this set.

(2) The base set of TF is the union of the set of roots and their sets of descendants:

$$TFPts =_d \Sigma \{TDescIds_r \mid r : TFRoots\}$$

(3) The relation $TFParentOf$ is the restriction of $TParentOf$ induced by $TFPts$:

$$TFParentOf =_d TFPts \diamond TParentOf$$

(4) The 'sibling order' of TF is likewise given by:

$$TFSibBef =_d TFPts \diamond TSibBef$$

(5) The value map is the domain restriction of TV induced by $TFPts$:

$$TFV =_d TFPts \langle TV$$

This implies that $TFVals =_d TVals = Vals$, by definition of $\langle$ (Section 3.6C).

As all the primary features of TF have been fixed, TF is entirely determined – the description is complete. We must, of course, check that the object defined satisfies all the conditions imposed on members of ForOV1. This is left to the reader.

The second method of defining TF is to use the operation Rem defined on TreeOV1, bearing in mind that this is not defined if $TSibNex(TE_1) = TE_2$. Thus TF is formally introduced as the object TF: ForOV1($Vals$) and fixed by the condition

$$TFPts =_{\mathrm{d}} \varnothing \qquad \text{if } TSibNex(TE_1) = TE_2;$$
$$(T', i, j, TF) =_{\mathrm{d}} \mathrm{Rem}(TTreeOV1, TE_1, TE_2) \qquad \text{otherwise.}$$

Here T' ($\in$ TreeOV1), i and j are dummy variables: they are required if the equation is to make sense, but we are only interested in TF. Also, we have introduced TF explicitly as a member of ForOV1($Vals$) as a way of ensuring that $TFVals = Vals$ in the case where $TFPts = \varnothing$. The reader may check that the definitions obtained by these two different methods are equivalent.

T: TreePtd1 Secondary Features I

$TI = (TI_1, TI_2): TPts^2$ — Internal cursors

$TDefPtd1$.:

(1) $TI_1 =_{\mathrm{d}} TSibNex(TE_1)$

(2) $TI_2 =_{\mathrm{d}} TSibPre(TE_2)$

TF: ForOV1 — Subforest delimited by TE (first definition)

$TDefPtd2$.:

(1) $TFRoots =_{\mathrm{d}} \{r: TPts \mid TE_1\ TSibBef\ r\ TSibBef\ TE_2\}$

(2) $TFPts =_{\mathrm{d}} \Sigma\ \{TDescIds_r \mid r: TFRoots\}$

(3) $TFParentOf =_{\mathrm{d}} TFPts \diamond TParentOf$

(4) $TFSibBef =_{\mathrm{d}} TFPts \diamond TSibBef$

(5) $TFV =_{\mathrm{d}} TFPts \langle TV$

16.3 Navigation operations in TEd

In TreePtd1, a navigation operation is a function which takes a tree T: TreePtd1 as argument and 'modifies' the cursor couple TE. More precisely, it returns a new T': TreePtd1 which may differ from T only by the value of $T'E$. In this section we describe navigation operations for this class of pointed trees.

Navigation operations in TreePtd1 fall into two natural groups. The first consists of those functions which leave $TParent(TE_1)$ unchanged, the second of those functions in which $T'Parent(T'E_1) \neq TParent(TE_1)$. These two groups are called Nav1 and Nav2 respectively. Recall that $TParent(TE_1) = TParent(TE_2)$ is always defined, on account of $TE_1 \neq TE_2$, which implies $TE_1 \neq TRoot$.

16.3A Group Nav1

This group comprises six operations. The first two are similar respectively to MoveToSibNex and MoveToSibPre defined in Section **12**.5B. Given

T: TreePtd1, MoveToSibNex2(T) 'moves' TE_2 to its next sibling if possible, and MoveToSibPre1(T) 'moves' TE_1 to its previous sibling if possible. It is easy to see that the former function is equivalent to MoveToSibNex with TE_2 substituted for TC, and the latter to MoveToSibPre with TE_1 substituted for TC. Only two minor adjustments are needed. First, the preconditions $TE_2 \neq TRoot$ and $TE_1 \neq TRoot$ need not be stated explicitly, as they are secondary features in any T: TreePtd1. Second, in each operation, the other external cursor must be defined as unchanged. It is easy to see that in each case, the result T' satisfies all the conditions implied by T': TreePtd1, in particular $T'CoPtd2$, i.e. $T'E_1$ $TSibBef$ $T'E_2$. Here are the definitions:

MoveToSibNex2

Move second external cursor to its next sibling if possible.
Given T: TreePtd1 such that

(Pre 1) $TE_2 \neq TChiLst_p$
where $p =_d TParent(TE_2)$

MoveToSibNex2(T) $=_d T'$ where T': TreePtd1 and

(1) $T'TreeOV1 =_d TTreeOV1$

(2) (a) $T'E_1 =_d TE_1$

(b) $T'E_2 =_d TSibNex(TE_2)$

MoveToSibPre1

Move first external cursor to its preceding sibling if possible.
Given T: TreePtd1 such that

(Pre 1) $TE_1 \neq TChiFst_p$
where $p =_d TParent(TE_1)$

MoveToSibPre1(T) $=_d T'$ where T': TreePtd1 and

(1) $T'TreeOV1 =_d TTreeOV1$

(2) (a) $T'E_1 =_d TSibPre(TE_1)$

(b) $T'E_2 =_d TE_2$

The next two operations are similar but somewhat more complicated, owing to the need to preserve the invariant $T'CoPtd2$ of T'. The first is MoveToSibNex1(T). Its primary purpose is to set $T'E_1$ to $TSibNex(TE_1)$ if possible. The second, MoveToSibPre2(T), aims to set $T'E_2$ to $TSibPre(TE_2)$ if possible.

We first develop MoveToSibNex1 in some detail, as a little case study in operation establishment, illustrating the interaction between analysis and specification. Then we derive MoveToSibPre2 from MoveToSibNex1 by 'inverting' the latter. Note that these two operations are symmetric (or dual) in an obvious sense, but are *not* functional inverses.

MoveToSibNex1

We establish MoveToSibNex1 in stages as follows. First, we express the main action desired. Then we examine under which circumstances this action can destroy a necessary property of the result T' and identify the 'minimum step' needed to restore the lost invariant. Finally, we determine on which condition this secondary step is infeasible, which leads to the *minimum* or *weakest* precondition required by the operation.

1 By the definition of a navigation operation, $T' =_d \text{MoveToSibNex1}(T)$ may differ from T only by the fact that $T'E \neq TE$. This means that

$$T'TreeOV1 =_d TTreeOV1$$

As T: TreePtd1 by hypothesis, *TTreeOV1* and therefore *T′TreeOV1* must satisfy all the conditions imposed on the features of any member of TreeOV1. Consequently, we only have to specify $T'E$ and ensure that the conditions imposed on this feature are satisfied. These constraints are:

(1) Both $T'E_1$ and $T'E_2$ are well-defined members of $T'Pts = TPts$
(2) $T'E_1 \; T'SibBef \; T'E_2$

Note

(a) We have already applied this reasoning implicitly in the establishment of the previous navigation operations; we state it here for completeness. (b) The fact that we may restrict our attention to this small subset of all the features of T' is a major benefit resulting from the modular design of TreePtd1. Similar reasoning has already been used several times before, and is perfectly natural. ■

2 The primary goal of MoveToSibNex1 is to 'move TE_1 forward'. This is represented by the equation

$$T'E_1 =_d TSibNex(TE_1)$$

3 What could go wrong with this equation? First, could $T'E_1$ fail to be defined? The answer is *no*. As we have seen, TE_1 must have a successor in T, as it is followed at least by TE_2. Consequently, $TSibNex(TE_1)$ is well defined in all cases and so is $T'E_1$.

Second, could $T'E_1 \; T'SibBef \; T'E_2$ fail to be satisfied as a result of this rule? The answer now is *yes*, and this may happen iff $TSibNex(TE_1) = TE_2$. Therefore if we want to define $T'E_1$ as desired, we must also redefine TE_2.

We naturally seek the *minimum* change in TE_2 necessary to preserve $T'E_1 \; T'SibBef \; T'E_2$, and this obviously is

$$T'E_2 =_d TSibNex(TE_2)$$

4 Again we must ask: 'What could go wrong with this second equation?' This time the answer is that $T'E_2 = TSibNex(TE_2)$ is defined iff TE_2 is not the last member of its sibling list, that is iff

$$TE_2 \neq TChiLst_p$$

where $p =_d TParent(TE_2)$. Therefore we conclude that if $TSibNex(TE_1) = TE_2$ then TE_2 must be redefined, which is possible iff $TE_2 \neq TChiLst_p$. This seems to give the minimum precondition required for the operation, namely

$$(TSibNex(TE_1) = TE_2) \Rightarrow (TE_2 \neq TChiLst_p)$$

5 We could keep this precondition as it is. However, a little reflection shows that it can be simplified. The final condition is

$$TSibNex(TE_1) \neq TChiLst_p$$

This is simpler and intuitively clearly correct (draw a diagram!). It is equivalent to the previous condition, *given the general properties of* T:TreePtd1. This equivalence is fairly easy to establish.

This concludes our establishment of MoveToSibNex1. We have carried it out systematically, by specifying a feature of T' and immediately analysing its consequences. As a result we have obtained simultaneously both a complete specification of MoveToSibNex1 and a proof that it is correct, in the sense that for any T:TreePtd1, the result $T' =$ MoveToSibNex1(T) is completely determined and satisfies all the conditions imposed on any member of TreePtd1.

The full specification is as follows:

MoveToSibNex1

Move first external cursor to its next sibling if possible.
Given T:TreePtd1 such that

(Pre 1) $TSibNex(TE_1) \neq TChiLst_p$
where $p =_d TParent(TE_1)$

MoveToSibNex1(T) $=_d T'$ where T':TreePtd1 and

(1)		$T'TreeOV1 =_d$	$TTreeOV1$	
(2)	(a)	$T'E_1 =_d$	$TSibNex(TE_1)$	
	(b)	$T'E_2 =_d$	TE_2	if $TSibNex(TE_1) \neq TE_2$;
			$TSibNex(TE_2)$	otherwise

MoveToSibPre2

As for MoveToSibPre2, this operation may be obtained either by repeating the above reasoning, or by formally and systematically 'inverting' the establishment

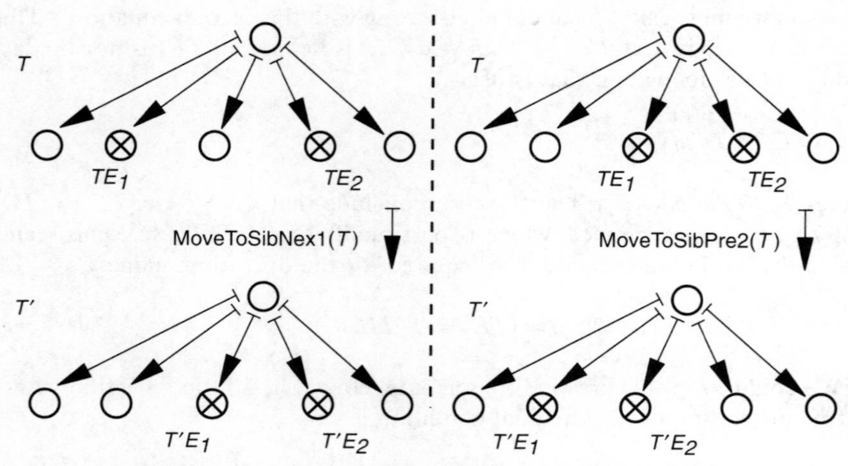

Figure 16.3A.1 Effects of MoveToSibNex1 and MoveToSibPre2.

of MoveToSibNex1. We choose the second method as it is simpler. The symbolic transformation rules, easily identified from Figure **16**.3A.1, are as follows:

(1) Replace 'MoveToSibNex1' by 'MoveToSibPre2'

(2) Replace '*TSibNex*' by '*TSibPre*'

(3) Replace '$TChiLst_p$' by '$TChiFst_p$'

(4) Swap 'TE_1' with 'TE_2' and '$T'E_1$' with '$T'E_2$'

The result follows.

<u>MoveToSibPre2</u>

Move second external cursor to its preceding sibling if possible.
Given T : TreePtd1 such that

(Pre 1) $TSibPre(TE_2) \neq TChiFst_p$
where $p =_d TParent(TE_2)$

MoveToSibPre2(T) $=_d$ T' where T' : TreePtd1 and

(1) $T'TreeOV1 =_d TTreeOV1$

(2) (a) $T'E_1 =_d TE_1$ if $TSibPre(TE_2) \neq TE_1$; $TSibPre(TE_1)$ otherwise

(b) $T'E_2 =_d TSibPre(TE_2)$

Tying the cursors

Finally, we introduce two simple navigation operations designed to make $T'E_1$ and $T'E_2$ adjacent. The first leaves TE_1 unchanged but 'ties' $T'E_2$ to TE_1, that is, sets $T'E_2$ to $TSibNex(TE_1)$. The second leaves TE_2 unchanged but sets $T'E_1$ to $TSibPre(TE_2)$. Clearly no preconditions are required. These two operations may be used to 'annihilate' the subforest TF.

TieTo1

Tie second external cursor to first one.
Given T:TreePtd1, TieTo1(T) $=_d$ T' where T':TreePtd1 and

(1) $T'TreeOV1 =_d TTreeOV1$
(2) (a) $T'E_1 =_d TE_1$
(b) $T'E_2 =_d TSibNex(TE_1)$

TieTo2

Tie first external cursor to second one.
Given T:TreePtd1, TieTo2(T) $=_d$ T' where T':TreePtd1 and

(1) $T'TreeOV1 =_d TTreeOV1$
(2) (a) $T'E_1 =_d TSibPre(TE_2)$
(b) $T'E_2 =_d TE_2$

16.3B Group Nav2

The second group of navigation operations involves a change in $p =_d TParent(TE_1)$. Our aim is to be able to 'move' $TE = (TE_1, TE_2)$ to any *couple* of distinct siblings in T. Equivalently, it is to be able to 'move' TE_1 to any i: $TPts$ such that $TSibNex(i)$ is defined, as the new value $T'E_1$ must always be followed by $T'E_2$ in the new tree T'.

There are many ways of doing this. We adopt one minimal solution, namely to apply the operations MoveToChiFst and MoveToParent, defined in TreePtd0, to TE_1. Accordingly, these two operations are renamed MoveToChiFst1 and MoveToParent1 in TreePtd1. Moreover, we call them 'basic' to distinguish them from further Nav2 operations.

As above, let T and T': TreePtd1 be the initial and final trees respectively in both operations, with $T'TreeOV1 =_d TTreeOV1$. Our specification so far is

(1) MoveToChiFst1(T) $=_d$ T' where $T'E_1 =_d TChiFst(TE_1)$
(2) MoveToParent1(T) $=_d$ T' where $T'E_1 =_d TParent(TE_1)$

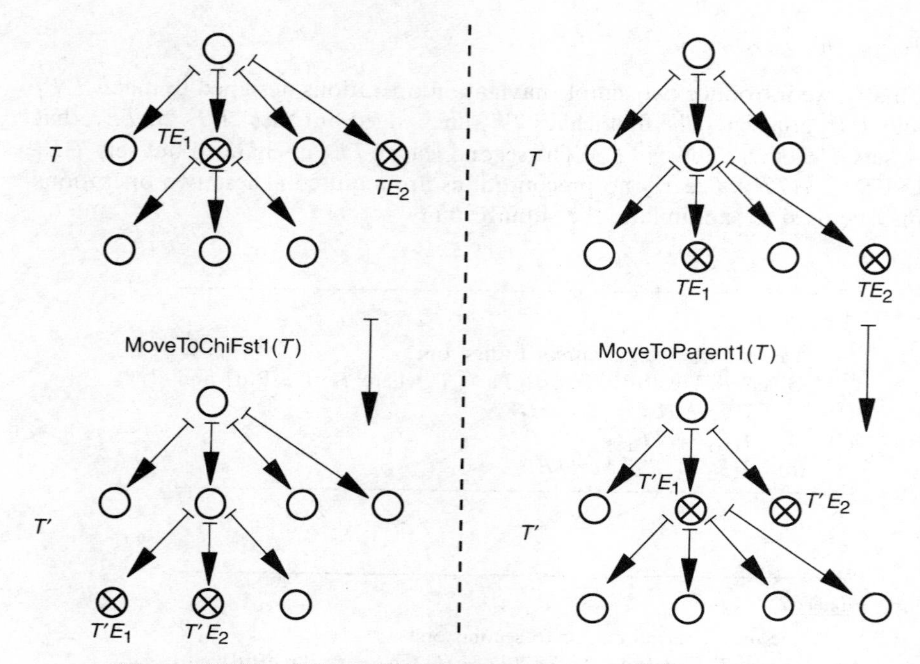

Figure 16.3B.1 Effects of MoveToChiFst1 and MoveToParent1.

Again, this is only a first approximation, which must be refined by analysis. The two key questions to ask for each operation are:

(a) In which cases is it well defined?

(b) Is it fully specified or should it be strengthened?

Consider each operation in turn, referring to Figure **16**.3B.1.

MoveToChiFst1

Let $j =_d TChiFst(TE_1)$. The condition '$T'E_1 = j$' is satisfiable iff j and $TSibNex(j)$ are defined, that is, iff $TChis(TE_1) \neq \emptyset$ and $j \neq TChiLst(TE_1)$. This establishes the *precondition* of MoveToChiFst1(T), and this condition is *minimum* or *weakest*.

Assuming this precondition is satisfied, is MoveToChiFst1(T) *fully* specified? The answer is 'no': the second cursor $T'E_2$ is still *underspecified*. By condition *T′CoPtd2*, $T'E_2$ may be any sibling following $T'E_1$, and we must *choose* one of these as the value of $T'E_2$. The most natural choice is the rule

(3) $T'E_2 =_d TSibNex(T'E_1)$

which we adopt. Here is the result:

MoveToChiFst1

Move first external cursor to its first child if possible.
Given T: TreePtd1 such that

(Pre 1) $TChis(TE_1) \neq \varnothing$
(Pre 2) $TChiFst(TE_1) \neq TChiLst(TE_1)$

MoveToChiFst1(T) $=_d T'$ where T': TreePtd1 and

(1) $T'TreeOV1 =_d TTreeOV1$
(2) (a) $T'E_1 =_d TChiFst(TE_1)$
(b) $T'E_2 =_d TSibNex(T'E_1)$

MoveToParent1

This operation is established in the same way as MoveToChiFst1(T). Let $i =_d TParent(TE_1)$; i is well defined as $TE_1 \neq TRoot$. The condition '$T'E_1 = i$' is satisfiable iff i has a next sibling, i.e. $TSibNex(i)$ is defined. In turn, $TSibNex(i)$ is defined iff (a) $i \in TChis_p$ for some $p: TPts$ and (b) $i \neq TChiLst_p$. This establishes the *precondition* of MoveToParent1(T), which is also *weakest*. If this precondition is satisfied, $T'E_2$ must be *selected* from among the siblings following i in T, and we again adopt rule (3).

MoveToParent1

Move first external cursor to its parent if possible.
Given T: TreePtd1 such that

(Pre 1) $\exists\, i, p: TPts \cdot$
(a) $i =_d TParent(TE_1) \in TChis_p$
(b) $i \neq TChiLst_p$

MoveToParent1(T) $=_d T'$ where T': TreePtd1 and

(1) $T'TreeOV1 =_d TTreeOV1$
(2) (a) $T'E_1 =_d TParent(TE_1)$
(b) $T'E_2 =_d TSibNex(T'E_1)$

This completes the establishment of these two operations.

16.3C Further Nav2 operations AT

Many other Nav2 operations could be added to MoveToParent1 and MoveToChiFst1, by operating primarily on TE_2 instead of TE_1, for instance, or selecting a child other than the first one as destination. The reader may work out various possible combinations.

One such function appears to be sufficiently useful in practice to warrant a precise establishment here. It is the operation which 'moves' TE_1 to its nth child and sets TE_2 to the next sibling if it exists, where n is a positive natural number. This operation is denoted by $\text{MoveToChi}_n(T)$, and is defined iff $n < \text{Num}(TChis(TE_1))$.

Let $TChi_n(i)$ denote the nth child of any $i: TPts$. It is a secondary variable feature of T specified as follows:

Definition 16.3C.1

For any $i: TPts$, $TChi_n(i)$ is defined recursively for all n: Nat such that $1 \leqslant n \leqslant \text{Num}(TChis(i))$ by

(1) $TChi_1(i) =_d TChiFst(i)$

(2) $TChi_{n+1}(i) =_d TSibNex(TChi_n(i))$
$1 \leqslant n < \text{Num}(TChis(i))$ ■

Using *TChi*, we may now establish MoveToChi formally as follows:

MoveToChi_n

Move first external cursor to its nth child if possible.
Given T: TreePtd1 and n: Nat such that
(Pre 1) $1 \leqslant n < \text{Num}(TChis(TE_1))$
$\text{MoveToChi}_n(T) =_d T'$ where T': TreePtd1 and
(1) $T'TreeOV1 =_d TTreeOV1$
(2) (a) $T'E_1 =_d TChi_n(TE_1)$
(b) $T'E_2 =_d TSibNex(T'E_1)$

16.4 Tree transformation operations in TEd

We now turn to the tree transformation operations of TEd. An operation in this group may take as argument a T: TreePtd1. Typically, it returns a new T': TreePtd1 with a new structure imposed on the base set. As a result, the value map $T'V: T'Pts \to Vals$ and the cursor couple $T'E$ may also be new. We begin with two closely related initialization operations.

16.4A Initialization

InitAuxV

This operation (Figure **16**.4A.1) creates a tree T': TreeOV1 with one *main point* $r =_d T'Root$ and two *sentinels*, the children of r. The value $T'V(r)$ is specified

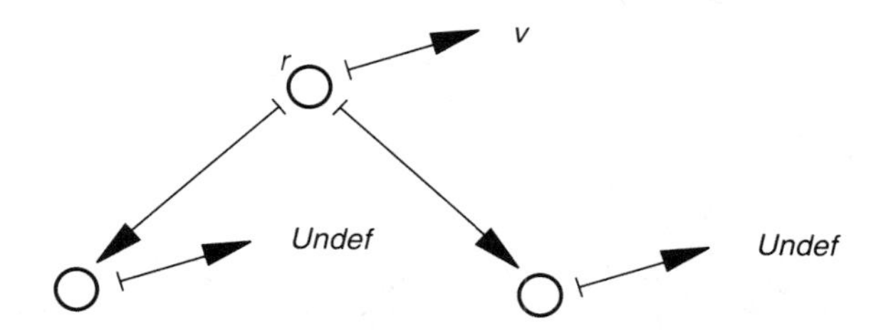

Figure 16.4A.1 Elementary tree InitAuxV(v) = T':TreeOV1.

by an argument v. Note that the tree T' is *not* pointed. The purpose of InitAuxV is to define a new valued main point with appropriate sentinels, to be inserted in a pointed tree by another operation (for example, InsPtV described below).

By the definition of InitAuxV(v) = T', the result T' is equipped with all necessary sentinels or auxiliaries. This is enough to ensure that every tree generated by repeated applications of TEd operations has sentinels.

InitAuxV

Create a valued tree (unpointed) with one main point and two sentinels. This operation uses the predefined set *Vals*.

Given v: *Vals*, InitAuxV(v) $=_d$ T':TreeOV1 where for $r =_d T'Root$

(1) (a) $T'Chis_r =_d \{T'ChiFst_r, T'ChiLst_r\}$
(b) $T'ChiFst_r \neq_d T'ChiLst_r$
(c) $\forall\, i : T'Chis_r \cdot T'Chis_i =_d \varnothing$

(2) (a) $T'Vals =_d Vals$
(b) $T'V(r) =_d v$
(c) $\forall\, i : T'Chis_r \cdot T'V(i) =_d Undef$

InitAuxPtd

This operation creates an initial *pointed* tree T':TreePtd1 with one *main point*, $r =_d T'Root$, and two *sentinels*, the children of r. The value $T'V(i)$ is *Undef* for all i: $T'Pts$. The result is the main tree which the user of TEd is presented with initially. See Figure **16**.4A.2.

InitAuxPtd

Create a pointed valued tree with one main point and two sentinels. The value of each base point i is undefined.

InitAuxPtd $=_d$ T' where T':TreePtd1 and

(1) $T'TreeOV1 =_d$ InitAuxV(*Undef*)

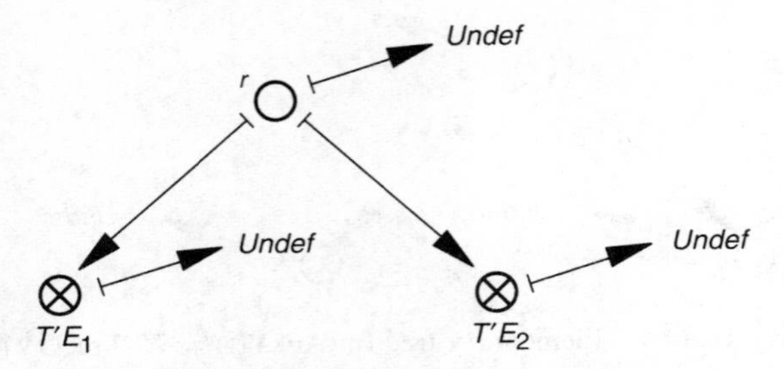

Figure 16.4A.2 Initial tree InitAuxPtd = T': TreePtd1.

Note that in T', the cursor couple $T'E$ is exactly determined. On account of condition *T'CoPtd2*, $T'E_1 = T'ChiFst_r$ and $T'E_2 = T'ChiLst_r$, necessarily.

16.4B General insertion and removal

Ins

The next tree transformation operation is based on the function Ins defined on TreeOV1. Given T: TreePtd1 and F: ForOV1(*Vals*), Ins returns the tree $T' =_d$ Ins(T, F): TreePtd1 obtained by 'inserting' F between TE_1 and TE_2 in T. The cursor couple TE itself is left unchanged, i.e. $T'E =_d TE$. The operation is defined iff TE_1 and TE_2 are adjacent, *FPts* is nonempty and *TPts* and *FPts* are disjoint. This is another overloading of Ins.

Ins

Insert forest F between TE_1 and TE_2 in T if possible.
Given T: TreePtd1 and F: ForOV1 such that

(Pre 1) $TSibNex(TE_1) = TE_2$
(Pre 2) $FPts \neq \varnothing$
(Pre 3) IsDisjoint(*TPts*, *FPts*)
(Pre 4) $FVals = Vals$

Ins(T, F) $=_d T'$ where T': TreePtd1 and
(1) $(T'TreeOV1, T'E_1, T'E_2) =_d$ Ins$(TTreeOV1, TE_1, TE_2, F)$

The effect of Ins is illustrated in Figure **16**.4B.1. Note that condition (1) implies $T'E = TE$, by definition of the operation Ins on TreeOV1. There is no need to specify the conservation of the cursors separately.

Rem

The inverse of Ins is Rem. This operation may be derived either from Rem defined in TreeOV1, or by inverting Ins. We follow the second route. Given a

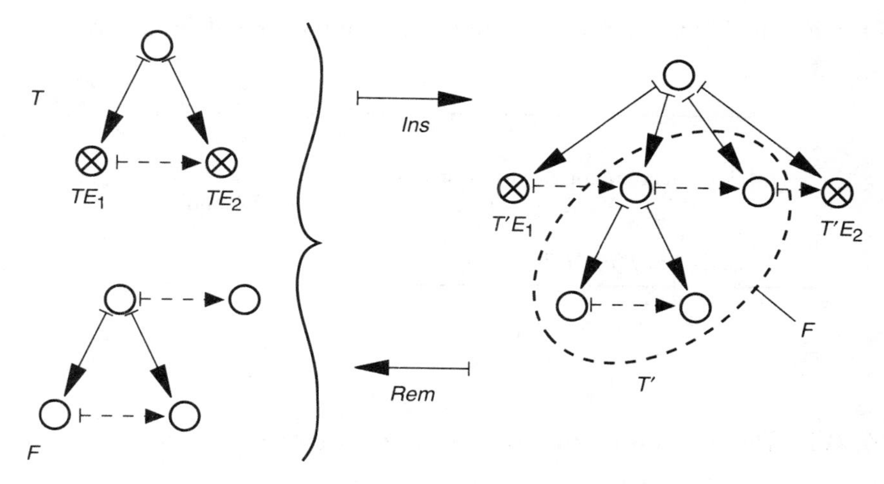

Figure 16.4B.1 Effects of Ins and Rem on TreePtd1.

pointed tree T': TreePtd1, Rem(T') returns a couple (T, F) where T: TreePtd1 and F: ForOV1. F is the subforest occurring between $T'E_1$ and $T'E_2$ in T' and T is what is left of T' when F is 'removed'. $T'E$ is left unchanged, i.e. $TE = T'E$.

<u>Rem</u>

Remove the subforest F located between $T'E_1$ and $T'E_2$ in T' if possible.
Given T': TreePtd1 such that

(Pre 1) $T'SibNex(T'E_1) \neq T'E_2$

Rem(T') $=_d (T, F)$ where T: TreePtd1, F: ForOV1 and

(1) $(TTreeOV1, TE_1, TE_2, F) =_d$ Rem($T'TreeOV1, T'E_1, T'E_2$)

The effect of Rem is also illustrated in Figure **16**.4B.1. As with Ins, $TE = T'E$ is implied by (1) and the definition of Rem on TreeOV1. Note that a possible equivalent definition of F is $F =_d T'F$.

The reader should compare Ins and Rem with the four corresponding TreePtd0 operations InsChiFst, RemChiFst, InsSibNex and RemSibNex established in Section **12**.5C. The relative simplicity of Ins and Rem is striking. This shows how different modelling strategies may lead to markedly different results.

Copy

In any word processor, one of the most useful operations is Copy, which enables the user to create a copy of a segment of the main text without altering the latter. An analogous facility, also called Copy, is provided in TEd. Given a forest F: ForOV1, Copy returns a forest F' isomorphic to, and disjoint from, F.

Copy

Make a disjoint copy of a forest F.
Given F: ForOV1, Copy(F) $=_d F'$ where F': ForOV1 and
(1) $F' \cong_d F$
(2) IsDisjoint($F'Pts$, $FPts$)

16.4C Point insertion and value update

InsPtV

In TEd, the basic method of expanding a tree with a new valued point is to define an elementary tree $T1 =_d$ InitAuxV(v) and then 'insert' $T1$ within the main tree. This is the purpose of InsPtV. Given T: TreePtd1 and v: *Vals*, this operation returns a new tree $T' =_d$ InsPtV(T, v): TreePtd1 with $T'E =_d TE$ and the root $T1Root$ of $T1$ inserted between $T'E_1$ and $T'E_2$ (see Figure **16**.4C.1). The natural way of establishing InsPtV is to compose InitAuxV with Ins.

Note that this operation imposes a constraint on InitAuxV, namely the condition IsDisjoint($TPts$, InitAuxV(v)Pts). This matter is to be treated separately, typically as 'implementation'.

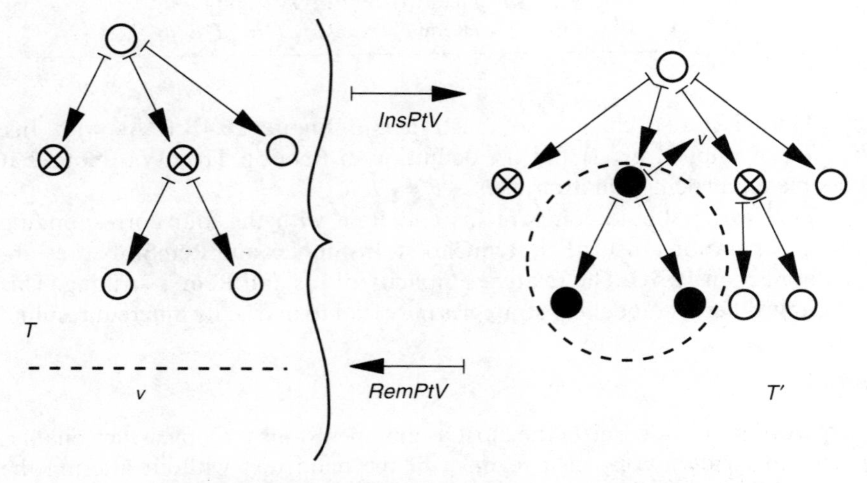

Figure 16.4C.1 Effects of InsPtV and RemPtV.

InsPtV

Insert a new valued point.
Given T: TreePtd1 and v: *Vals*, such that
(Pre 1) $TSibNex(TE_1) = TE_2$
InsPtV(T, v) $=_d$ T' where T': TreePtd1 and
(1) $T' =_d$ Ins(T, InitAuxV(v)*ForOV1*)

RemPtV

This is the inverse of InsPtV. Given a tree T': TreePtd1 such that $T' =_d$ InsPtV(T, v), RemPtV(T') $=_d$ (T, v) where T: TreePtd1. At point level, the precondition of RemPtV is that $T'F \cong$ InitAuxV(v) for some value v: *Vals*.

Note that in the establishment of RemPtV the function InitAuxV may be used to define the precondition only *up to isomorphism* as the base set of InitAuxV(v) is independent of points in T'. However, this is all that is needed. Note also that, whereas RemPtV is an exact left inverse of InsPtV, InsPtV is a left inverse of RemPtV only up to isomorphism, as the individual base points in InitAuxV(v) are undetermined.

RemPtV

Remove one point.
Given T': TreePtd1 such that for some v': *Vals*
(Pre 1) $T'F \cong$ InitAuxV(v') (implying $T'F$ is a tree)
RemPtV(T') $=_d$ (T, v) where T: TreePtd1 and v: *Vals*.
Let $T1$: TreeOV1.
(1) (T, $T1ForOV1$) $=_d$ Rem(T')
(2) $v =_d T1V(T1Root)$

Redefining a value: SetV

The purpose of SetV is to 'replace' the value $TV(TI_1)$ of TI_1 by a new value v in a T: TreePtd1. The effect of this operation is similar to that of InsPtV. The operation is defined iff TI_1 is not a sentinel.

SetV has two arguments, T and the new value v. It returns T': TreePtd1 such that T' differs from T only by $T'V(TI_1)$, equal to v.

SetV

Reset the value of TI_1 if it is a main point.
Given T: TreePtd1 and v: *Vals* such that
(Pre 1) $TI_1 \neq TChiLst(TParent(TI_1))$
SetV(T, v) $=_d$ T' where T' : TreePtd1 and
(1) $T'TreeOrd =_d TTreeOrd$
(2) $T'V =_d (TV | TI_1 \mapsto v)$
(3) $T'E =_d TE$

16.5 The tree editor as an interactive system

16.5A Introduction

We now move to the second stage of the construction of TEd. Our purpose is to draw up a blueprint for a certain computer system, the tree editor TEd, based on the theoretical model developed so far. What is the description or model appropriate at this stage?

In a narrow sense, a computer system is a machine whose behaviour is controlled by a certain program. However, it is important to recall that this view is too limited. A more comprehensive description of a computer system is that it is a *couple* (*User*, *Machine*), that is, a combination of two interacting agents: a user on the one hand, and a machine on the other. Our aim is to describe the two agents, how they behave individually and how they interact.

The user–machine interaction is a process that unfolds over time. At any time, both agents are in a certain *state*. The user's 'state' is a certain perception or *conception* of the machine's own state and functions, together with certain objectives to achieve. The machine's state includes the state of its internal registers or store, and the state of its 'output devices', such as its screen. The former is *hidden* from the user, whereas the latter is *visible*. Although this distinction is important, it must not mislead us. *The user's conception covers both the visible and the hidden features of the machine*, and it is this total picture that matters.

Both agents perform actions in time. The user sends a succession of *commands* to the machine, one at a time. In response to each command, the machine performs a certain function which brings it into a *new state*. The visible part of this new state – for instance, a message, an icon or a diagram displayed on the screen – represents information returned by the machine to the user. This information is then interpreted by the user, who therefore acquires a new conception of the machine, on the basis of which the next command is selected. This 'input–output' cycle is repeated indefinitely.

From this general description of a computer system, it follows that the establishment of a specific system requires a definition of the following elements:

(1) The possible states of the machine

(2) The commands available in each state

(3) For each command, the new machine state resulting from its execution by the machine

Our aim now is to provide such a description for TEd. This description is an extension of the theoretical model of pointed trees T: TreePtd1 and associated operations previously developed. We begin with the following outline.

1 A *state* *St* of TEd is mainly (a physical representation of) a pointed tree *T*: TreePtd1. More precisely, *T* is the principal component of *St*; a second component is specified below.

2 The main effect of a command is to apply to the current state *St* of TEd one or several of the operations established earlier. Thus the new state of TEd is primarily the pointed tree *T′* resulting from the operation invoked by the command. The new state is denoted by *St′*.

Note that in our definition of a machine state, we ignore both the internal and the visible *physical* representation of *T*. Our description is purely conceptual or logical, and is perfectly proper. The representation of *T* in machine store is entirely a matter of implementation; it does not concern the user. The *screen* representation *does* concern the user, but it is a complex matter which must be treated separately, as another extension of the theoretical model developed here. We do not touch upon this aspect in the present study.

Under these circumstances, how does the present modelling stage differ from the previous one? Have we not completed our description? The answer is 'no': four questions remain to be considered.

1 The description of a state *St* of TEd as a tree *T*: TreePtd1 is only partial, as already mentioned. We must now establish appropriate auxiliary elements.

2 It may be convenient now to make a distinction between (a) 'input variables', which are part of a command, (b) 'output variables', which define changes in the *visible* components of the machine's state, and (c) 'internal variables', the hidden components of the machine's state.

3 Any command need not invoke only *one* function. It may be defined as a combination of several functions, typically navigation and tree transformation operations. We may regard our theoretical model as providing an intermediate 'programming language' in which commands are constructed. If several operations are invoked, one of them is regarded as the main operation of the command.

4 Most functions in TEd are partial. Consequently an attempt to apply a function when its precondition is not satisfied is an *error*. It is necessary to establish when a command is erroneous and what the response of the machine should be to such a command.

We examine these questions in turn and then describe the commands of TEd in detail. To simplify, if an operation has several preconditions we call their conjunction 'the precondition' of the operation.

16.5B Full state description

The symbol '*St*' denotes the *complete* state of TEd at any time. We have already defined the main component of *St*, namely a certain tree *T*: TreePtd1. To this, we add only one second component, namely a certain forest F: ForOV1, with the constraint IsDisjoint($TPts$, $FPts$). Thus we may write

$$St =_{\mathrm{d}} (T, F)$$

Both components are always defined. However, at any time the second component F may be empty or nonempty. At the start of the process, F is empty, i.e. $FPts =_{\mathrm{d}} \varnothing$. F is redefined as the subforest returned by Rem(T) or Copy(TF) whenever either function is invoked *by a command.* Conversely, F serves as a *copy* of the second argument of Ins whenever this function is invoked *by a command.* Thus, F itself is left unchanged by such a command, and in fact by any command that does not invoke Rem or Copy.

The forest F may be viewed as a *buffer* between the application of Rem (or Copy) on the one hand and that of Ins on the other. Specifically, the user may apply Rem creating F, perform a sequence of navigation (and possibly other) steps and finally apply Ins to the main tree. Thus, the executions of Rem and Ins are *decoupled* by the intermediate actions. This makes it possible, for instance, to transfer a subforest from its current position to any other location in the main tree. The area of store used to represent F is sometimes called the *paste buffer*, as a reminder of the traditional 'cut' and 'paste' editing operations which Rem and Ins model.

16.5C Input, output and internal variables

For any command in TEd, the new state St' depends on two factors: (a) the elements of the initial state St and (b) the command input by the user. The command is primarily a reference to the main operation of TreePtd1 to be applied to St. However, in some cases it is natural to extend it with additional information, specifically with *some* of the arguments of the operation referred to. The command augmented in this way is called an *extended command.*

For instance, it is natural to define the command to insert a new point with a value v: $Vals$ as consisting of (a reference to) the function InsPtV and the value v itself. The latter is the second argument of InsPtV. The first argument of InsPtV is not needed as part of the command, as it is the main component T of the current state St, by definition.

Conversely, we must establish what information must be returned by the machine to the user in response to any command. This is equivalent to specifying how the machine is to modify the visible part of its state – for example, by displaying a new message or altering a displayed picture. This decision should be made at this stage, if only to provide a starting-point for the next stage, namely the specification of the form in which the visible components should be presented to the user.

Consequently, at this modelling stage it may be useful to distinguish the three types of variable already alluded to: (a) *input* variables, which are part of a command; (b) *internal* variables, each of which is a component of the machine's current or new *hidden* state; and (c) *output* variables, each of which is a component of the information returned by the machine to the user in response to a command. A common convention is to distinguish *input* variables by decorating them with the suffix '?', and *output* variables with the suffix '!'. This is a matter of convenience; there is nothing essential about the distinction between input, internal and output variables in their names. We apply this convention in a limited way, for illustration purposes.

Conceptual versus physical input and output

It is emphasized again that the input and output variables referred to in the present model are purely conceptual or logical. They must be carefully distinguished from their physical representation.

Consider the input side in particular. The standard command input device nowadays is the keyboard. Consequently any command is physically represented as a keyboard character or a sequence of characters. This sequence need not be the *name* of the invoked function used in the conceptual model. For instance, navigation operations, which are frequently applied, are usually physically represented by a single character, often an arrow key, and not by a word like 'MoveToSibNex1'.

Likewise on the output side, the output variables and their physical representation are two separate matters. The logical information to be provided is the starting-point, and it is typically much simpler than its physical expression. One reason is that the latter must allow for all the physical characteristics of the output device, such as screen dimensions, character set available, speed of display, and so on.

The distinction between conceptual input and output information flows and their physical counterpart is a major application of the principle of *separation of concerns*. It is useful to reflect upon the significance of this principle in this case. The separation may be justified on the following grounds:

1 Conceptual input and output variables are typically much simpler than their physical representation. Once the former have been established, the latter may be developed from the former, independently of the other features of the overall system. The conceptual variables may be regarded as forming an *interface* between their physical representation and other parts of the system.

2 Conceptual and physical variables are affected by different criteria. The main example is given by the physical characteristics of the input and output devices, as mentioned above. Another example is the expected relative frequency of each information flow. It may even be appropriate to relate the form of commands to the representation of the output. All these factors should be allowed for in specifying the physical form of information flows, but they do not affect the conceptual variables.

3 The separation of conceptual variables from their physical representation makes it possible to *vary* the latter while keeping the former fixed. This means that the choice of input and output devices may be left open and may be altered during the life of the system without affecting it at the conceptual level.

16.5D Commands and error handling

Commands as combinations of operations

A TEd command is the application of a certain function *Com* to the current machine state *St*, returning the new state *St'*. The function *Com* is a combination of some of the operations defined in Sections **16**.3 and **16**.4. In every case the arguments of *Com* consist mainly of the two components *T* and *F* of the initial state *St*. In a few cases, *Com* has a third argument, namely an input variable specified by the user as a command parameter.

Likewise, for every command the result of *Com* is in three parts: the two components *T'* and *F'* of the new machine state *St'*, and an output variable *Mes!*. *Mes!* denotes any signal or message returned by the machine, either to confirm execution of the command or inform the user of a wrong command.

There are two main ways in which component operations are combined to form the function *Com*. First, for each command, *Com* consists of a combination of the three subfunctions which return *T'*, *F'* and *Mes!* respectively. These are *executed 'in parallel'*, which is one form of combination. The second form is the *composition* of more elementary functions in the sense of function theory; it occurs in a few commands.

The definition of commands as combinations of basic functions is another example of modular construction. This method is quite flexible, as it offers many alternatives to choose from. This in turn raises the question of the design principles which should be used in this construction.

One such principle must be mentioned here, as it is illustrated by several commands of the tree editor. This is that, when defining any command, we should not consider it in isolation but *as part of the possible sequences of commands* within which it is likely to occur frequently. For instance, when constructing a new tree *T*, the user is likely to insert not just one new valued point but several siblings at a time in the order in which they are to occur in the tree. Therefore the one-point insertion command should be such that the creation of several successive siblings may be achieved by repeatedly inputting this command only, that is, no other operations should be needed in conjunction with it.

Error handling

The designer of a computer system should allow for every possible error which the user may make. In other words, the system should behave 'sensibly' – for instance, it should not 'crash' – for every possible input, however unlikely or 'absurd'. This leads to three general questions about the commands of the system:

(1) When is a command correct and what are the causes of incorrect commands?

(2) If an incorrect command is input, what should be the response of the machine?

(3) In particular, what message should the machine output in response to an incorrect command?

There are four main causes of an incorrect input command:

1 The input does not correspond to any *available* command. For instance, it has been misspelt.

2 The combination of functions invoked by the command is partial and not defined in the current state *St* of the system. In other words, the precondition of this combination is not satisfied by *St*.

3 The application of the invoked functions to *St* would be judged incorrect by a rational, competent user. For instance, if the auxiliary forest *F* is empty, i.e. $FPts = \varnothing$, inserting *F* into the current tree *T* has no effect. This step is regarded as incorrect as it probably betrays an error or misconception on the part of the user.

4 The execution of the invoked functions is not feasible on account of physical constraints imposed on the implementation of the system, such as a storage limitation. Although we are not concerned with implementation details at this stage, we should at least allow for the possible infeasibility of an operation for reasons of this type, even if these are not determined yet.

These four cases apply to the command together with its parameter(s), if any.

In TEd, the behaviour of the system is defined (sensibly) for every possible input from the user. Thus there is *no precondition* imposed on the user's commands in the strict sense of the term: a strict precondition is such that, if it is not satisfied, the machine behaviour resulting from the input is *undefined*, i.e. may be anything. This should never be allowed in a program.

However, with each command is associated what we call a *normal precondition*. This is analogous to a precondition in the usual sense. It indicates under which circumstances a command input will produce the 'normal' or 'expected' response from the machine, essentially the application of the operations invoked by it. In particular, the normal precondition always implies the preconditions of the invoked functions.

If the normal precondition is not satisfied, then the state of the system is left unchanged, that is, $St =_{d} St'$. We can also say that in this case the function *Com* is the identity function. If the normal precondition is satisfied, then *Com* is the combination of the operations invoked by the command, and these are applied to *St*. Consequently, the result *St'* is well defined in all cases, and *Com* is a *total* function.

The normal precondition is related to the four cases of command incorrectness given above, as follows: it is satisfied iff none of these cases obtains. Thus the normal precondition is satisfied by the user's input iff (1) the input corresponds to an available command; (2) the preconditions of the operation(s) invoked are all satisfied; (3) any additional 'sensible' condition is satisfied; and (4) any additional implementation constraint is met.

Nothing else can be said at this stage about cases (1) and (4). The elements of the normal precondition corresponding to cases (2) and (3) are given with each individual command in the next section.

The output variable *Mes!* plays a role in error handling. If for any command the normal precondition is satisfied, then *Mes!* is either a symbol denoting the 'empty message' or a report confirming the execution of the command and its effect on *St*. Otherwise, *Mes!* is an error message outlining the cause of the error, for instance, or a symbol denoting a simple signal such as an 'alarm bell'.

We do not specify *Mes!* further at this stage. As mentioned above, this feature of TEd should be treated separately, as part of the design of all the visible aspects of the system. At this stage, *Mes!* should be regarded essentially as a *marker*, a reminder of an important aspect to be developed elsewhere.

16.5E Details of TEd commands

The commands of TEd are set out below. For each command the following details are given:

(1) Command name and parameter, if any
(2) Purpose of the command in outline
(3) Normal precondition
(4) Effects of the command in terms of basic functions, assuming the normal precondition is satisfied

The name of each command consists of the prefix 'Com' followed by an identifier. As a rule, this identifier is the name of the main operation invoked. As mentioned above, the components of the normal condition explicitly listed correspond to cases (2) and (3) of command correctness only.

The commands fall into two main groups. The first contains two commands: ComStart and ComEnd. The second contains all other commands. ComStart initiates the execution of TEd and ComEnd terminates it. While TEd is not being executed, ComStart is the only available command. At every stage during the execution of TEd, all commands are available except ComStart. Thus nested executions of TEd are not considered here.

We stated above that every command requires an initial state $St = (T, F)$ and transforms it into a new state $St' = (T', F')$. This rule must be qualified slightly. It holds in full only for commands in the second group. For the two commands in the first group, the rule holds only partially. ComStart does not require an initial state St but returns a final state St'. Conversely, ComEnd is available only if the initial state St exists, but it returns no final state St'. The symmetry between these two commands may be noted.

The execution of each command, except ComEnd, must satisfy the required general property IsDisjoint($T'Pts$, $F'Pts$), together with any other similar precondition of any operation invoked by the command. These conditions are not restated in the establishment of individual commands below. Recall that ensuring they are satisfied is a separate, 'implementation' concern.

We use the function Min(x, y) where x, y : Nat, defined in the usual way by

$$\text{Min}(x, y) =_d x \text{ if } x < y; \quad y \text{ otherwise}$$

Initialization and termination commands

ComStart

Aim: Initialize execution of TEd.
Effect:
$F'Pts =_d \varnothing$
$T' =_d$ InitAuxPtd

ComEnd

Aim: Terminate execution of TEd.
Effect: $St' = (T', F')$ undefined

Navigation commands

A navigation command invokes a navigation function. We describe only two commands in this group, namely ComMoveToSibNex1 and ComMoveToChi. All other navigation commands are defined in the same way as ComMoveTo-SibNex1.

ComMoveToSibNex1

Aim: Move cursor TE_1 to its next sibling in T.
Normal precondition: Precondition of MoveToSibNex1(T)
Effect:
$F' =_d F$
$T' =_d$ MoveToSibNex1(T)

A general description of all navigation operations may be obtained from this definition as follows. Replace MoveToSibNex1 by the variable OpNav ranging over the set of navigation function names. Then each definition of a navigation command other than ComMoveToChi may be obtained by replacing 'OpNav' by a navigation function name in this general definition. This illustrates the process of *generalization*. For the record:

ComOpNav

Aim: Redefine cursor TE.
Normal precondition: Precondition of OpNav(T)
Effect:
$F' =_d F$
$T' =_d$ OpNav(T)

We now turn to the special navigation command ComMoveToChi. This differs from the others by the parameter $n?$: Pos specifying the target of the cursor.

ComMoveToChi $n?$

Aim: Move cursor TE_1 to the $n?$th child of TE_1.
Normal precondition: Precondition of MoveToChi$_{n?}$(T)
Effect:
$F' =_d F$
$T' =_d$ MoveToChi$_{n?}$(T)

An alternative and more liberal version of ComMoveToChi may be defined. The idea is to abolish the maximum value imposed on $n?$ in the normal precondition, but to replace $n?$ by this maximum if the value input is greater.

ComMoveToChiVer1 $n?$

Aim: Move cursor TE_1 to the $n?$th child of TE_1. If $n?$ is greater than the maximum allowed, move TE_1 to the last child but one of TE_1.
Normal precondition:
$n?$: Pos
Num($TChis(TE_1)$) $\geqslant 2$
Effect: Let p: Pos.
$F' =_d F$
$T' =_d$ MoveToChi$_p$(T), where $p =_d$ Min($n?$, Num($TChis(TE_1)$) $- 1$)

Tree transformation commands

A tree transformation command invokes a tree transformation function as main operation. This is combined with the application of other operations, such as navigation operations in some cases.

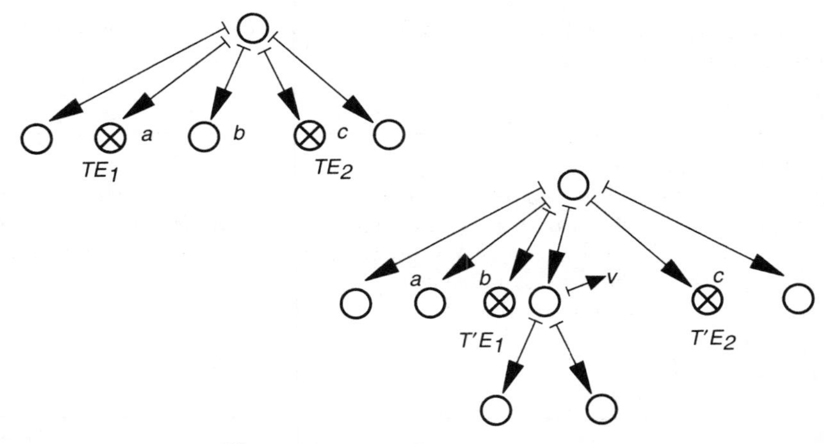

Figure 16.5E.1 Effect of ComInsPtV.

We begin with ComInsPtV. This command is input with a parameter $v?$. It inserts a new point with value $v?$ immediately before TE_2. The value of TE_2 is unchanged, but TE_1 is first 'moved forward' if it is separated from TE_2 in T. The effect of this command is illustrated in Figure **16**.5E.1. Recall TI_1 is the point which immediately follows TE_1 in T.

ComInsPtV $v?$

Aim: Insert a new point with value $v?$ immediately before TE_2. In St', $T'E_2 =_d TE_2$ and the new point is $T'I_1$ *surrounded by* $T'E_1$ and $T'E_2$. Consequently the repeated application of ComInsPtV will create a list of siblings ordered according to their insertion.

Normal precondition:

$v?$: *Vals*

Effect: Let $T1$: TreePtd1.

$F' =_d F$

$T1 =_d$ TieTo2(T)

The application of TieTo2 causes $T1SibNex(T1E_1) = T1E_2$, the precondition of InsPtV($T1$, $v?$), and $T1E_2 = TE_2$.

$T' =_d$ InsPtV($T1$, $v?$)

Note that the external cursor is unchanged: $T'E = T1E$.

Implications:

$T'E_2 = TE_2$

$T'I_1 = T'I_2$ (new point)

Note that in this establishment the intermediate variable $T1$ is introduced solely in order to formulate the two comments made on the effect of the command. We could as well use the description

$$T' =_d \text{InsPtV(TieTo2}(T), v?)$$

which is perfectly clear.

The next commands are straightforward applications of the remaining tree transformation functions.

ComSetV *v?*

Aim: Replace the value of TI_1 by the new value *v?*. If this command is input immediately after ComInsPtV, it updates the value of the point inserted by ComInsPtV. Also, if ComSetV is used repeatedly, each application modifies the value of the same point, namely TI_1.
Normal precondition: Precondition of SetV(T, *v?*)
Effect:

$F' =_d F$
$T' =_d$ SetV(T, *v?*)

ComIns

Aim: Insert a copy of the auxiliary forest F between TE_1 and TE_2.
Normal precondition:

$FPts \neq \varnothing$
$TSibNex(TE_1) = TE_2$

Effect:

$F' =_d F$
$T' =_d$ Ins(T, Copy(F))

The insertion of a copy of F rather than F ensures IsDisjoint($T'Pts$, $F'Pts$).

More liberal versions of ComIns may be devised. In the following alternative version, the normal precondition $TSibNex(TE_1) = TE_2$ is dropped.

ComInsVer1

Aim: Insert a copy of the auxiliary forest F between TE_1 and TE_2. If the subforest TF is not empty, the copy of F is inserted immediately after TF in T'. Consequently this command may be used repeatedly to insert several copies of F after one another. It may also be used in alternation with ComInsPtV repeatedly, with a similar effect on the order in which inserted objects will occur in the final tree.
Normal precondition:

$FPts \neq \varnothing$

Effect:

$F' =_d F$
$T' =_d$ Ins(TieTo2(T), Copy(F))

The application of TieTo2 ensures that the precondition of Ins is satisfied and that the copy of F is placed immediately after TF.

ComRem

Aim: Remove the subforest TF from T and save TF as the new auxiliary forest F'.

Normal precondition:

$TSibNex(TE_1) \neq TE_2$

That is, TF is not empty.

Effect:

$(T', F') =_d \text{Rem}(T)$

Note that the original F is lost.

ComDel

Aim: Remove the subforest TF from T without saving it. The original auxiliary forest F is saved.

Normal precondition:

$TSibNex(TE_1) \neq TE_2$

That is, TF is not empty.

Effect: Let $F1$: ForOV1.

$F' =_d F$

$(T', F1) =_d \text{Rem}(T)$

$F1$ is a dummy variable.

ComCopy

Aim: Copy the subforest TF into F'.

Normal precondition:

$TSibNex(TE_1) \neq TE_2$

That is, TF is not empty.

Effect:

$F' =_d \text{Copy}(TF)$

$T' =_d T$

Here we rely on the general constraint IsDisjoint($T'Pts$, $F'Pts$) imposed on St'.

---

17 A General Resource Allocation Model (ResAll)

17.1 Introduction

17.1A Resource allocation systems

A *resource allocation system* is a collection of related entities which evolve in time. At any time, the entities and their relations are *fixed*; they form the *state* of the system at this time. The fact that they evolve in time means that the system goes through *successive states*, each following from the previous one according to some transformation rule.

The entities fall into three main categories:

(1) Tasks to be performed

(2) Resource units of various types, also simply called 'resources'

(3) Agents of various types, such as 'employees', 'customers' or 'users'

These entities are related in multiple ways. For instance, each task *requires* various resources in certain quantities. A task is either *active* – that is;

being performed, or *inactive* – that is, suspended. If it is active, a task must be *allocated* all the resources necessary to meet its requirements. The resources are fixed, in the sense that they are not consumed by being used and may be allocated to several tasks, albeit one at a time. Any task may be '*owned*' by a customer or user and *assigned* to an employee. The latter must have the *authority level* required by the task.

In general, resources and employees are controlled by some organization. Although this fact is not essential here, it may be useful to bear it in mind. A resource may be allocated to a task only if it is controlled or owned by the organization. Thus we make the distinction between resources in general and *owned resources*.

Example 17.1A.1

As mentioned in Section **13**.3B, a *conference centre* may be described as a resource allocation system. Typically, it involves the following entities:

Tasks Events such as lectures and seminars

Resources Rooms of various seating capacities; audio-visual facilities of various types; operators for certain facilities; etc.

Agents Employees and customers or users of the centre

Any event requires a room of adequate capacity, together with the various facilities needed by the lecturer. An event is an 'active task' while it is being held. It is during this time that its resource requirements must be met, and consequently that the necessary resources are allocated to it. ■

In general, the entities involved in a resource allocation system form various *sets*: owned resources of various types, inactive tasks, active tasks, employees, users and so on. As for the relations between entities, these may be relatively numerous and varied. To simplify, no distinction is made here between *attributes* of entities and *relations* between entities. The former are treated as a special case of the latter.

As already mentioned, a resource allocation system may be described as a *succession of states* determined by certain transformation rules. Each rule is a *function* which sends a state of the system to the following state. Thus, it is an *operation* on the class of all possible system states.

The main operations governing the system are as follows.

(1) All the sets involved are made empty. This is the usual initialization (nullary) operation.

(2) An additional resource unit is acquired.

(3) An owned resource is disposed of.

(4) A new task arises. At this stage it is inactive.

(5) An inactive task is made active, i.e. its performance is either started or resumed.

(6) A task is suspended, possibly completed.

(7) An agent joins the organization, either as employee or as customer.

(8) An agent leaves the organization.

It is easy to see how each operation transforms a system state into a new state, and this in an *elementary* way. Also, it should be clear that these operations are sufficient to describe the evolution of the system, in its essential aspects at least. For instance, if in reality several changes may occur simultaneously, these may be described as occurring in some arbitrary order. This may be a slight distortion of reality, but it is likely to be entirely valid in most applications – such 'harmless distortions' are typical of the art of modelling.

Another application of ResAll is the description of a lending library. This was also outlined in Section **13**.3B. Many other examples could be given.

17.1B Aim of the chapter

In this chapter, we develop a theoretical model of a resource allocation system in general. This model is called ResAll and is built on the description given above. This is done by formally establishing (a) the various states in which the system may be at any time and (b) the operations which define possible transitions between states.

ResAll is a generic model. It is designed to capture only the most common features of allocation systems, and to serve as a basis for special cases. The generic nature of ResAll is illustrated in particular by the two applications mentioned above.

We develop ResAll in stages, as another illustration of modular design. Each stage introduces a *distinct type of concern*. First, we consider only tasks, resources and relations between these entities. These, together with the corresponding state transformation operations, form the *core* of ResAll. Second, we add agents and authority levels, their relations to tasks, additional constraints they impose on core operations and any additional operations they may entail in their own right. Third, we add error-handling and report features.

This order of development is not arbitrary but based on a careful *analysis* of resource allocation systems. It is justified by two criteria mainly.

First, priority is given to those features of resource allocation systems judged to be *commonest*. These include the fact that in all cases there is a set of tasks whose execution requires certain fixed resources, and no resource may be allocated to more than one task at a time. Hence resources, tasks and relations between them are given first priority.

Second, the various components of a resource allocation system, namely entities, relations and operations, are subject to further logical dependencies.

These impose a partial order on these components, which must be allowed for in model development. For instance, the establishment of operations must follow the establishment of the objects on which they operate. Errors and error-handling may arise only if certain constraints may be breached, so these constraints must be established first. Finally, reports may only return information on certain aspects of the system modelled: these aspects must be determined first.

17.1C General remarks

ResAll is a general model. Consequently in some applications some of its features may prove irrelevant. A general technique in such cases is to use the model with *dummy variables* standing for the irrelevant features. This is illustrated by the lending library service case, where in reality the 'tasks' for which books are borrowed are usually unknown to the service itself. We may easily assume that each loan of a book copy corresponds to a separate implicit task.

Conversely, although general, ResAll may be insufficient to represent all the essential features of a given situation. In this case the model may still be applicable if it can be extended, or combined with other models, to allow for the missing features. An example of such an extension is the construction of a timetable for a complex project (a set of tasks related by various precedence and resource constraints). The main difficulty in this case is to add an explicit time dimension to the basic model, but this can be done quite naturally.

It is important to make a distinction between a resource allocation system and a *computer* system representing it. As it is defined above, the former is a *part of the real world*. It is a collection of *physical* entities and relations between them, that is, a 'distant system' in the sense of Section **1**.1B. The latter is a computer-based model of the former. In this chapter we are concerned first with developing a theoretical description *of the former*, the distant system, and second with deriving a computer system representing it.

Another distinction must be made between ResAll and the resource allocation models of the type developed in operational research or management science, for instance. In these disciplines, resource allocation models are usually intended for *optimization*. This means that they typically include a 'measure of goodness' which is to be maximized, and they rely on *decision rules* or *algorithms* to produce a resource allocation which satisfies all constraints and maximizes the measure. ResAll is *not* an optimization model in this sense. The aim of the model is to capture only *some* of the features of optimization models, namely the entities and physical constraints (relations) imposed on them. However, ResAll could serve as a basis for the more ambitious optimization models.

In our establishment of ResAll, operations are not overloaded. This somewhat facilitates the description of extensions. The reader is invited to compare this style of establishment with that of previous models.

17.2 Core model: tasks and resources

Henceforth, we use the term 'ResAll' both as the name of the model established here and as an abbreviation for 'resource allocation'.

In the core model of ResAll, the only features considered are sets of tasks, sets of resources of various types and relations between these elements. The aim of the model is to define what these features may be at any time, that is, in any state of the ResAll system described, and the operations which determine the possible state transformations of the system.

Among the features we need to consider, some are *constant* over the set of possible system states, while others vary with these states. It is appropriate to distinguish these two types of feature. Consequently we first establish the constant features of the core model and their relations. Then we establish the variable features of the model and their relations. Finally, we establish the operations on the system states or, more precisely, on these variable features.

In order to emphasize the distinction between constant and variable features, we prefix the names of the former with '*K*'. (This symbol is borrowed from combinatory logic, where it is used to express a constant function.) The prefix '*K*' is also applied to names of relations between constant features.

In this model, we tend to use the term 'class' for a collection of existing or potential objects and the term set for a collection of actual objects, physically present at a given time. All the classes we consider are constant features of the model. Note that all the collections we establish, whether called 'classes' or 'sets', are strict sets in the sense of set theory. Also recall that in an elementary identifier, the suffix 's' is generally used to denote a set.

17.2A Constant features

In any model of a ResAll system, the first constant feature to establish is the class of possible tasks. This is denoted by *KTasks*. It includes both the actual and the potential tasks which may have to be performed.

In the case of a conference centre, these are the various events which the centre is designed to host: lectures, seminars, and so on. In the case of a library service, the tasks are the various uses for which books are or may be needed by library users. In this case, the tasks may in reality be implicit; nevertheless they are an explicit feature of the model.

The second constant feature to establish is the class of possible *types* of resource which may occur at any time, that is, in any state of the system. This class is denoted by *KReTypes*.

For instance, in a model describing a conference centre, this class could be something like

$$KReTypes =_{\mathrm{d}} \{\text{50-seat-room, 200-seat-room, Overhead-projector, Video-recorder, Operator}\}$$

Thus at any time, any resource may be of one of the five listed types.

In a model of a library lending service, *KReTypes* would typically be the class of all possible *books*, actual or potential. For, as we have seen, in such a ResAll system, a resource is a *copy* of a given book.

Given the class *KReTypes* of possible resource types, the third constant feature to establish is the class of all possible resources of any type $r : KReTypes$. This class is denoted by $KReSet_r$.

In the case of a conference centre, for $r =_d$ 50-seat-room, the set $KReSet_r$ is the class of all possible 50-seat rooms, whether actual and owned by the centre or another organization, or potential – for example, to be built later. In the case of a library service, $KReSet_r$ is the class of all possible *copies* of a *book* r, whether already in existence and owned by the library, another library, the publisher etc., or to be printed in the future.

From the definition of $KReSet_r$, it follows that *KReSet* is a function

$$KReSet : KReTypes \rightarrow \text{Set}$$

We stipulate that any resource may have only one type. This rule is likely to reflect reality in most cases. Also, it greatly facilitates the development of the model, by ensuring that resources of different types may be treated separately. This is our first condition on constant features:

$$KCond1 \,.\!: \text{IsDisjointPairwise}\,(KReSet_r | r : KReTypes)$$

that is:

$$\forall\, r, r' : KReTypes \text{ with } r \neq r' \cdot KReSet_r \cap KReSet_{r'} =_d \varnothing$$

The remaining features are two functions relating tasks and resources. The first of these expresses the fact that any task $Ta : KTasks$ requires certain types of resource. These form a *finite* set, denoted by $KReqTypes(Ta)$, which must be a subset of *KReTypes*:

$$KReqTypes(Ta) \subseteq_d KReTypes$$

From this definition, it follows that *KReqTypes* is a total function

$$KReqTypes : KTasks \rightarrow \text{Powf}(KReTypes)$$

The second function is a key feature of ResAll. It gives for each resource type r and each task Ta the number of resources of type r required by Ta. This is denoted by $KReqNum_r(Ta)$ and it is assumed to be a natural number. *KReqNum* may be read as short for 'required number (of resources)' or 'requirement number'.

There is an important difference between the resource *requirements* of a task Ta and the resources *allocated* to Ta when it is active. For each resource type r, the requirement of Ta is defined as a *quantity* of resources, not as a specific set of resource units. This means that *any set* of resource units of type r may be allocated to Ta, provided its cardinality is equal to $KReqNum_r(Ta)$. In other words, the *resources of any type r are regarded as interchangeable* in ResAll. This interchangeability is the fundamental property of resource types: we could define a set of resources of a given type as any set whose members may be substituted for one another in any allocation.

It follows that *KReqNum* is a total binary function

$$KReqNum : KReTypes \times KTasks \rightarrow \text{Nat}$$

This function must satisfy the following constraint: for any resource *type* $r : KReTypes$ and any task $Ta : KTasks$, r is required by Ta iff the quantity of units of type r required by Ta is positive. This is formally expressed as

$$KCond2 .: \forall r : KReTypes,\ Ta : KTasks \cdot$$
$$r \in KReqTypes(Ta) \Leftrightarrow_d KReqNum_r(Ta) > 0$$

Note that $KReqNum_r(Ta)$ is defined for *all* $r : KReTypes$, and not just the members r of $KReqTypes(Ta)$. It is for this reason that the conditional '$\Leftarrow$' in *KCond2* is needed. This choice simplifies the establishment of the model, owing to the fact that *KReTypes* is constant, whereas $KReqTypes(Ta)$ varies with Ta.

In addition to the special conditions described above, a general condition is imposed on any constant set, of the form *KSet*. This is that *no such set is empty*. This general condition holds not only for the present features, but also for all additional constant sets to be introduced later.

This completes our description of the constant features of the core model of ResAll. We group them in the joint definition shown below in Feature Notation format:

K : AllocConstants

$KTasks$: Set	Class of tasks
$KReTypes$: Set	Class of resource types
$KReSet_r$: Set	Class of resources of type r
($r : KReTypes$)	
$KCond1 .:$ IsDisjointPairwise($KReSet_r \mid r : KReTypes$)	
$KReqTypes(Ta) \subseteq_d KReTypes$	Set of types of resource required by task Ta
($Ta : KTasks$)	
$KReqNum_r(Ta)$: Nat	Number of resources of type r required by task Ta
($r : KReTypes$)	
($Ta : KTasks$)	
$KCond2 .: \forall r : KReTypes,\ Ta : KTasks \cdot$	
$r \in KReqTypes(Ta) \Leftrightarrow_d KReqNum_r(Ta) > 0$	
$KCond3 .:$ For any $KSet$: Set, $KSet \neq \varnothing$	

17.2B Variable features

We now turn to the core variable features of a ResAll system. Recall that these are the task and resource features which may vary in time or, which is the same, with the possible states of the system.

These variable elements are either sets or functions. All the functions are total. Moreover, their domains and codomains are *constant*, based on the two sets *KTasks* and *KReTypes* in most cases. This modelling strategy necessitates some extra conditions, but it greatly simplifies the establishment of the model.

The features we introduce naturally fall into three groups: features involving tasks only; features involving resources only; and features involving both resources and tasks. These three groups are described as three separate modules.

Task features

At any time, the state of a ResAll system includes a set of tasks to be performed. This set is denoted by *TasksTotal*. Its members are *actual* tasks, in contrast to the class *KTasks* of all *possible* tasks, actual or potential. Therefore, *TasksTotal* must be a (finite) subset of *KTasks*:

$$TasksTotal \subseteq_{d} KTasks$$

At any time, an actual task *Ta*: *TasksTotal* is either *active* (being performed) or *inactive* (not being performed). Therefore, the set *TasksTotal* is partitioned into two subsets, the set *TasksAct* of active tasks and the set *TasksInact* of inactive tasks. This is expressed formally by the relation

$$TasksCond.: TasksTotal =_{d} TasksAct + TasksInact$$

Example 17.2B.1

1 In the case of a conference centre, *KTasks* is the set of all possible events (lectures, seminars, and so on) that are or could be taking place in the centre. At any time, *TasksTotal* is the set of all such events which either are being held or have at least been planned. *TasksAct* is the set of events being held now. *TasksInact* is the set of events which have been planned, so their resource requirements are known, but are not taking place now.

2 In the case of a library service, *KTasks* is the set of all possible uses to which books may be put. *TasksTotal* is the set of all actual uses, known by the users at least. *TasksAct* contains all the uses for which a book copy has been obtained by a user. *TasksInact* contains any task which a user wishes to carry out and for which a certain book is needed but has not been obtained yet. ■

The state of actual tasks, which clearly varies in time, is described in Feature Notation format below. In the definition, *Tasks* is a typical variable representing any such state. Two features are classified as *primary*, which is indicated by an asterisk (*). These are *TasksTotal* and *TasksAct*. This means that all the variable features of *Tasks* are entirely determined when these two features are fixed. This is so of *TasksInact* in particular, on account of condition *TasksCond.*

<u>*Tasks*: TaskStates</u>

*	$TasksTotal,$	Total set of tasks in hand
*	$TasksAct,$	Set of active tasks, i.e. being performed
	$TasksInact \subseteq_d KTasks$	Set of inactive tasks, i.e. not being performed

$TasksCond.: TasksTotal =_d TasksAct + TasksInact$

Resource features

Next, consider the resource features. At any time in the life of a ResAll system, there is a set of actual resources *owned* by the organization and therefore either allocated or available for allocation to tasks. For instance, in the case of a conference centre this is the set of rooms, overhead projectors, video recorders, and so on, owned by the centre at a given time. In the case of a library service, this is the stock of book copies owned by the library at a given time.

The set of owned resources is clearly a variable feature of the ResAll system under consideration. As time passes, the set grows with the acquisition of new resources and shrinks with the disposal or loss of existing resources. Each owned resource must be of some type $r: KReTypes$. Consequently we may identify two variable features of owned resources: (a) the set *ReTypes* of the *types* of owned resource and (b) for each resource type $r: KReTypes$, the set $ReSet_r$ of owned resources of type r. The total set of resources owned is the set sum of the various $ReSet_r$,

$$\Sigma \{ReSet_r | r: ReTypes\}$$

We do not give a name to this total set as it is rarely referred to. Clearly, the set *ReTypes* must be a subset of the class of possible resource types:

$$ReTypes \subseteq_d KReTypes$$

Likewise, for any type $r: KReTypes$, the set $ReSet_r$ of owned resources of type r must be a subset of the class of all possible resources of type r:

$$ReSet_r \subseteq_d KReSet_r \qquad (r: KReTypes)$$

Example 17.2B.2

Consider the case of a conference centre. Suppose that at a given time the centre owns two 50-seat rooms, say Room1 and Room2, and three overhead projectors, say OP1, OP2 and OP3. Then in this state,

$$ReTypes =_{\mathrm{d}} \{\text{50-seat-room, Overhead-projector}\}$$

Moreover, for the resource type $r =_{\mathrm{d}}$ 50-seat-room,

$$ReSet_r =_{\mathrm{d}} \{\text{Room1, Room2}\}$$

and for $r =_{\mathrm{d}}$ Overhead-projector,

$$ReSet_r =_{\mathrm{d}} \{\text{OP1, OP2, OP3}\}$$

■

ReSet is a function from *KReTypes* to the set of all finite sets of possible resources. Note that $ReSet_r$ is defined for each possible resource type r: *KReTypes*, not just for those r in *ReTypes*. This makes it necessary to express the fact that $ReSet_r$ is empty if r is not a member of *ReTypes*. The reverse condition is also adopted, namely that for any r in *ReTypes*, $ReSet_r$ is not empty. Moreover, the finiteness of any set $ReSet_r$ is explicitly imposed, so that Num($ReSet_r$) is a well-defined natural number in all cases. These three conditions are formulated as

$$\begin{aligned} ReCond.: \quad &(1) \quad \forall r: KReTypes - ReTypes \cdot ReSet_r =_{\mathrm{d}} \varnothing \\ &(2) \quad \forall r: ReTypes \cdot ReSet_r \neq_{\mathrm{d}} \varnothing \\ &(3) \quad \forall r: ReTypes \cdot \mathrm{IsFinite}(ReSet_r) \end{aligned}$$

This completes the description of the pure resource features of a ResAll system. These features define the state of its owned resources at any time. It is established below in Feature Notation format, with *ReSet* labelled primary. (Clearly, *ReTypes* is entirely determined by *Reset*, on account of *ReCond.*)

<u>*Re*: ResourceStates</u>

	$ReTypes \subseteq_{\mathrm{d}} KReTypes$	Set of types of owned resource
*	$ReSet_r \subseteq_{\mathrm{d}} KReSet_r$ $(r: KReTypes)$	Set of owned resources of type r

$$\begin{aligned} ReCond.: \quad &(1) \quad \forall r: KReTypes - ReTypes \cdot ReSet_r =_{\mathrm{d}} \varnothing \\ &(2) \quad \forall r: ReTypes \cdot ReSet_r \neq_{\mathrm{d}} \varnothing \\ &(3) \quad \forall r: ReTypes \cdot \mathrm{IsFinite}(ReSet_r) \end{aligned}$$

Task and resource features

We are now in a position to describe the core states of a ResAll system in full. Any such state is a variable S with three major features:

$STasks$: TaskStates, grouping the task features of S;

SRe: ResourceStates, grouping the resource features of S;

$SRes$, which represents the allocation of owned resources to tasks and some of its implications, and which remains to be defined.

The primary component of $SRes$ is the function $SResAll_r(Ta)$. For any resource type $r: KReTypes$ and any task $Ta: KTasks$, $SResAll_r(Ta)$ is the set of resources of type r allocated to Ta. This must be a subset of all possible resources of type r. Thus:

$$SResAll_r(Ta) \subseteq_{\mathrm{d}} KReSet_r \qquad (r: KReTypes,\ Ta: KTasks)$$

Note that in contrast to resource requirements, ResAll expresses the fact that when a task is activated, it is allocated *individual* resources. This simply reflects reality more accurately and in a way which may be crucial in some applications.

From our previous informal description of a ResAll system, the various sets $SResAll_r(Ta)$ must satisfy three conditions. First, if Ta is an actual active task, then it must be allocated $KReqNum_r(Ta)$ resources of type r; otherwise, Ta must be allocated no resources of this type. This is formally expressed as

$$\begin{aligned} &SCond1 .: \forall r: KReTypes,\ Ta: KTasks \cdot \\ &\quad (1)\quad Ta \in STasksAct \Rightarrow \\ &\qquad\qquad\qquad \mathrm{Num}(SResAll_r(Ta)) =_{\mathrm{d}} KReqNum_r(Ta) \\ &\quad (2)\quad Ta \notin STasksAct \Rightarrow SResAll_r(Ta) =_{\mathrm{d}} \varnothing \end{aligned}$$

Note that $Ta \notin STasksAct$ means that either $Ta \in STasksInact$ or $Ta \notin STasksTotal$. $SResAll_r(Ta)$ is defined in all cases, that is, whether Ta is active or not. When Ta is not an active task, $SResAll_r(Ta)$ is simply specified as the empty set.

Second, for any resource type r, a unit of this type may not be allocated to more than one task. This is expressed by stating that the various sets $ResAll_r(Ta)$ must be disjoint, that is

$$SCond2 .: \forall r: KReTypes \cdot \mathrm{IsDisjointPairwise}\ (ResAll_r(Ta) \mid Ta: STasksAct)$$

Third, for any task Ta, the resources of any type r allocated to Ta must be owned. This is expressed as

$$SCond3 .: \forall r: KReTypes,\ Ta: KTasks \cdot SResAll_r(Ta) \subseteq SReSet_r$$

This completes our establishment of the primary core features of a ResAll system, which is summarized as follows. These primary features have multiple implications, which are analysed next.

S: Alloc

* $STasks$: TaskStates
* SRe: ResourceStates
* $SResAll_r(Ta) \subseteq_d KReSet_r$ — Set of resources of type r allocated to task Ta
  $(r: KReTypes)$
  $(Ta: KTasks)$
  $SCond1 .: \forall r: KReTypes,\ Ta: KTasks \cdot$
  (1) $Ta \in STasksAct \Rightarrow$
  $\text{Num}(SResAll_r(Ta)) =_d KReqNum_r(Ta)$
  (2) $Ta \notin STasksAct \Rightarrow SResAll_r(Ta) =_d \varnothing$
  $SCond2 .: \forall r: KReTypes \cdot$
  $\text{IsDisjointPairwise}\ (ResAll_r(Ta) \mid Ta: STasksAct)$
  $SCond3 .: \forall r: KReTypes,\ Ta: KTasks \cdot SResAll_r(Ta) \subseteq_d SReSet_r$

17.2C Secondary core features

Consider any core state S: Alloc of a ResAll sytem. We have just described its *primary* features, which determine S completely. What we now do is identify some of the *secondary* features of S, those implied by the primary ones. These again fall into two categories: (a) variable secondary features and (b) fixed secondary features. This identification process is the *analysis* part of the establishment of S.

Recall from Section **10**.3A that a *variable secondary feature* of S is a well-defined total function of its primary features. To say that it is well defined is the same as to say that it is entirely determined by the primary features of S: whenever all these are fixed, the secondary variable feature has a determined value – *exactly one*.

A *fixed secondary feature* of S is a property implied by its primary features. It may be regarded as a predicate whose value is true in every state S of the system, *as a consequence of the primary features*. Fixed features, whether primary or secondary, are also called *invariants*.

We begin with two features which may be described as global implications of the resource allocation of S. They are determined mainly by $SResAll_r(Ta)$ and $SReSet_r$. The first is the total set of allocated resources of any type $r: KReTypes$, and is denoted by $SResAlloc_r$. The second is the residual set of *free* – that is, unallocated – owned resources; this is denoted by $SResFree_r$. For any resource type $r: KReTypes$, $SResAlloc_r$ must be a subset of all possible resources of type r. Hence this variable is given by

$$SResAlloc_r \subseteq_d KReSet_r$$

Moreover, the various sets $SResAll_r(Ta)$ are nonempty only for active tasks Ta, by *SCond1*, and pairwise disjoint, by *SCond2*. Consequently $SResAlloc_r$ is defined as the following set sum:

$$SDef1 .: \forall r : KReTypes \cdot SResAlloc_r =_d \Sigma \{SResAll_r(Ta) \mid Ta : STasksAct\}$$

The set $SResFree_r$ of free resources of type r may now be defined. It is introduced by

$$SResFree_r \subseteq_d KReSet_r$$

Only owned resources may be allocated, by *SCond3*, and an owned resource is either allocated or free. Therefore, $SResFree_r$ is well-defined by the relation

$$SDef2 .: \forall r : KReTypes \cdot SReSet_r =_d SResAlloc_r + SResFree_r$$

This implies that for any r, $SResAlloc_r$ and $SResFree_r$ are disjoint.

We introduce a third related variable feature, determined by *SResFree*. This is a predicate named $SIsCapAdeq(Ta)$ and defined for any task $Ta : KTasks$. It is specified as true iff there are enough free resources in S to accommodate Ta in addition to the currently active tasks. Thus, *SIsCapAdeq* is formally specified by

$$SDef3 .: \forall\ Ta : KTasks \cdot SIsCapAdeq(Ta) \Leftrightarrow_d \\ \forall r : KReTypes \cdot KReqNum_r(Ta) \leqslant \mathrm{Num}(SResFree_r)$$

These additional features are grouped below, in what we may regard as a *noncreative extension* of Alloc (see Section **9**.1D).

S: Alloc Secondary Features I

$SResAlloc_r \subseteq_d KReSet_r$	Total set of allocated resources of type r
$SDef1 .: \forall r : KReTypes \cdot$ $SResAlloc_r =_d \Sigma \{SResAll_r(Ta) \mid Ta : STasksAct\}$	
$SResFree_r \subseteq_d KReSet_r$	Set of owned resources of type r free i.e. unallocated
$SDef2 .: \forall r : KReTypes \cdot$ $SReSet_r =_d SResAlloc_r + SResFree_r$	
$SIsCapAdeq(Ta)$: Bool $(Ta : KTasks)$	True iff spare resource capacity is adequate to accommodate task Ta
$SDef3 .: \forall\ Ta : KTasks \cdot SIsCapAdeq(Ta) \Leftrightarrow_d$ $\forall r : KReTypes \cdot KReqNum_r(Ta) \leqslant \mathrm{Num}(SResFree_r)$	

17.2D Further implications of the core model

We now establish a number of secondary properties or fixed features implied by the primary features of any S: Alloc. These are relatively obvious but important to bear in mind. Brief justifications of proof steps are given enclosed in square brackets.

SImp1 The first property is that in any S: Alloc, the set $SResFree_r$ is well defined, that is, exists uniquely for each resource type r. This is implied by *SDef1*, *SCond3* and *SDef2*.

$$SImp1 .: \forall r : KReTypes \cdot SResFree_r \text{ is well defined, given by}$$
$$SResFree_r = SReSet_r - SResAlloc_r$$
$$[SDef1, SCond3, SDef2]$$

SImp2 The second property is that any active task *Ta* requires a certain resource type *r* iff *Ta* is allocated a nonempty set of resources of type *r*. This follows from condition *KCond2*, which states that *Ta* requires *r* iff the quantity of resources of type *r* required by *Ta* is positive, and from *SCond1*(1), which states that the resource requirements of an active task must be met. Formally:

$$\begin{aligned} &SImp2 .: \forall r : KReTypes, Ta : STasksAct \cdot \\ &\qquad r \in KReqTypes(Ta) \\ &\Leftrightarrow \qquad\qquad\qquad\qquad [KCond2, SCond1(1)] \\ &\qquad \text{Num}(SResAll_r(Ta)) \neq 0 \\ &\Leftrightarrow \qquad\qquad\qquad\qquad [\text{Property of Num}] \\ &\qquad SResAll_r(Ta) \neq \varnothing \end{aligned}$$

Note in connection with this property that in the definition of K: Alloc-Constants we have not excluded the possibility of a task *Ta* having *no* resource requirements. For such a task $Ta : KTasks$, $KReqTypes(Ta) = \varnothing$, and consequently $SResAll_r(Ta) = \varnothing$ for all $r : KReTypes$, even if *Ta* is active.

SImp3 The third property is that for any allocated resource unit of any type *r*, there exists *exactly one* active task *Ta* to which this resource is allocated.

$$\begin{aligned} &SImp3 .: \forall r : KReTypes \cdot \\ &\qquad \forall u : SResAlloc_r \; \exists 1 \; Ta : STasksAct \cdot u \in SResAll_r(Ta) \\ &\qquad\qquad [SCond2, SDef1] \end{aligned}$$

For the description of the next two properties, we introduce the function *KReqTypes1* derived from *KReqTypes*. Given a finite subset *Tas* of tasks, *KReqTypes1*(*Tas*) is the subset of resource types required by the members of *Tas*. This set is defined by the relation

$$KDef1 .: KReqTypes1(Tas) =_{\mathrm{d}} \cup \{KReqTypes(Ta) \mid Ta : Tas\}$$

SImp4 The fourth property is that the union of the resource types required by the active tasks is a subset of the types of owned resources.

$$SImp4.:KReqTypes1(STasksAct) \subseteq SReTypes \qquad [KDef1, SImp2, SCond3, SReCond]$$

SImp5 The fifth property is in two parts. First, a resource type r is in the set required by the active tasks iff some resources of this type are allocated to some tasks. Second, if any r is not in the set of types of owned resources, then there are no allocated resources of type r.

$SImp5.:\forall r:KReTypes\cdot$

(1) $r \in KReqTypes1(STasksAct) \Leftrightarrow SResAlloc_r \neq \emptyset$ [KDef1, SImp2, SDef1]

(2) $r \notin SReTypes \Rightarrow SResAlloc_r = \emptyset$ [SReCond, SCond3, SDef1]

These results are grouped as follows:

S:Alloc   Secondary Features II

$SImp1.:\forall r:KReTypes\cdot SResFree_r$ is well defined, given by

$SResFree_r = SReSet_r - SResAlloc_r$ [SDef1, SCond3, SDef2]

$SImp2.:\forall r:KReTypes, Ta:STasksAct\cdot$

$r \in KReqTypes(Ta)$

$\Leftrightarrow$ [KCond2, SCond1(1)]

$\text{Num}(SResAll_r(Ta)) \neq 0$

$\Leftrightarrow$ [Property of Num]

$SResAll_r(Ta) \neq \emptyset$

$SImp3.:\forall r:KReTypes\cdot \forall u:SResAlloc_r\ \exists 1\ Ta:STasksAct\cdot u \in SResAll_r(Ta)$ [SCond2, SDef1]

$SImp4.:KReqTypes1(STasksAct) \subseteq SReTypes$ [KDef1, SImp2, SCond3, SReCond]

$SImp5.:\forall r:KReTypes\cdot$

(1) $r \in KReqTypes1(STasksAct) \Leftrightarrow SResAlloc_r \neq \emptyset$ [KDef1, SImp2, SDef1]

(2) $r \notin SReTypes \Rightarrow SResAlloc_r = \emptyset$ [SReCond, SCond3, SDef1]

17.3 Core operations

As stated in Section **17**.1A, a ResAll system evolves in time. Each state of the system is transformed into a new state as a result of an elementary operation. We now describe the operations affecting the core features of the system, namely tasks, resources and their relations. Recall that the set of possible states is denoted by Alloc.

These operations may take as argument(s) an initial state S: Alloc and possibly other variables, and they return a new state S': Alloc. For each operation we first establish its *preconditions*, if any, and its *primary effects*. The preconditions determine the definition domain of the operation. The primary effects are conditions imposed on the new state S' and sufficient to determine all the variable features of S'. This forms the specification proper of the operation.

In principle the primary effects should be *minimal*: any additional constraint should be either redundant, because implied by them, or inconsistent with them (Section **10**.3B). Note that in order to establish that the primary effects determine *all* the variable features of S', it is sufficient to show that they determine all the *primary* variable features of S'.

The specification proper of an operation is followed by an *analysis* of its primary effects, namely the identification of some key features of S' which they imply. The derivation of these consequences is given in outline.

17.3A Initialization

There is one initialization operation, namely the nullary function Emp. This returns the 'empty' state S': Alloc in which all primary sets are empty. For this operation, it is not necessary to specify all the primary variable features of the result S'. Because of its special nature, S' is entirely determined by imposing emptiness explicitly on only two sets: $S'TasksTotal$ and $S'ReTypes$. The formal establishment of Emp is as follows:

Emp

Emp $=_d S'$: Alloc where
(1) $S'TasksTotal =_d \varnothing$
(2) $S'ReTypes =_d \varnothing$

We must verify that this definition determines all the variable features of $S' =$ Emp, and that for each such feature the implied value is as expected. Consider each primary variable feature of S' in turn.

1 It is clear that the constraint $S'TasksTotal = \varnothing$ implies that all the task sets of S' must be empty, by $S'TasksCond$.

2 Likewise, if $S'ReTypes = \varnothing$, then each resource set $S'ReSet_r$ must be empty, by $S'ReCond(1)$.

3 In turn, if there are no owned resources, then there are no resources to allocate and consequently every set $S'ResAll_r(Ta)$ must be empty, by $S'Cond3$.

We conclude that all the primary variable features of S' are determined as expected. On the other hand, it is also clear that the two conditions defining

Emp are *minimal*: they are needed jointly to specify S' completely. We put these implied features together as a 'noncreative extension' of Emp. We include in the list two implied variable features, namely $S'ResAlloc_r$ and $S'ResFree_r$, and show that these too are exactly determined.

Emp	Implied Features I	
Implications of (1)		
(I1.1)	$S'TasksAct = \varnothing$	[$S'TasksCond$, (1)]
(I1.2)	$S'TasksInact = \varnothing$	[$S'TasksCond$, (1)]
Implications of (2)		
(I2.1)	$\forall r{:}KReTypes \cdot S'ReSet_r = \varnothing$	[$S'ReCond$(1), (2)]
(I2.2)	$\forall r{:}KReTypes, Ta{:}KTasks \cdot S'ResAll_r(Ta) = \varnothing$	[$S'Cond3$, (I2.1)]
(I2.3)	$\forall r{:}KReTypes \cdot S'ResAlloc_r = \varnothing$	[$S'Def2$, (I2.1)]
(I2.4)	$\forall r{:}KReTypes \cdot S'ResFree_r = \varnothing$	[$S'Def2$, (I2.1)]

Note that some implications may be reached by several routes. For instance, (I2.3) – there are no allocated resources – also follows from $S'Def1$ and (I2.2). On the other hand, (I2.1) – the absence of owned resources – does *not* imply $S'TasksAct = \varnothing$. (Why?) As a rule, we give the most direct derivation.

17.3B Task operations

Next, we introduce two operations on sets of tasks. Both operations transform an initial state S:Alloc into a new state S':Alloc. The first adds a new task Ta to $STasksTotal$, with 'inactive' status. The second removes a task Ta from this set, provided Ta is inactive. We begin with the insertion of a new task in $STasksTotal$.

InsTask

Given S:Alloc and $Ta{:}KTasks$ with

(Pre 1) $Ta \notin STasksTotal$

InsTask(S, Ta) $=_d S'$ where S':Alloc and

(1) $S'TasksTotal =_d STasksTotal + \{Ta\}$

(2) $S'TasksInact =_d STasksInact + \{Ta\}$

(3) $S'Re =_d SRe$

(4) $S'ResAll =_d SResAll$

As for Emp, we must verify that $S' =_d$ InsTask(S, Ta) is completely determined. This follows immediately from (3) and (4) for the primary resource features and the function $S'ResAll$. As for the tasks features, two sets are directly specified by (1) and (2). The third, the set $S'TasksAct$ of active tasks, is determined by (1), (2) and $STasksCond$. These imply that $S'TasksAct = STasksAct$, that is, the active tasks are unchanged, as expected intuitively.

We add two further obvious implications, namely the conservation of the total set $SResAlloc_r$ of allocated resources, and of the set $SResFree_r$ of free resources, for each resource type r.

InsTask Implied Features I

Implications of (1) and (2)

(I1.1) $S'TasksAct = STasksAct$ [$STasksCond$, $S'TasksCond$, (1), (2)]

Implications of (1), (2) and (4)

(I2.1) $\forall r: KReTypes \cdot S'ResAlloc_r = SResAlloc_r$ [$SDef1$, $S'Def1$, (I1.1), (4)]

Implications of (1)–(4)

(I3.1) $\forall r: KReTypes \cdot S'ResFree_r = SResFree_r$ [$SDef2$, $S'Def2$, (3), (I2.1)]

The next operation, RemTask, reverses the effect of InsTask: it removes an inactive task Ta from $STasksTotal$. Note the slight asymmetry between these two operations. While in InsTask the precondition is that Ta is not an actual task, in RemTask the precondition is that Ta is both actual and inactive.

RemTask

Given S: Alloc and $Ta: KTasks$ with

(Pre 1) $Ta \in STasksInact$

RemTask(S, Ta) $=_d S'$ where S': Alloc and

(1) $S'TasksTotal =_d STasksTotal - \{Ta\}$

(2) $S'TasksInact =_d STasksInact - \{Ta\}$

(3) $S'Re =_d SRe$

(4) $S'ResAll =_d SResAll$

In this operation again, the set $STasksAct$ is left unchanged as an implication. Moreover, as in InsTask, the resource features SRe and the function $SResAll$ are unchanged by (3) and (4). Consequently the global resource allocation features also are left unchanged (implications (I2.1), (I3.1)).

RemTask Implied Features I

Implications of (1) and (2)

(I1.1) $S'TasksAct = STasksAct$ [$STasksCond$, $S'TasksCond$, (1), (2)]

Implications of (1), (2) and (4)

(I2.1) $\forall r: KReTypes \cdot S'ResAlloc_r = SResAlloc_r$ [$SDef1$, $S'Def1$, (I1.1), (4)]

Implications of (1)–(4)

(I3.1) $\forall r: KReTypes \cdot S'ResFree_r = SResFree_r$ [$SDef2$, $S'Def2$, (3), (I2.1)]

17.3C Resource operations

Next, we establish two operations on resources. The first adds a resource unit u of a given type ru to $SReSet_{ru}$ and the second removes u from $SReSet_{ru}$, provided it is free in S. These two operations are analogous to the previous ones on tasks. They may be established by systematically transforming the latter in a fairly obvious way.

InsRes

Given S: Alloc, $ru: KReTypes$ and $u: KReSet_{ru}$ with

(Pre 1) $u \notin SReSet_{ru}$

InsRes(S, u) $=_d S'$ where S': Alloc and

(1) $S'Tasks =_d STasks$

(2) $S'ReSet_{ru} =_d SReSet_{ru} + \{u\}$

(3) $\forall r: KReTypes - \{ru\} \cdot S'ReSet_r =_d SReSet_r$

(4) $S'ResAll =_d SResAll$

In the case of InsRes, we must again verify that all the features of the result S' are determined entirely and correctly. This is directly so for all the task features, by (1). For each resource type r, the set $S'ReSet_r$ is exactly determined by (2) and (3). This in turn determines the *type* set $S'ReTypes$, by $SReCond$. The function $S'ResAll$ is directly determined by (4). This in turn determines $S'ResAlloc_r$ and $S'ResFree_r$.

InsRes Implied Features I

Implications of (1) and (4)

(I1.1) $\forall r: KReTypes \cdot S'ResAlloc_r = SResAlloc_r$ [$SDef1$, $S'Def1$, (1), (4)]

Implications of (2), (3)

(I2.1) $S'ReTypes = SReTypes \cup \{ru\}$ [$SReCond$, $S'ReCond$, (2), (3)]

Implications of (1)–(4)

(I3.1) $S'ResFree_{ru} = SResFree_{ru} + \{u\}$ [$SDef2$, $S'Def2$, (2), (I1.1)]

(I3.2) $\forall r: KReTypes - \{ru\} \cdot S'ResFree_r = SResFree_r$ [$SDef2$, $S'Def2$, (3), (I1.1)]

The next operation reverses the effect of InsRes: it removes a resource unit u of type ru from $SReSet_{ru}$, provided u is free. Here, the precondition is that the unit removed is a free owned resource.

On account of the symmetry between InsRes and RemRes, we verify the latter in the same way as the former: the above comments on the implications of InsRes hold *mutatis mutandis*.

RemRes

Given S: Alloc, ru: $KReTypes$ and u: $KReSet_{ru}$ with

(Pre 1) $u \in SResFree_{ru}$

RemRes(S, u) $=_d S'$ where S': Alloc and

(1) $S'Tasks =_d STasks$

(2) $S'ReSet_{ru} =_d SReSet_{ru} - \{u\}$

(3) $\forall r: KReTypes - \{ru\} \cdot S'ReSet_r =_d SReSet_r$

(4) $S'ResAll =_d SResAll$

RemRes Implied Features I

Implications of (1) and (4)

(I1.1) $\forall r: KReTypes \cdot S'ResAlloc_r = SResAlloc_r$ [$SDef1$, $S'Def1$, (1), (4)]

Implications of (Pre 1), (2), (3)

(I2.1) $u \in SReSet_{ru} \neq \varnothing$ [$SDef2$, (Pre 1)]

(I2.2) $ru \in SReTypes$ [$SReCond$, (I2.1)]

(I2.3) $S'ReTypes = SReTypes - \{ru\}$ if $SReSet_{ru} = \{u\}$;
$SReTypes$ otherwise [$SReCond$, $S'ReCond$, (2), (3), (I2.2)]

Implications of (1)–(4)

(I3.1) $S'ResFree_{ru} = SResFree_{ru} - \{u\}$ [$SDef2$, $S'Def2$, (2), (I1.1)]

(I3.2) $\forall r: KReTypes - \{ru\} \cdot S'ResFree_r = SResFree_r$ [$SDef2$, $S'Def2$, (3), (I1.1)]

17.3D Resource allocation operations

The last two operations 'activate' and 'deactivate' an actual task Ta in $STasksTotal$. In other words, they respectively transfer Ta from $STasksInact$ to $STasksAct$ and vice versa. This has a corresponding effect on the resource allocation of S.

The first operation is named Activate. It is *underspecified* in the sense that the resources allocated to the activated task are not individually determined by the operation: they must be fixed by some auxiliary mechanism or choice function to be provided separately, as an 'implementation feature'.

Activate

Given S: Alloc and Ta: $KTasks$ with

(Pre 1) $Ta \in STasksInact$

(Pre 2) $SIsCapAdeq(Ta)$

Activate(S, Ta) $=_d S'$ where S': Alloc and

(1) $S'TasksInact =_d STasksInact - \{Ta\}$

(2) $S'TasksAct =_d STasksAct + \{Ta\}$

(3) $S'Re =_d SRe$

(4) $\forall r: KReTypes, Ta': STasksAct \cdot S'ResAll_r(Ta') =_d SResAll_r(Ta')$

We use the predicate *SIsCapAdeq* in the precondition of Activate. Recall that by *SDef3*, for any task *Ta*, *SIsCapAdeq*(*Ta*) is true iff all the resource requirements of *Ta* may be satisfied by the spare resource capacity of *S*.

We verify that the result *S′* is entirely and correctly determined.

1 All the task sets are determined as expected, two directly by (1) and (2), and the third, *S′TasksTotal*, indirectly by (1), (2) and *STasksCond*.

2 The resource features of *S* are conserved, by (3).

3 As for the function *ResAll*, this is only partly specified. For each resource type *r* and all tasks *Ta′* different from *Ta*, $SResAll_r(Ta')$ is left unchanged by (4). $S'ResAll_r(Ta)$ is *underdetermined*. It must be a subset of $SResFree_r$, by (2), (3) and (4), and its cardinality must be equal to $KReqNum_r(Ta)$ by *S′Cond1*(1). Subject to these constraints, the actual units allocated to *Ta* are left unspecified.

4 In view of the precondition (Pre 2), it is clear that the two sets $S'ResAlloc_r$ and $S'ResFree_r$ are well determined by

$$S'ResAlloc_r = SResAlloc_r + S'ResAll_r(Ta)$$
$$S'ResFree_r = SResFree_r - S'ResAll_r(Ta)$$

Activate Implied Features I

Implications of (1) and (2)

(I1.1) $S'TasksTotal = STasksTotal$ [*STasksCond*, *S′TasksCond*, (1), (2)]

Implications of (2) and (4)

(I2.1) $\forall r: KReTypes \cdot S'ResAlloc_r = SResAlloc_r + S'ResAll_r(Ta)$ [*SDef1*, *S′Def1*, (2), (4)]

Implications of (2), (3) and (4)

(I3.1) $\forall r: KReTypes \cdot S'ResAll_r(Ta) \subseteq SResFree_r$
[*S′Cond3*, *SDef1*, *S′Def1*, *SDef2*, (2), (3), (4)]

(I3.2) $\forall r: KReTypes \cdot S'ResFree_r = SResFree_r - S'ResAll_r(Ta)$
[*SDef2*, *S′Def2*, (3), (I2.1), (I3.1)]

The underdeterminacy of Activitate may prove inappropriate in some applications. As an alternative, we may make this operation entirely deterministic by passing the resources to be allocated to *Ta* as a third explicit parameter *ReAll*. This is a function which defines for each *r*:*KReTypes* the specific set $ReAll_r$ of resources of type *r* to be allocated to *Ta*. As a new precondition (Pre 2), $ReAll_r$ must be a subset of the free owned resources of *S*. Moreover, its cardinality must meet the requirements of *Ta*, that is, must be equal to $KReqNum_r(Ta)$. The establishment of this alternative, called Activate1, follows without analysis of its implications.

Activate1

Given S: Alloc, $Ta: KTasks$ and $(ReAll_r \subseteq_d KReSet_r | r: KReTypes)$ with

(Pre 1) $Ta \in STasksInact$

(Pre 2) (a) $\forall r: KReTypes \cdot ReAll_r \subseteq_d SResFree_r$

(b) $\forall r: KReTypes \cdot \text{Num}(ReAll_r) = KReqNum_r(Ta)$

Activate1$(S, Ta, ReAll) =_d S'$ where S': Alloc and

(1) $S'TasksInact =_d STasksInact - \{Ta\}$

(2) $S'TasksAct =_d STasksAct + \{Ta\}$

(3) $S'Re =_d SRe$

(4) $\forall r: KReTypes, Ta': STasksAct \cdot S'ResAll_r(Ta') =_d SResAll_r(Ta')$

(5) $\forall r: KReTypes \cdot S'ResAll_r(Ta) =_d ReAll_r$

The inverse of Activate is Deactivate. There is a slight asymmetry between these two functions. First, there is no precondition imposed on the owned resources in Deactivate: any active task may always be suspended at any time, as this can only free some resources. Second, unlike its predecessor, Deactivate is entirely deterministic.

Deactivate

Given S: Alloc and $Ta: KTasks$ with

(Pre 1) $Ta \in STasksAct$

Deactivate$(S, Ta) =_d S'$ where S': Alloc and

(1) $S'TasksInact =_d STasksInact + \{Ta\}$

(2) $S'TasksAct =_d STasksAct - \{Ta\}$

(3) $S'Re =_d SRe$

(4) $\forall r: KReTypes, Ta': S'TasksAct \cdot S'ResAll_r(Ta') =_d SResAll_r(Ta')$

The implications of this description are similar to those of Activate. Thus, the result S' is entirely determined. In particular, in S' the set $S'ResAll_r(Ta)$ is determined: it must be equal to $\varnothing$, by (2) and $S'Cond1$(2).

Deactivate — Implied Features I

Implications of (2)

(I1.1) $\forall r: KReTypes \cdot S'ResAll_r(Ta) = \varnothing$ [$S'Cond1$(2), (2)]

Implications of (1) and (2)

(I2.1) $S'TasksTotal = STasksTotal$ [$STasksCond$, $S'TasksCond$, (1), (2)]

Implications of (2) and (4)

(I3.1) $\forall r: KReTypes \cdot S'ResAlloc_r = SResAlloc_r - SResAll_r(Ta)$

[$SDef1$, $S'Def1$, (2), (4)]

Implications of (2), (3) and (4)

(I4.1) $\forall r: KReTypes \cdot S'ResFree_r = SResFree_r + SResAll_r(Ta)$

[$SDef2$, $S'Def2$, (3), (I3.1)]

17.4 Agents and authority

In this section, we extend the core model of ResAll by introducing *agents* and various relations between these and core features.

First, we add new constant features to allow for agents. This is done as an extension of the original class AllocConstants of constant features.

Second, we establish the various sets of agents which may actually exist at any time and the relations which connect these sets. These new features are described in a new module named AgentStates, similar to TaskStates and ResourceStates. It is at this level that we make the distinction between *users*, or customers, and *members of staff* or employees.

Third, we combine these new elements with the core model of ResAll as described by the class Alloc. This is done by adding the new elements to the features of the members of Alloc, together with further functions and relations connecting core and new features. The result is a new class AllocA.

Finally, we adapt the original core operations as appropriate and establish new operations to allow for agents.

17.4A Constant features

Three constant features are added at this stage, as an extension of the establishment of K: AllocConstants.

The first feature is the set *KAgents*. This is the class of all agents, actual or potential. If defined, an agent is either a user, or a member of staff, or both. However, this distinction is made only at the state level – that is, between variable features.

The second feature is a special value *KAgUndef* of *KAgents*, standing for 'undefined'. In any function to *KAgents*, this value is assigned to any domain member x to represent the fact that x is not mapped to any actual or potential agent. This is required by our strategy of defining all functions as total, with constant domain and codomain.

The third new feature of K is the set *KAuthoLevels* of so-called *authority levels*. This is a finite subset of the natural numbers. It is used to represent the rule that any member of staff and any task is assigned an authority level, and a staff member may be assigned a task only if the authority level of the former is no less than the authority level of the latter. *KAuthoLevels* must contain at least one value, the number 0. The functions defining authority levels are themselves established as variable features.

These new features are established as an extension of AllocConstants in the usual format.

K: AllocAConstants (Extended AllocConstants)	
K[*AllocConstants*]: AllocConstants	Core constant features
KAgents: Set	Class of agents: users, staff, etc.
KAgUndef: *KAgents*	Undefined agent
$KAuthoLevels \subseteq_d \mathrm{Nat}$	Set of authority levels
$KAutCond .\!: 0 \in KAuthoLevels$	

Recall from Section **10**.3D that in this definition *KAllocConstants* is a group feature. It stands for all the features imported from AllocConstants: *KTasks*, *KReTypes*, and so on.

17.4B Agent features

Next, we introduce actual agents. These fall into four groups. The total set of agents existing at a given time, or actual agents, is *AgentsTotal.* This includes two subsets: the set *AgentsStaff* of *members of staff* or employees, and the set *AgentsUser* of *users* or customers. Any actual agent must belong to one of these two subsets and may be a member of both. Consequently, we also introduce the subset *AgentsUserExt* of those users who are not members of staff, or *external users.*

These four sets must satisfy three obvious conditions. The first is that an actual agent may not be the special value *KAgUndef,* which stands for 'non-existent'. This is expressed formally as

$$AgentsCond1 .\!: KAgUndef \notin AgentsTotal$$

The other two conditions reflect the above informal introduction of agent sets. The second is that *AgentsTotal* must be the union of *AgentsStaff* and *AgentsUser.*

$$AgentsCond2 .\!: AgentsTotal =_d AgentsStaff \cup AgentsUser$$

In this union the two operands are not necessarily disjoint, which is reflected in the use of the standard operator '$\cup$'.

The third condition expresses the fact that *AgentsUserExt* is the set of those actual users who are not members of staff:

$$AgentsCond3 .\!: AgentsUserExt =_d AgentsUser \setminus AgentsStaff$$

Note that the relative complement operator '\' indicates that *AgentsStaff* need not be a subset of *AgentsUser.*

These various features characterize the actual agents of a ResAll system state. They are grouped below in the usual way. In the definition *AgentsStaff* and *AgentsUser* are labelled as *primary features*. They determine the other two variable features exactly, on account of *AgentsCond2* and *AgentsCond3*.

Agents: AgentStates

*	*AgentsStaff*,	Set of members of staff
*	*AgentsUser*,	Set of users (nonstaff or staff)
	AgentsTotal,	Total set of agents
	$AgentsUserExt \subseteq_d KAgents$	External, i.e. nonstaff users

$AgentsCond1 .: KAgUndef \notin AgentsTotal$

$AgentsCond2 .: AgentsTotal =_d AgentsStaff \cup AgentsUser$

$AgentsCond3 .: AgentsUserExt =_d AgentsUser \setminus AgentsStaff$

17.4C Agent and core features

We may now integrate the core features of ResAll with the new elements just introduced. This is done by augmenting the features of any ResAll state *S*: Alloc with the agent features we have established. Within *S*, these are denoted by *SAgents*: AgentStates in Feature Notation. In addition, we introduce various functions and relations connecting core and agent features. These fall into two groups: task–agent relations on the one hand, and authority relations on the other. We establish these in turn.

Task–agent relations

The task–agent relations involve two functions related to previous features. First, it is assumed that any actual task *Ta* may be carried out for the benefit of a user or customer. The beneficiary is called the *owner* of *Ta* and denoted by *SAgOwner*(*Ta*) as part of state *S*. *SAgOwner* is a total function

$$SAgOwner: KTasks \rightarrow KAgents$$

This function must satisfy the following two-part condition. For any task *Ta*: *KTasks*, if *Ta* is an actual task – i.e. $Ta \in STasksTotal$ – the owner of *Ta* either is a user or is undefined; otherwise, the owner is undefined.

$SAgCond1 .: \forall\ Ta: KTasks \cdot$

(1) $Ta \in STasksTotal \Rightarrow$
$\quad SAgOwner(Ta) \in SAgentsUser + \{KAgUndef\}$

(2) $Ta \notin STasksTotal \Rightarrow SAgOwner(Ta) =_d KAgUndef$

Second, it is assumed that any actual task *Ta* may be assigned to a member of staff, which means that the latter is responsible for the proper execution of the former. The employee to whom *Ta* is assigned is called the *agent responsible* for *Ta* and denoted by *SAgResp(Ta)* within *S*. *SAgResp* is a total function

$$SAgResp: KTasks \rightarrow KAgents$$

This function must satisfy a condition similar to that imposed on *SAgOwner*. For any task *Ta*: *KTasks*, if *Ta* is an actual task, the agent responsible for *Ta* either is a member of staff or is undefined; otherwise, no one is assigned to *Ta*.

$$\begin{aligned} &SAgCond2 .: \forall\ Ta: KTasks \cdot \\ &\quad (1) \quad Ta \in STasksTotal \Rightarrow \\ &\qquad\qquad SAgResp(Ta) \in SAgentsStaff + \{KAgUndef\} \\ &\quad (2) \quad Ta \notin STasksTotal \Rightarrow SAgResp(Ta) =_{\mathrm{d}} KAgUndef \end{aligned}$$

Authority relations

The authority relations involve two functions. The first assigns a natural number called authority level to any agent *Ag*: *KAgents*. This is denoted by *SAutLev(Ag)* and must be a member of *KAuthoLevels*. *SAutLev* is a function

$$SAutLev: KAgents \rightarrow KAuthoLevels$$

It must satisfy the condition that for any agent who is not a member of staff, the corresponding level is equal to 0:

$$SAutCond1 .: \forall\ Ag: KAgents \cdot Ag \notin SAgentsStaff \Rightarrow SAutLev(Ag) =_{\mathrm{d}} 0$$

Note that this requirement can always be satisfied, in view of *KAutCond*.

The second function is similar to the first. It assigns an *authority required* level to any task *Ta*: *KTasks*. This is denoted by *SAutReq(Ta)*, and must also be a member of *KAuthoLevels*. *SAutReq* is a function

$$SAutReq: KTasks \rightarrow KAuthoLevels$$

The main condition relating these two functions is that for any task *Ta*, the authority level required by *Ta* must not exceed the authority level of the employee responsible for it:

$$SAutCond2 .: \forall\ Ta: STasksTotal \cdot SAutReq(Ta) \leqslant SAutLev(SAgResp(Ta))$$

This completes our first extension of the core model of ResAll. The various elements presented above are summarized below. In this definition, all four new functions are primary features.

S: AllocA (Extended Alloc)

*	$S[Alloc]$: Alloc	Core features
*	$SAgents$: AgentStates	
	Task–Agent Relations	
*	$SAgOwner(Ta): KAgents$	Owner or beneficiary of task Ta
	$(Ta: KTasks)$	
	$SAgCond1 .: \forall\ Ta: KTasks \cdot$	
	(1) $Ta \in STasksTotal \Rightarrow$	
	$SAgOwner(Ta) \in SAgentsUser + \{KAgUndef\}$	
	(2) $Ta \notin STasksTotal \Rightarrow SAgOwner(Ta) =_{\mathrm{d}} KAgUndef$	
*	$SAgResp(Ta): KAgents$	Employee responsible for task Ta
	$(Ta: KTasks)$	
	$SAgCond2 .: \forall\ Ta: KTasks \cdot$	
	(1) $Ta \in STasksTotal \Rightarrow$	
	$SAgResp(Ta) \in SAgentsStaff + \{KAgUndef\}$	
	(2) $Ta \notin STasksTotal \Rightarrow SAgResp(Ta) =_{\mathrm{d}} KAgUndef$	
	Authority Relations	
*	$SAutLev(Ag): KAuthoLevels$	Agent's authority level
	$(Ag: KAgents)$	
	$SAutCond1 .: \forall\ Ag: KAgents \cdot$	
	$Ag \notin SAgentsStaff \Rightarrow SAutLev(Ag) =_{\mathrm{d}} 0$	
*	$SAutReq(Ta): KAuthoLevels$	Authority level required by task Ta
	$(Ta: KTasks)$	
	$SAutCond2 .: \forall\ Ta: STasksTotal \cdot$	
	$SAutReq(Ta) \leqslant SAutLev(SAgResp(Ta))$	

Recall from Section **10**.3D that in this definition $SAlloc$ is the group feature representing all the features imported from Alloc: $STasks$, SRe, and so on. In $SAlloc$, '$Alloc$' is a 'dispensable' feature name.

17.5 Agent-extended operations

The addition of agents has two effects on ResAll operations. The core operations must be extended, and new operations must be established to allow for the new features.

First, we consider the core operations in turn. For each of them, we establish how it must be transformed to allow for agent features. The new version is given the name of the original function extended with the suffix 'A'. Second, we establish the new operations required by the new features.

Recall that for any S: AllocA, the group of features inherited from Alloc is denoted by $SAlloc$. Operations on any S: AllocA are constructed as extensions of operations on $SAlloc$.

17.5A Initialization

Recall that there is one initialization function, namely the nullary Emp, which returns a certain ResAll state S' : Alloc. Emp must be extended to a new function EmpA returning a state S' : AllocA. We must add to the specification of Emp that in the state S' the set $S'AgentsTotal$ is empty. This in turn implies that all the other features of $S'Agents$ are empty sets and so satisfy all three conditions $S'AgentsCond$. We shall see below that the four new functions defining task–agent and authority relations are also determined *as far as necessary* in S' and satisfy all the conditions imposed on them.

EmpA

EmpA $=_d S'$: AllocA where
(1) $S'Alloc =_d$ Emp
(2) $S'AgentsTotal =_d \varnothing$

Implications of EmpA

Condition EmpA(1) implies that all the consequences of Emp are satisfied by S'. Furthermore, as stated above, condition EmpA(2) implies that all the set features of $S'Agents$ are empty and so all the conditions stated in the definition of $S'Agents$ are met. It remains to consider the features of S' introduced under the headings 'tasks–agent relations' and 'authority relations'.

S'AgOwner For any Ta : $KTasks$, $Ta \notin S'TasksTotal = \varnothing$ by EmpA(1). Consequently $S'AgOwner(Ta) = KAgUndef$ by $S'AgCond1$(2). Therefore, the function $S'AgOwner$ is entirely determined.

S'AgResp By the same argument, for any Ta : $KTasks$, $Ta \notin S'TasksTotal$ and so $S'AgResp(Ta) = KAgUndef$ by $S'AgCond2$(2). Therefore, $S'AgResp$ is entirely determined.

S'AutLev Likewise, for any P : $KAgents$, $P \notin S'AgentsTotal = \varnothing$ by EmpA(2), hence $P \notin S'AgentsStaff$ by $S'AgentsCond2$ and so $S'AutLev(P) = 0$ by $S'AutCond1$. Therefore, $S'AutLev$ is entirely determined.

S'AutReq Unlike the previous three functions, $S'AutReq$ is not determined anywhere on its domain, as no definition of $S'AutReq(Ta)$ has been given for *any* Ta : $KTasks$. This reflects the modelling decision that the authority level required by a task should be determined only while this task is a member of $S'TasksTotal$, and should also be open to revision during this period.

This underdeterminacy does no harm. In particular, condition *S′AutCond2* is satisfied vacuously as it constrains the value *S′AutReq(Ta)* of a task *Ta* only if $Ta \in S'TasksTotal$, and this set is empty. Note that this analysis provides a useful reminder to ensure that the authority level of a new actual task is specified when this is added to a set *STasksTotal*.

17.5B Task operations

Next, we extend the two operations InsTask and RemTask. Recall that both operations take as argument a pair (*S*, *Ta*) where *S*: Alloc and *Ta*: *KTasks*, and return a new state *S′*: Alloc. The first adds *Ta* to *STasksTotal*, with 'inactive' status. The second removes *Ta* from this set, provided *Ta* is inactive.

InsTaskA

Consider first InsTaskA, the extended version of InsTask. When a task *Ta* is added to *STasksTotal*, we must ensure that all new functions of *Ta* are defined in *S′*. The relevant values are *S′AgOwner(Ta)*, *S′AgResp(Ta)* and *S′AutReq(Ta)*. These are passed as additional explicit arguments of InsTaskA, named *User*, *Resp* and *AuReq* respectively. Moreover, we must ensure that the values assigned to these arguments are consistent with all the constraints imposed on *S′* by the specification of AllocA.

As for the other features of *S′*, these are determined by the general aim to minimize the difference between *S* and *S′*, or *principle of minimum change*. Consider the preconditions of InsTaskA. These must include the original precondition of InsTask, namely $Ta \notin STasksTotal$. To this, we must add constraints on *Resp* and *AuReq* imposed by the the new conditions *S′AgCond* and *S′AutCond*. These are:

(1) *Resp*, the employee to be made responsible for *Ta*, must be either undefined or a member of staff in *S*:

$$Resp \in SAgentsStaff + \{KAgUndef\}$$

(2) *AuReq*, the authority level required by *Ta*, must not exceed the authority level of *Resp*:

$$AuReq \leqslant SAutLev(Resp)$$

There are no constraints imposed on *User*. We make sure that *User* is added to the set of users if necessary.

Next, consider the desired effects of InsTaskA. First, these must include all the effects of InsTask on the core features of *S*. This is expressed as

$$S'Alloc =_{\mathrm{d}} \mathrm{InsTask}(SAlloc, Ta)$$

Second, the agent sets of S' must be specified. These are entirely determined by fixing $S'AgentsStaff$ and $S'AgentsUser$, the primary features of $S'Agents$. As for members of staff, these do not change:

$$S'AgentsStaff =_d SAgentsStaff$$

To ensure that *User*, the intended owner of *Ta*, is recorded as an actual user in *S*, we specify

$$S'AgentsUser =_d SAgentsUser \cup \{User\}$$

Third, the four new functions must be specified. *SAutLev* defines the authority of employees, which does not change:

$$S'AutLev =_d SAutLev$$

The other three functions assign attributes to tasks. All three must be redefined for *Ta*, using the relevant arguments of InsTaskA. For all other tasks $Ta' : KTasks$, these functions do not change. A transformation of this kind may be described using the function-overriding operation defined in Section **3**.6C. Recall that for any function $F, x : FDom$ and $v : FCod$, $(F | x \mapsto v)$ denotes the function which assigns v to x and $F(y)$ to every other point $y : FDef$. We obtain respectively

$$S'AgOwner =_d (SAgOwner | Ta \mapsto User)$$
$$S'AgResp =_d (SAgResp | Ta \mapsto Resp)$$
$$S'AutReq =_d (SAutReq \mid Ta \mapsto AuReq)$$

These various conditions are put together in the usual form:

InsTaskA

Given S : AllocA, $Ta : KTasks$, $User, Resp : KAgents$, $AuReq : KAuthoLevels$ with

(Pre 1) $Ta \notin STasksTotal$

(Pre 2) $Resp \in SAgentsStaff + \{KAgUndef\}$

(Pre 3) $AuReq \leqslant SAutLev(Resp)$

InsTaskA(S, Ta, $User$, $Resp$, $AuReq$) $=_d S'$ where S' : AllocA and

(1) $S'Alloc =_d$ InsTask($SAlloc$, Ta)

(2) (a) $S'AgentsStaff =_d SAgentsStaff$

(b) $S'AgentsUser =_d SAgentsUser \cup \{User\}$

(3) (a) $S'AgOwner =_d (SAgOwner | Ta \mapsto User)$

(b) $S'AgResp =_d (SAgResp | Ta \mapsto Resp)$

(c) $S'AutLev =_d SAutLev$

(d) $S'AutReq =_d (SAutReq | Ta \mapsto AuReq)$

Implications of InsTaskA

1 On account of (1), all the implications of InsTask are inherited by InsTaskA.

2 Precondition (Pre 3) has the following consequence. If a task is specified with a positive authority requirement then an employee (with sufficient authority) must be assigned to *Ta*. That is, if $AuReq > 0$ then *Resp* may not be specified as *KAgUndef*. This is because for any S: AllocA, $SAutLev(KAgUndef) = 0$ by *SAgentsCond1*, *SAgentsCond2* and *SAutCond1*, and with this value (Pre 3) is not satisfied.

RemTaskA

Given a state S: AllocA and a task Ta: *KTasks* in *STasksTotal*, the aim of RemTaskA is to remove *Ta* from *STasksTotal*, giving a new state S': AllocA. This is a straightforward extension of RemTask. As RemTaskA partially reverses the effect of InsTaskA, we seek to derive it from the latter systematically.

The other effects of RemTaskA are determined by the conditions imposed on any member of AllocA, combined with the principle of minimum change: subject to the elimination of *Ta*, the difference between S and S' must be as small as possible.

The arguments of RemTaskA are the pair (S, Ta), and the result is the new state S'. Clearly the operation is well defined iff the precondition of RemTask is satisfied; this is $Ta \in STasksInact$.

As with InsTaskA, we define the main effect of RemTaskA as the application of RemTask to SAlloc. As a result, all the implications of RemTask are inherited by S'. Thus:

$$S'Alloc =_{\mathrm{d}} \mathrm{RemTask}(SAlloc, Ta)$$

Next, the primary agent sets of S' must be specified, that is, *S′AgentsStaff* and *S′AgentsUser*. The set *SAgentsStaff* is left unchanged. As for the set of users, two alternatives may be considered. The first is to leave the set *SAgentsUser* unchanged, by a strict application of the principle of minimum change. The second is to remove the owner of *Ta* from *SAgentsUser* if this agent does not own any other actual task. Although this second option is consistent with the definition of any S: AllocA and is justifiable, the first seems more appropriate: it reflects the practice of keeping records of past customers. Thus we may write $S'AgentsStaff =_{\mathrm{d}} SAgentsStaff$ and $S'AgentsUser =_{\mathrm{d}} SAgentsUser$ or, globally, $S'Agents =_{\mathrm{d}} SAgents$.

Finally, the variable features grouped under $S'Ag$ and $S'Aut$ must be established. The function *SAutLev* again is left unchanged, as it does not involve tasks: $S'AutLev =_{\mathrm{d}} SAutLev$.

The other features are three functions with domain *KTasks*. The values they assign to any task Ta' different from *Ta* are left unchanged by the principle of minimum change. It remains to establish the values assigned to *Ta*.

As $Ta \notin S'TasksTotal$ by condition RemTask(1), $S'AgOwner(Ta) = KAgUndef$ by $S'AgCond1$(2) and $S'AgResp(Ta) = KAgUndef$ by $S'AgCond2$(2). Hence we may write:

$$S'AgOwner =_{\text{d}} (SAgOwner \mid Ta \mapsto KAgUndef)$$

$$S'AgResp =_{\text{d}} (SAgResp \mid Ta \mapsto KAgUndef)$$

(Note this specification is slightly redundant – why?)

As for $S'AutReq(Ta)$, this is not constrained in any way, so we leave this value unchanged by the principle of minimum change: $S'AutReq =_{\text{d}} SAutReq$. This condition, combined with $S'AutLev =_{\text{d}} SAutLev$, is simply expressed as $S'Aut =_{\text{d}} SAut$. The formal definition of RemTaskA is as follows:

RemTaskA

Given S: AllocA and Ta: $KTasks$ with
(Pre 1) $Ta \in STasksInact$
RemTaskA(S, Ta) $=_{\text{d}} S'$ where S': AllocA and
(1) $S'Alloc =_{\text{d}}$ RemTask($SAlloc$, Ta)
(2) $S'Agents =_{\text{d}} SAgents$
(3) (a) $S'AgOwner =_{\text{d}} (SAgOwner \mid Ta \mapsto KAgUndef)$
(b) $S'AgResp =_{\text{d}} (SAgResp \mid Ta \mapsto KAgUndef)$
(c) $S'Aut =_{\text{d}} SAut$

17.5C Other operations

The extension of remaining core operations is entirely straightforward. The reason is that none of them modifies a relation between a task and an agent. Therefore in every case, all we need to do is replace operands S: Alloc by operands S: AllocA and apply the original core operation. In addition, we must specify that all the new, agent-related features of the initial state S are left unchanged. For each extended operation OpA, the application of the original operation Op takes the form

$$S'Alloc =_{\text{d}} \text{Op}(SAlloc, \text{—})$$

where '—' stands for any arguments of Op occurring in addition to S. The conservation of the agent-related features of S is an application of the principle of minimum change. It always takes the form

(a) $S'Agents =_{\text{d}} SAgents$

(b) $S'Ag =_{\text{d}} SAg$

(c) $S'Aut =_{\text{d}} SAut$

The formal definitions may be given without more ado.

<u>InsResA</u>

Given S: AllocA, ru: $KReTypes$ and u: $KReSet_{ru}$ with

(Pre 1) $u \notin SReSet_{ru}$

InsResA(S, u) $=_d$ S' where S': AllocA and

(1) $S'Alloc =_d \text{InsRes}(SAlloc, u)$

(2) (a) $S'Agents =_d SAgents$

(b) $S'Ag =_d SAg$

(c) $S'Aut =_d SAut$

<u>RemResA</u>

Given S: AllocA, ru: $KReTypes$ and u: $KReSet_{ru}$ with

(Pre 1) $u \in SResFree_{ru}$

RemResA(S, u) $=_d$ S' where S': AllocA and

(1) $S'Alloc =_d \text{RemRes}(SAlloc, u)$

(2) (a) $S'Agents =_d SAgents$

(b) $S'Ag =_d SAg$

(c) $S'Aut =_d SAut$

<u>ActivateA</u>

Given S: Alloc and Ta: $KTasks$ with

(Pre 1) $Ta \in STasksInact$

(Pre 2) $SIsCapAdeq(Ta)$

ActivateA(S, Ta) $=_d$ S' where S': AllocA and

(1) $S'Alloc =_d \text{Activate}(SAlloc, Ta)$

(2) (a) $S'Agents =_d SAgents$

(b) $S'Ag =_d SAg$

(c) $S'Aut =_d SAut$

<u>Activate1A</u>

Given S: Alloc, Ta: $KTasks$ and $(ReAll_r \subseteq_d KReSet_r | r: KReTypes)$ with

(Pre 1) $Ta \in STasksInact$

(Pre 2) (a) $\forall r: KReTypes \cdot ReAll_r \subseteq_d SResFree_r$

(b) $\forall r: KReTypes \cdot \text{Num}(ReAll_r) = KReqNum_r(Ta)$

Activate1A(S, Ta, $ReAll$) $=_d$ S' where S': AllocA and

(1) $S'Alloc =_d \text{Activate1}(SAlloc, Ta, ReAll)$

(2) (a) $S'Agents =_d SAgents$

(b) $S'Ag =_d SAg$

(c) $S'Aut =_d SAut$

DeactivateA

Given S: AllocA and Ta: $KTasks$ with

(Pre 1) $Ta \in STasksAct$

DeactivateA(S, Ta) $=_d S'$ where S': AllocA and

(1) $S'Alloc =_d$ Deactivate($SAlloc$, Ta)

(2) (a) $S'Agents =_d SAgents$

(b) $S'Ag =_d SAg$

(c) $S'Aut =_d SAut$

17.6 New agent-related operations

In addition to their effects on core operations, the agent-related features entail new operations. These may be outlined as follows.

First, there are two operations to insert and remove a user from the set $SAgentsUser$ of a state S: AllocA. These are named InsUserA and RemUserA.

Second, there are two similar operations acting on the set $SAgentsStaff$ of members of staff of S. These are named InsStaffA and RemStaffA.

Third, there are two operations designed to update the authority level $SAutLev(Ag)$ of an agent Ag, and the authority level required $SAutReq(Ta)$ of an actual task Ta. These are named SetAutLevA and SetAutReqA.

In each case, the operation converts an initial state S: AllocA to a new state S': AllocA. This is subject to the rule of minimum change: given the explicit change specified in the operation, the difference between S and S' is minimized.

These six operations are straightforward. The main point of interest in each case is the analysis of the weakest precondition which each function requires in order to preserve the invariants of S: AllocA. Note that the precondition is weakest given the application of the rule of minimum change.

Other operations could be added to this list: for instance, functions to redefine the owner of a task or the employee responsible for it. These are not developed here as they do not seem to offer additional insights into the model.

17.6A User operations

InsUserA

Given a state S: AllocA and an agent Ag: $KAgents$, InsUserA adds Ag to the set $SAgentsUser$ of S, giving the new state S': AllocA. The operation is defined iff Ag is not already a user in S. Note that this condition is not essential: the operation could be defined more liberally, without this precondition.

The other features of S are left unchanged, by the minimum change rule. In particular the set of tasks owned by Ag is the same in both states; this set is empty, as Ag is a new user in S'. The establishment of InsUserA is thus entirely straightforward.

InsUserA

Given S: AllocA and $Ag: KAgents$ with

(Pre 1) $Ag \neq KAgUndef$

(Pre 2) $Ag \notin SAgentsUser$

InsUserA(S, Ag) $=_d S'$ where S': AllocA and

(1) $S'Alloc =_d SAlloc$

(2) (a) $S'AgentsStaff =_d SAgentsStaff$

(b) $S'AgentsUser =_d SAgentsUser + \{Ag\}$

(3) (a) $S'Ag =_d SAg$

(b) $S'Aut =_d SAut$

RemUserA

Given a state S: AllocA and an agent $User: KAgents$ such that $User$ is a member of $SAgentsUser$, RemUserA removes $User$ from this set, giving the new state S': AllocA.The minimum precondition of this operation is in two parts. First, $User$ must be a member of $SAgentsUser$:

$$User \in SAgentsUser$$

Second, $User$ must not own any tasks in S. This is formally expressed by

$$\forall\, Ta: STasksTotal \cdot SAgOwner(Ta) \neq User$$

The other features of S are unchanged.

RemUserA

Given S: AllocA and $User: KAgents$ with

(Pre 1) $User \in SAgentsUser$

(Pre 2) $\forall\, Ta: STasksTotal \cdot SAgOwner(Ta) \neq User$

RemUserA(S, $User$) $=_d S'$ where S': AllocA and

(1) $S'Alloc =_d SAlloc$

(2) (a) $S'AgentsStaff =_d SAgentsStaff$

(b) $S'AgentsUser =_d SAgentsUser - \{User\}$

(3) (a) $S'Ag =_d SAg$

(b) $S'Aut =_d SAut$

17.6B Employee operations

Employee operations are similar to user operations. They are developed on the pattern of the latter. The comments made on user operations apply to employee operations *mutatis mutandis.*

InsStaffA

Given a state S: AllocA and an agent Ag: *KAgents*, InsStaffA adds Ag to the set *SAgentsStaff* of S, giving the new state S': AllocA. The operation is defined iff Ag is not already a member of staff in S.

The other features of S are unchanged. This applies in particular to the authority level of Ag and the set of tasks for which Ag is responsible. In S, the former is equal to 0. This is not modified, which implies that Ag is treated as a very junior member of staff on appointment. Likewise, in S Ag may not be responsible for any task, and this remains so in S': you first get a job, then you are assigned specific tasks.

InsStaffA

Given S: AllocA and Ag: *KAgents* with
(Pre 1) $Ag \neq KAgUndef$
(Pre 2) $Ag \notin SAgentsStaff$
InsStaffA(S, Ag) $=_d S'$ where S': AllocA and
(1) $S'Alloc =_d SAlloc$
(2) (a) $S'AgentsStaff =_d SAgentsStaff + \{Ag\}$
(b) $S'AgentsUser =_d SAgentsUser$
(3) (a) $S'Ag =_d SAg$
(b) $S'Aut =_d SAut$

RemStaffA

Given a state S: AllocA and an agent *Empl*: *KAgents* such that *Empl* is a member of *SAgentsStaff*, RemStaffA removes *Empl* from this set, giving the new state S': AllocA.

As for RemUser, the minimum precondition of this operation is twofold. First, *Empl* must be a member of *SAgentsStaff*:

$$Empl \in SAgentsStaff$$

Second, *Empl* must not be responsible for any tasks in S. This is formally expressed by

$$\forall\, Ta : STasksTotal \cdot SAgResp(Ta) \neq Empl$$

Furthermore, the authority of *Empl* must be cancelled:

$$S'AutLev =_d (SAutLev \mid Empl \mapsto 0)$$

(This, again, is slightly redundant.) The other features of S are unchanged.

<u>RemStaffA</u>

Given S: AllocA and $Empl$: $KAgents$ with

(Pre 1) $Empl \in SAgentsStaff$

(Pre 2) $\forall\ Ta : STasksTotal \cdot SAgResp(Ta) \neq Empl$

RemStaffA(S, $Empl$) $=_d S'$ where S' : AllocA and

(1) $S'Alloc =_d SAlloc$

(2) (a) $S'AgentsStaff =_d SAgentsStaff - \{Empl\}$

(b) $S'AgentsUser =_d SAgentsUser$

(3) (a) $S'Ag =_d SAg$

(b) (i) $S'AutLev =_d (SAutLev \mid Empl \mapsto 0)$

(ii) $S'AutReq =_d SAutReq$

17.6C Authority level operations

The last two operations update the authority level $SAutLev(Ag)$ of an agent Ag, and the authority-required level $SAutReq(Ta)$ of an actual task Ta respectively. Each one is described as a function-overriding operation.

SetAutLevA

Consider any state S: AllocA and any agent $Empl$: $KAgents$ that is a member of $SAgentsStaff$. The purpose of SetAutLevA is to redefine $SAutLev(Empl)$ without modifying the other features of S, giving the new state S': AllocA. The new authority level assigned to *Empl* is passed as an argument $AuLev$: $KAuthoLevels$ of the operation, in addition to S and *Empl*.

The main difficulty here is to ensure that *AuLev* is sufficient for all the tasks already assigned to *Empl* in S. Therefore the preconditions of SetAutLevA are

$$Empl \in SAgentsStaff$$

$$\forall\ Ta : STasksTotal \cdot SAgResp(Ta) = Empl \Rightarrow SAutReq(Ta) \leqslant AuLev$$

The formal definition of SetAutLevA follows.

SetAutLevA

Given S: AllocA, $Empl: KAgents$ and $AuLev: KAuthoLevels$ with

(Pre 1) $Empl \in SAgentsStaff$

(Pre 2) $\forall\, Ta: STasksTotal \cdot SAgResp(Ta) = Empl \Rightarrow SAutReq(Ta) \leqslant AuLev$

SetAutLevA(S, $Empl$, $AuLev$) $=_{\mathrm{d}} S'$ where S': AllocA and

(1) $S'Alloc =_{\mathrm{d}} SAlloc$

(2) $S'Agents =_{\mathrm{d}} SAgents$

(3) $S'Ag =_{\mathrm{d}} SAg$

(4) (a) $S'AutLev =_{\mathrm{d}} (SAutLev \mid Empl \mapsto AuLev)$

(b) $S'AutReq =_{\mathrm{d}} SAutReq$

SetAutReqA

The last operation, SetAutReqA, is to tasks what SetAutLevA is to employees; indeed there is a certain symmetry between these two operations, which we exploit in developing the former. Given any state S: AllocA and any task $Ta: KTasks$ that is a member of $STasksTotal$, SetAutReqA redefines $SAutReq(Ta)$ without modifying the other features of S. The result is the new state S': AllocA.

The new authority-required level assigned to Ta is passed as an argument $AuReq: KAuthoLevels$ of the operation, in addition to S and Ta. Again, the main difficulty is to ensure that $AuReq$ does not exceed the authority level of the employee assigned to Ta. Consequently, the preconditions of SetAutReqA are

$$Ta \in STasksTotal$$
$$AuReq \leqslant SAutLev(SAgResp(Ta))$$

SetAutReqA

Given S: AllocA, $Ta: KTasks$ and $AuReq: KAuthoLevels$ with

(Pre 1) $Ta \in STasksTotal$

(Pre 2) $AuReq \leqslant SAutLev(SAgResp(Ta))$

SetAutReqA(S, Ta, $AuReq$) $=_{\mathrm{d}} S'$ where S': AllocA and

(1) $S'Alloc =_{\mathrm{d}} SAlloc$

(2) $S'Agents =_{\mathrm{d}} SAgents$

(3) $S'Ag =_{\mathrm{d}} SAg$

(4) (a) $S'AutLev =_{\mathrm{d}} SAutLev$

(b) $S'AutReq =_{\mathrm{d}} (SAutReq \mid Ta \mapsto AuReq)$

17.7 Decisions, errors and reports

So far, we have described the possible states of a ResAll system and their transformation rules, or operations. A state S is a collection of sets and relations holding at a certain time: sets of actual tasks to perform, owned resources, agents, and so on; relations such as the allocation of resources to tasks or the assignment of tasks to employees, and so on.

An operation transforms a state S into a new state S'. For instance, it adds a new task to the set of tasks or removes a resource from the set of owned resources. The life of the system may be described as a succession of states, each resulting from the application of an operation to the previous state.

In general, the transformations determining the successive states do not occur at random. They are the result of *decisions* made by people, employees and users mainly. In a library lending service for instance, a user decides to borrow a book, and this decision may or may not be sanctioned by an employee. The management decides to hire a new member of staff, or an employee decides to leave the organization.

Any decision is not necessarily consistent with the rules of the system: *errors* may be made and must be allowed for. Moreover, in order to make correct decisions, people need information on the system: for example, on its operating rules, its present state or, perhaps, its past performance. The provision of such information takes the form of *reports* of various types, including *error reports*.

We now incorporate these elements into our model. This last extension completes our development of ResAll.

17.7A Error handling

With regard to errors, two questions must be addressed. First, we must establish what constitutes an error. Second, we must establish the effect of erroneous decisions.

Two types of error may affect a decision. The first type consists in expressing the decision incorrectly: whatever is formulated does not correspond to any operation and therefore cannot be understood as a proper decision.

The second type of error consists in making a decision inconsistent with the present state of the system. The ResAll model developed so far contains all we need to establish precisely what this means. A decision is an attempt, made at a certain time, to apply a certain operation to the current state S: AllocA of the system. We say that *the decision is consistent iff all the preconditions of the operation are satisfied by S.* Thus, each precondition corresponds to a possible error, when the precondition is *not* satisfied, and the various preconditions established in previous sections give us a ready-made catalogue of possible errors.

This is a minimalist solution. It is chosen simply to guarantee that any state S' resulting from a consistent decision, or sequence of decisions, satisfies all the rules defining allowed states, that is, members of AllocA. Further conditions could be imposed, but this option is not considered here.

Next, we turn to the effect of an incorrect decision on the system state S obtaining at the time of the decision. We again adopt the simplest specification. If a decision is erroneous for whatever reason, then the state S is unchanged. More accurately, the new state S' is defined by the equation $S' =_d S$.

17.7B Reports

The main effect of a decision is to transform the state S of the system into a new state S'. We now assume that in addition to this main result, any decision also produces a *set* of reports. These are designed to meet the agents' information needs, and represent one further aspect of reality. The possibility of this set being empty is included. Note that we regard a report as just another object that may arise in the physical world and worthy of consideration. Whether it is to be generated by computer or by other means does not matter.

By *report* or *message*, we mean any piece of information. We follow the usual convention that a report has the form of a string of characters. However, this is only one possible alternative, adopted to fix the reader's ideas. There is no essential need to specify the concept of a report beyond the fact that it is a member of some predefined unbounded class.

We distinguish two main types of report. A *normal report* is produced in response to a correct decision or, in some cases, any decision. An *error report* is produced in response to an incorrect decision. Thus for a correct decision, all the reports produced are normal. For an erroneous one, the set produced may contain both normal and error reports. An example of a normal report that is returned whether the decision is correct or not is an acknowledgement that the decision is being considered or 'processed'.

We may now translate these ideas into the final extension of our theoretical model. First, we postulate the existence of two further constant features. These are the class *KRepsNorm*: Set, consisting of all possible normal reports, and the class *KRepsErr*: Set, consisting of all possible error reports. As normal reports must clearly be distinct from error messages, these two sets are constrained to be disjoint:

$$KRepsCond .: \text{IsDisjoint}(KRepsNorm, KRepsErr)$$

These two classes are added to our collection of constant features in the usual way. Alternatively, these two classes could be established more specifically as sets of character strings, by the definition $KRepsNorm, KRepsErr \subseteq_d \text{String}$ ($=_d \text{ListV1}(Char)$ for some character set $Char$).

K: AllocRConstants	(Extended AllocAConstants)
$K[AllocAConstants]$: AllocAConstants	Core and agent features
$KRepsNorm$,	Class of normal reports
$KRepsErr$: Set	Class of error messages
$KRepsCond$.: IsDisjoint($KRepsNorm$, $KRepsErr$)	

Second, we introduce one additional variable feature *Reps*. This is a pair of two sets: a finite set $RepsNorm \subseteq_d KRepsNorm$ of actual normal reports, and a finite set $RepsErr \subseteq_d KRepsErr$ of actual error reports. They are defined as follows:

$Reps$: ReportSets
$RepsNorm \subseteq_d KRepsNorm$
$RepsErr \subseteq_d KRepsErr$

This new feature is added to the list of features of a system state S. As part of S, it is named $SReps$: ReportSets. Our interpretation of $SReps$ is as follows. If S is the result of a decision, correct or incorrect, then $SRepsNorm$ ($SRepsErr$) is the set of normal (error) reports generated as a by-product of the decision; otherwise, both sets are empty.

This completes our final extension of the set of possible system states. In this last form, this set is named AllocR.

S: AllocR	(Extended AllocA)
$S[AllocA]$: AllocA	Core and agent features
$SReps$: ReportSets	

17.7C Extended operations

Turning now to functions, each operation defined on states S: AllocA must be extended to a corresponding operation, called *decision*, on states S: AllocR. This must be done in the light of the rules on errors and reports established in Sections **17**.7A and **17**.7B.

Recall that each operation on AllocA we have established is of the form OpA or OpA(S, —) where S: AllocA and '—' stands for additional arguments, if any. Moreover, given (S, —), OpA returns the state OpA(S, —) $=_d S'$: AllocA.

For each operation OpA, the corresponding extension is denoted by OpR, with the suffix 'A' replaced by 'R'. If OpA has arguments (S^-, —), then OpR has arguments (S, —) where S: AllocR, $S^- =_d SAllocA$ and the other arguments are the same as in OpA. Moreover the result OpR(S, —) $=_d S'$: AllocR.

Each extension OpR is derived from OpA by the same set of rules. We first establish these common rules and then give two examples.

1 Consider any operation OpA. In general, OpA(S^-, —) is defined iff its arguments satisfy a set of preconditions referred to as (Pre1), (Pre2), etc. Let Preconds be the set of these preconditions. Thus,

$$\text{Preconds} =_d \{(\text{Pre1}), (\text{Pre2}), \ldots\}$$

Note that there is a different set Preconds for each operation OpA.

The extension OpR(S, —) has no preconditions: provided the decision is well formulated, OpR is a total function. However, if any precondition (Pre i) of OpA is unsatisfied, then the decision is incorrect in the sense defined in Section **17**.7A, and $S^- =_d S AllocA$ is left unchanged in the final state S'.

Thus any (Pre i) is a condition which should *normally* be satisfied by (S, —), and we call it a *normal precondition* of OpR. A normal precondition is *not* a precondition in the strict sense of the term: if it is not satisfied, OpR(S, —) is defined all the same. If (Pre i) is not satisfied then the application of OpR is simply labelled 'incorrect', and the result is different from the effect of applying OpR in the absence of error.

2 Consider a fixed set of arguments (S, —) for OpR, and again let $S^- =_d S AllocA$. Given (S, —), we may now form the set of those preconditions (Pre i): Preconds which are *not* satisfied by (S, —). This set is denoted by PrecondsUnsat. Thus, using Pr to denote any precondition,

$$\text{PrecondsUnsat} =_d \{Pr : \text{Preconds} \mid \neg\, Pr\}$$

Clearly if PrecondsUnsat $= \varnothing$, then the decision is correct and OpA(S^-, —) is defined. Otherwise, the decision is incorrect, OpA(S^-, —) is undefined, and PrecondsUnsat is the nonempty set of unsatisfied normal preconditions. This subset fully *explains* why the decision is in error and may be used to determine the set of error reports to produce.

3 We may now formally define the effect of OpR(S, —) on S^-, that is, on all features preceding the reports in S. If all normal preconditions are satisfied then S^- is sent to OpA(S^-, —); otherwise, S^- is left unchanged. Formally:

$$S' AllocA =_d \begin{array}{ll} \text{OpA}(S^-) & \text{if PrecondsUnsat} = \varnothing; \\ S^- & \text{otherwise} \end{array}$$

4 It remains to establish the reports of the result S'. We do not specify the normal reports. As for the error reports, we introduce a function ErrMes, which, for each normal precondition Pr of OpR, returns an error message

ErrMes(Pr): $KRepsErr$. Thus ErrMes is a total function

$$\text{ErrMes}: \text{Preconds} \rightarrow KRepsErr$$

Note again that there is a different function ErrMess for each operation OpA. Each report ErrMes(Pr) is meant to be a description of the precondition Pr, that is, one cause of error. We assume only that all these descriptions are different. This is tantamount to asking that ErrMes be injective. Consequently there is the same number of error reports as of unsatisfied preconditions. We may now define the set $S'RepsErr$ of error reports in S'. This is given by

$$S'RepsErr =_{d} \{ERep: KRepsErr \mid \exists\, Pr: \text{PrecondsUnsat} \cdot ERep = \text{ErrMes}(Pr)\}$$

We put these elements together in the following generic format:

OpR

Let Preconds and ErrMes be defined as above, depending on OpR.
Given (S, —) where S: AllocR and '—' stands for further arguments,
OpR(S, —) $=_d$ S' where S': AllocR and

(1) PrecondsUnsat $=_d \{Pr: \text{Preconds} \mid \neg\, Pr\}$

(2) $S'AllocA =_d$ OpA($SAllocA$, —) if PrecondsUnsat $= \varnothing$;
$\quad SAllocA$ otherwise

(3) $S'RepsErr =_d$
$\{ERep: KRepsErr \mid \exists\, Pr: \text{PrecondsUnsat} \cdot ERep = \text{ErrMes}(Pr)\}$

One operation OpR has no arguments: EmpR. The above definition is still applicable – in this case simply ignore the arguments and the normal preconditions. We obtain the following result:

EmpR

EmpR $=_d$ S': AllocR where

(1) $S'AllocA =_d$ EmpA

(2) $S'RepsErr =_d \varnothing$

We do not list all the instances of OpR but treat only one further example, namely InsTaskR. First, we must establish the set Preconds and the function ErrMes. Refer to the establishment of InsTaskA. For this operation:

$$\text{Preconds} =_d \{(\text{Pre 1}), (\text{Pre 2}), (\text{Pre 3})\}$$

Recall the definition of these three normal preconditions:

(Pre 1) $\quad Ta \notin STasksTotal$

(Pre 2) $\quad Resp \in SAgentsStaff + \{KAgUndef\}$

(Pre 3) $\quad AuReq \leqslant SAutLev(Resp)$

We assume that $KRepsErr \subseteq_d$ String. For each normal precondition Pr: Preconds, ErrMes(Pr) must be a message expressing the *negation* of Pr. ErrMes is given in the following table, which is essentially a specification of the graph of the function.

ErrMes

Pr	ErrMes(Pr)
(Pre 1)	'Task *Ta* is already in *STasksTotal*'
(Pre 2)	'*Resp* is a defined agent but is not a member of staff'
(Pre 3)	'*AuReq* exceeds the authority level of *Resp*'

We are now in a position to derive InsTaskR, by instantiating the definition of OpR with the help of the definition of InsTaskA.

InsTaskR

Given S:AllocR, Ta:*KTasks*, *User*, *Resp*:*KAgents* and *AuReq*: *KAuthoLevels*, let Preconds and ErrMes be defined as above. Then InsTaskR (S, Ta, *User*, *Resp*, *AuReq*) $=_d S'$ where S':AllocR and

(1) $\text{PrecondsUnsat} =_d \{Pr : \text{Preconds} \mid \neg\, Pr\}$

(2) $S'AllocA =_d$

$$\begin{cases} \text{InsTaskA}(SAllocA, Ta, User, Resp, AuReq) & \text{if PrecondsUnsat} = \varnothing; \\ SAllocA & \text{otherwise} \end{cases}$$

(3) $S'RepsErr =_d$

$$\{ERep : KRepsErr \mid \exists\, Pr : \text{PrecondsUnsat} \cdot ERep = \text{ErrMes}(Pr)\}$$

17.7D Query operations

The reports introduced so far are by-products of state transformation operations. However, in practice agents also need reports on the state of the system, or its historical behaviour, which are independent of any state transformation. In order to meet these needs, we introduce a new class of functions called *query* or *retrieve operations*. The distinctive feature of these operations is to return a report or a set of reports without modifying the non-informational features of the initial state of the system.

In this model, we consider only query operations returning information on the *current* state S:AllocR of the system. Moreover, we give only a few typical examples of such functions. We begin with a general description of this class of operations.

Let QueR denote any query operation on AllocR. QueR operates on a set (S, —) of arguments, where S:AllocR, and returns a new state S':AllocR.

The fact that QueR does not modify the non-informational features of S is represented by the general condition

$$S'AllocA =_{\mathrm{d}} SAllocA$$

The main purpose of QueR is to return a description of some variable feature F of S, primary or secondary. Recall that a secondary feature is a function of primary ones. In general, F is a partial function and therefore it is defined iff some set Preconds of preconditions is satisfied. These preconditions are treated as *normal*, as in any operation OpR.

Given $(S, \text{—})$, let PrecondsUnsat again denote the subset of preconditions unsatisfied by $(S, \text{—})$:

$$\text{PrecondsUnsat} =_{\mathrm{d}} \{Pr : \text{Preconds} \mid \neg\, Pr\}$$

If PrecondsUnsat $= \varnothing$ then F is defined and its description is provided as a normal report, that is, a member of $S'RepsNorm$. Otherwise no such description is returned but each unsatisfied precondition gives rise to an error report in $S'RepsErr$. In the instances of query operations set out below, we specify only the feature F and its associated preconditions, *not* the way in which F is described as a normal report if all preconditions are satisfied by S. Thus, as with other OpR operations, the set $S'RepsNorm$ of normal reports is not further specified.

As for the set $S'RepsErr$ of error reports, it is defined in the same way as for other OpR operations. A function

$$\text{ErrMes} : \text{Preconds} \rightarrow KRepsErr$$

is defined, and $S'RepsErr$ is derived from ErrMes and PrecondsUnsat by condition OpR(3).

To sum up, QueR is established by a schema similar to the definition of OpR and based on the latter, as follows:

<u>QueR</u>

Let Preconds and ErrMes be defined as above, depending on QueR. Given $(S, \text{—})$ where S: AllocR and '—' stands for further arguments, QueR$(S, \text{—}) =_{\mathrm{d}} S'$ where S': AllocR and

(1) $\text{PrecondsUnsat} =_{\mathrm{d}} \{Pr : \text{Preconds} \mid \neg\, Pr\}$
(2) $S'AllocA =_{\mathrm{d}} SAllocA$
(3) If PrecondsUnsat $= \varnothing$ then $F =_{\mathrm{d}} \ldots$
(4) $S'RepsNorm =_{\mathrm{d}} \begin{cases} \varnothing & \text{if PrecondsUnsat} \neq \varnothing; \\ \{\ldots\} & \text{otherwise (description of } F) \end{cases}$
(5) $S'RepsErr =_{\mathrm{d}} \{ERep : KRepsErr \mid \exists\, Pr : \text{PrecondsUnsat} \cdot ERep = \text{ErrMes}(Pr)\}$

The main difference between the definition of OpR and that of QueR is that, in the latter, *SAllocA* does not change.

We now establish some typical examples of query operations.

Que1R: set of active tasks

The first query operation, called Que1R, returns the set of active tasks in the current ResAll state *S*, namely *STasksAct*. This is a primary feature of *S*. As this set is always defined, Que1R has no normal preconditions: Preconds = $\varnothing$. The formal specification is therefore a simplified instance of the establishment of QueR.

Que1R

Given S: AllocR, Que1R(S) $=_d S'$ where S': AllocR and

(1) $S'AllocA =_d SAllocA$

(2) $F =_d STasksAct$

(3) $S'RepsNorm =_d$ {...} (description of F)

(4) $S'RepsErr =_d \varnothing$

Que2R: sets of allocated and free resources

Next, the operation Que2R returns two features of *S*, namely the pair

$$F =_d (SResAlloc, SResFree)$$

The first component of *F* is the function which, for each r: *KReTypes*, indicates which resources of this type are allocated to active tasks in *S*. The second component is the function which for each r: *KReTypes* gives the set of free, that is, unallocated resources of type *r*. Here again there are no preconditions.

Que2R

Given S: AllocR, Que2R(S) $=_d S'$ where S': AllocR and

(1) $S'AllocA =_d SAllocA$

(2) $F =_d (SResAlloc, SResFree)$

(3) $S'RepsNorm =_d$ {...} (description of F)

(4) $S'RepsErr =_d \varnothing$

This operation returns *SResAlloc* and *SResFree* as two separate functions from *KReTypes*. An alternative is to return *one* function, giving the pair

($SResAlloc_r$, $SResFree_r$) for each r:*KReTypes*. Moreover, it is clear that there is no need to take *KReTypes* as domain of any of these functions: we may explicitly restrict them to *SReTypes*, as for any r:*KReTypes* − *SReTypes*, $SResAlloc_r = SResFree_r = \varnothing$.

We specify F as the graph of this second alternative:

$$F =_d \{(r, (SResAlloc_r, SResFree_r)) \mid r : SReTypes\}$$

Que3R: set of active tasks requiring k resources of type r

The previous example illustrates an implied feature F described by an elementary expression. Next, we illustrate a retrieved feature F consisting of a set described by a complex expression.

In this case, the operation requires two arguments in addition to S. These are r:*SReTypes* and k:Nat. The returned feature is the set F of active tasks which require k or more resources of type r.

In this example, the current state S must satisfy two normal preconditions. First, r must be a member of *SReTypes*. Second, k must be a positive number. Thus we establish Que3R as an instance of the general definition of an operation QueR as follows:

Que3R

Given S:AllocR, r:*KReTypes* and k:Nat. Let
(Pre 1) $=_d$ $r \in SReTypes$
(Pre 2) $=_d$ $k > 0$
Also, let Preconds $=_d$ {(Pre 1), (Pre 2)}, and ErrMes: Preconds → *KRepsErr* be the function with the following graph:

ErrMes

Pr	ErrMes(*Pr*)
(Pre 1)	'r is not the type of an owned resource'
(Pre 2)	'k must be a positive number'

Que3R(S, r, k) $=_d$ S' where S':AllocR and

(1) PrecondsUnsat $=_d \{Pr : \text{Preconds} \mid \neg\, Pr\}$
(2) $S'AllocA =_d SAllocA$
(3) If PrecondsUnsat $= \varnothing$ then
$F =_d \{Ta : KTasks \mid Ta \in STasksAct \wedge r \in KReqTypes(Ta) \wedge KReqNum_r(Ta) \geq k\}$
(4) $S'RepsNorm =_d$ $\varnothing$ If PrecondsUnsat $\neq \varnothing$;
{...} otherwise (description of F)
(5) $S'RepsErr =_d$
$\{ERep : KRepsErr \mid \exists\, Pr : \text{PrecondsUnsat} \cdot ERep = \text{ErrMes}(Pr)\}$

Que4R: conflicts of interest

In S, any actual task Ta may have an 'owner' or beneficiary, $SAgOwner(Ta)$, and may be assigned to an agent responsible for it, $SAgResp(Ta)$. If defined, $SAgOwner(Ta)$ must be a user and $SAgResp(Ta)$ an employee. However, an employee may also be a user of the organization's services. Consequently it is possible for an employee to be responsiblible for a task of which he or she is the beneficiary. This may create conflicts of interest, which the organization may at least wish to monitor.

The purpose of the next query, Que4R, is to retrieve the set of all tasks Ta for which the owner and the employee responsible are the same person, together with the name of the owner. In formulating this query, we must not overlook the following point: the mythical agent $KAgUndef$, which represents 'undefined', must not be included among the possible employee owners. Note that here there are no normal preconditions.

Que4R

Given S : AllocR, Que4R(S) $=_d S'$ where S' : AllocR and

(1) $S'AllocA =_d SAllocA$

(2) $F =_d \{(Ta, SAgOwner(Ta)) \mid Ta : STasksTotal \wedge SAgOwner(Ta) \neq KAgUndef \wedge SAgOwner(Ta) = SAgResp(Ta)\}$

(3) $S'RepsNorm =_d \{\ldots\}$ (description of F)

(4) $S'RepsErr =_d \varnothing$

The reader may enjoy devising further similar queries.

References

Aho A. V., Hopcroft J. E. and Ullman J. D. (1974). *The Design and Analysis of Computer Algorithms.* Reading, MA: Addison-Wesley

Andrews P. B. (1986). *An Introduction to Mathematical Logic and Types Theory: To Truth through Proof.* New York: Academic Press

Backus J. W. (1978). Can programming be liberated from the Von Neumann style? A functional style and its algebra of programs. *Comm. ACM*, **21**, 612–41

Berge C. (1962). *The Theory of Graphs and Its Applications.* London: Methuen

Bird R. and Wadler P. (1988). *Introduction to Functional Programming.* New York: Prentice-Hall

Birkhoff G. and Mac Lane S. (1965). *A Survey of Modern Algebra* 3rd edn. New York: Macmillan

Brookes F. P., Jr. (1975). *The Mythical Man-Month.* Reading, MA: Addison-Wesley

Dijkstra E. W. (1989). On the cruelty of really teaching computing science. *Comm. ACM*, **32**, 1398–1404

Dijkstra E. W. and Scholten C. S. (1990). *Predicate Calculus and Program Semantics.* New York: Springer-Verlag

Dowsing R. D., Rayward-Smith V. J. and Walter C. D. (1986). *A First Course in Formal Logic and its Applications in Computer Science.* Oxford: Blackwell

Enderton H. B. (1972). *A Mathematical Introduction to Logic.* New York: Academic Press

Enderton H. B. (1977). *Elements of Set Theory.* New York: Academic Press

Gries D. (1981). *The Science of Programming.* New York: Springer-Verlag

Halmos P. R. (1974). *Naive Set Theory.* New York: Springer-Verlag

Hayes I. (Ed.) (1987). *Specification Case Studies.* Englewood Cliffs, NJ: Prentice-Hall

Hopcroft J. E. and Ullman J. D. (1979). *Introduction to Automata Theory, Languages and Computation.* Reading, MA: Addison-Wesley

Hunt R. and Shelley, J. (1983). *Computers and Commonsense.* Englewood Cliffs, NJ: Prentice-Hall

Ince D. C. (1988). *An Introduction to Discrete Mathematics and Formal System Specification.* Oxford: Clarendon Press

Jones C. B. (1990). *Systematic Software Development Using VDM* 2nd edn. New York: Prentice-Hall

Latham J. T., Bush V. J. and Cottam I. D. (1990). *The Programming Process: An Introduction Using VDM and Pascal.* Wokingham: Addison-Wesley

Liskov B. and Guttag J. (1986). *Abstraction and Specification in Program Development.* Cambridge, MA: MIT Press

Mac Lane S. (1971). *Categories for the Working Mathematician.* New York: Springer-Verlag

Mac Lane S. and Birkhoff G. (1979). *Algebra* 2nd edn. New York: Macmillan

Manes E. G. and Arbib M. A. (1986). *Algebraic Approaches to Program Semantics.* New York: Springer-Verlag

Manna Z. and Waldinger R. (1985). *The Logical Basis for Computer Programming.*

Vol. I: Deductive Reasoning. Reading, MA: Addison-Wesley

Manna Z. and Waldinger R. (1990). *The Logical Basis for Computer Programming. Vol. II: Deductive Systems*. Reading, MA: Addison-Wesley

McDermid J. A. (Ed.) (1989). *The Theory and Practice of Refinement*. London: Butterworths

Nordström B., Petersson K. and Smith J. M. (1990). *Programming in Martin-Löf's Type Theory*. Oxford: Clarendon Press

Reeves S. and Clarke M. (1990). *Logic for Computer Science*. Wokingham: Addison-Wesley

Simon H. A. (1960). *The New Science of Management Decision*. Englewood Cliffs, NJ: Prentice-Hall

Sommerville I. (1989). *Software Engineering*. Wokingham: Addison-Wesley

Spivey J. M. (1989). *The Z Notation: A Reference Manual*. New York: Prentice-Hall

Wiener N. (1954). *The Human Use of Human Beings: Cybernetics and Society* 2nd edn. Houghton Mifflin. Also: London: Free Association Books, 1989

Wirth N. (1976). *Algorithms + Data Structures = Programs*. London: Prentice-Hall International

Wood D. (1987). *Theory of Computation*. New York: Wiley

Wordsworth J. B. (1992). *Software Development with Z*. Wokingham: Addison-Wesley

Index

A

B

E

F

G

H

I

J

K

L

N

O

P

S

T

U

V

W

Y

Z